HIGHER

MATHEMATICS

SECOND EDITION

Robert Barclay
Brian J. Logan
& Mike Smith

Acknowledgements

Material used in Appendix 2 on page 298 adapted from SQA Higher Mathematics course specification May 2018, used with permission © Scottish Qualifications Authority.

The authors and publisher would like to extend thanks to Jeremy Beard for the assistance and advice offered at the manuscript stage.

Every effort has been made to trace all copyright holders, but if any have been inadvertently overlooked the Publishers will be pleased to make the necessary arrangements at the first opportunity.

Although every effort has been made to ensure that website addresses are correct at time of going to press, Hodder Gibson cannot be held responsible for the content of any website mentioned in this book. It is sometimes possible to find a relocated web page by typing in the address of the home page for a website in the URL window of your browser.

Hachette UK's policy is to use papers that are natural, renewable and recyclable products and made from wood grown in well-managed forests and other controlled sources. The logging and manufacturing processes are expected to conform to the environmental regulations of the country of origin.

Orders: please contact Bookpoint Ltd, 130 Park Drive, Milton Park, Abingdon, Oxon OX14 4SE. Telephone: (44) 01235 827827. Fax: (44) 01235 400454. Email education@bookpoint.co.uk. Lines are open 9.00–5.00, Monday to Saturday, with a 24-hour message answering service. Visit our website at www.hoddereducation.co.uk. Hodder Gibson can be contacted directly at hoddergibson@hodder.co.uk.

© Robert Barclay, Brian J. Logan and Mike Smith 2019

First published in 2015 © Robert Barclay, Brian J. Logan and Mike Smith
This second edition published in 2019 by
Hodder Gibson, an imprint of Hodder Education,
An Hachette UK Company
211 St Vincent Street
Glasgow G2 5QY

Impression number	5	4	3	2	1
Year	2023	2022	2021	2020	2019

All rights reserved. Apart from any use permitted under UK copyright law, no part of this publication may be reproduced or transmitted in any form or by any means, electronic or mechanical, including photocopying and recording, or held within any information storage and retrieval system, without permission in writing from the publisher or under licence from the Copyright Licensing Agency Limited. Further details of such licences (for reprographic reproduction) may be obtained from the Copyright Licensing Agency Limited, Saffron House, www.cla.co.uk

Cover photo © Baloncici/Shutterstock.com
Illustrations by Integra Software Services Pvt. Ltd, Pondicherry, India.
Typeset in 10/11.5 Gill Sans Std/Regular by Integra Software Services Pvt. Ltd, Pondicherry, India.
Printed in Italy

A catalogue record for this title is available from the British Library

ISBN: 978 1 5104 5773 7

CONTENTS

INTRODUCTION/PREFACE

Higher Mathematics has been specifically written to meet the requirements of the SQA Higher Mathematics Course and provides full coverage of the syllabus as set out in the SQA Higher Mathematics Course Specification.

In preparing the text, full account has been made of the requirements for students to be able to use and apply mathematics in written examinations and to solve problems with and without a calculator.

Each chapter contains the following features:

- **What I am learning** – from the SQA course specification, detailing the skills covered in each chapter
- **What I should already know/be able to do** – background skills and knowledge required for this topic
- A '**Quick check**' feature to give the student confidence in their background knowledge.

The main part of each chapter consists of fully worked examples with explanatory notes and commentary, carefully graded questions, a summary of key points and a 'Checkout' exercise at the end, to enable the student to show that the topic has been consolidated. These Checkouts could also provide opportunities, throughout the course, to consolidate topics met during the chapter and to monitor progress.

Some chapters include areas for investigation. These give the student the opportunity to improve and practise their skills in using and applying mathematics. Indeed, they also help a student to meet the four capacities of Curriculum for Excellence (CfE); in particular, successful learner, effective contributor and perhaps a more confident individual!

Most exercises in each chapter will feature our unique **HPQ** and **ACE** icons:

What are these?

HPQ	Hinge-Point Questions	Allow the student to determine whether to continue with next part of the exercise or spend some more time consolidating skills covered in the first part of the exercise.
ACE	Application, Communication, Enquiry	A chance for the student to show application of problem-solving skills; communicating a solution with justification; using enquiry skills to solve a problem.

The overall aim of this textbook is to enable the student to develop a range of mathematical operational and reasoning skills that can be used to solve mathematical and real-life problems.

It is hoped the structure of this book allows for approaches to learning and teaching which are engaging, and which provide opportunities for personalisation and choice.

A final word of advice for all students from Lewis Carroll (a mathematician as well as noted writer):

'Then you should say what you mean,' the March Hare went on.

'I do,' Alice hastily replied; 'at least I mean what I say, that's the same thing, you know.'

'Not the same thing a bit!' said the Hatter. 'Why, you might just as well say that "I see what I eat" is the same thing as "I eat what I see!"'

Lewis Carroll, *Alice in Wonderland*

So make sure you say what you mean, you write down what you mean to write down, and that you check that any conclusions you draw or justifications you state make sense!

Wishing you every success in your Higher Mathematics studies,

Robert Barclay, Brian J. Logan and Mike Smith

CHAPTER

1 The Straight Line

You should already be familiar with finding the gradient and equation of straight lines.

In this chapter, your knowledge of the straight line will be extended and applied to cover work on lines associated with triangles such as the median and the altitude, and the perpendicular bisector of a line.

What I am learning

* The distance formula
* How to find the midpoint of a straight line
* The relationship between gradient and the tangent of an angle
* How to determine whether a given set of points is collinear
* The relationship between the gradients of perpendicular lines
* How to work with equations of altitudes, medians and perpendicular bisectors
* How to determine whether a given set of lines is concurrent
* The meaning of the orthocentre, the centroid and the circumcentre in a triangle
* How to solve problems like this:

  AB is a line perpendicular to the line with equation $3x + 2y = 6$

  Find the equation of AB if A has coordinates $(5, -2)$.

What I should already know/be able to do

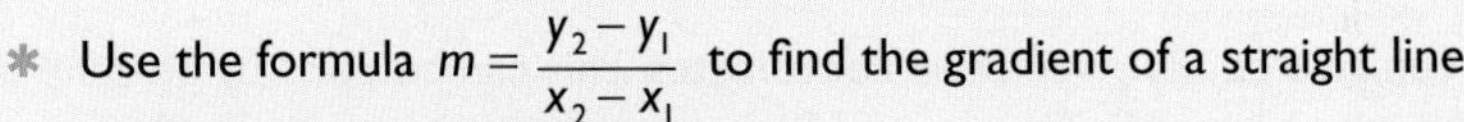

* Use the formula $m = \frac{y_2 - y_1}{x_2 - x_1}$ to find the gradient of a straight line
* Parallel lines have equal gradients
* The gradient of a line that slopes up from left to right is positive and the gradient of a line that slopes down from left to right is negative
* The gradient of a horizontal line is zero and the line has an equation of the form the form $y = k$
* The gradient of a vertical line is undefined and the line has an equation of the form $x = h$
* Use the formula $y - b = m(x - a)$ to find the equation of a straight line
* Use the formula $y = mx + c$ to find the equation of a straight line
* Identify the gradient and the y-intercept of a straight line from the equation $y = mx + c$
* Express the equation of a straight line in the form $ax + by + c = 0$
* Identify the gradient and the y-intercept of the straight line $ax + by + c = 0$
* Use Pythagoras' Theorem to find the distance between two points
* Use the converse of Pythagoras' Theorem
* Find the point of intersection of two straight lines by using simultaneous equations

Quick check!

1 What is the gradient of the line joining C(4, −3) and D(−2, −4)?
2 Find the equation of the straight line joining the points K(4, 3) and L(−2, 7).
3 What is the equation of the line joining C(2, −4) and D(2, 5)?
4 Find the gradient of a line parallel to the line with equation $3y + 4x + 2 = 0$.
5 What is the gradient and y-intercept of the line with equation $2y - 3x = 4$?
6 What is the length of the line segment joining A(3, −2) and B(6, 4)?
7 A triangle has sides of length 24 centimetres, 15 centimetres and 20 centimetres. Is the triangle right-angled?
8 Find the point of intersection of the lines $3x + y = 6$ and $7x - 2y = 40$.

Quick check! – *Solutions*

1 $\frac{1}{6}$
2 $2x + 3y - 17 = 0$
3 $x = 2$
4 $-\frac{4}{3}$
5 $\frac{3}{2}$, (0, 2)
6 $\sqrt{45}$
7 No, since $24^2 \neq 15^2 + 20^2$
8 (4, −6)

The distance formula

You already know how to find the distance between two points given their coordinates. This can be done by plotting the points, forming a right-angled triangle (if possible) and applying the Theorem of Pythagoras. You can use these ideas to find a more general formula for the distance, d, between two points A (x_1, y_1) and B (x_2, y_2).

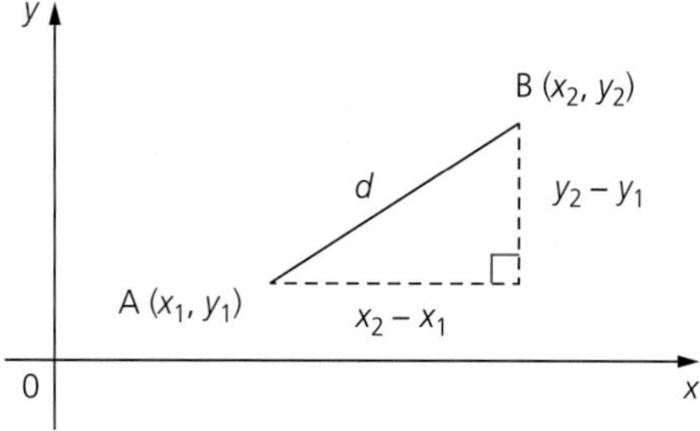

The distance from A (x_1, y_1) to B (x_2, y_2) can be given by the formula

$$d = \sqrt{(x_2 - x_1)^2 + (y_2 - y_1)^2}$$

This formula is known as the **distance formula**.

Example

Find the distance between the points (3, −2) and (−1, 4).

SOLUTION

$$\begin{aligned} d &= \sqrt{(x_2 - x_1)^2 + (y_2 - y_1)^2} \\ &= \sqrt{(-1-3)^2 + (4-(-2))^2} \\ &= \sqrt{(-4)^2 + 6^2} \\ &= \sqrt{16+36} \\ &= \sqrt{52} \\ &= 2\sqrt{13} \end{aligned}$$

Exercise 1.1

1 Calculate the distance between the following pairs of points. Where appropriate, leave your answer as a surd in simplest form. HPQ

a) (2, 1) and (5, 2) **b)** (−3, −2) and (1, 1) **c)** (0, −4) and (2, −7)

d) (6, −2) and (3, 5) **e)** (−2, 8) and (3, −4) **f)** (2, −1) and (−3, −1)

g) (2, −2) and (0, 0) **h)** (−3, −1) and (2, −4) **i)** (5, −3) and (0, 1)

2 Show that the triangle with coordinates A(−6, 7), B(6, 3) and C(1, 8) is isosceles.

3 Show that the triangle with coordinates D(−1, 4), E(2, 5) and F(1, 2) is isosceles.

4 Use the distance formula and the converse of the Theorem of Pythagoras to show that the triangle with vertices P(5, 1), Q(11, 7) and R(8, 10) is right-angled.

5 Repeat Question 4 for a triangle with vertices K(1, −2), L(−1, 1) and M(7, 2).

6 Find the values of k if M is the point (4, −3), N is the point (6, k) and the distance between M and N is $\sqrt{20}$. ACE

The midpoint of a line

You can find the coordinates of the midpoint of the line joining the points A (x_1, y_1) and B (x_2, y_2) by finding the mean of the x-coordinates and the mean of the y-coordinates. If M is the midpoint of the line AB, the coordinates of M are given by

$$\left(\frac{x_1 + x_2}{2}, \frac{y_1 + y_2}{2}\right)$$

Example

Find the coordinates of the midpoint, M, of the line AB where A is (3, −8) and B is (−1, 14).

SOLUTION

M is $\left(\frac{3+(-1)}{2}, \frac{-8+14}{2}\right) = (1, 3)$.

Algebraic Skills

Exercise 1.2

1 Write down the coordinates of the midpoint of the line joining:

a) (2, 1) and (10, 7) **b)** (−3, 2) and (5, −4) **c)** (0, −8) and (6, 0)

d) (−3, 2) and (1, −4) **e)** (−2, 6) and (−2, −4) **f)** (2, −1) and (−3, 2)

g) (6, −8) and (0, 0) **h)** (−7 −1) and (−9 −3) HPQ **i)** (8, −6) and (6, −2)

2 M (10, −3) is the midpoint of line AB. If A is the point (6, −5), find the coordinates of B.

3 M (4, −2) is the midpoint of line PQ. If P is the point (−1, 1), find the coordinates of Q.

4 PQRS is a quadrilateral with vertices P (6, −3) Q (10, 7) R (4, 15) and S (0, 5).

a) Find the coordinates of the midpoint of PR.
b) Find the coordinates of the midpoint of QS.
c) What can you say about the diagonals of PQRS?

5 In triangle ABC, A is (−4, 5) B (2, 9) and C (−8, 3)

a) Find the coordinates of M, the midpoint of BC.
b) Find the equation of the line BM.

Gradient: $m = \tan\theta$

When you first studied gradient, you used the formula $m = \dfrac{\text{vertical height}}{\text{horizontal distance}}$

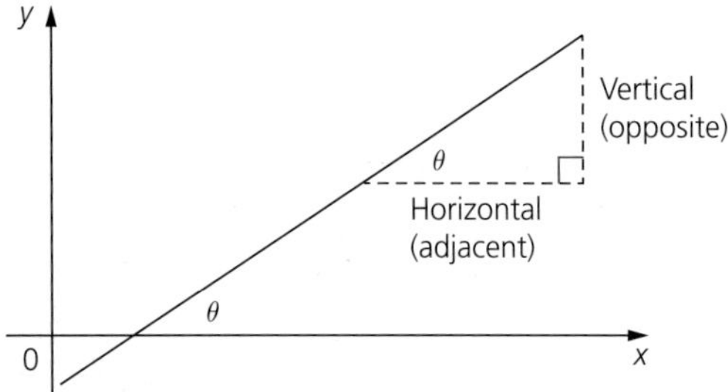

By looking at the triangle, you can see that the vertical side is *opposite* to the angle θ (theta) and the horizontal side is *adjacent* to the angle θ. So

$$m = \frac{\text{vertical height}}{\text{horizontal distance}} = \frac{\text{opposite}}{\text{adjacent}} = \tan\theta$$

The formula $m = \tan\theta$ tells us that the **gradient** of a straight line is the **tangent** of the angle that the line makes with the positive direction of the x-axis.

- A line making an angle of 45° with the positive *x*-axis has gradient 1 as $\tan 45° = 1$.
- A line with gradient 2 makes an angle of $\tan^{-1} 2 = 63{\cdot}4°$ with the positive *x*-axis.
- A line with zero gradient is parallel to the *x*-axis.
- A line with an undefined gradient is perpendicular to the positive *x*-axis.
- A line with a negative gradient makes an obtuse angle with the positive *x*-axis. For example, a line with gradient −2 makes an angle of $\tan^{-1}(-2) = 116{\cdot}6°$ with the positive *x*-axis.

Algebraic Skills

Example

What angle does the line joining points A (–3, 5) and B (2, –1) make with the positive direction of the *x*-axis?

SOLUTION

$$m_{AB}=\frac{y_2-y_1}{x_2-x_1}=\frac{-1-5}{2-(-3)}=-\frac{6}{5}\Rightarrow \tan\theta=-\frac{6}{5}\Rightarrow \theta=129\cdot 8 \text{ (correct to one decimal place)}$$

Hence the line makes an angle of $129\cdot 8°$ with the positive direction of the *x*-axis.

Exercise 1.3

(Unless otherwise stated give angles correct to one decimal place and gradients correct to two decimal places.)

1 Find the size of the angle between the positive *x*-axis and a line with gradient:

a) 4 **b)** $\frac{1}{\sqrt{3}}$ **c)** –1

d) 0·5 **e)** $-\sqrt{3}$ **f)** 57

2 Find the gradient of a line inclined to the positive *x*-axis at an angle of:

a) 20° **b)** 120° **c)** 55°

d) 90° **e)** 78·7° **f)** 164°

3 a) Calculate the gradient of the line joining points A (5, 3) and B (8, 4). HPQ

b) What angle does this line make with the positive *x*-axis?

4 a) Calculate the gradient of the line joining points A (–3, 3) and B (4, –2).

b) What angle does this line make with the positive *x*-axis?

5 What angle does the line joining points P (2, 1) and Q (3, 7) make with the positive direction of the *x*-axis?

6 What angle does the line joining points R (–3, –3) and B (–7, –7) make with the positive direction of the *x*-axis?

7 What angle does the line joining points T (–1, 4) and U (3, 8) make with the positive direction of the *x*-axis?

8 Calculate the gradient, correct to two decimal places, of:

a) AB

b) AC

c) BC

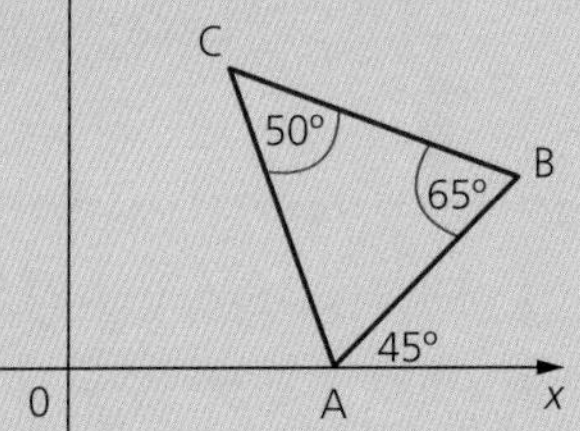

9 The acute angle between two intersecting lines is 50°. One of the lines has gradient 3. Make a sketch and find the possible gradients of other line. Give your answers correct to one decimal place.

10 Line l_1 has gradient 4; line l_2 has gradient $-\frac{1}{4}$.

a) Calculate the size of the angles marked *a* and *b*.

b) Calculate the angle between lines l_1 and l_2.

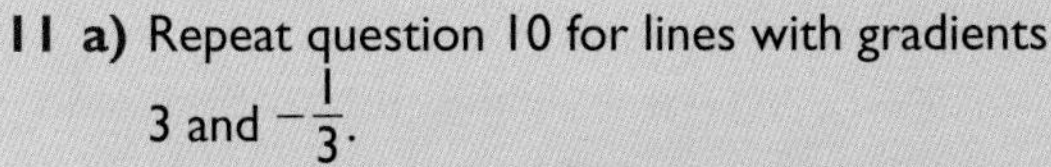

11 a) Repeat question 10 for lines with gradients 3 and $-\frac{1}{3}$.

b) Comment on your findings.

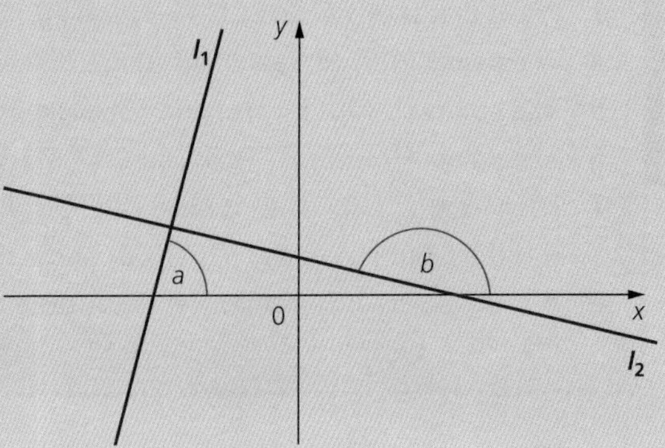

Collinear points

When you first started to plot straight lines, you were probably told that you should always plot at least three points, because two points can always be joined by a straight line but you would not know if you had made a mistake! So the third point acts as a check.

You can use this idea to determine if three points lie in a straight line. Points which lie in a straight line are said to be **collinear**.

The property of lying on the same straight line is known as **collinearity**.

Example

Show that points A (−6, −2), B (−1, 1) and C (9, 7) are collinear.

SOLUTION

There are three possible line segments to consider, AB, BC and AC. You should find the gradients of any *two* of them.

$$m_{AB} = \frac{y_2 - y_1}{x_2 - x_1} = \frac{1-(-2)}{-1-(-6)} = \frac{3}{5} \qquad m_{BC} = \frac{y_2 - y_1}{x_2 - x_1} = \frac{7-1}{9-(-1)} = \frac{6}{10} = \frac{3}{5}$$

Because $m_{AB} = m_{BC}$, AB and BC are parallel.

Since point B is common to both lines, points A, B and C are collinear.

Note

To prove **collinearity**:

- Show that the **gradients** of two line segments are **equal**, which means the lines are parallel.
- State that there is a **common point**.

Later, when you study vectors, you will find another way of proving collinearity.

Exercise 1.4

1. Show that points A (1, 3), B (3, 11) and C (5, 19) are collinear. HPQ
2. Show that points D (2, −5), E (4, −11) and F (7, −20) are collinear.
3. Prove that points G (2, 2), H (6, 4) and J (8, 5) all lie on the same straight line.
4. The points (4, 5), (8, 8) and (12, k) are collinear. Find the value of k.
5. The points (1, 10), (2, 13) and (t, 16) all lie on the same straight line. Find t.
6. The points A (3, −2), B (−1, 4) and C (7, q) are collinear. Find q.
7. P is the point (10, −4), Q is (8, 4) and M is the midpoint of PQ.
   R is the point (1, −6) and S is (13, 3). Show that R, S and M are collinear.
8. A is the point (3, 7) and B is (9, 19). A third point C lies directly between A and B such that the ratio AC:CB is 1:2. Find the coordinates of C. ACE

Perpendicular lines

If two lines with gradients m_1 and m_2 are parallel, then $m_1 = m_2$.

In this section we shall consider two lines with gradients m_1 and m_2 which are perpendicular (look back to questions 10 and 11 in Exercise 1.3).

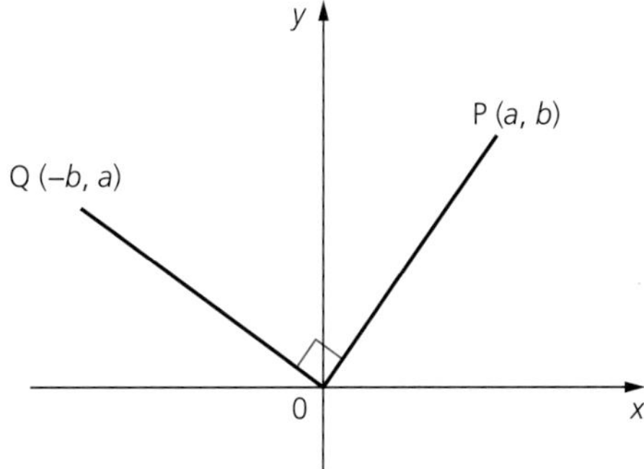

In the above diagram the line OP, where P is the point (a, b) has been rotated 90° anti-clockwise about the origin to OQ, so that Q is the point $(-b, a)$.

Check that $m_{OP} = \frac{b}{a}$ and $m_{OQ} = -\frac{a}{b}$.

Therefore $m_{OP} \times m_{OQ} = \frac{b}{a} \times \left(-\frac{a}{b}\right) = -1$.

This leads to the important result that if two lines with gradients m_1 and m_2 are perpendicular, then $m_1 \times m_2 = -1$.

- To decide if two lines are perpendicular, calculate the product of their gradients.
  They are perpendicular if the product equals -1.
- If a line has gradient $\frac{e}{f}$ you can find the gradient of a perpendicular line by inverting $\frac{e}{f}$ and changing the sign, leading to $-\frac{f}{e}$.
  For example, $\frac{5}{2}$ and $-\frac{2}{5}$ are gradients of perpendicular lines.

Example

AB is a line perpendicular to the line with equation $3x + 2y = 6$.

Find the equation of AB if A has coordinates $(5, -2)$.

SOLUTION

Rearrange $3x + 2y = 6$ into the form $y = mx + c$.

$$2y = -3x + 6$$

$$\Rightarrow y = -\frac{3}{2}x + 3$$

$$\Rightarrow m = -\frac{3}{2}$$

As AB is perpendicular to the line $3x + 2y = 6$, $m_{AB} = \frac{2}{3}$.

Use the formula $y - b = m(x - a)$ to find the equation of AB.

$$y + 2 = \frac{2}{3}(x - 5)$$

$$\Rightarrow \quad 3y + 6 = 2x - 10$$

$$\Rightarrow 2x - 3y - 16 = 0$$

Algebraic Skills

Note Remember that the equation of a line can appear in numerous different forms, e.g. $y = mx + c$ or $ax + by + c = 0$. It is good practice to tidy up any fractions and simplify as far as possible.

Exercise 1.5

1 The gradients of six lines are given below:

AB $\frac{1}{2}$ CD $-\frac{2}{5}$ EF -2 GH 3 IJ 3 KL $2{\cdot}5$

State which pairs of lines which are:

a) parallel
b) perpendicular

2 Write down the gradient of a line which is perpendicular to a line with gradient:

a) 4 **b)** -3 **c)** $\frac{1}{4}$

d) $-0{\cdot}4$ **e)** $-\frac{3}{4}$ **f)** $\frac{7}{2}$

3 Explain why the straight lines with equations $y = 4x + 5$ and $y = -\frac{1}{4}x - 3$ are perpendicular.

4 Write down the equation of the line through the origin perpendicular to the line with equation:

a) $y = 5x$ **b)** $y = -2x$

c) $y = \frac{1}{2}x$ **d)** $y = -\frac{1}{6}x$

5 P is the point (6, 5) and Q is (–3, 4)

a) Write down the gradient of a line parallel to PQ.
b) Write down the gradient of a line perpendicular to PQ.

6 a) Find the gradient of the line joining points U (–1, 3) and V (5, –2).
b) Hence find the equation of the line perpendicular to UV which passes through the point W (2, 4).

7 A is the point (0, –4) and B (3, 2). Find the equation of the line which is **perpendicular** to AB and passes through the point (5, 1). HPQ

8 A line passes through the points G (1, 3) and H (6, 2). Find the equation of the line which is **parallel** to the given line and passes through the point (–3, 7).

9 Find the equation of the line passing through C (–2, 2) perpendicular to the line joining A (–4, 8) and B (1, –3).

10 Find the equation of the line passing through L (4, –1) perpendicular to the line joining M (–3, 0) and N (6, 6).

11 G is the point (–5, –6) and H (–3, –3). Find the equation of the line **perpendicular** to GH which passes through the point (–4, 0).

12 Given that K, L and M are the points (–4, 0), (–1, 3) and (3, –1) respectively, prove that triangle KLM is right-angled. ACE

13 A triangle has vertices A (–3, –3), B (–1, 1) and C (7, –3). Show that the triangle is right-angled at B.

14 A line has equation $4x + 3y - 4 = 0$. Find the equation of the line perpendicular to this line which passes through the point (0, –3).

15 AB is a line perpendicular to the line with equation $2x + 4y = 5$.
Find the equation of AB if A has coordinates (3, 1).

16 UV is a line perpendicular to the line with equation $2x + 7y - 1 = 0$.
Find the equation of UV if V has coordinates (–4, 0).

Perpendicular bisectors

As the name suggests, the **perpendicular bisector** of a line is a straight line which crosses the midpoint of the line at right angles.

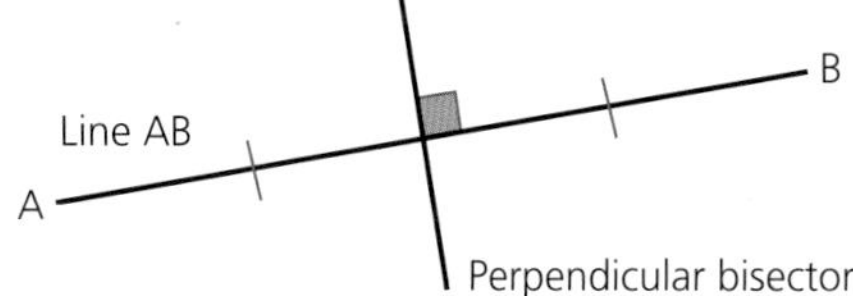

Example

Find the equation of the perpendicular bisector of the line joining P (–2, 4) to Q (6, 10).

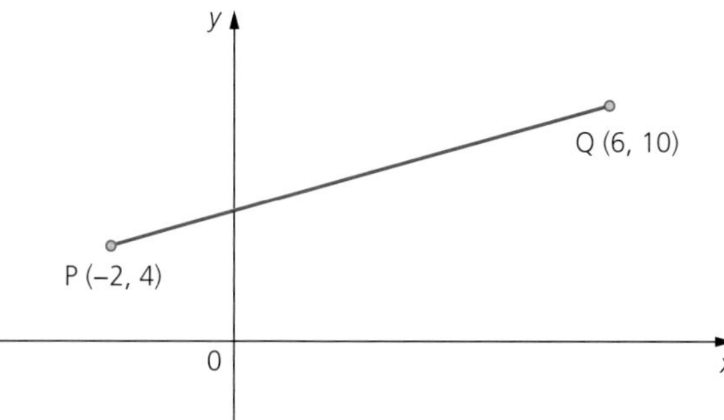

SOLUTION

Carry out the following steps:

* Find the midpoint of PQ.
* Find the gradient of PQ.
* Find the gradient of the perpendicular bisector.
* Substitute into $y - b = m(x - a)$.

The midpoint of PQ is $\left(\frac{-2+6}{2}, \frac{4+10}{2}\right) = (2, 7)$.

$$m_{PQ} = \frac{y_2 - y_1}{x_2 - x_1} = \frac{10-4}{6-(-2)} = \frac{6}{8} = \frac{3}{4}$$

Therefore the gradient of the perpendicular bisector is $-\frac{4}{3}$.

Substitute into $y - b = m(x - a)$:

$$y - 7 = -\frac{4}{3}(x - 2)$$

$$\Rightarrow \quad 3y - 21 = -4x + 8$$

$$\Rightarrow 4x + 3y - 29 = 0$$

Algebraic Skills

Exercise 1.6

1 Find the equation of the perpendicular bisector of the line joining each pair of points:

a) A (1, 3) and B (7, 9)
b) C (−2, 6) and D (4, 2)
c) E (−4, −4) and F (6, 2)
d) G (−2, 5) and H (4, −3)
e) J (3, 1) and K (3, −5)
f) L (−5, −1) and M (5, 7)

2 A triangle has vertices P (−2, −3), Q (6, 1) and R (5, 8).
Find the equation of the perpendicular bisector of the line PQ.

3 The diagram shows triangle DEF. HPQ
D has coordinates (1, 9), E (7, 5) and F (1, −2).
Find the equation of the perpendicular bisector of the line DF.

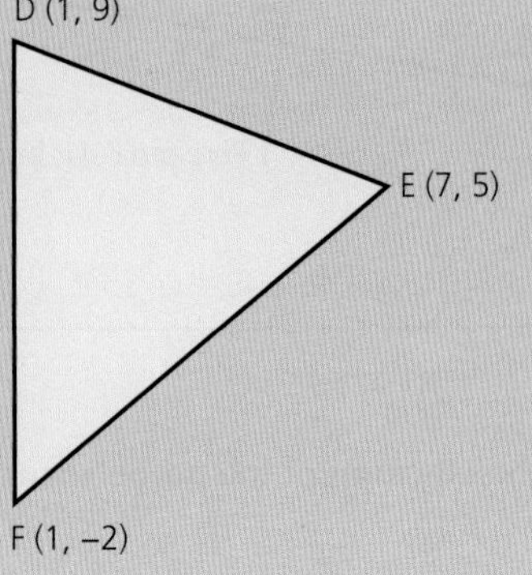

The altitude of a triangle

The **altitude** of a triangle is a straight line from a vertex perpendicular to the opposite side.

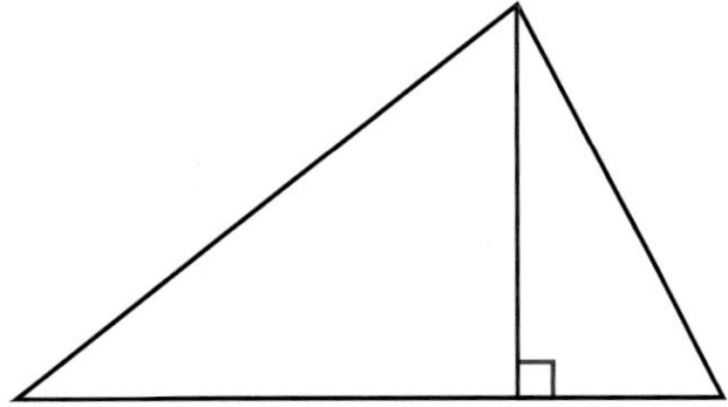

Example

A (−6, 4), B (−1, −4) and C (5, 3) are vertices of triangle ABC.
Find the equation of CD, the altitude from C.

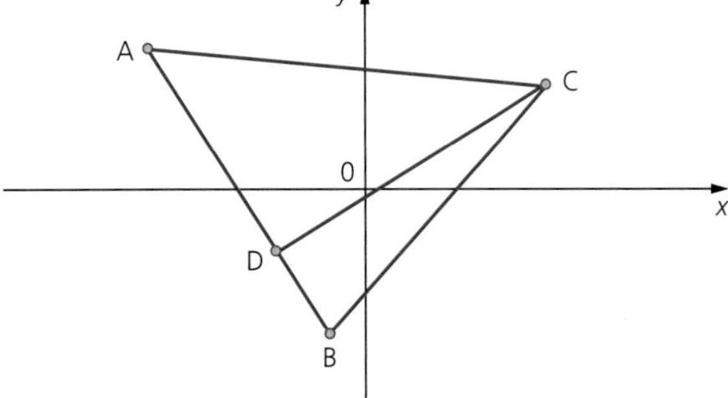

Algebraic Skills

SOLUTION

Carry out the following steps:

* Find the gradient of AB.
* Find the gradient of CD.
* Substitute into $y - b = m(x - a)$.

$$m_{AB} = \frac{y_2 - y_1}{x_2 - x_1} = \frac{-4-4}{-1-(-6)} = \frac{-8}{5} = -\frac{8}{5}$$

Therefore the gradient of the altitude is $\frac{5}{8}$.

Substitute into $y - b = m(x - a)$:

$$y - 3 = \frac{5}{8}(x - 5)$$

$$\Rightarrow \quad 8y - 24 = 5x - 25$$

$$\Rightarrow 5x - 8y - 1 = 0$$

Exercise 1.7

1 Find the equation of the altitude from K in a triangle with vertices K (4, −2), L (−3, −1), and M (1, 3).

2 P (−4, 5), Q (−2, −2) and R (4, 1) are vertices of triangle PQR.
Find the equation of PS, the altitude from P.

3 In triangle ABC, A is the point (3, −2), B is (5, −3) and C is (2, 1).

a) Find the equation of the altitude from A.

b) Find the equation of the altitude from B.

4 Find the equation of all three altitudes in a triangle with vertices A (7, 8), B (6, 2) and C (−5, 2). HPQ

5 STU is a triangle where T has coordinates (3, −1) and the line SU has equation $2y = 6x - 1$. ACE
Find the equation of the altitude from T.

The median of a triangle

The **median** of a triangle is a straight line from a vertex to the **midpoint** of the opposite side.

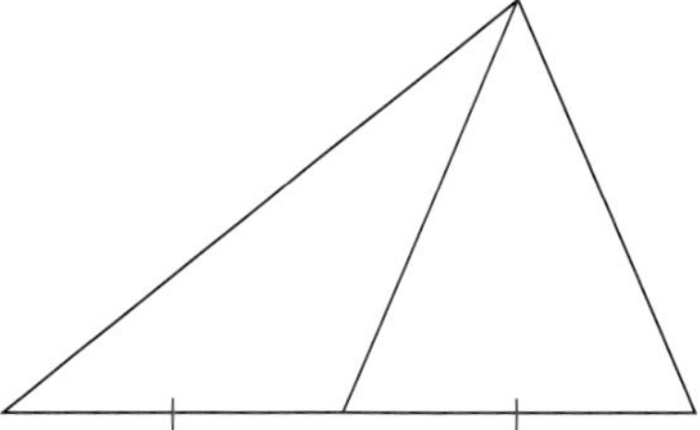

Algebraic Skills

Example

A triangle has vertices T (−1, 3), U (5, 2) and V (9, −6)
Find the equation of the TM, the median from T.

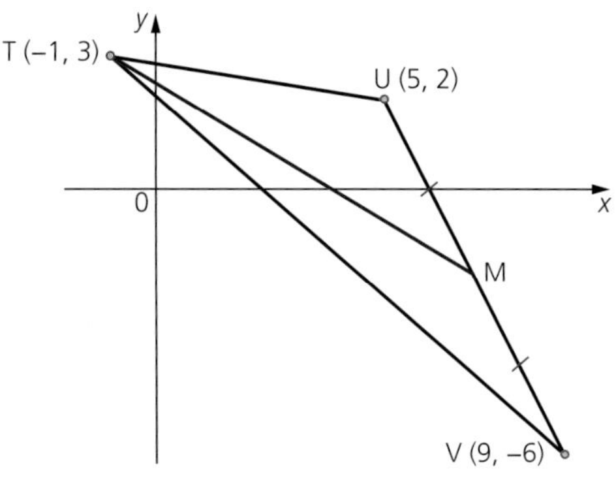

SOLUTION

Carry out the following steps:

* Find M, the midpoint of UV.
* Find the gradient of TM.
* Substitute into $y - b = m(x - a)$.

The midpoint of UV is $\left(\frac{5+9}{2}, \frac{2+(-6)}{2}\right) = (7, -2)$.

$$m_{TM} = \frac{y_2 - y_1}{x_2 - x_1} = \frac{-2-3}{7-(-1)} = \frac{-5}{8} = -\frac{5}{8}$$

Substitute into $y - b = m(x - a)$:

$$y + 2 = -\frac{5}{8}(x - 7)$$

$$\Rightarrow \quad 8y + 16 = -5x + 35$$

$$\Rightarrow 5x + 8y - 19 = 0$$

Exercise 1.8

1. A triangle has vertices P (−2, −3), Q (6, 1) and R (5, 8).
   Find the equation of RM, the median from R.
2. In triangle ABC, A is point (−3, −3), B is (−1, 1) and C is (7, −3).
   a) Find the equation of the median AM, the median from A.
   b) Find the equation of BN, the median from B.
3. Find the equations of all three medians in a triangle with vertices P (2, 6), Q (8, −4) and R (−2, 4). HPQ
4. A triangle has vertices K (−1, −4), L (3, 6) and M (1, 12). HPQ
   a) Find the equation of the perpendicular bisector of the line KL.
   b) Find the equation of the altitude from K.
   c) Find the equation of the median from M.

→

5 Triangle PQR has vertices P (3, 4), Q (−6, 6) and R (−4, −2). ACE

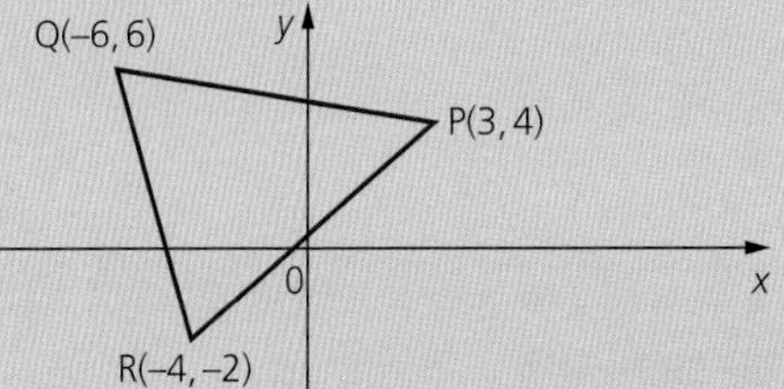

a) Find the equation of the altitude through P.
b) Find the equation of the median through P.
c) What kind of triangle is PQR? Justify your answer.

Intersecting lines

In this section you will study how to find points of intersection of straight lines associated with triangles.

Example

Triangle XYZ has vertices X (9, 0), Y (−1, −6) and Z (2, 6).
The median ZM and the altitude XA meet at the point K.

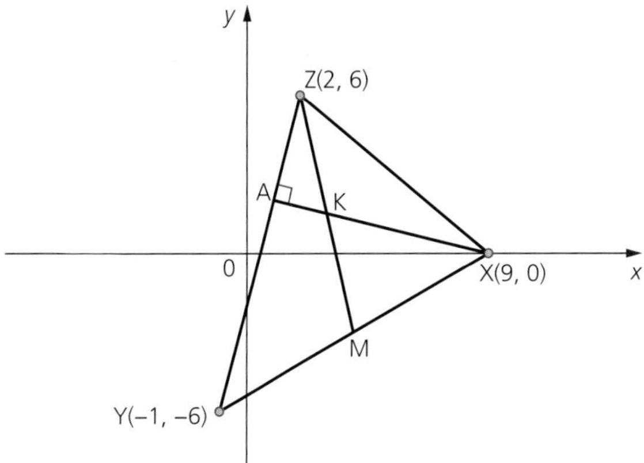

a) Find the equation of ZM.
b) Find the equation of XA.
c) Find the coordinates of K.

SOLUTION

a) The median ZM joins Z to M, the midpoint of XY.

As X is (9, 0) and Y is (−1, −6), M is $\left(\frac{9+(-1)}{2}, \frac{0+(-6)}{2}\right) = (4, -3)$.

The gradient of ZM is $\frac{y_2 - y_1}{x_2 - x_1} = \frac{-3-6}{4-2} = -\frac{9}{2}$.

The equation of ZM is $y - b = m(x - a) \Rightarrow y - 6 = -\frac{9}{2}(x - 2)$.

This simplifies to $2y - 12 = -9x + 18 \Rightarrow 9x + 2y - 30 = 0$.

b) The altitude XA is perpendicular to YZ.

The gradient of YZ is $\frac{y_2 - y_1}{x_2 - x_1} = \frac{6-(-6)}{2-(-1)} = \frac{12}{3} = 4.$

Therefore the gradient of XA is $-\frac{1}{4}$.

The equation of XA is $y - b = m(x - a) \Rightarrow y - 0 = -\frac{1}{4}(x - 9)$

This simplifies to $4y = -x + 9 \Rightarrow x + 4y - 9 = 0.$

c) To find the point of intersection of ZM and XA, solve simultaneous equations.

$$\begin{aligned} 9x + 2y &= 30 && (1) \\ x + 4y &= 9 && (2) \\ (1)\times 2: \quad 18x + 4y &= 60 && (3) \\ (3)-(2) \quad 17x &= 51 && \\ x &= 3 && \end{aligned}$$

By substitution in (1): $9 \times 3 + 2y = 30 \Rightarrow y = 1{\cdot}5$

Hence the coordinates of K are $(3, 1{\cdot}5)$

Exercise 1.9

1 In triangle ABC, A is the point (–3, –3), B is (–1, 1) and C is (7, –3).

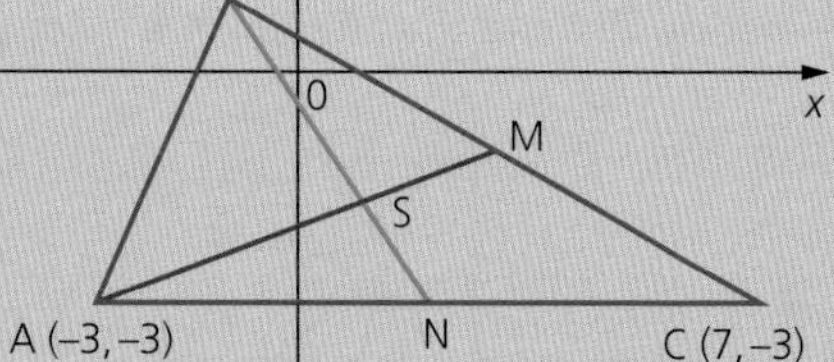

a) Find the equation of the median AM.
b) Find the equation of the median BN.
c) The medians AM and BN intersect at S. Find the coordinates of S.

2 In triangle PQR, P is the point (6, 6), Q is (–3, 0), and R is (0, –3).

a) Find the equation of the altitude from P.
b) Find the equation of the altitude from Q.
c) Find the coordinates of the point of intersection of the altitudes from P to Q.

3 Triangle ABC has vertices A (1, 8), B (8, –6) and C (–12, –2). HPQ

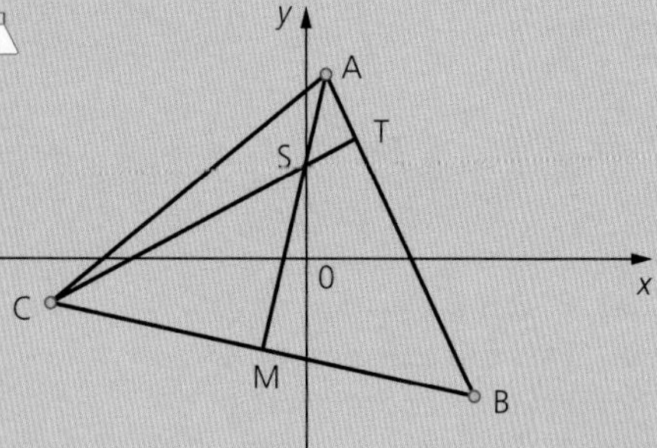

a) Find the equation of median AM.
b) Find the equation of altitude CT.
c) Find the coordinates of S, the point of intersection of AM and CT.

4 Triangle KLM has vertices K (–1, 12), L (–2, –5) and M (7, –2).

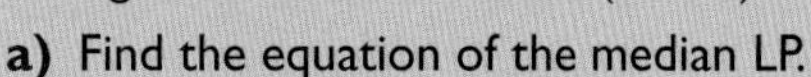

a) Find the equation of the median LP.
b) Find the equation of the altitude KT.
c) Find the coordinates of the point of intersection of LP and KT.

→

5 Triangle ABC has vertices A $(-1, 6)$, B $(-3, -2)$ and C $(5, 2)$. ACE

a) Find the equation of the line l_1, the median from vertex C.

b) Find the equation of the line l_2, the perpendicular bisector of BC.

c) Find the coordinates of the point S, the intersection of l_1 and l_2.

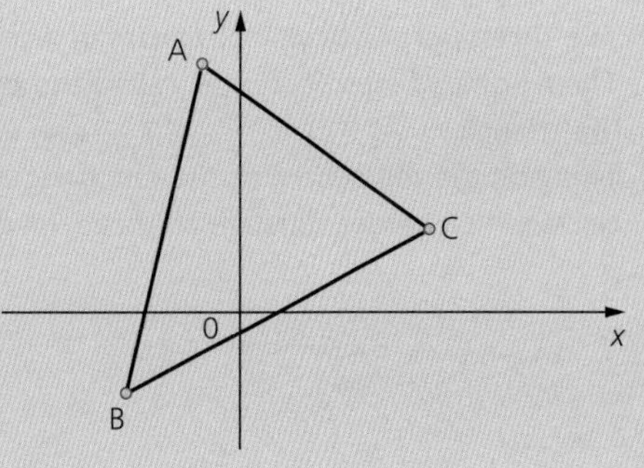

Concurrent lines

Three or more lines are said to be **concurrent** if they intersect at a single point.

Example

Three lines have equations $3x + 2y - 14 = 0$, $2x - 5y - 3 = 0$ and $x + 6y - 10 = 0$.

Determine whether these lines are concurrent.

SOLUTION

You answer this question by solving simultaneous equations. You do not need to solve every pair of equations – simply solve the easiest pair then check if the coordinates of the point of intersection satisfy the remaining equation.

The easiest pair of equations to solve appear to be $2x - 5y - 3 = 0$ and $x + 6y - 10 = 0$.

$$\begin{aligned} & 2x - 5y - 3 = 0 && (1) \\ & x + 6y - 10 = 0 && (2) \\ (2) \times 2: \quad & 2x + 12y - 20 = 0 && (3) \\ (1) - (3): \quad & -17y + 17 = 0 && \\ & \Rightarrow y = 1 && \end{aligned}$$

Substitute $y = 1$ in equation (1): $2x - 5 \times 1 - 3 = 0 \Rightarrow x = 4$

Hence the lines $2x - 5y - 3 = 0$ and $x + 6y - 10 = 0$ intersect at $(4, 1)$.

Now substitute $(4, 1)$ into the remaining line $3x + 2y - 14 = 0$.

$3 \times 4 + 2 \times 1 - 14 = 12 + 2 - 14 = 0$

Therefore all three lines pass through $(4, 1)$ so they are concurrent.

Exercise 1.10

1 Find which of the following sets of lines are concurrent:

a) $x + y = 8$, $3x - 2y = 9$, $5x - y = 22$

b) $y = 2x + 5$, $y = \frac{1}{2}x + 8$, $y = 3x - 1$

c) $3x + 2y - 3 = 0$, $2x - 3y + 11 = 0$, $x + 2y - 5 = 0$

d) $5x - 2y = 3$, $4x + y = 18$, $3x - 5y = -16$

2 Find the value of k if the lines $x + 3y = 1$, $2x - 5y = 13$ and $x - 2y + k = 0$ are concurrent.

Concurrent lines associated with triangles

- The three perpendicular bisectors in a triangle are concurrent.
- Their point of intersection is called the **circumcentre** of the triangle.
- This point is the centre of the **circumcircle**, i.e. the circle which passes through all three vertices of the triangle.

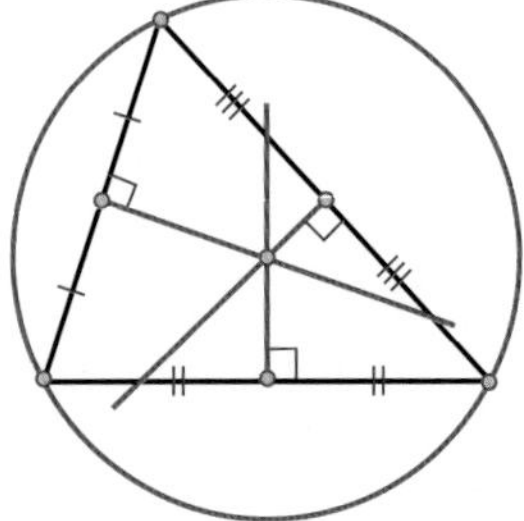

- The three altitudes in a triangle are concurrent.
- Their point of intersection is called the **orthocentre** of the triangle.
- If the triangle is acute-angled, the orthocentre will be inside the triangle.

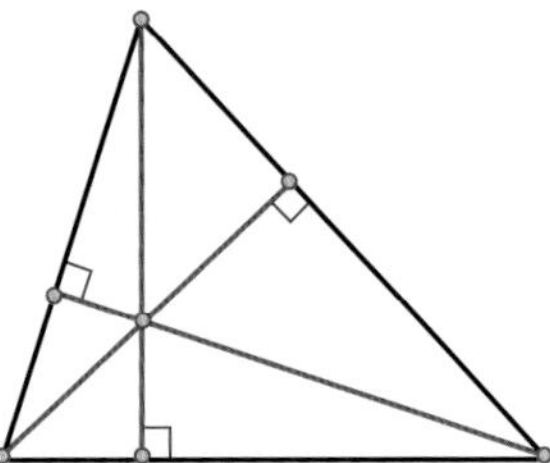

- The three medians in a triangle are concurrent.
- Their point of intersection is called the **centroid** of the triangle.
- The centroid cuts each median in the ratio 2:1.
  It is the 'centre of gravity' of the triangle.

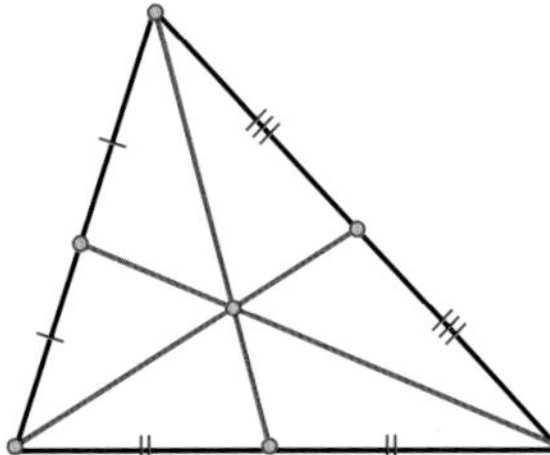

Exercise 1.11

All the questions in this exercise are ACE.

1 a) Find the equation of all three altitudes in a triangle with vertices A (2, −3), B (8, −2) and C (8, 6).
  b) Find the coordinates of the **orthocentre** of the triangle.

2 a) Find the equation of all three medians in a triangle with vertices P (−6, 9), Q (6, 1) and R (−6, −7).
  b) Find the coordinates of the **centroid** of the triangle.

3 a) Find the equation of all three perpendicular bisectors in a triangle with vertices D (0, 2), E (2, −4) and F (4, −6).
  b) Find the coordinates of the **circumcentre** of the triangle.

4 A funfair owner wants to tidy up the environment of his funfair. He intends to place a new rubbish bin for each group of three rides.

To make it efficient and easy to access for his customers, he intends to place the bin at the **circumcentre** of the three rides.

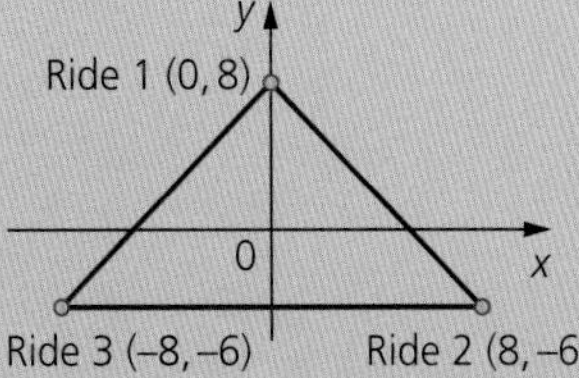

Find the coordinates of the spot where he should place the bin for this set of rides.

Algebraic Skills

Investigation

Draw a large scalene triangle.

Mark in the **perpendicular bisectors** in one colour, and mark in the point of intersection.

Mark in the **altitudes** in another colour, and mark in the point of intersection.

Mark in the **medians** in a third colour, and mark in the point of intersection.

Look at the three points of intersection. Join them up. Are you surprised?

This is known as **Euler's line** – you may wish to put this term in a search engine and find out a little more.

In a different scalene triangle, draw the three angle bisectors (the lines which bisect the angles at each vertex of the triangle).

Find out the name of the point where the three angle bisectors intersect.

Checkout

1 Find the distance between the points $(-2, -1)$ and $(-6, 4)$.

2 ABCD is a parallelogram. A has coordinates $(2, 3)$, B is $(4, 7)$ and C is $(8, 11)$. Find the equation of DC.

3 L, M and N are vertices of a triangle as shown. Find the equation of LS, the altitude from L.

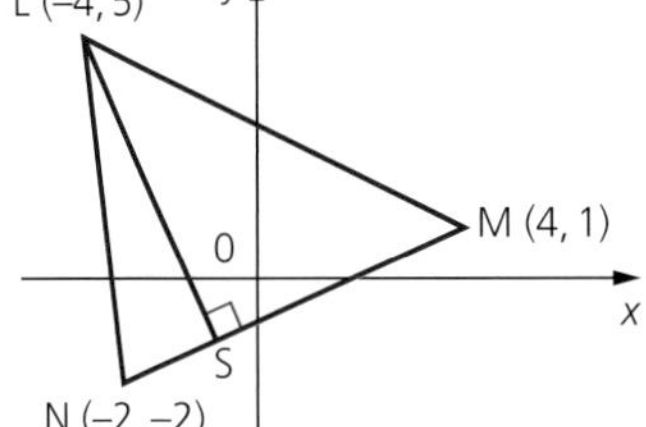

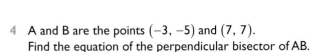

4 A and B are the points $(-3, -5)$ and $(7, 7)$. Find the equation of the perpendicular bisector of AB.

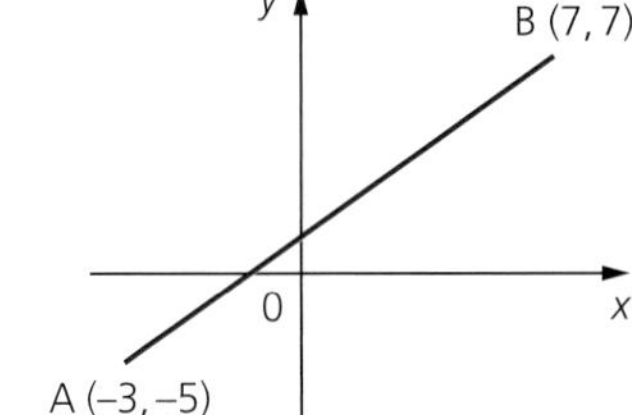

5 Three lines have equations $5x + 2y = 11$, $x + y = 7$ and $3x - 4y + 35 = 0$. Determine whether these lines are concurrent.

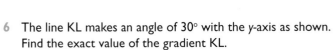

6 The line KL makes an angle of 30° with the y-axis as shown. Find the exact value of the gradient KL.

7 a) Find the equation of the straight line through the points A $(-1, 5)$ and B $(3, 1)$.
b) Find size of the angle which the line AB makes with the positive x-axis.

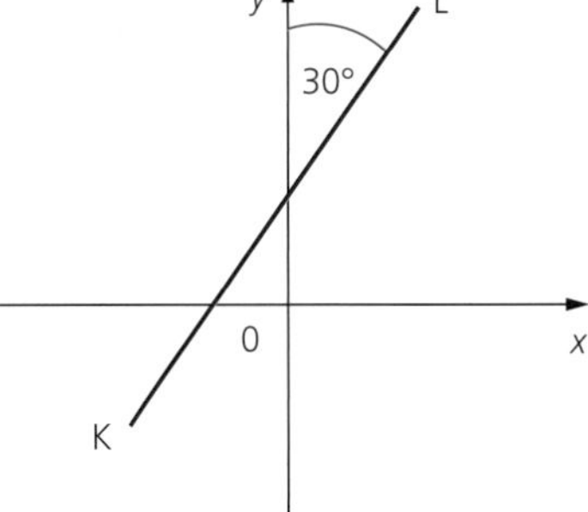

8 A chord joins the points A $(1, 0)$ and B $(5, 4)$ as shown. Show that the equation of the perpendicular bisector of chord AB is $x + y = 5$.

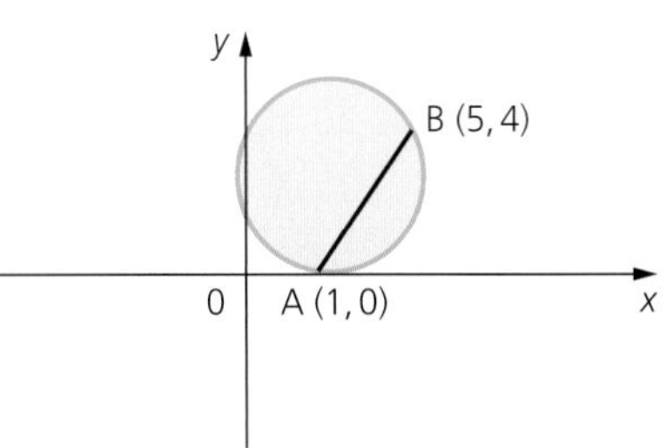

9 Show that the points A $(-1, -7)$, B $(1, 3)$ and C $(4, 18)$ are collinear.

10 Triangle DEF has vertices D $(-1, 12)$, E $(-2, -5)$ and F $(7, -2)$.
a) Find the equation of the median from E.
b) Find the equation of the altitude from D.
c) Find the point of intersection of the median and altitude.

Summary

The Straight Line

1 The distance from A (x_1, y_1) to B (x_2, y_2) is given by the **distance formula**:
$d = \sqrt{(x_2 - x_1)^2 + (y_2 - y_1)^2}$.

2 The midpoint of the line joining the points A (x_1, y_1) and B (x_2, y_2) has coordinates given by $\left(\frac{x_1 + x_2}{2}, \frac{y_1 + y_2}{2}\right)$.

3 The gradient of the line which makes an angle of θ with the positive direction of the x-axis is given by $m = \tan\theta$.

y
$m = \tan\theta$
θ
0
x

4 Points which lie in a straight line are said to be **collinear**. To show that points A, B and C are collinear, use gradients to check that lines AB and BC are parallel, and state that B is a point common to both lines.

5 If two lines with gradients m_1 and m_2 are perpendicular, then $m_1 m_2 = -1$.

6 The **perpendicular bisector** of a line is a straight line which crosses the midpoint of the line at right angles.

7 The **altitude** of a triangle is a straight line from a vertex perpendicular to the opposite side.

8 The **median** of a triangle is a straight line from a vertex to the midpoint of the opposite side.

9 Three or more lines are said to be **concurrent** if they intersect at a single point. To check whether a set of lines is concurrent, use simultaneous equations to find the point of intersection of one pair of the lines, then check that the coordinates of this point satisfy the remaining equations.

10 The perpendicular bisectors in a triangle are concurrent, as are the altitudes and the medians.

* The perpendicular bisectors intersect at the **circumcentre** of the triangle.
* The altitudes intersect at the **orthocentre** of the triangle.
* The medians intersect at the **centroid** of the triangle.

CHAPTER 2

Sequences and Recurrence Relations

In this chapter we will study sequences of numbers defined by recurrence relations. A **recurrence relation** is a formula connecting each term in a sequence to the previous term.

What I am learning

- How to determine a recurrence relation from given information
- How to determine a required term in a sequence
- How to determine if a limit exists for a given sequence/recurrence relation
- How to find the limit of a sequence, where it exists
- How to interpret the meaning of the limit of a given sequence, where it exists
- How to solve problems like this:
  A sequence is defined by the recurrence relation $u_{n+1} = \frac{1}{2}u_n + 5$, $u_0 = 3$.
  Explain why this sequence has a limit as $n \to \infty$ and find the limit.

What I should already know/be able to do

- Determine required terms in a sequence given a formula for the nth term
- Determine a formula for the nth term of a simple sequence given some of the terms in the sequence

Quick check!

1 Write down the first four terms of each of the following sequences whose n^{th} term is given below:
  a) $2n+3$
  b) $7n-2$
  c) $50-3n$

2 Write down an expression for the nth term of each of the following sequences:
  a) 4, 7, 10, 13, 16, …
  b) 1, 6, 11, 16, 21, …
  c) 19, 18, 17, 16, 15, …

Quick check! – *Solutions*

1 a) 5, 7, 9, 11
  b) 5, 12, 19, 26
  c) 47, 44, 41, 38

2 a) $3n+1$
  b) $5n-4$
  c) $20-n$

The nth term of a sequence

Note The nth term of a sequence is usually denoted by u_n. The first term is u_1, the second term is u_2, the third term is u_3, and so on.

Example 1

The nth term of a sequence is given by the formula $u_n = 3n + 2$. Find the first four terms of the sequence and the 50th term of the sequence.

SOLUTION

The first four terms are: $u_1 = 3(1) + 2 = 5$

$u_2 = 3(2) + 2 = 8$

$u_3 = 3(3) + 2 = 11$

$u_4 = 3(4) + 2 = 14$

The 50th term is: $u_{50} = 3(50) + 2 = 152$

When the difference between pairs consecutive terms of a sequence is the same, it is called a **linear sequence**. The formula for the nth term of a linear sequence is of the form $u_n = dn + b$, where d represents the common difference between consecutive terms.

Example 2

Find a formula for u_n, the nth term of the sequence 4, 10, 16, 22, 28, ...

SOLUTION

This is a linear sequence because the common difference between successive terms is 6.

Therefore the formula for the nth term is of the form $u_n = 6n + b$.

$$u_1 = 6(1) + b = 6 + b = 4$$
$$u_2 = 6(2) + b = 12 + b = 10$$
$$u_3 = 6(3) + b = 18 + b = 16$$
$$u_4 = 6(4) + b = 24 + b = 22$$
$$u_5 = 6(5) + b = 30 + b = 28$$

So $b = -2$ and therefore the formula for the nth term is $u_n = 6n - 2$.

Exercise 2.1

1 The formulae for the nth term of some sequences are given below.
Write down the first four terms and the 20th term of each sequence.

a) $u_n = 2n - 1$ **b)** $u_n = \frac{1}{2}n + 2$ **c)** $u_n = 4n - 10$

d) $u_n = 5n^2$ **e)** $u_n = n^3$ **f)** $u_n = 3^n$

g) $u_n = 7 - \frac{1}{n}$ **h)** $u_n = 5\cos(180n°)$

2 Find a formula for u_n, the nth term of each sequence below.

a) 6, 10, 14, 18, 22, ... **b)** 7, 15, 23, 31, 39, ... **c)** −5, −3, −1, 1, 3, ...

d) 21, 17, 13, 9, 5, ... **e)** 1, 4, 9, 16, 25, ... **f)** 2, 4, 8, 16, 32, ...

Recurrence relations

The terms in a sequence may be defined by a recurrence relation.

A recurrence relation is a formula that gives the connection between two consecutive terms in a sequence.

The consecutive terms are usually labelled u_{n+1} and u_n; however, they may be given as u_n and u_{n-1}. The starting value is usually denoted by u_0.

Example

A sequence is defined by the recurrence relation $u_{n+1} = 2u_n + 1,\ \ u_0 = 4$. Calculate the value of u_4.

SOLUTION

$$u_1 = 2u_0 + 1 = 2(4) + 1 = 9$$
$$u_2 = 2u_1 + 1 = 2(9) + 1 = 19$$
$$u_3 = 2u_2 + 1 = 2(19) + 1 = 39$$
$$u_4 = 2u_3 + 1 = 2(39) + 1 = 79$$

Note A recurrence relation of the form $u_{n+1} = au_n + b,\ \ a \neq 0$, is called a **linear recurrence relation.** This is sometimes written in the form $u_n = au_{n-1} + b,\ \ a \neq 0$.

Exercise 2.2

1 For each recurrence relation calculate the value of u_5:

a) $u_{n+1} = 3u_n + 1,\ \ u_0 = 2$

b) $u_n = 0{\cdot}5u_{n-1} + 2,\ \ u_0 = 12$

c) $u_{n+1} = -4u_n + 3,\ \ u_0 = 1$

d) $u_{n+1} = \frac{1}{3}u_n - 1,\ \ u_0 = 120$

2 A recurrence relation is given by $u_n = 2u_{n-1} + 1{\cdot}5$, $u_0 = 10$.

a) Calculate the values of u_2 and u_3.

b) Find the smallest value of n such that $u_n > 200$.

3 A recurrence relation is given by $u_{n+1} = 0{\cdot}3u_n - 4,\ \ u_0 = 8$. HPQ

a) Calculate the values of u_2 and u_3.

b) Find the smallest value of n such that $u_n < -5{\cdot}7$.

Problems involving recurrence relations

Example 1

Rory deposits £1000 into a savings account which earns 3% interest per year.

He also deposits a further £100 at the end of each year.

a) How much will he have in the account after 3 years?

b) Write down a recurrence relation for the amount in his savings account.

SOLUTION

a) $u_0 = 1000$

$u_1 = 103\%$ of $u_0 + 100 = 1{\cdot}03(1000) + 100 = 1130$

$u_2 = 1{\cdot}03(1130) + 100 = 1263{\cdot}9$

$u_2 = 1{\cdot}03(1263{\cdot}90) + 100 = 1401{\cdot}817$

Rory has £1401·82 in his account after 3 years.

b) $u_{n+1} = 1{\cdot}03u_n + 100,\ \ u_0 = 1000$, where u_n is the amount in the account after n years.

Note The [ANS] key on a scientific calculator can be used to speed up the calculation of successive terms of a sequence defined by a recurrence relation as described below.

For the recurrence relation $u_{n+1} = 1 \cdot 03u_n + 100,\ u_0 = 1000$:

* press [1000][=] to enter the starting value
* press [1·03][ANS][+][100] to set up the recurrence relation
* press [=] to get u_1
* press [=] again to get u_2
* press [=] again to get u_3
* and so on to get successive terms.

1000
1130
1263·9
1401·817

Example 2

A sequence is defined by the linear recurrence relation $u_{n+1} = au_n + b$.
Given that $u_0 = 10$, $u_1 = 8$ and $u_2 = 7{\cdot}4$, calculate the values of a and b.

SOLUTION

$u_{n+1} = au_n + b$

$u_1 = au_0 + b \Rightarrow 8 = 10a + b$

$u_2 = au_1 + b \Rightarrow 7{\cdot}4 = 8a + b$

We can now solve the pair of simultaneous equations:

$$8 = 10a + b \quad (1)$$
$$7{\cdot}4 = 8a + b \quad (2)$$
(1) – (2): $0{\cdot}6 = 2a$
$$a = 0{\cdot}3$$
Substitute $a = 0{\cdot}3$ into (1): $8 = 10(0{\cdot}3) + b$
$$8 = 3 + b$$
$$b = 5$$

Exercise 2.3

All questions in Exercise 2.3 are ACE questions.

1 Ali was given £100 on his 10th birthday and £50 on each birthday thereafter.
He invests this money in a savings account that pays interest at 2·5% per annum.

a) Write down a recurrence relation to model this situation.
b) How much will he have in his account on his 16th birthday?

2 Dave, who is retired, has £150 000 invested in a pension fund.
This fund earns Dave interest at the rate of 5% per annum.
At the end of each year Dave takes out £15 000 for living expenses for the following year.

a) Write down a recurrence relation to model this situation.
b) Dave's financial advisor tells him his pension fund will 'easily last 15 years'
Is this sound advice? Justify your answer.

3 Gemma borrows £2000 from a finance company on February 1st.
On the last day of each month she is charged 1·5% interest on the outstanding balance.
She makes repayments on the first of each subsequent month. Each repayment is £250 except for the smaller final amount which will pay off the loan.

a) Write down a recurrence relation for the outstanding balance on the first of each month.
b) Find the date and the amount of the final payment.

4 Joan has a balloon which contains 1500 millilitres of air. She blows more air into it.
Each puff she gives it increases the amount of air in the balloon by 15%.
However, 100 millilitres of air escapes at the same time.

a) Write down a recurrence relation to model this situation.
b) How much air will be in the balloon after 5 puffs?
c) The balloon will burst when it reaches 3000 millilitres. After how many puffs should Joan stop?

5 Mike's dog is ill. The vet gives the dog an injection of 100 millilitres of drug.
Every 4 hours, 12% of the drug passes through the dog's bloodstream.
To compensate, a further 10 millilitre dose is given every 4 hours.

a) Write down a recurrence relation to model this situation.
b) How much drug will be in Mike's dog after 24 hours?

6 A sequence is defined by the recurrence relation $u_{n+1} = au_n + b$.
If $u_1 = -3$, $u_2 = 7$ and $u_3 = 10$, find the values of a and b.

7 A sequence is defined by the recurrence relation $u_n = mu_{n-1} + c$.
If $u_0 = 100$, $u_1 = 30$ and $u_2 = 2$, find the values of m and c.

8 The amounts in a bank account at the end of three consecutive years were £2800, £3112 and £3436·48 respectively. The interest rate remained constant over this period and an extra fixed amount was also invested each year.
What was the interest and the fixed amount invested each year?

9 A recurrence relation is defined by $u_{n+1} = au_n - 4$, $u_0 = 2$.

a) Find expressions for u_1 and u_2 in terms of a.
b) Given $u_2 = 26$, find the values of a.

10 A recurrence relation is defined by $u_n = mu_{n-1} + 1$, $u_0 = 3$.

a) Find expressions for u_1 and u_2 in terms of m.
b) If $u_2 = 5$, find the values of m.

Convergent, divergent and oscillating sequences

We shall now look at three different ways in which a sequence can **converge** to a limit.

1 The recurrence relation $u_{n+1} = 0{\cdot}2u_n + 4,\ u_0 = 2$, generates the sequence $2,\ 4{\cdot}4,\ 4{\cdot}88,\ 4{\cdot}976,\ \ldots$
The terms of this sequence *increase* by smaller and smaller amounts until they eventually settle at 5.
As $n \to \infty$, $u_n \to 5$, and we say that the sequence converges to a limit of 5.

2 The recurrence relation $u_{n+1} = 0{\cdot}5u_n + 1{\cdot}5,\ u_0 = 7$, generates the sequence $7,\ 5,\ 4,\ 3{\cdot}5,\ 3{\cdot}25,\ 3{\cdot}125,\ \ldots$
The terms of this sequence *decrease* by smaller and smaller amounts until they eventually settle at 3.
As $n \to \infty$, $u_n \to 3$, and we say that the sequence converges to a limit of 3.

3 The recurrence relation $u_{n+1} = -0{\cdot}5u_n + 2,\ u_0 = 2$, generates the sequence $2,\ 1,\ 1{\cdot}5,\ 1{\cdot}25,\ 1{\cdot}375,\ 1{\cdot}3125,\ \ldots$
The terms of this sequence *oscillate* (alternately increasing and decreasing) by smaller and smaller amounts until they eventually settle at $1\frac{1}{3}$. As $n \to \infty$, $u_n \to 1\frac{1}{3}$, and we say that the sequence converges to a limit of $1\frac{1}{3}$.

Converging to a limit

1. 2. 3.

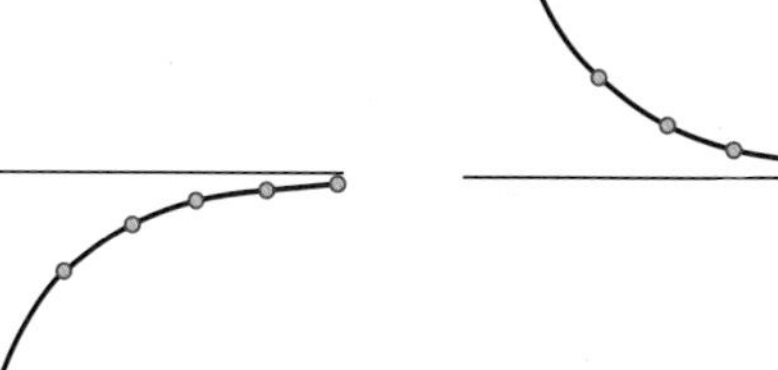

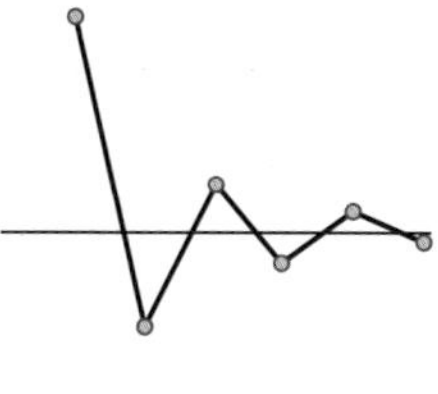

Next we shall look at three different ways in which a sequence can **diverge**.

1 The recurrence relation $u_{n+1} = 4u_n + 3,\ u_0 = 1$, generates the sequence $1,\ 7,\ 31,\ 127,\ 511,\ \ldots$
The terms of this sequence increase by larger and larger amounts.
As $n \to \infty$, $u_n \to \infty$, and we say that the sequence diverges.

2 The recurrence relation $u_{n+1} = 3u_n - 5,\ u_0 = 1$, generates the sequence $1,\ -2,\ -11,\ -38,\ -119,\ -362,\ \ldots$
The terms of this sequence decrease by larger and larger amounts.
As $n \to \infty$, $u_n \to -\infty$, and we say that the sequence diverges.

3 The recurrence relation $u_{n+1} = -2u_n + 1,\ u_0 = 8$, generates the sequence $8,\ -15,\ 31,\ -61,\ 123,\ -245,\ \ldots$
The terms of this sequence oscillate and the sequence diverges.

Diverging

1. 2. 3.

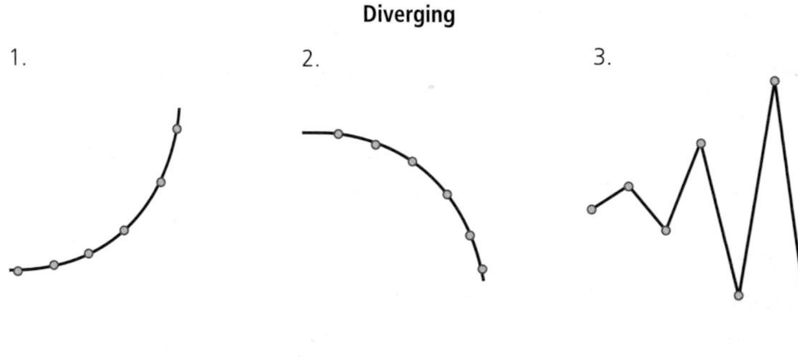

Some sequences oscillate between two values. An example of this is the recurrence relation $u_{n+1} = -u_n + 2, \quad u_0 = 3,$ which generates the sequence $3, -1, 3, -1, 3, -1, \ldots$

Oscillating between two values

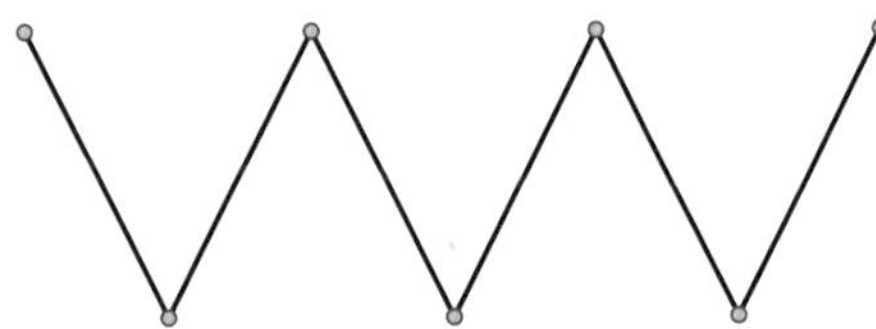

Exercise 2.4

1 Determine which of the following recurrence relations generate sequences that:
i) are convergent;
ii) are divergent;
iii) oscillate between two values.

a) $u_{n+1} = 3u_n + 1, \quad u_0 = 2$
b) $u_{n+1} = 0{\cdot}5u_n + 2, \quad u_0 = 10$
c) $u_{n+1} = -2u_n + 7, \quad u_0 = 1$
d) $u_{n+1} = -0{\cdot}6u_n + 2, \quad u_0 = 15$
e) $u_n = u_{n-1} - 20, \quad u_0 = 25$
f) $u_{n+1} = -u_n + 4, \quad u_0 = 100$
g) $u_{n+1} = 0{\cdot}8u_n - 3, \quad u_0 = 5$

2 For those sequences in question 1 which are convergent, find the limit of the sequence.

3 Find the limit of the sequence generated by the recurrence relation $u_{n+1} = 0{\cdot}75u_n + 3$ for each of the following starting values:
a) $u_0 = 4$
b) $u_0 = 200$
c) $u_0 = -30$

4 Find the limit of the sequence generated by the recurrence relation $u_{n+1} = -0{\cdot}2u_n - 10$ for each of the following starting values:
a) $u_0 = 4$
b) $u_0 = 200$
c) $u_0 = -30$

5 How can you tell if the sequence generated by the linear recurrence relation $u_{n+1} = au_n + b$ converges to a limit? Make a conjecture based on your answers to the questions in this exercise. ACE

The limit of a recurrence relation

The sequence generated by the linear recurrence relation $u_{n+1} = au_n + b$ converges to a limit if $-1 < a < 1$. We usually denote the limit by L.

Once the limit has been reached, the next term in the sequence, u_{n+1}, is the same as the previous term, u_n. That is, as $n \to \infty, \quad u_{n+1} = u_n = L$.

Hence, as $n \to \infty$

$$
\begin{aligned}
u_{n+1} = au_n + b \Rightarrow \quad & L = aL + b \\
\Rightarrow \quad & L - aL = b \\
\Rightarrow \quad & L(1-a) = b \\
\Rightarrow \quad & L = \frac{b}{1-a}
\end{aligned}
$$

Note that the limit is independent of the starting value, u_0.

Algebraic Skills

Example

A sequence is defined by the recurrence relation $u_{n+1} = \frac{1}{2}u_n + 5, \ u_0 = 3.$

Explain why this sequence has a limit as $n \to \infty$, and find the limit.

SOLUTION

The sequence has a limit since $-1 < \frac{1}{2} < 1.$

$$\begin{aligned} L &= \frac{b}{1-a} \\ &= \frac{5}{1-\frac{1}{2}} \\ &= \frac{5}{\frac{1}{2}} \\ &= 10 \end{aligned}$$

Exercise 2.5

1 For each of the following recurrence relations:

- explain why the sequence generated by it converges or diverges;
- where the sequence converges, find the limit.

a) $u_{n+1} = 0{\cdot}6u_n + 12, \ u_0 = 4$ **b)** $u_{n+1} = 0{\cdot}25u_n - 9, \ u_0 = 6$

c) $u_{n+1} = 2u_n + 5, \ u_0 = 1$ **d)** $u_{n+1} = -0{\cdot}5u_n + 3, \ u_0 = 10$

e) $u_{n+1} = u_n + 10, \ u_0 = 3$ **f)** $u_{n+1} = -\frac{2}{3}u_n - 4, \ u_0 = 5$

2 A sequence is defined by the recurrence relation $u_{n+1} = 0{\cdot}3u_n + 2, \ u_0 = 2.$

a) Explain why this sequence has a limit as $n \to \infty$.

b) Find the **exact** value of this limit.

3 A sequence is defined by the recurrence relation $u_{n+1} = \frac{4}{7}u_n + 4, \ u_0 = 5.$

a) Explain why this sequence has a limit as $n \to \infty$.

b) Find the **exact** value of this limit.

4 Two sequences are defined by the recurrence relations. HPQ

$u_{n+1} = 4u_n - 0{\cdot}7, \ u_0 = 2,$ and $w_{n+1} = 0{\cdot}4w_n + 3, \ w_0 = 2.$

a) Explain why only one of these sequences has a limit as $n \to \infty$.

b) Find this limit.

5 A sequence, defined by the recurrence relation $u_{n+1} = 0{\cdot}84u_n + b, \ u_0 = 6,$ converges to a limit of 25. Find the value of b.

6 A sequence, defined by the recurrence relation $u_{n+1} = au_n + 40, \ u_0 = 10,$ converges to a limit of 50. Find the value of a.

7 Two sequences are defined by the recurrence relations

$u_{n+1} = 0{\cdot}4u_n + p, \ u_0 = 1,$ and $w_{n+1} = 0{\cdot}7w_n + q, \ w_0 = 4.$

If both sequences have the same limit, express p in terms of q.

8 For the recurrence relation $u_{n+1} = au_n + b$, it is known that $u_0 = 6$, $u_1 = 12$ and $u_2 = 21$. ACE

a) Calculate the values of a and b.

b) Explain whether or not a limit exists for this sequence.

Recurrence relations in context

Example

The squirrel population in a forest decreases by 7% per year.

Each year 25 new squirrels are introduced to the forest.

The initial squirrel population is 200.

a) What will the squirrel population be after 3 years?
b) What will be the long-term effect on the squirrel population?

SOLUTION

a) The population decreases by 7%, so the population left is $100\% - 7\% = 93\% = 0{\cdot}93$.
A recurrence relation which models this situation is $P_{n+1} = aP_n + b$, where P_n is the squirrel population after n years, $P_0 = 200$, $a = 0{\cdot}93$ and $b = 25$.
This leads to the recurrence relation $P_{n+1} = 0{\cdot}93P_n + 25$. Hence

$$P_1 = 0{\cdot}93P_0 + 25 = 0{\cdot}93(200) + 25 = 211$$
$$P_2 = 0{\cdot}93P_1 + 25 = 0{\cdot}93(211) + 25 = 221{\cdot}23$$
$$P_3 = 0{\cdot}93P_2 + 25 = 0{\cdot}93(221{\cdot}23) + 25 = 230{\cdot}7439$$

After 3 years, the squirrel population will be about 231.

Note When you decide to use the limit formula, you must state that a limit exists and give a reason why.

b) The sequence converges to a limit since $-1 < 0{\cdot}93 < 1$.

Hence $L = \dfrac{b}{1-a}$

$$= \frac{25}{1-0{\cdot}93}$$

$$= \frac{25}{0{\cdot}07}$$

$$= 357{\cdot}14\ldots$$

In the long term, the population of squirrels converges to a limit of around 357.

Exercise 2.6

All questions in Exercise 2.6 are ACE questions.

1 In a pond, 35% of the existing tadpoles die off each day but during the night 800 tadpoles are hatched. There are t_n tadpoles at the start of a given day.

a) Write down a recurrence relation for t_{n+1}, the number of tadpoles at the start of the next day.
b) Find the limit of this sequence.
c) Explain what this limit means in the context of the question.

2 A farmer has 200 chickens. Unfortunately, 27% of the chickens are killed by foxes each month. At the end of each month the farmer buys 20 chickens to replenish his stock.

a) Set up a recurrence relation to model this situation.
b) State why a limit exists for this sequence.
c) Calculate this limit.
d) Explain what this limit means in the context of the question.

3 Algae grow in a pond at a rate of 275 grams per week. The pond is cleaned every week using a process which removes 55% of any algae present.

a) Set up a recurrence relation to model this situation.
b) What will happen, in the long run, to the mass of algae in the pond?

4 A hospital patient is put on medication which is taken once per day.
The dose is 35 milligrams, and each day the patient's metabolism burns off 65% of the drug in her system.
If the level of drug reaches 50 milligrams the consequences are very serious.
Is it safe for the patient to take this drug indefinitely?

5 A factory wishes to release waste containing 2 tonnes of pollutant chemical annually into a sea loch.
The natural action of the sea loch will remove 70% of the pollutant chemical each year.
The maximum amount that the authorities will allow to be in the loch in total is 3 tonnes.
Would the factory meet this requirement in the long run? Justify your answer.

6 Once a month, the environmental health department removes sticky gum from the pavements in Dalburgh town centre. This operation removes 85% of the gum. However, each month, the public drop another 3 kilograms of gum on the pavements.

a) In the long run, how much gum will there be on the pavements in Dalburgh?
b) The council runs an awareness-raising campaign which they think will reduce the monthly amount of gum dropped to 2 kilograms. How will this affect the sticky gum problem in the long run?

7 In a membership drive a health club is trying to recruit new members.
In any month it estimates that it loses 2·5% of its members to competitors and attracts 30 new members.
It has 1250 members at the start of the recruitment drive.

a) What would happen to the number of members in the long term if this situation continued?
b) How many new members would the club have to recruit each month in order to maintain its membership level at 1400?

8 Maurice decides to plant some trees as a boundary between him and his neighbour.
The trees are expected to grow 75 centimetres each year.

a) If Maurice cuts 20% off their height each year, to what height would the trees grow in the long term?
b) Maurice's neighbour is not too happy and would like the height of the trees to not exceed 2·5 metres. What percentage should Maurice cut off each year to achieve this?

Investigation

Two utility companies share 90 000 customers.

We'R'Electric loses 30% of its customers to Edison Electrics each year.

Edison Electrics loses 20% of its customers to We'R'Electric each year.

If this trend continues over a long period of time, how many customers would each company have?

Checkout

1 A recurrence relation is given by $u_n = 1{\cdot}5u_{n-1} - 2,\ \ u_0 = 8$.
a) Calculate the values of u_2 and u_3.
b) Find the smallest value of n such that $u_n > 50$.

2 A sequence is defined by the recurrence relation $u_{n+1} = 0{\cdot}4u_n + 5,\ \ u_0 = 10$.
a) Explain why this sequence has a limit as $n \to \infty$.
b) Find the **exact** value of this limit.

3 A sequence is defined by the recurrence relation $u_{n+1} = au_n + 5,\ \ u_0 = 6$.
Find the value of a which will produce a sequence with a limit of 4.

4 Two sequences are defined by the recurrence relations $u_{n+1} = 0{\cdot}2u_n + p,\ \ u_0 = 1$, and $v_{n+1} = 0{\cdot}4v_n + q,\ \ v_0 = 10$.
If both sequences have the same limit, express p in terms of q.

5 Two sequences are defined by the recurrence relations $u_{n+1} = au_n + 10$, $u_0 = 2$, and $v_{n+1} = a^2 v_n + 8$, $v_0 = 2$. If both sequences have the same limit, find the value of a, and hence evaluate the limit.

6 A sequence is defined by the recurrence relation $u_{n+1} = mu_n + c$, where $-1 < m < 1$ and $u_0 = 12$.
a) If $u_1 = 15$ and $u_2 = 16$, find the values of m and c.
b) Find the limit of this sequence as $n \to \infty$.

7 John takes out a mortgage for £90000 on a flat. The interest charged on this sum is 4·5% per annum. He pays back £6000 each year.
How much will he still owe after 4 years?

8 Garden shrubs are sprayed weekly with the pesticide 'Bugs Away', whose manufacturer claims it will destroy 65% of all pests. Between the weekly sprayings, it is estimated that 200 new pests will invade the shrubs. A new pesticide, OutBug, is developed and comes on the market. The manufacturer claims that it will destroy 80% of existing pests, but it is estimated that 250 new pests will invade the shrubs each week.
Which pesticide will be more effective in the long run? Justify your answer.

Summary

Sequences and Recurrence Relations

1 A recurrence relation is a formula that gives the connection between two consecutive terms in a sequence.

2 A recurrence relation of the form $u_{n+1} = au_n + b$, $a \neq 0$, is called a linear recurrence relation. This is sometimes written in the form $u_n = au_{n-1} + b$.

3 The linear recurrence relation $u_{n+1} = au_n + b$ tends to a limit if $-1 < a < 1$.
The limit, L, is given by $L = \dfrac{b}{1-a}$.

Algebraic Skills

CHAPTER

3 Polynomial Expressions and Equations

You have already studied linear functions, e.g. $f(x) = 3x + 7$, and quadratic functions, e.g. $f(x) = x^2 + 6x + 8$. In this chapter, you will study polynomials including cubic and quartic functions. These expressions involve powers of x greater than 2, e.g. $x^3 + 3x^2 + 3x + 1$, $2x^4 + 4x^3 - 8x + 5$.

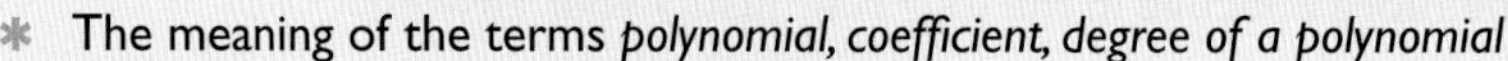

What I am learning

* The meaning of the terms *polynomial, coefficient, degree of a polynomial*
* How to evaluate a polynomial expression
* The Remainder and Factor Theorems
* How to factorise cubic and quartic expressions
* How to solve cubic and quartic equations
* How to find the point(s) of intersection of two graphs
* How to solve problems using the discriminant
* How to solve quadratic inequalities
* How to solve problems like this: Factorise $2t^3 + 5t^2 - 28t - 15$ fully.

What I should already know/be able to do

* How to solve linear equations and inequalities
* How to factorise a quadratic expression
* How to solve a quadratic expression
* How to sketch the graph of a quadratic function
* How to determine the nature of the roots of a quadratic equation using the discriminant
* The terms *factor, roots* and *zeros*

Quick check!

1 Solve the equations:
   a) $4x - 3 = 17$
   b) $3(2x + 5) = 24$
   c) $5x - 2 = 2x + 7$
2 Solve the inequality $2(3 - x) \le 4$.
3 Factorise:
   a) $4xy - y^2$
   b) $9x^2 - 25$
   c) $2x^2 - 5x - 3$
4 Find the roots of the equation $3x^2 - 10x - 8 = 0$.
5 Sketch the graph of $f(x) = (x + 1)(x - 3)$ showing where it crosses the coordinate axes.
6 Use the discriminant to determine the nature of the roots of the equation $3x^2 + 5x - 2 = 0$.

Quick check! – *Solutions*

1 a) $x = 5$
 b) $x = 1{\cdot}5$
 c) $x = 3$
2 $x \geqslant 1$
3 a) $y(4x - y)$
 b) $(3x + 5)(3x - 5)$
 c) $(2x + 1)(x - 3)$
4 $x = -\frac{2}{3}$ or $x = 4$
5

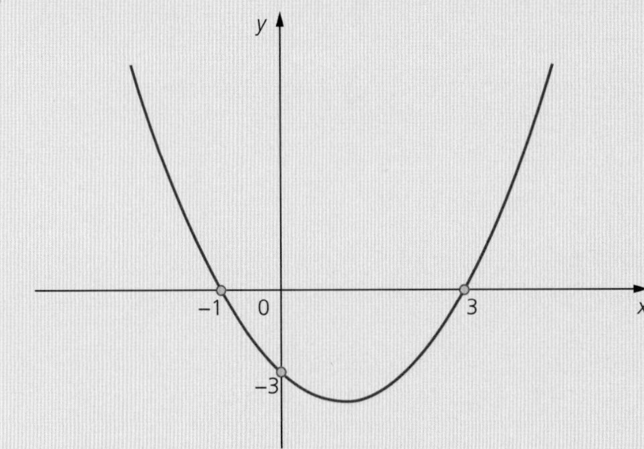

6 Two distinct real rational roots (as $b^2 - 4ac = 49 > 0$ and a perfect square)

What is a polynomial?

$x^3 + 3x^2 + 3x + 1$ and $2x^4 + 4x^3 - 8x + 5$ are examples of **polynomials**.

The **degree** of a polynomial is the value of the highest power.

$x^3 + 3x^2 + 3x + 1$ is a polynomial of degree 3. A polynomial of degree 3 is called a **cubic**.

$2x^4 + 4x^3 - 8x + 5$ is a polynomial of degree 4. A polynomial of degree 4 is called a **quartic**.

In the polynomial $2x^4 + 4x^3 - 8x + 5$, the **coefficient** of the x^4 term is 2. The coefficients of the x^3, x^2 and x terms are 4, 0 and −8 respectively. The coefficient of the x^0 term is 5; it is called the **constant** term.

In general, $a_nx^n + a_{n-1}x^{n-1} + a_{n-2}x^{n-2} + \ldots + a_3x^3 + a_2x^2 + a_1x + a_0, x \neq 0$ is a polynomial of degree n, where n is a whole number and $a_n, \ldots, a_0$ are the coefficients.

Polynomials are often expressed in functional notation.

Example

Evaluate $f(2)$ where $f(x) = 3x^3 - 5x^2 - 4x + 1$.

SOLUTION

$f(2) = 3 \times 2^3 - 5 \times 2^2 - 4 \times 2 + 1 = 24 - 20 - 8 + 1 = -3$

Exercise 3.1

1 State the coefficient of x in:

a) x^3+3x^2+3x+1 **b)** $5-8x+6x^3-2x^4$ **c)** $3-4x^3-x^5$

2 State the constant term in:

a) x^3+3x^2+3x+1 **b)** $5-8x+6x^3-2x^4$ **c)** $3-4x^3-x^5$

3 State the coefficient of x^2 in:

a) x^3+3x^2+3x+1 **b)** $5-8x+6x^3-2x^4$ **c)** $3-4x^2-x^5$
d) $(3x^2-1)^2$ **e)** $(5-x)^3$

4 State the degree of the polynomial:

a) $f(x)=4x-1$ **b)** $f(x)=3x^4+2x-3$ **c)** $f(x)=3x^6-x$
d) $f(x)=5x^2-2x+1$ **e)** $f(x)=x^2(2x-3)$ **f)** $f(x)=x(x^2-1)+x^2(x^2+2)$

5 Which of the following are polynomials? HPQ

a) $f(x)=0\cdot5x-3$ **b)** $f(x)=3x^4+2x-3$ **c)** $f(x)=3x^{\frac{1}{2}}+2x+4$
d) $f(x)=2x^{-3}+5x^2-2x+1$ **e)** $f(x)=\sqrt{(x^2+2)}$

6 Arrange in descending powers of x:

a) $(1+5x)^2$ **b)** $x(4-x)^2$

7 Arrange in ascending powers of x:

a) $x^2+3-4x-5x^3$ **b)** $(x+2)^3$

8 State the coefficient of

a) x in $(3x-2)(2x-4)$ **b)** x^2 in $(2-x)(4-3x)$ **c)** x^3 in $x(2x-1)^2$

9 State the constant term in $(4x-3)^2$.

10 Evaluate:

a) $f(-3)$ where $f(x)=x^2-5x$ **b)** $f(2)$ where $f(x)=5x^2-3x+7$
c) $f(-1)$ where $f(x)=2x^3-2x^2+x+4$ **d)** $f(-2)$ where $f(x)=x^4-3x^3-4x^2-7x+8$

Evaluating polynomials

Polynomials are often evaluated by substitution (see question 10 in the previous exercise).
We are now going to study another method for evaluating polynomials.

Example

Evaluate $f(2)$ where $f(x)=3x^3-5x^2-4x+1$.

SOLUTION

Arrange the polynomial into **nested form**.

$$\begin{aligned} f(x) &= 3x^3-5x^2-4x+1 \\ &= (3x^2-5x-4)x+1 \\ &= [(3x-5)\,x-4]x+1 \end{aligned}$$

Hence
$$\begin{aligned} f(2) &= [(3\times2-5)\times2-4]\times2+1 \\ &= [(6-5)\times2-4]\times2+1 \\ &= [1\times2-4]\times2+1 \\ &= [2-4]\times2+1 \\ &= -2\times2+1 \\ &= -3 \end{aligned}$$

The nested form method can be laid out in a table as follows:

2	3	−5	−4	1
		6	2	−4
	3	1	−2	−3

$\Rightarrow f(2) = -3$

Steps for completing the table

1 To evaluate $f(2)$, start with 2 on the top row to the left of the table.
2 Write the coefficients of $f(x)$ along the top row of the table.
3 Copy down the leading coefficient, 3, from the top row to the bottom row.
4 Multiply diagonally by 2 to get 6 in the middle row.
5 Add the −5 in the top row and the 6 in the middle row to get 1.
6 Continue to multiply and add twice more.
7 The value of the polynomial is the final number in the third row, namely −3.

This table provides a quick and simple way of evaluating polynomials in nested form. It is particularly useful when working without a calculator.

Note

When evaluating a polynomial in nested form:
- the polynomial should be arranged in descending powers of x
- any 'missing' powers should be assigned coefficient 0

Example

Evaluate $f(-3)$ for the function $f(x) = 4 - 3x + 2x^2 - x^4$.

SOLUTION

Arrange $f(x)$ into descending powers of x and make 0 the coefficient of x^3.

$f(x) = -x^4 + 0x^3 + 2x^2 - 3x + 4$

−3	−1	0	2	−3	4
		3	−9	21	−54
	−1	3	−7	18	**−50**

$\Rightarrow f(-3) = -50$

Exercise 3.2

1 Evaluate: HPQ

a) $f(4)$ where $f(x) = 2x^2 + 6x - 10$
b) $f(1)$ where $f(x) = 2x^3 - 4x^2 + 5x - 3$
c) $f(-5)$ where $f(x) = x^4 + x^3 + x^2 - 5x + 3$
d) $f(8)$ where $f(x) = 11 - 2x - x^2$
e) $f(3)$ where $f(x) = 2x^3 - 3x - 4$
f) $g(5)$ where $g(t) = t^3 + 2t^2 + 30$
g) $h(-1)$ where $h(n) = 12 - n - n^3$
h) $f(2)$ where $f(p) = 1 + 3p^2 - 2p^4$

2 Find the value of:

a) $2x^3 - x^2 - 4x + 3$ when $x = 2{\cdot}5$
b) $6n^3 + 3n^2 - 2n + 7$ when $n = -0{\cdot}5$
c) $5t^4 + 4t^3 - 12t^2 + 6t - 7$ when $t = 1{\cdot}2$
d) $4x^4 - 3x^3 + 7x^2 + 1$ when $x = -0{\cdot}25$

3 A function is defined by $f(x) = 3x^3 - 4x^2 - 5x + k$. ACE
Find the value of k if $f(2) = 5$.

Dividing polynomials and the Remainder Theorem

Consider when you did division in arithmetic.

9	÷	4	=	2	+1
Dividend		Divisor		Quotient	Remainder

We can rewrite this calculation as $9 = 4 \times 2 + 1$.

In this section, we shall look at the division of polynomials where the same ideas apply.

Suppose we divide a polynomial $f(x)$ by the expression $(x-h)$. We will get a quotient $q(x)$ and a remainder r so that $f(x) = (x-h)\,q(x) + r$, where r is a constant.

Example

A function is defined by $f(x) = 2x^2 - 3x + 4$. Divide $f(x)$ by $(x-3)$.

SOLUTION

Carry out a long division.

$$
\begin{array}{r|l}
 & 2x + 3 \\
\hline
x-3 & 2x^2 - 3x + 4 \\
 & \underline{2x^2 - 6x} \\
 & \quad\quad 3x + 4 \\
 & \quad\quad \underline{3x - 9} \\
 & \quad\quad\quad \underline{13}
\end{array}
$$

In the above format

$2x^2 - 3x + 4$	÷	$(x-3)$	=	$(2x + 3)$	$+13$
Dividend		Divisor		Quotient	Remainder

Hence $2x^2 - 3x + 4 = (x-3)(2x + 3) + 13$

Consider using the nested form table to evaluate $f(3)$.

$$
\begin{array}{c|ccc}
3 & 2 & -3 & 4 \\
 & & 6 & 9 \\
\hline
 & 2 & 3 & \mathbf{13}
\end{array}
$$

Notice the following:

- The value of $f(3)$ is 13, which is the remainder when $f(x)$ is divided by $(x-3)$.
  This result is called the **Remainder Theorem**.

> If $f(x)$ is divided by $(x - h)$, the remainder is $f(h)$.

- The other values in the bottom row of the table, 2 and 3, are the coefficients of the quotient, $2x + 3$.
  This method of dividing $f(x)$ by $(x-h)$ is called **synthetic division**.

Algebraic Skills

Example 1

Find the quotient and remainder on dividing $2x^3+x^2-7x+4$ by $(x+2)$.

SOLUTION

Let $f(x)=2x^3+x^2-7x+4$. Then the remainder is $f(-2)$.

−2	2	1	−7	4
		−4	6	2
	2	−3	−1	**6**

$\Rightarrow$ The remainder $f(-2)$ equals 6.

The quotient is $2x^2-3x-1$ and the remainder is 6.

Therefore $2x^3+x^2-7x+4=(2x^2-3x-1)(x+2)+6$.

Example 2

Find the value of k if the remainder on dividing $x^3+3x^2+kx-14$ by $(x-3)$ is 10.

SOLUTION

Let $f(x)=x^3+3x^2+kx-14$. Then the remainder is $f(3)$.

3	1	3	k	-14
		3	18	$3k+54$
	1	6	$k+18$	$3k+40$

$\Rightarrow 3k+40=10$

$\Rightarrow k=-10$

Exercise 3.3

1 Find the quotient and remainder on dividing: HPQ

a) x^3+3x^2-4x+2 by $(x-1)$

b) x^3-2x^2+x-7 by $(x+2)$

c) x^4-3x-6 by $(x-2)$

d) x^3-5x^2-6x+2 by $(x+3)$

e) x^3-5 by $(x-4)$

f) $2x^3-6x^2+x-4$ by $(x+4)$

g) x^3+x^2-12 by $(x-2)$

h) $6x^3-25x^2+x+60$ by $(x-3)$

i) $1+x+x^2+x^3-x^4$ by $(x-2)$

j) $3x^2+x^3-x^4+3x^5$ by $(x+4)$

2 Find the value of a given that x^3-2x^2-5x+a has remainder 2 on division by $(x-3)$.

3 Find the value of h given that $2x^3+x^2+hx-5$ has remainder 11 on division by $(x+2)$.

4 Find the value of p given that $5x^3-px^2-4x-6$ has remainder -10 on division by $(x+1)$.

5 Find the value of q given that qx^3-x^2+7x-3 has remainder 117 on division by $(x-3)$.

The Remainder Theorem can be adapted for division by $(ax-b)$.

If $f(x)$ is divided by $(ax-b)$, the remainder is $f\left(\frac{b}{a}\right)$.

Example

Find the quotient and remainder on dividing $3x^3+4x^2+11x-6$ by $(3x-2)$.

SOLUTION

The remainder is $f\left(\frac{2}{3}\right)$.

$\frac{2}{3}$	3	4	11	−6
		2	4	10
	3	6	15	**4**

$\Rightarrow$ The remainder $f\left(\frac{2}{3}\right)$ equals 4.

Hence $3x^3+4x^2+11x-6 = \left(x-\frac{2}{3}\right)(3x^2+6x+15)+4$

$=(3x-2)(x^2+2x+5)+4$

So the quotient is x^2+2x+5 and the remainder is 4.

Exercise 3.4

1 Find the quotient and remainder on dividing:

a) $2x^3+3x^2-6x-7$ by $(2x-1)$
b) $4x^3-6x^2-2x+12$ by $(2x+1)$
c) $3x^3+8x^2+6x-5$ by $(3x-1)$
d) $3x^3+7x^2+17x-2$ by $(3x+1)$
e) $10x^4-4x^3+15x^2+14x-3$ by $(5x-2)$

Factorising polynomials

In Exercise 3.3, question 1(h), you were asked to find the quotient and the remainder when $6x^3-25x^2+x+60$ was divided by $(x-3)$. The solution to this question is shown below.

Let $f(x)=6x^3-25x^2+x+60$. Then the remainder is $f(3)$.

3	6	−25	1	60
		18	−21	−60
	6	−7	−20	0

$\Rightarrow$ The remainder $f(3)$ equals 0.

The quotient is $6x^2-7x-20$ and the remainder is 0.

The fact that the remainder is 0 indicates that $(x-3)$ divides into $6x^3-25x^2+x+60$ exactly and is therefore a **factor** of $6x^3-25x^2+x+60$.

Algebraic Skills

This idea is a particular example of the Remainder Theorem and is called the **Factor Theorem**. This is given below along with its converse.

> If $f(a)=0$, then $(x-a)$ is a factor of a polynomial $f(x)$.
>
> If $(x-a)$ is a factor of a polynomial $f(x)$, then $f(a)=0$.

We can use the Factor Theorem to factorise polynomial expressions.

Example 1

Factorise $6x^3-25x^2+x+60$ fully.

SOLUTION

From the synthetic division table above, since $f(3)=0$, then $(x-3)$ is a factor of $6x^3-25x^2+x+60$.

$$\begin{aligned}\text{Hence } 6x^3-25x^2+x+60 &= (x-3)(6x^2-7x-20)\\ &= (x-3)(3x+4)(2x-5)\end{aligned}$$

Example 2

Factorise $2t^3+5t^2-28t-15$ fully.

SOLUTION

We must use trial and error to find the first factor, $(t-h)$.

As the constant term is -15, try factors of -15, i.e. $h = \pm1, \pm3, \pm5, \pm15$, until we obtain a value of h for which the remainder $f(h)$ is 0.

Let $f(t)=2t^3+5t^2-28t-15$.

1	2	5	−28	−15	
		2	7	−21	
	2	7	−21	**−36**	⇒ The remainder $f(1)\neq 0$, so $(t-1)$ is not a factor.
−1	2	5	−28	−15	
		−2	−3	31	
	2	3	−31	**16**	⇒ The remainder $f(-1)\neq 0$, so $(t+1)$ is not a factor.
3	2	5	−28	−15	
		6	33	15	
	2	11	5	**0**	⇒ The remainder $f(3)=0$, so $(t-3)$ is a factor.

$$\begin{aligned}\text{Hence } 2t^3+5t^2-28t-15 &= (t-3)(2t^2+11t+5)\\ &= (t-3)(2t+1)(t+5)\end{aligned}$$

Algebraic Skills

Exercise 3.5

1 Fully factorise x^3-4x^2+x+6 given that $(x-2)$ is a factor.

2 Fully factorise x^3-4x^2+5x-2 given that $(x-1)$ is a factor.

3 Fully factorise $x^3+3x^2-10x-24$ given that $(x+2)$ is a factor.

4 Fully factorise $x^3-4x^2-4x+16$ given that $(x-2)$ is a factor.

5 Fully factorise $2x^3+2x^2-x-1$ given that $(x+1)$ is a factor.

6 **a)** Show that $(x-1)$ is a factor of x^3-7x+6.
b) Hence, or otherwise, factorise x^3-7x+6 fully.

7 **a)** Show that $(x-1)$ is a factor of x^3+x^2-5x+3.
b) Hence, or otherwise, factorise x^3+x^2-5x+3 fully.

8 Fully factorise the following polynomials: HPQ

a) x^3-2x^2-5x+6 **b)** x^3-x^2-2x **c)** $2x^3+9x^2+7x-6$

d) $2x^3+11x^2+17x+6$ **e)** $2t^3-3t^2-39t+20$

Now consider an example where the given factor is in the form $(ax-b)$. Compare this with the example before Exercise 3.4.

Example 3

Fully factorise $2x^3+5x^2-28x-15$ given that $(2x+1)$ is a factor.

SOLUTION

The remainder is $f\left(-\frac{1}{2}\right)$.

$-\frac{1}{2}$	2	5	−28	−15
		−1	−2	15
	2	4	−30	**0**

$\Rightarrow$ The remainder $f\left(-\frac{1}{2}\right)=0$,

so $\left(x+\frac{1}{2}\right)$ is a factor.

Hence
$$2x^3+5x^2-28x-15=\left(x+\frac{1}{2}\right)\left(2x^2+4x-30\right)$$
$$=(2x+1)\left(x^2+2x-15\right)$$
$$=(2x+1)(x-3)(x+5)$$

Algebraic Skills

Exercise 3.5 (continued)

9 Fully factorise $2x^3+x^2-5x+2$ given that $(2x-1)$ is a factor.

10 Fully factorise $3x^3+4x^2-5x-2$ given that $(3x+1)$ is a factor.

11 Fully factorise $2x^3-9x^2+x+3$ given that $(2x+1)$ is a factor.

12 a) Show that $(x+1)^2$ is a factor of $x^4+5x^3+9x^2+7x+2$. ACE
b) Hence factorise $x^4+5x^3+9x^2+7x+2$ fully.

13 a) Show that $(x+1)$ is a factor of $x^4+4x^3+8x^2+8x+3$.
b) Hence factorise $x^4+4x^3+8x^2+8x+3$ fully.

14 a) Find c given that $(x+1)$ is a factor of x^3+x^2-4x+c.
b) Hence factorise x^3+x^2-4x+c fully.

15 Find b given that $(x+2)$ is a factor of $4x^3+12x^2+bx-10$.

16 The polynomial $6x^3+7x^2+ax+b$ has a remainder of 72 when divided by $(x-2)$ and is exactly divisible by $(x+1)$. Find the values of a and b. ACE

17 Find the values of p and q given that $(x+3)$ and $(x-3)$ are both factors of $2x^3-x^2+px+q$.

Polynomial equations

You will remember solving quadratic equations by factorisation. A similar method can be used to solve most polynomial equations: first factorise them and then find the roots by equating each factor in turn to zero.

Example

Solve the equation $x^3+5x^2+3x-9=0$.

SOLUTION

Try factors of -9, i.e. ±1, ±3, ±9.

1	1	5	3	−9
		1	6	9
	1	6	9	0

$\Rightarrow$ The remainder $f(1)=0$, so $(x-1)$ is a factor.

Hence $x^3+5x^2+3x-9=(x-1)(x^2+6x+9)$
$=(x-1)(x+3)(x+3)$

Therefore $x^3+5x^2+3x-9=0$

$\Rightarrow (x-1)(x+3)(x+3)=0$

$\Rightarrow x-1=0$ or $x+3=0$ (twice)

$\Rightarrow x=1$ or $x=-3$ (twice)

Note

- $x = 1$ and $x = -3$ are called the roots of the equation $x^3 + 5x^2 + 3x - 9 = 0$.
- 1 and -3 are called the **zeros** of the function $f(x) = x^3 + 5x^2 + 3x - 9$.
- The graph of the function $f(x) = x^3 + 5x^2 + 3x - 9$ cuts the x-axis at the point $(1, 0)$. The repeated root at $x = -3$ indicates that the graph only touches the x-axis at the point $(-3, 0)$ so that the x-axis is a tangent to the curve at this point.

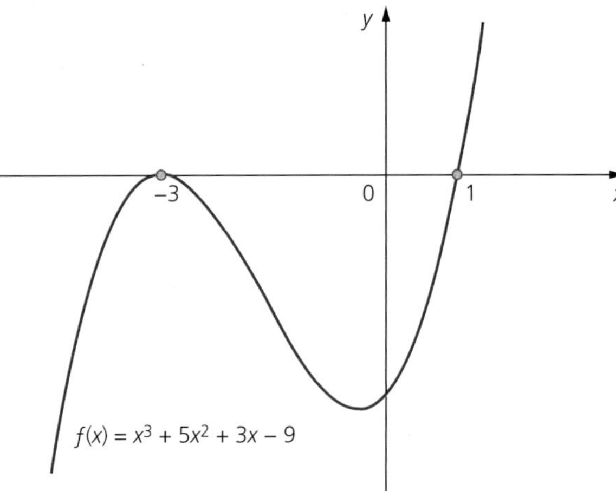

Exercise 3.6

1 a) Show that $x = 1$ is a solution of the equation $x^3 + x^2 - 10x + 8 = 0$.
b) Hence find all the solutions.

2 a) Show that $x = -1$ is a root of the equation $6x^3 + 7x^2 - x - 2 = 0$.
b) Hence find all other roots.

3 a) Show that $x = 1$ and $x = -1$ are roots of the equation $x^4 - 3x^3 + x^2 + 3x - 2 = 0$.
b) Hence find all the roots.

4 Solve the following equations: HPQ
a) $x^3 - 3x^2 - 4x + 12 = 0$
b) $x^3 + 6x^2 + 5x - 12 = 0$
c) $x^3 - 12x^2 + 44x - 48 = 0$
d) $10x^3 - 11x^2 - x + 2 = 0$

5 Show that $x = \frac{2}{3}$ is a root of the equation $6x^3 - 7x^2 - x + 2 = 0$, and hence find all the roots of the equation.

6 Solve the following equations:
a) $x^4 - 2x^3 - 5x^2 + 6x = 0$
b) $x^4 - 6x^3 + 13x^2 - 12x + 4 = 0$
c) $2x^4 - 5x^3 + 5x - 2 = 0$

7 a) Find the value of k if $(x - 4)$ is a factor of $f(x) = 2x^3 - 5x^2 + kx - 20$. ACE
b) Hence show that $f(x) = 0$ has only one solution.

8 Find the coordinates of the points where the following graphs cut the x-axis:
a) $y = x^3 - 5x^2 - 8x + 12$
b) $y = x^3 - x^2 - 5x - 3$

Algebraic Skills

Graphs of polynomial functions

You have already studied graphs of linear functions and quadratic functions.

You will consider how to sketch graphs of cubic functions in Chapter 14 in the calculus section of this book.

In this section you will learn how to find the equation of a polynomial function from its graph.

Example 1

Find the equation of the function shown in this graph.

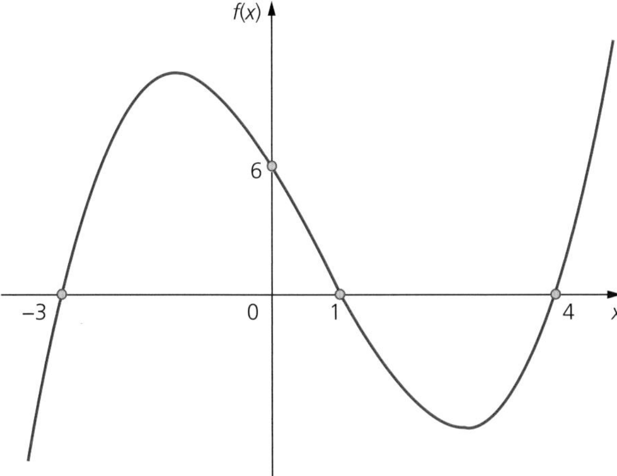

SOLUTION

The graph has zeros at $x=-3$, $x=1$ and $x=4$.

The zeros are roots of the equation $f(x)=0$

$\Rightarrow k(x+3)(x-1)(x-4)=0$, where k is a constant.

Hence the equation of the function is $f(x)=k(x+3)(x-1)(x-4)$.

From the graph, $f(0)=6$

$$\Rightarrow 6=k(0+3)(0-1)(0-4)$$

$$\Rightarrow 12k=6$$

$$\Rightarrow k=\frac{1}{2}$$

Hence $f(x)=\frac{1}{2}(x+3)(x-1)(x-4)$

$$=\frac{1}{2}x^3-x^2-\frac{11}{2}x+6$$

Algebraic Skills

Example 2

The graph of the function shown in the diagram below passes through the point $(3, -72)$. Find the equation of the function.

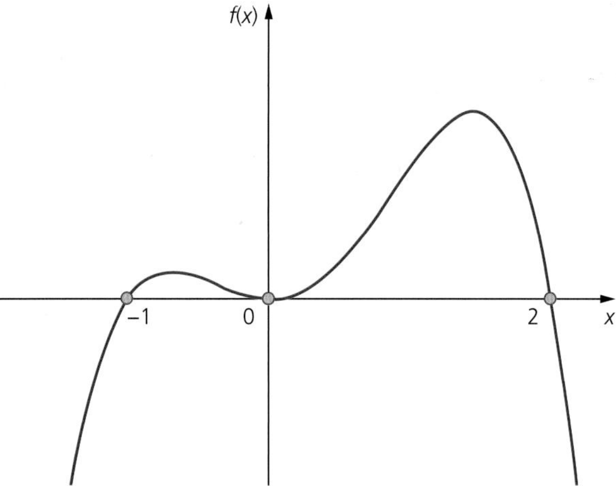

SOLUTION

The graph has zeros at $x = -1$, $x = 0$ (repeated root), and $x = 2$.

The zeros are roots of the equation $f(x) = 0$

$\Rightarrow \quad k(x+1)(x-0)^2(x-2) = 0$, where k is a constant.

Hence the equation of the function is $f(x) = kx^2(x+1)(x-2)$.

From the graph, $f(3) = -72$

$$\Rightarrow -72 = k \times 3^2(3+1)(3-2)$$
$$\Rightarrow 36k = -72$$
$$\Rightarrow k = -2$$

Hence $f(x) = -2x^2(x+1)(x-2)$
$$= 4x^2 + 2x^3 - 2x^4$$

Exercise 3.7

Find the equation of the function shown in each graph.

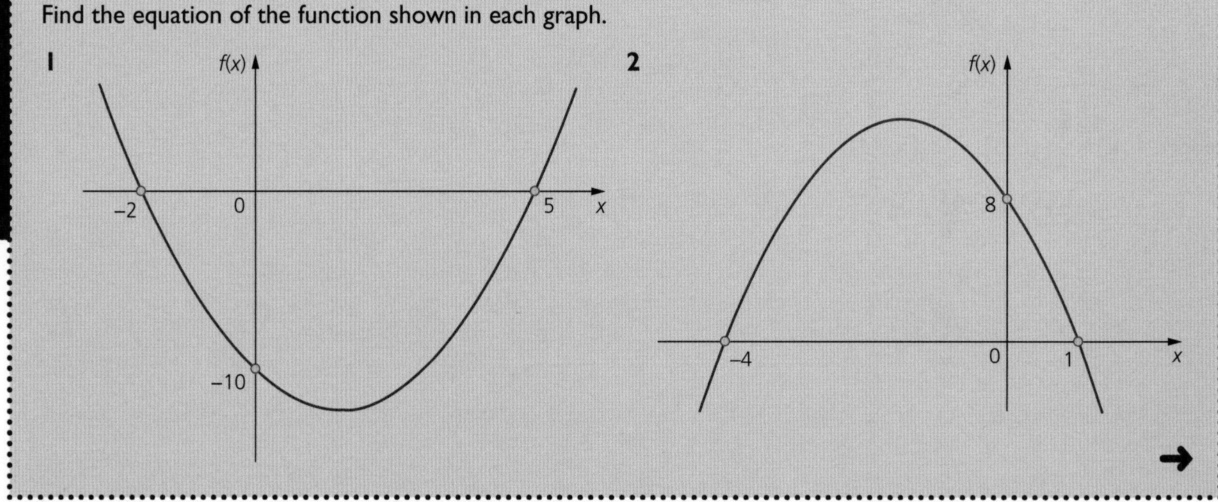

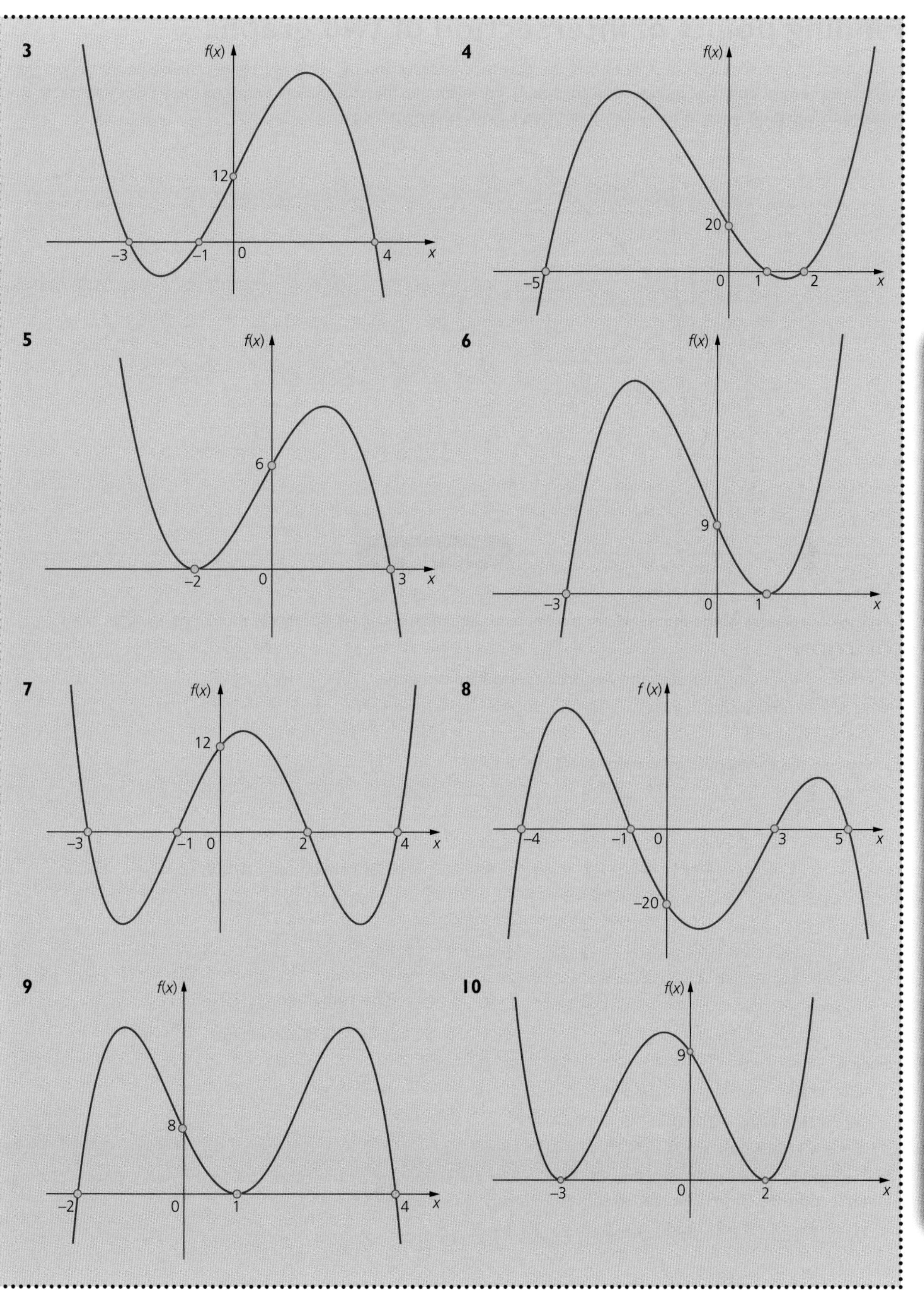

3
f(x)
12
–3
–1
0
4
x
4
f(x)
20
–5
0
1
2
x
5
f(x)
6
–2
0
3
x
6
f(x)
9
–3
0
1
x
7
f(x)
12
–3
–1
0
2
4
x
8
f (x)
–4
–1
0
3
5
x
–20
9
f(x)
8
–2
0
1
4
x
10
f(x)
9
–3
0
2
x

Finding points of intersection of two graphs

In this section you shall look at how to find the points of intersection of two graphs given their equations. Two graphs could have several points of intersection (or none). For example, the straight line with equation $y = x$ intersects the cubic curve with equation $y = x^3 + 5x^2 + 3x - 9$ in three points as shown below.

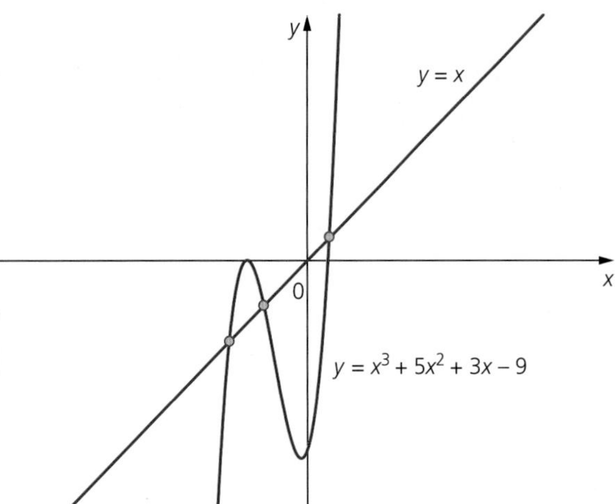

Example

Find the coordinates of the points where the line with equation $y = x + 3$ intersects the curve $y = x^3 - 2x + 1$.

SOLUTION

Where the two graphs intersect, the *y*-coordinates will be the same.

Hence $x^3 - 2x + 1 = x + 3$

$\Rightarrow x^3 - 3x - 2 = 0$

To factorise the polynomial, try factors of −2, i.e. ±1, ±2.

1	1	0	−3	−2	
		1	1	−2	
	1	1	−2	**−4**	$\Rightarrow$ The remainder $f(1) \neq 0$, so $(x - 1)$ is not a factor
−1	1	0	−3	−2	
		−1	1	2	
	1	−1	−2	**0**	$\Rightarrow$ The remainder $f(-1) = 0$, so $(x + 1)$ is not a factor

Hence $x^3 - 3x - 2 = 0$

$\Rightarrow (x+1)(x^2 - x - 2) = 0$

$\Rightarrow (x+1)(x+1)(x-2) = 0$

$\Rightarrow x = -1$ (twice) or $x = 2$

Now substitute both values for *x* into the equation of either the line or the curve to find the *y*-coordinates of the points of intersection. It is clearly simpler to substitute into $y = x + 3$ in this case:

$x = -1 \Rightarrow y = -1 + 3 = 2$ and $x = 2 \Rightarrow y = 2 + 3 = 5$

Algebraic Skills

Hence the points of intersection are $(-1, 2)$ and $(2, 5)$.

Note that the repeated root at $x=-1$ indicates that the straight line is a tangent to the curve at the point $(-1, 2)$

Exercise 3.8

1 A curve has equation $y=2x^3+3x^2-6x-4$.

a) Show that the straight line with equation $y=3x+6$ cuts the curve at the point $(2, 12)$

b) Find the coordinates of the other points of intersection of the curve and the line.

2 Find the coordinates of the points where the line $y=4x+8$ intersects the curve $y=x^3-5x+8$.

3 The line $y=4$ intersects the graph of $f(x)=3x^2-x^3$ at A and B as shown. HPQ

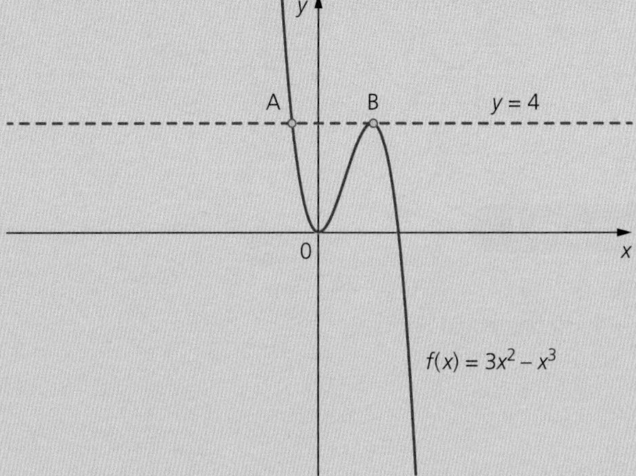

Determine the coordinates of A and B.

4 Find the coordinates of the points where the line $y=2x+3$ intersects the curve $y=x^3+2x^2+x+1$.

5 Find the coordinates of the points of intersection of the line $y=3x-1$ and the curve $y=2x^3-5x^2+4x+1$.

6 Show that the line $y=1-2x$ and the curve $y=x^3-5x+3$ intersect at two points and find the coordinates of these points of intersection.

7 Find the coordinates of the points of intersection of the line $y=1-4x$ and the curve $y=x^3-4x^2+1$.

8 Find the coordinates of all the points of intersection of the curves with equations $y=7x^3-5x^2+3x+2$ and $y=x^3+5x+1$. ACE

The discriminant

Reminder The roots of $ax^2+bx+c=0, (a\neq 0)$ are given by the quadratic formula $x=\dfrac{-b\pm\sqrt{(b^2-4ac)}}{2a}$. The discriminant is b^2-4ac.

* $b^2 - 4ac > 0 \Rightarrow$ quadratic equation has two distinct real roots.
If the discriminant is a perfect square the roots are rational.
If the discriminant is not a perfect square the roots are irrational.

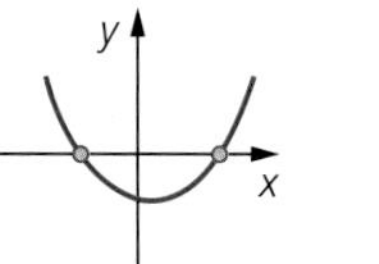

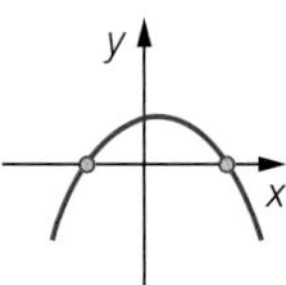

* $b^2 - 4ac = 0 \Rightarrow$ quadratic equation has one real root.
(In this case we often say the equation has two equal roots.)

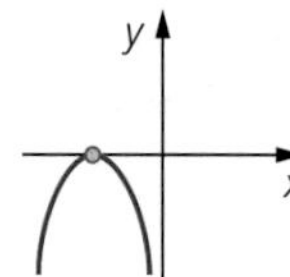

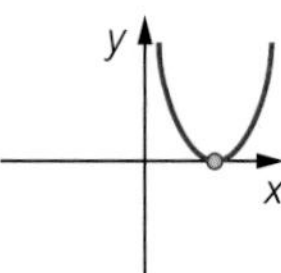

* $b^2 - 4ac < 0 \Rightarrow$ quadratic equation has no real roots.

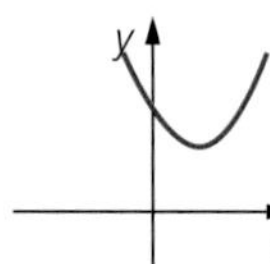

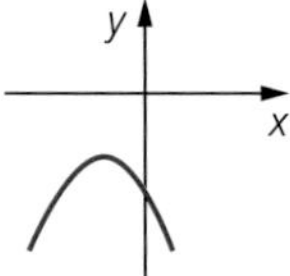

Example 1

Find the value of p such that the equation $px^2+(3p-4)x+4=0$ has equal roots.

SOLUTION

$a=p,\ b=(3p-4),\ c=4.$

Hence $b^2-4ac = (3p-4)^2-4\times p\times 4$

$= 9p^2-24p+16-16p$

$= 9p^2-40p+16$

Equal roots $\Rightarrow b^2-4ac=0$

$\Rightarrow 9p^2-40p+16=0$

$\Rightarrow (9p-4)(p-4)=0$

$\Rightarrow p=\frac{4}{9}$ or 4

Example 2

Show that the roots of the equation $2x^2+tx-3=0$ are real for all values of t.

SOLUTION

$a=2,\ b=t,\ c=-3.$

Hence $b^2-4ac=t^2-4\times 2\times(-3)$

$=t^2+24$

$\geqslant 24$ (since $t^2 \geqslant 0$ for all values of t)

Hence the roots are real for all values of t since $b^2-4ac \geqslant 0$.

Example 3

Find the equation of the tangent to the parabola $y = x^2 + 3x + 1$ with gradient 7, and state the coordinates of the point of contact.

SOLUTION

The equation of the tangent is $y = 7x + k$ where $(0, k)$ is the y-intercept.

At the point where the line meets the parabola the y-coordinates will be the same.

Hence $x^2 + 3x + 1 = 7x + k$

$\Rightarrow x^2 - 4x + 1 - k = 0$

Since the line is a tangent to the parabola there is only one point of contact, so this equation will have equal roots and therefore $b^2 - 4ac = 0$.

$a = 1,\ b = -4,\ c = (1 - k)$

Hence $(-4)^2 - 4 \times 1 \times (1 - k) = 0$

$\Rightarrow 16 - 4 + 4k = 0$

$\Rightarrow k = -3$

Hence the equation of the tangent is $y = 7x - 3$.

This line meets the parabola where $x^2 - 4x + 4 = 0$

$\Rightarrow (x - 2)(x - 2) = 0$

$\Rightarrow x = 2$

$x = 2 \Rightarrow y = 7 \times 2 - 3 = 11$

Hence the point of contact is $(2, 11)$

Exercise 3.9

1 Determine the nature of the roots of these quadratic equations:

a) $x^2 + 3x + 1 = 0$ **b)** $m^2 - 3m + 4 = 0$

c) $4t^2 - 20t + 25 = 0$ **d)** $5g^2 + 4g - 1 = 0$

2 Determine the nature of the roots of the equation $3u(u - 2) = -2$.

3 Show that the equation $x(x + 1) = 3x - 2$ has no real roots.

4 Show that $x = 4$ is the only real root of the equation $3x^3 - 11x^2 - 16 = 0$.

5 Show that the line with equation $y = 2x + 1$ does not intersect the parabola with equation $y = x^2 + 3x + 4$.

6 Mark rolls a die which is numbered from 1 to 6.
Whichever number comes up, he substitutes for b in $x^2 + bx + 4 = 0$.
What is the probability that the resulting equation will have:

a) no real solution

b) exactly one real solution

c) two real distinct solutions?

7 For what values of p does the equation $x^2 - 6x + p = 0$ have: HPQ

a) equal roots

b) two real distinct roots

c) no real roots?

8 Find k given that $x^2 + (k + 1)x + 16 = 0$ has equal roots. HPQ

9 Given that the roots of the equation $(x + 5)(x + q) = -16$ are equal, find the two possible values of q.

10 Find the range of values of k for which $kx^2 + 2x - 6 = 0$ has no real roots.

➜

11 a) Given that $\frac{x}{k}+\frac{k+2}{x+1}=2$, prove that $x^2+(1-2k)x+k^2=0$.

b) Hence find the values of k for which x is real.

12 Show that the roots of the equation $(x-1)(x-3)=k^2$ are always real.

13 Show that the roots of the equation $(k-2)x^2-(3k-2)x+2k=0$ are always real. ACE

14 Show that the equation $(1-2k)x^2-5kx-2k=0$ has real roots for all integer values of k.

15 Find the values of p for which the straight line with equation $y=-3x-1$ is a tangent to the parabola with equation $y=x(x-p)$.) ACE

16 The line $y=5x+k$ is a tangent to the curve $y=2x^2+x-5$. Determine the value of k.

17 Find the equation of the tangent to the parabola $y=x^2+6x-2$ with gradient 8, and state the coordinates of the point of contact. ACE

Quadratic inequalities

We can solve a quadratic inequality by sketching the graph of the related quadratic function and considering which parts of the graph are above and below the x-axis. Start by finding the roots of the corresponding quadratic equation.

Example

Solve the inequality $20-8x-x^2<0$.

SOLUTION

Start by finding the roots of the equation $20-8x-x^2=0$.

$$20-8x-x^2=0$$
$$\Rightarrow (2-x)(10+x)=0$$
$$\Rightarrow x=2 \text{ and } x=-10$$

Next sketch the graph of $y=20-8x-x^2$. It crosses the x-axis at $(2,0)$ and $(-10,0)$ and it has a maximum turning point as the x^2 term is negative. These are the *only* pieces of information required for the sketch graph.

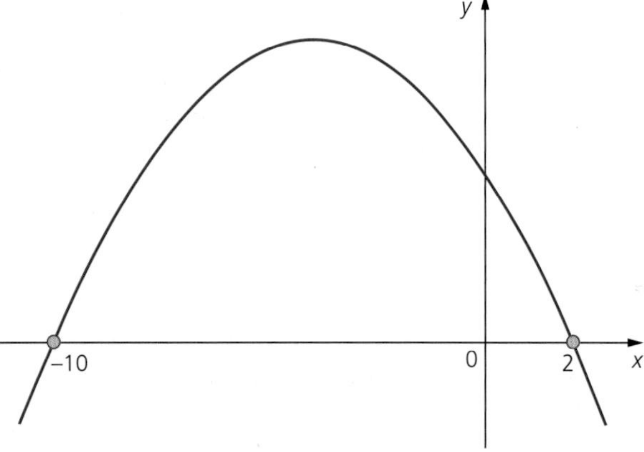

From the graph, the value of $20-8x-x^2$ is negative on the part of the graph which is below the x-axis. Hence the solution is $x<-10$ and $x>2$.

Algebraic Skills

Note

The value of $20-8x-x^2$ is positive on the part of the graph which is above the x-axis, so the solution of $20-8x-x^2>0$ is $-10<x<2$.
Similarly the solution of $20-8x-x^2\geqslant 0$ is $-10\leq x\leq 2$.

The graphs of some quadratic functions do not cut the x-axis, e.g. $y=x^2+2$ which lies completely *above* the x-axis. Therefore the solution to the inequality $x^2+2>0$ would be R, the set of real numbers. There is no real solution to the inequality $x^2+2\leqslant 0$.

If you are in doubt about a quadratic equation, you can check the nature of its roots using the discriminant. Remember that if $b^2-4ac>0$ and a perfect square, then the roots are rational and the quadratic expression will factorise.

Exercise 3.10

Solve these quadratic inequalities:

1 $x^2+5x+6>0$
2 $x^2+2x-8<0$
3 $x^2-x-6\geq 0$
4 $x^2+2x-15\leq 0$
5 $10x^2+31x+15>0$
6 $5+8x-4x^2>0$
7 $16+6x-x^2\leq 0$
8 $x^2-25\leq 0$
9 $4x-3x^2<0$
10 Find the range of values of k for which $x^2+(k-1)x+9=0$ has no real roots.
11 Find the range of values of t for which $tx^2-2tx+4=0$ has real roots.
12 Find the range of values of p for which the graph of $y=x^2+px+4$ crosses the x-axis.
13 Find the range of values of k for which the graph of $y=x^2-2kx+k+6$ does not cross or touch the x-axis.

Approximate roots

Investigation

You solved a number of polynomial equations earlier in Exercise 3.6. In all the questions, the polynomial expressions factorised. This meant that the roots of the equations belonged to Q, the set of rational numbers. However, when a polynomial expression does not factorise, the roots are irrational numbers and we can use a calculator to find approximate roots.

Example

Show that the equation $3x^3-2x^2-4=0$ has a root between 1 and 2 and find it, correct to two decimal places.

SOLUTION

Because the graphs of polynomials are continuous, a change in the sign of the value of the polynomial from + to – or vice versa indicates that there is a root in between.

First, let $f(x)=3x^3-2x^2-4$ and then gradually close in on the required solution by repeated substitutions into your calculator. The process of trial and improvement is known as **iteration**. Working can be neatly illustrated in a table.

x	$f(x)$	Root lies between
1	−3	
2	12	1 and 2
1·5	1·625	1 and 1·5
1·25	−1·2656	1·25 and 1·5
1·375	0·0175	1·25 and 1·375 (looks close to 1·375)
1·37	−0·0397	1·37 and 1·375 (so root is 1·37 to 2 decimal places)

It is generally a good idea to choose the midpoint of an interval e.g. 1·375 is the midpoint of 1·25 and 1·5, then once $f(x)$ gets closer to zero you can hone in on the solution more quickly.

Investigate the process of iteration and try the example below.

Example

Show that the equation $x^3 - 2x^2 + 4x - 5 = 0$ has a root between 0 and 4 and find it, correct to two decimal places.

Checkout

1 A function f is defined on the set of real numbers by $f(x) = x^3 - x^2 + x + 3$.
What is the quotient and the remainder when $f(x)$ is divided by $(x - 1)$?

2 a) Show that $(x - 1)$ is a factor of $f(x) = 2x^3 + x^2 - 8x + 5$.
b) Hence factorise $f(x)$ fully.
c) Solve the equation $2x^3 + x^2 - 8x + 5 = 0$.

3 The line with equation $y = 5x + 3$ is a tangent to the curve with equation $y = x^3 - x^2$ at the point G.
Find the coordinates of G.

4 a) Show that $(x - 3)$ is a factor of $f(x) = 4x^3 - 12x^2 - x + 3$.
b) Hence solve the equation $4x^3 - 12x^2 - x + 3 = 0$.

5 a) Show that $x = 1$ is a root of the equation $x^3 + 8x^2 + 11x - 20 = 0$.
b) Hence factorise $x^3 + 8x^2 + 11x - 20$.

6 The graph of the curve with equation $y = 2x^3 + x^2 - 13x + a$ cuts the x-axis at the point $(2, 0)$.

a) Find the value of a.
b) Hence find the coordinates of the point where the graph cuts the y-axis.
c) Find algebraically the coordinates of the other points where the curve cuts the x-axis.

7 The graph of the function $f(x) = ax^3 + bx^2 + cx + d$ crosses the x-axis at the points $(-3, 0)$, $(1, 0)$ and $(2, 0)$. It crosses the y-axis at the point $(0, 6)$. Find the values of a, b, c and d.

8 The roots of the equation $px^2 - 3x + 2 = 0$ are equal. What is the value of p?

9 Find the range of values of t for which the quadratic equation $tx(x + 1) = 3 - t$ has no real roots.

10 Solve the inequality $x^2 - 4x - 32 \leqslant 0$.

Summary

Polynomial Expressions and Equations

1 When $f(x)$ is divided by $(x-h)$, the quotient and remainder can be found by synthetic division.

2 The Remainder Theorem.
When $f(x)$ is divided by $(x-h)$, the remainder is $f(h)$.

3 The Factor Theorem.
$f(a)=0 \Leftrightarrow (x-a)$ is a factor of $f(x)$.

4 To solve $f(x)=0$, factorise and then find the roots by equating each factor in turn to zero.

5 If the graph of $f(x)$ crosses the x-axis at $(a, 0)$, $(b, 0)$ and $(c, 0)$, then its equation is $f(x)=k(x-a)(x-b)(x-c)$. The value of k can be found by substituting in the coordinates of any other known point on the graph.

6 For the quadratic equation $ax^2+bx+c=0$, b^2-4ac is called the discriminant.

* $b^2-4ac < 0 \Rightarrow$ there are no real roots
* $b^2-4ac = 0 \Rightarrow$ the roots are real and equal
* $b^2-4ac > 0 \Rightarrow$ the roots are real and distinct

(If b^2-4ac is also a perfect square then the roots are rational; otherwise they are irrational.)

7 To solve a quadratic inequality, sketch the graph of the related quadratic function and consider which parts of the graph are above and below the x-axis.

CHAPTER 4

Circles

In this chapter we will study different forms of the equation of a circle and use these equations to solve problems involving circles.

What I am learning

* The equation of a circle in the form:
  * $x^2 + y^2 = r^2$
  * $(x - a)^2 + (y - b)^2 = r^2$
  * $x^2 + y^2 + 2gx + 2fy + c = 0$
* How to use the equation of the circle to solve problems
* How to find the equation of a tangent to a circle
* How to use the properties of the tangent to solve problems
* How to find the intersection of a line and a circle
* How to check whether circles overlap, touch or do not overlap
* How to solve problems like this:

  The point P (4, 3) lies on a circle with centre C (−2, −1).
  Find the equation of the tangent at P.

What I should already know/be able to do

* Use vocabulary relating to circles, e.g. radius, diameter, chord, circumference
* How to find the equation of a straight line
* Solve simultaneous equations
* Solve inequalities
* Factorise and solve quadratic equations
* Complete the square in a quadratic expression
* Use the discriminant to find the nature of the roots of a quadratic equation
* Find the midpoint of a line segment
* Use the distance formula
* Change the subject of a formula

Quick check!

1 Find the equation of the line passing through the points (3, −2) and (5, 4).
2 Find the equation of the line with gradient 2 passing through the point (−3, 5).
3 Solve the equations $3x + y = 8$, $4x - y = 13$.
4 Solve the inequality $4(3 - x) < 16$.
5 Solve the equation $x^2 - 8x - 48 = 0$.
6 Express $x^2 + 6x - 1$ in the form $(x + p)^2 + q$.
7 Find the nature of the roots of the equation $2x^2 - 12x + 18 = 0$.
8 Calculate the distance between the points (3, −4) and (2, −8).
9 Change the subject of the formula $3x - 2y = 8$ to y.

Quick check! – *Solutions*

1 $y = 3x - 11$	2 $y = 2x + 11$	3 $x = 3,\ y = -1$
4 $x > -1$	5 $x = -4$ or 12	6 $(x+3)^2 - 10$
7 Equal real roots	8 $\sqrt{17}$	9 $y = \dfrac{3x-8}{2}$

The circle with centre the origin and radius *r*

Definition

A circle is a locus of points equidistant from a fixed point (the centre).

The circle C is a set of points at distance *r* from the origin.

A point P (x, y) is marked on the circumference.

By applying the Theorem of Pythagoras, it can be seen that $x^2 + y^2 = r^2$.

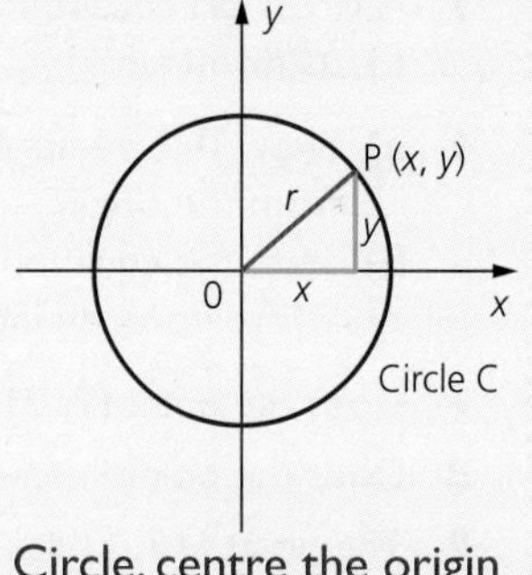

Circle, centre the origin (0, 0) and radius *r*

The equation of a circle with centre (0, 0) and radius *r* is $x^2 + y^2 = r^2$.

For example, the circle with centre at the origin and radius 3 has equation $x^2 + y^2 = 3^2$.

This can be simplified to $x^2 + y^2 = 9$.

Similarly the circle with equation $x^2 + y^2 = 16$ has centre (0, 0) and radius 4.

Example

Find the equation of a circle with centre (0, 0) passing through the point (3, −4).

SOLUTION

Use the distance formula to find the radius.

$r^2 = (3-0)^2 + (-4-0)^2 = 9 + 16 = 25$

Therefore the radius $r = 5$.

Hence the equation of the circle is $x^2 + y^2 = 25$.

Note

Although the distance formula is $d = \sqrt{(x_2 - x_1)^2 + (y_2 - y_1)^2}$, it is simpler to use $d^2 = (x_2 - x_1)^2 + (y_2 - y_1)^2$ to find r^2 directly.

Exercise 4.1

1 Write down the equation of the circle with centre at the origin and radius:
a) 2 **b)** 6 **c)** 8 **d)** 15

2 State the centre and radius of each of these circles: HPQ
a) $x^2+y^2=49$ **b)** $x^2+y^2=100$ **c)** $x^2+y^2=25$ **d)** $x^2+y^2=81$

3 Find the equation of the circle with centre at the origin and passing through the point: HPQ
a) (5, 12) **b)** (−3, 4) **c)** (0, 4) **d)** (8, −6)

4 Find the equation of the concentric circle which has radius twice that of the circle with equation:
a) $x^2+y^2=36$ **b)** $x^2+y^2=10$

5 A circle has equation $x^2+y^2=16$. Find:
a) its diameter **b)** its circumference **c)** its area

Note Concentric circles have the same centre.

6 **a)** Show that points A (4, −3), B (0, 5) and C (3, 4) are equidistant from the origin.
b) State the equation of the circle which passes through A, B and C.
c) Write down an inequality which describes the set of points inside the circle.

7 Does the point (7, 3) lie inside, outside or on the circle with equation $x^2+y^2=64$?

8 Does the point (−4, −5) lie inside, outside or on the circle with equation $x^2+y^2=40$?

9 The point (15, p) lies on the circumference of the circle with centre the origin and equation $x^2+y^2=289$. Find two possible values for p.

10 **a)** Sketch the lines with equations $x=3$, $x=-3$, $y=5$ and $y=-5$. ACE
b) These lines define a rectangle. Find the equation of the circle which passes through the vertices of the rectangle.

11 PQ is a diameter of the circle with equation $x^2+y^2=52$. Write down the coordinates of Q if P is the point (6, −4). ACE

The circle with centre (a, b) and radius r

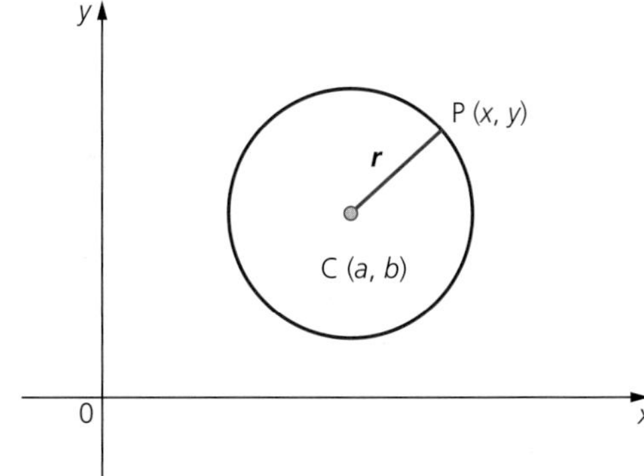

In the diagram, the circle has centre C (a, b).

A point P (x, y) lies on the circumference of the circle.

The radius of the circle is r.

By applying the distance formula, we can find the equation of the circle.

The equation of a circle with centre (a, b) and radius r is $(x-a)^2+(y-b)^2=r^2$.

For example, the circle with centre (6, −2) and radius 7 has equation $(x-6)^2+(y+2)^2=49$.

Similarly, the circle with equation $(x+5)^2+y^2=16$ has centre (−5, 0) and radius 4.

Example

A circle has the line AB as its diameter where A is the point (5, −3) and B is (3, 7).
Find the equation of the circle.

SOLUTION

As AB is a diameter of the circle, the centre, C, is the midpoint of AB.

The centre is $\left(\frac{5+3}{2}, \frac{-3+7}{2}\right) = (4, 2)$.

The radius is the distance from C (4, 2) to A (5, −3) [or the distance from C to B].

$r^2 = CA^2 = (5-4)^2 + (-3-2)^2 = 1^2 + (-5)^2 = 26$

The equation of the circle is $(x-a)^2 + (y-b)^2 = r^2$, where (a, b) is (4, 2) and $r^2 = 26$, i.e.

$(x-4)^2 + (y-2)^2 = 26$

Exercise 4.2

1 Write down the equation of the circle with centre (3, 5) and radius 4.

2 Write down the equation of the circle with centre (3, −1) and radius 7.

3 Write down the equation of the circle with centre (−5, −7) and radius 5.

4 Write down the equation of the circle with centre (−4, 0) and radius 3·5.

5 State the centre and radius of each of these circles:

a) $(x-5)^2 + (y-7)^2 = 16$
b) $(x-3)^2 + (y+6)^2 = 4$
c) $x^2 + (y-3)^2 = 6{\cdot}25$
d) $(x+2)^2 + (y+2)^2 = 47$

6 In each pair of points below, H is the centre of a circle passing through K. HPQ
For each pair of points, find the equation of the circle.

a) H (3, 2), K (7, 5)
b) H (−2, 2), K (−8, 10)
c) H (−4, −3), K (8, 2)
d) H (0, −3), K (3, 0)
e) H (x_1, y_1), K (x_2, y_2)

7 The circle shown has centre (7, 24) and passes through the origin. Find its equation.

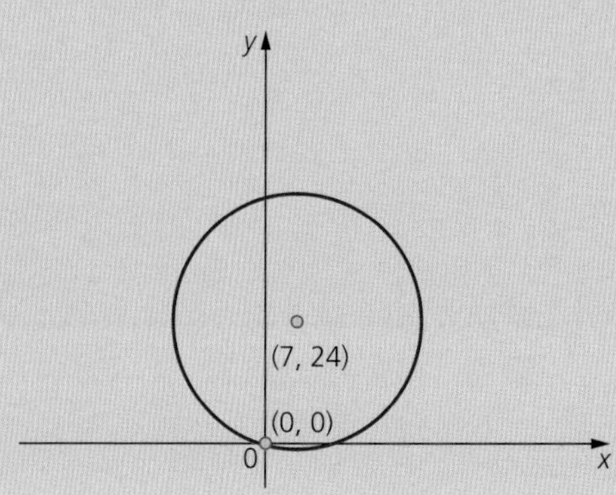

→

Algebraic Skills

8 The x-axis is a tangent to the circle shown below. Find the equation of this circle.

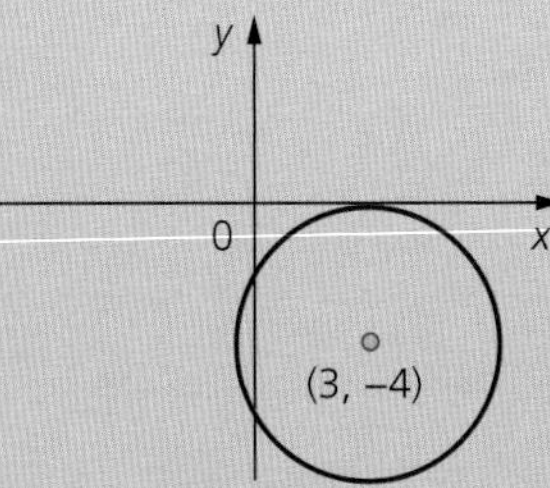

9 A circle has equation $(x-1)^2+(y+3)^2=196$. A smaller concentric circle has half the radius of this larger one. Find the equation of the smaller circle.

10 Does the point P (−3, 1) lie inside, outside or on the circle with equation $(x-2)^2+(y-5)^2=25$?

11 Does the point Q (−1, 2) lie inside, outside or on the circle with equation $(x+4)^2+(y-1)^2=12$?

12 The points (8, −3) and (−2, 15) lie at opposite ends of a diameter of a circle. Find the equation of the circle.

13 A circle has the line EF as its diameter where E is the point (−6, 4) and F is (−4, 10) Find the equation of the circle.

14 Show that the point A (5, −1) lies on the circle with equation $(x-2)^2+(y+3)^2=13$. Find the coordinates of the other end of the diameter through A.

15 A circle passes through the origin, P (0, 6) and Q (8, 0) ACE

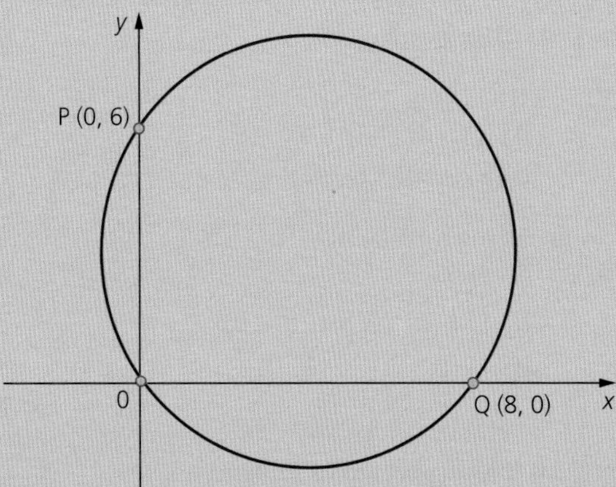

a) Explain why PQ must be a diameter of the circle.
b) Find the equation of the circle.

16 Circle A has equation $(x-5)^2+(y-7)^2=16$. ACE
Circle B has equation $(x+1)^2+(y+1)^2=36$.
Do these circles overlap? Justify your answer.

Algebraic Skills

Expanding the brackets

The equation of a circle can be written in expanded form.

For example, the circle with centre (4, –2) and radius 5 has equation

$$(x-4)^2+(y+2)^2=25$$

$\Rightarrow\ x^2-8x+16+y^2+4y+4=25$ [by expanding the brackets]

$\Rightarrow\ x^2-8x+y^2+4y=5$

$\Rightarrow\ x^2+y^2-8x+4y-5=0$

This form of the equation is called the **general equation of the circle.**

Working in reverse from the general equation you can find the centre and radius of the circle.

$$x^2+y^2-8x+4y-5=0$$

$\Rightarrow\ x^2-8x+y^2+4y=5$

$\Rightarrow\ (x-4)^2-16+(y+2)^2-4=5$ [by completing the square for the x and y terms]

$\Rightarrow\ (x-4)^2+(y+2)^2=25$

This is the equation of the circle with centre (4, –2) and radius 5.

Exercise 4.3

Show that each of the following equations represents a circle.
Find the centre and radius in each case.

1 $x^2+y^2-2x-4y-3=0$
2 $x^2+y^2+4x+6y=0$
3 $x^2+y^2+6x-4y-12=0$
4 $x^2+y^2-8x+10y+5=0$

The general equation of a circle

Following the method shown above, we can find a quicker way of identifying the centre and radius of any circle whose equation is given in the form $x^2+y^2+2gx+2fy+c=0$.

$$x^2+y^2+2gx+2fy+c=0$$

$\Rightarrow\ x^2+2gx+y^2+2fy=-c$

$\Rightarrow\ (x+g)^2-g^2+(y+f)^2-f^2=-c$

$\Rightarrow\ (x+g)^2+(y+f)^2=g^2+f^2-c$

This is now in the form $(x-a)^2+(y-b)^2=r^2$, so the centre of the circle is $(-g, -f)$ and the radius is $\sqrt{g^2+f^2-c}$.
Note that this equation is only valid if $g^2+f^2-c>0$.

The equation $x^2+y^2+2gx+2fy+c=0$ is the **general equation** of a circle with centre $(-g, -f)$ and radius $\sqrt{g^2+f^2-c}$, provided that $g^2+f^2-c>0$.

Example

Find the centre and radius of the circle with equation $x^2+y^2+10x-6y-2=0$.

SOLUTION

$x^2+y^2+2gx+2fy+c=0$

$x^2+y^2+10x-6y-2=0$

$2g=10 \Rightarrow g=5 \Rightarrow -g=-5$

$2f=-6 \Rightarrow f=-3 \Rightarrow -f=3$

Hence the centre is $(-5, 3)$, and the radius is $r=\sqrt{g^2+f^2-c}=\sqrt{5^2+(-3)^2+2}=\sqrt{25+9+2}=\sqrt{36}=6$.

Exercise 4.4

1 By evaluating g^2+f^2-c, state which of the following equations represent a circle. For those which represent a circle, find the coordinates of the centre and the length of the radius.

a) $x^2+y^2-4x-8y+16=0$ **b)** $x^2+y^2-6x-10y-2=0$

c) $x^2+y^2-2x+2y+35=0$ **d)** $x^2+y^2+6x-2y+10=0$

e) $x^2+y^2-8x-2y+13=0$ **f)** $x^2+y^2+4x+6y+4=0$

2 Find the centre and radius of the following circles: HPQ

a) $x^2+y^2-10x-6y-2=0$ **b)** $x^2+y^2+6x+4y+4=0$

c) $x^2+y^2+8x+12=0$ **d)** $x^2+y^2-8x+4y+17=0$

e) $x^2+y^2+10x-14y+65=0$

3 A circle has equation $x^2+y^2+2x-4y-7=0$. The radius of a larger concentric circle is three times the radius of this smaller one.
Find the equation of the larger circle.

4 Determine whether the points A (5, 7), B (6, 6) and C (8, −1) lie inside, outside or on the circle with equation $x^2+y^2-6x-10y+26=0$.

5 A circle has equation $2x^2+2y^2+12x-8y-46=0$.
Find the centre and radius of this circle.

In question 5, start by dividing throughout by 2.

6 Find the coordinates of the centre and the radius of the following circles:

a) $3x^2+3y^2+12x-18y-36=0$

b) $\frac{1}{2}x^2+\frac{1}{2}y^2+3x+4y=0$

7 Show that the point S(3, −5) lies on the circle with equation $x^2+y^2-4x-22=0$.
Find the coordinates of point T which is diametrically opposite S.

8 Find two possible values of m if the point $(m, 1)$ lies on the circle with equation $x^2+y^2+6x-16y-12=0$.

9 Points P (2, 5) and Q (−2, 1) lie on the circle $x^2+y^2+2gx+2fy+7=0$.

a) Form two equations in f and g.

b) Solve the system of equations to find the values of f and g.

c) Write down the equation of the circle.

d) State its centre and radius.

10 Find the equation of the circle passing through the points (7, 1), (9, −3) and (0, −6). ACE

Equation of a tangent to a circle

In this section we shall look at how to find the equation of a tangent to a circle at a point on the circumference.

Example 1

The point P (4, 3) lies on a circle with centre C (−2, −1).
Find the equation of the tangent at P.

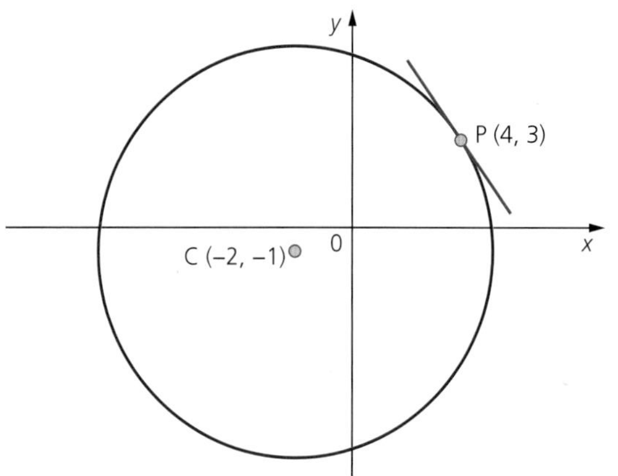

SOLUTION

The gradient of the radius joining C to P is

$$\frac{y_2 - y_1}{x_2 - x_1} = \frac{-1-3}{-2-4} = \frac{-4}{-6} = \frac{2}{3}$$

Gradient of tangent $= -\frac{3}{2}$ (as tangent is perpendicular to radius)

Substitute in equation $y - b = m(x - a)$

$$\Rightarrow \quad y - 3 = -\frac{3}{2}(x - 4)$$

$$\Rightarrow \quad 2y - 6 = -3x + 12$$

$$\Rightarrow \quad 3x + 2y = 18$$

Hence the equation of the tangent is $3x + 2y = 18$.

Example 2

The diagram shows the circle, centre A, with equation $(x+5)^2 + (y-4)^2 = 40$.

a) Prove that point B (1, 6) lies on the circumference of the circle.

b) Find the equation of the tangent to the circle at point B.

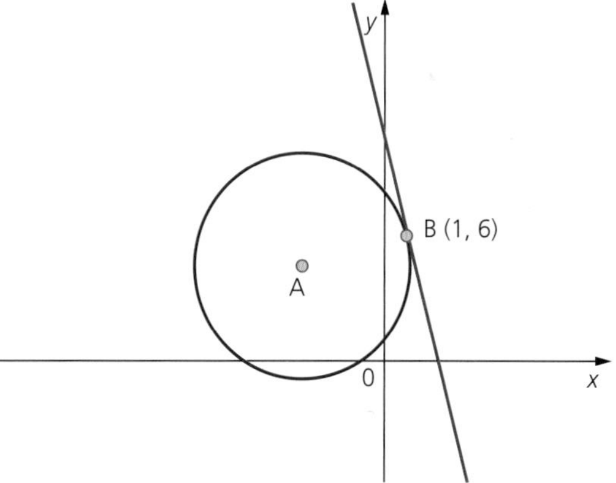

SOLUTION

a) Substitute $x = 1$, $y = 6$ into $(x+5)^2 + (y-4)^2$.
Hence $(1+5)^2 + (6-4)^2 = 6^2 + 2^2 = 36 + 4 = 40$.
Therefore B (1, 6) lies on the circumference of the circle.

b) A is the point (−5, 4).

Gradient of radius AB $= \frac{y_2 - y_1}{x_2 - x_1} = \frac{6-4}{1+5} = \frac{2}{6} = \frac{1}{3}$

Hence gradient of tangent at B $= -3$ (as tangent is perpendicular to radius)
Substitute into equation $y - b = m(x - a)$

$$\Rightarrow \quad y - 6 = -3(x - 1)$$

$$\Rightarrow \quad y - 6 = -3x + 3$$

$$\Rightarrow \quad 3x + y = 9$$

Hence the equation of the tangent is $3x + y = 9$.

Exercise 4.5

1 Find the equation of the tangent at the point:

a) P (1, 2) to the circle with equation $(x-3)^2+(y+4)^2=40$
b) Q (−1, 2) to the circle with equation $x^2+y^2=5$

2 A circle has equation $x^2+y^2-6x-4y+8=0$. Find the equation of the tangent to this circle at the point T (5, 1)

3 Determine the equation of the tangent to the circle with equation $(x-4)^2+(y+1)^2=20$ at the point (2, 3).

4 Find the equation of the tangent at the point S (−5, 1) to the circle with equation $x^2+y^2+6x+4=0$.

5 **a)** Show that the point W (6, 1) lies on the circle with equation $x^2+y^2+4x-10y-51=0$. HPQ
b) Find the equation of the tangent at the point (6, 1) on this circle.

6 The diagram shows a circle, centre C, with equation $x^2+y^2+6x+4y+8=0$. ACE

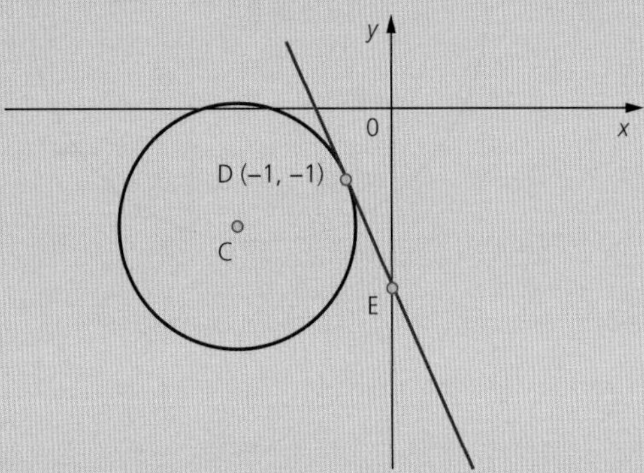

a) Find the equation of the tangent to the circle at the point D (−1, −1).
b) The tangent cuts the *y*-axis at E as shown. Find the equation of the circle which has DE as diameter.

7 The diagram shows a circle centre (−2, 3) which passes through the point A (−5, 0). ACE

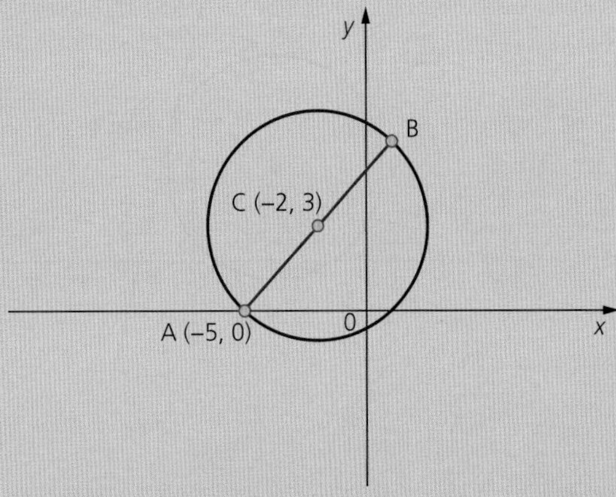

a) Find the equation of the circle.
b) AB is a diameter of the circle. Find the equation of the tangent to the circle at B.

Algebraic Skills

Intersection of a line and a circle

In the previous chapter we studied how to find the point(s) of intersection of two graphs.

We shall now consider how to find the point(s) of intersection of a straight line and a circle.

There are three possibilities:

- two points of intersection
- one point of intersection (i.e. the line is a tangent to the circle)
- no points of intersection.

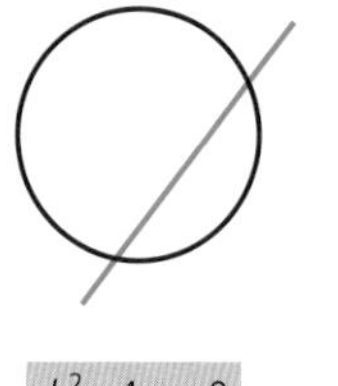

$b^2 - 4ac > 0$

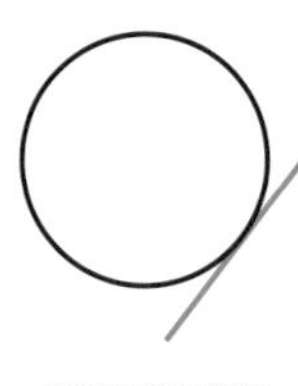

$b^2 - 4ac = 0$

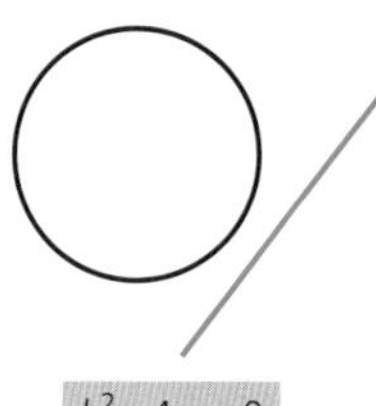

$b^2 - 4ac < 0$

Example 1

Find the coordinates of the points where the line $y = 2x - 1$ and the circle $x^2 + y^2 - 3x - 4y + 5 = 0$ meet.

SOLUTION

Substitute $y = 2x - 1$ into $x^2 + y^2 - 3x - 4y + 5 = 0$:

$$x^2 + (2x - 1)^2 - 3x - 4(2x - 1) + 5 = 0$$

$$\Rightarrow x^2 + 4x^2 - 4x + 1 - 3x - 8x + 4 + 5 = 0$$

$$\Rightarrow 5x^2 - 15x + 10 = 0$$

$$\Rightarrow x^2 - 3x + 2 = 0$$

$$\Rightarrow (x - 1)(x - 2) = 0$$

$$\Rightarrow x = 1 \text{ or } x = 2$$

Now substitute both values for x into the equation of either the line or the circle to find the y-coordinates of the points of intersection. It is clearly simpler to substitute into $y = 2x - 1$ in this case:

$x = 1 \Rightarrow y = 2 \times 1 - 1 = 1$ and $x = 2 \Rightarrow y = 2 \times 2 - 1 = 3$

Hence the points of intersection are $(1, 1)$ and $(2, 3)$.

Note

We can use the value of the discriminant to find how many points of intersection there are:

- $b^2 - 4ac > 0 \Rightarrow$ two points of intersection
- $b^2 - 4ac = 0 \Rightarrow$ one point of intersection (i.e. the line is a tangent to the circle)
- $b^2 - 4ac < 0 \Rightarrow$ no points of intersection.

In the example above,

$$x^2 - 3x + 2 = 0 \Rightarrow b^2 - 4ac = (-3)^2 - 4\times1\times2 = 1$$
$$\Rightarrow b^2 - 4ac > 0$$
$\Rightarrow$ the equation has two distinct roots

$\Rightarrow$ there are two points of intersection.

Example 2

a) Show that the line with equation $2y - x = 19$ is a tangent to the circle with equation $x^2 + y^2 + 8x - 10y + 36 = 0$.

b) State the coordinates of the point of contact.

SOLUTION

a) First re-arrange the equation of the straight line to make x or y the subject of the equation. Avoid fractions if possible, so in this case make x the subject:

$2y - x = 19 \Rightarrow x = 2y - 19$

Now substitute $x = 2y - 19$ into $x^2 + y^2 + 8x - 10y + 36 = 0$:

$(2y - 19)^2 + y^2 + 8(2y - 19) - 10y + 36 = 0$

$\Rightarrow 4y^2 - 76y + 361 + y^2 + 16y - 152 - 10y + 36 = 0$

$\Rightarrow 5y^2 - 70y + 245 = 0$

$\Rightarrow y^2 - 14y + 49 = 0$

Hence $b^2 - 4ac = (-14)^2 - 4\times1\times49 = 0$

$\Rightarrow$ the equation has equal roots

$\Rightarrow$ there is only one point of contact

$\Rightarrow$ the line is a tangent to the circle.

b) $y^2 - 14y + 49 = 0$

$\Rightarrow (y - 7)(y - 7) = 0$

$\Rightarrow y = 7$

Substitute $y = 7$ into $x = 2y - 19$ to find the point of contact.

Hence the point of contact is (7, –5).

Exercise 4.6

1 The equations of a straight line and a circle are given in each part.
Find out if they intersect. If they do, calculate the coordinates of the point(s) of intersection.

a) $y = 1,\ x^2 + y^2 = 17$

b) $y = 3,\ x^2 + y^2 = 34$

c) $y = 4,\ x^2 + y^2 = 9$

d) $y = x + 1,\ x^2 + y^2 = 5$

e) $y = 3x - 10,\ x^2 + y^2 + 2x + 6y - 10 = 0$

2 In each part, show that the line is a tangent to the given circle and find the coordinates of the point of contact.

a) $x = 4,\ x^2 + y^2 = 16$

b) $y = 4x + 7,\ (x - 3)^2 + (y - 2)^2 = 17$

c) $y = 2x - 4,\ x^2 + y^2 - 2x - 6y + 5 = 0$

3 Show that the line with equation $y = 2x - 10$ is a tangent to the circle with the equation $x^2 + y^2 = 20$ and find the coordinates of the point of contact. HPQ

→

4 Show that the line with equation $y=3x+2$ is a tangent to the circle with the equation $x^2+y^2-14x-6y+18=0$ and find the coordinates of the point of contact.

5 The circle with equation $x^2+y^2-4x+2y+3=0$ cuts the *x*-axis at two points. Find the coordinates of these points.

6 The line with equation $y=3x+5$ cuts the circle with equation $x^2+y^2=65$ at two points. Determine the coordinates of these points.

7 Find the coordinates of the points of intersection of the line $y=x-4$ and the circle $(x+2)^2+y^2=36$.

8 The circle with equation $x^2+y^2+4x+2y-20=0$ and the line $y=2x+8$ meet at the points A and B. HPQ
Determine the coordinates of A and B.

9 Find the points where the line $y=x+1$ and the circle $x^2+y^2-4x-8y+7=0$ intersect.

10 The equation of a circle is $x^2+y^2-8x-4y=0$. ACE

a) State the coordinates of the centre and the radius of the circle.

b) Find the coordinates of the points of intersection, A and B, of the line $x+y=8$ and the given circle.

c) Write down the coordinates of M, the midpoint of AB.

d) A second circle has the same centre as the given circle and has AB as a tangent. What is the equation of the second circle?

11 A circle has equation $x^2+y^2-6x-10y+26=0$. ACE

a) State the coordinates of C, the centre of the circle.

b) Find the equation of the chord with midpoint M (4, 6).

c) Show that the line $x+y=12$ is a tangent to the circle and find the coordinates of P, the point of contact.

12 Show that the straight line with equation $4x+3y+7=0$ is a tangent to the circle with equation $x^2+y^2-6x-4y-12=0$ and find the coordinates of the point of contact. ACE

13 Find the possible values of *k* for which the line with equation $x-y=k$ is a tangent to the circle $x^2+y^2=18$. ACE

Intersection of circles

In this section, we consider different ways in which circles can be positioned relative to each other. Two circles may intersect in two, one or no points.

Consider two circles, one with radius *R* and the other with radius *r*.

If the distance between their centres is *d*, then the two circles:

- do not touch (and the circles are separate) if $d > R + r$

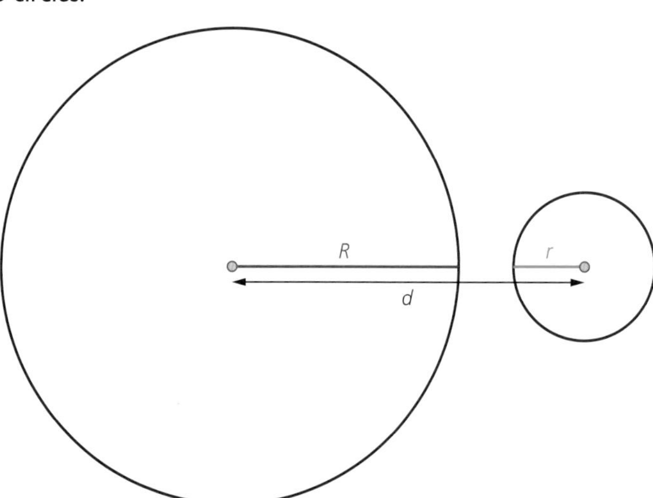

Algebraic Skills

- touch externally if $d = R + r$

- intersect in two points if $d < R + r$

- touch internally if $R = d + r$

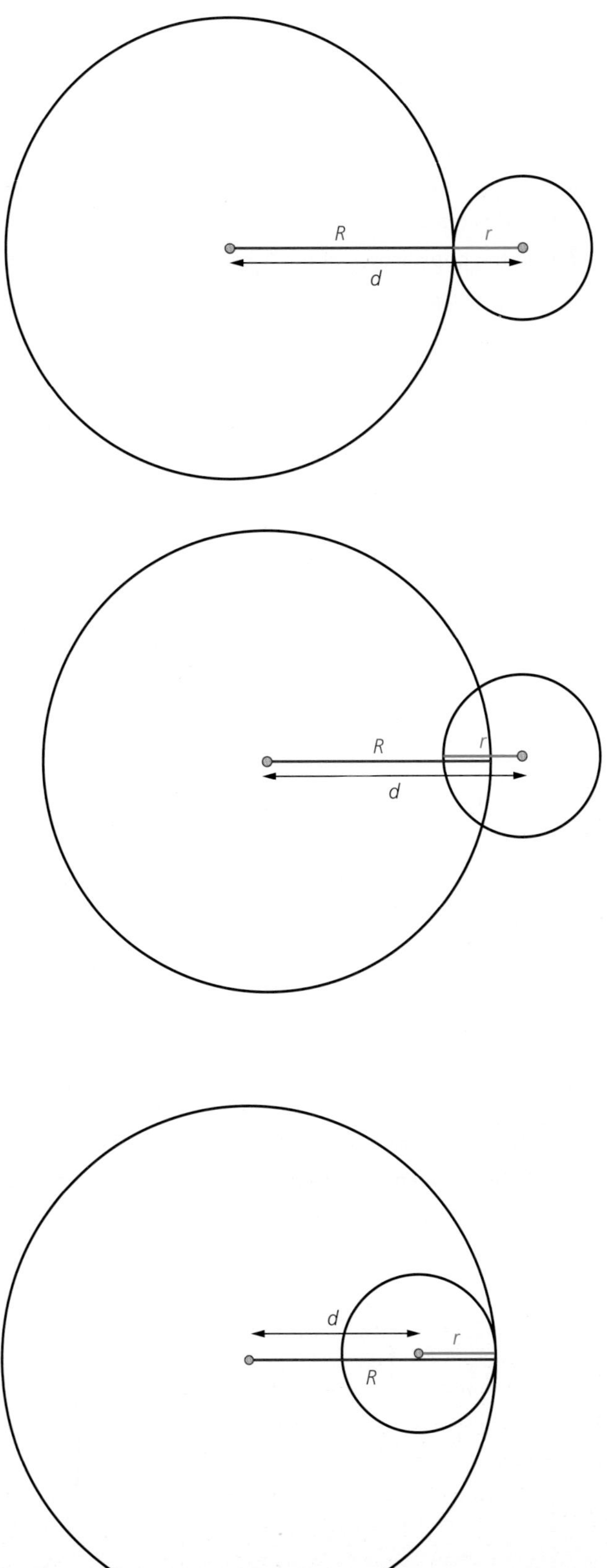

- do not touch (and one circle is enclosed by the other) if $R > d + r$.

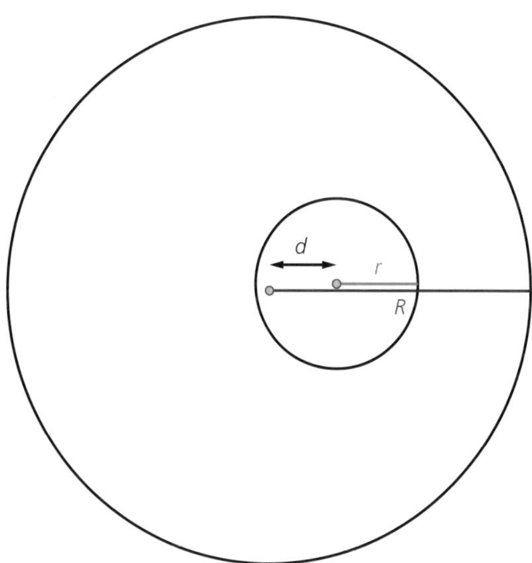

Example

Two congruent circles have equations $x^2 + y^2 + 6x + 4y - 12 = 0$ and $x^2 + y^2 - 6x - 12y + 20 = 0$.
Show that these circles touch externally.

SOLUTION

The circle $x^2 + y^2 + 6x + 4y - 12 = 0$ has centre $(-g, -f) = (-3, -2)$ and radius $\sqrt{g^2 + f^2 - c} = \sqrt{3^2 + 2^2 + 12} = \sqrt{9 + 4 + 12} = \sqrt{25} = 5$.

The circle $x^2 + y^2 - 6x - 12y + 20 = 0$ has centre $(-g, -f) = (3, 6)$ and radius 5 (as the circles are congruent).

The sum of the two radii is 10.

The distance between the centres is:

$$\begin{aligned} d &= \sqrt{(x_2 - x_1)^2 + (y_2 - y_1)^2} \\ &= \sqrt{(3+3)^2 + (6+2)^2} \\ &= \sqrt{6^2 + 8^2} \\ &= \sqrt{36 + 64} = \sqrt{100} = 10 \end{aligned}$$

So the sum of the radii = the distance between the centres; therefore the circles **touch externally**.

Exercise 4.7

Hint Make a rough sketch for each question.

1 Circle A has equation $(x-6)^2 + (y-8)^2 = 100$.
Circle B has equation $x^2 + y^2 - 6x - 8y = 0$.
Do these circles touch internally or externally?

2 Do the circles with equations $(x-2)^2 + (y-3)^2 = 9$ and $(x-1)^2 + (y+1)^2 = 16$ overlap?

3 Determine the relationship between each of the following pairs of circles. HPQ

a) $x^2 + y^2 + 6x - 10y + 18 = 0$ and $x^2 + y^2 - 6x + 2y + 6 = 0$

b) $x^2 + y^2 - 6x - 4y - 36 = 0$ and $x^2 + y^2 - 2x + 2y - 2 = 0$

→

4 Two circles have equations $x^2+y^2+4x+8y+15=0$ and $x^2+y^2-12x-9=0$. Show that these circles touch externally.

5 Two circles have equations $x^2+y^2-4x-8y+16=0$ and $x^2+y^2+6x-8y+16=0$.

a) Prove that circles touch externally.

b) Find the coordinates of the point of contact of the circles.

6 Two circles have equations $x^2+y^2-6y=0$ and $x^2+y^2-24x-16y+172=0$.

a) Show that the circles do not overlap.

b) Calculate the smallest distance between the two circles.

7 Two congruent circles touch externally at the point (7, 6). ACE
One of the circles has equation $x^2+y^2-8x-2y-17=0$.
Find the equation of the other circle.

8 Three rollers in a printing machine can be represented by three circles with collinear centres as shown. ACE

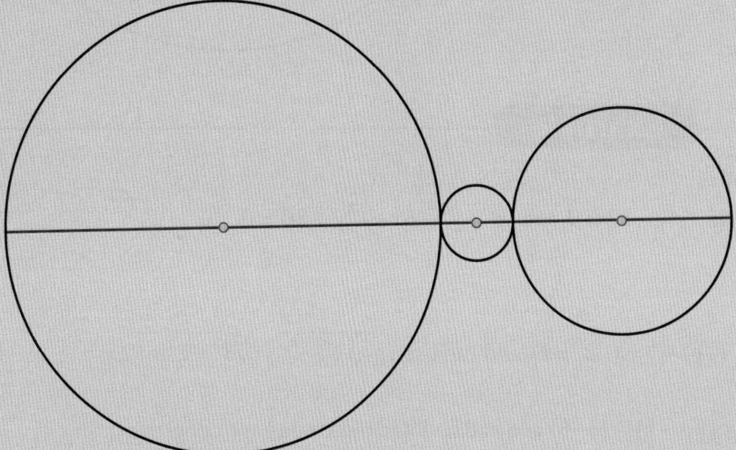

The equations of the outer circles are $x^2+y^2-2x-6y-215=0$ and $x^2+y^2-58x-48y+1317=0$.
Find the equation of the middle circle.

9 Point A (2, 0) lies on circle C_1 with equation $(x+2)^2+(y-3)^2=25$. ACE
Two circles C_2 and C_3 touch circle C_1 externally and internally respectively at A.
The radius of each of these circles is twice the radius of circle C_1.
Find the equations of circles C_2 and C_3.

Checkout

1 Write down the equation of a circle with centre (5, −1) and radius 3.

2 Find the equation of a circle that has a diameter with endpoints A (−4, 2) and B (4, −2).

3 A circle has equation $(x-5)^2+(y-2)^2=9$.

a) Find the coordinates of the centre C and the length of the diameter.

b) Does the point K (7, 2) lie inside, outside or on the circle?

c) Does the line with equation $y=2x$ cut the circle?

Algebraic Skills

4 The points P $(-1,\ 1)$ and Q $(7,\ -5)$ lie on the circumference of of the circle with equation $x^2+y^2-6x+4y-12=0$. Show that PQ is a diameter of the circle.

5 A baker makes gingerbread snowmen. Each snowman is 12 units high with a circular head and body.

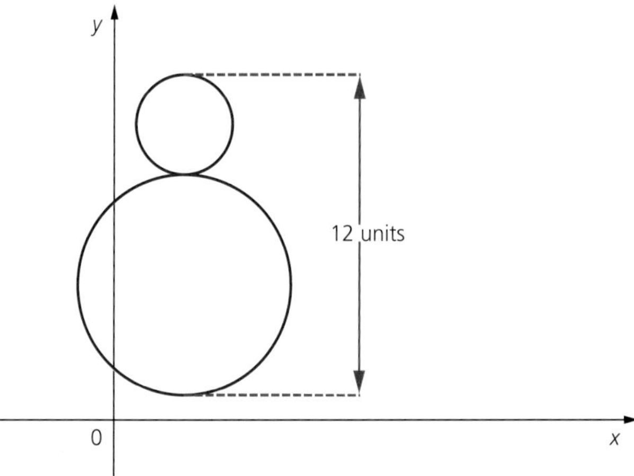

The equation of the body is $x^2+y^2-6x-12y+29=0$.
The line joining the centres is parallel to the y-axis. Find the equation of the head.

6 The point P (2, 4) lies on the circle $(x+1)^2+(y-2)^2=13$.
Find the equation of the tangent at P.

7 A circle has centre C $(-2,\ 4)$. Show that the tangent to the circle at the point T $(-5,\ 8)$ has equation $3x-4y+47=0$.

8 Prove that the line $3y=x+20$ is a common tangent to the circles $x^2+y^2=40$ and $x^2+y^2-22x-14y+160=0$.

9 A circle has equation $x^2+y^2+4x-2y-11=0$.
a) Find its centre and radius.
b) Find the coordinates of the points where the circle cuts the y-axis.
Leave your answer in simplified surd form.

10 Two circles have equations $x^2+y^2-4x-10y+16=0$ and $x^2+y^2+8x-2y-100=0$. Prove that circles touch internally.

11 The small circle, centre B, has equation $(x+2)^2+(y+1)^2=25$.
The large circles, centres A and C, touch the small circle as shown. AC is parallel to the x-axis.

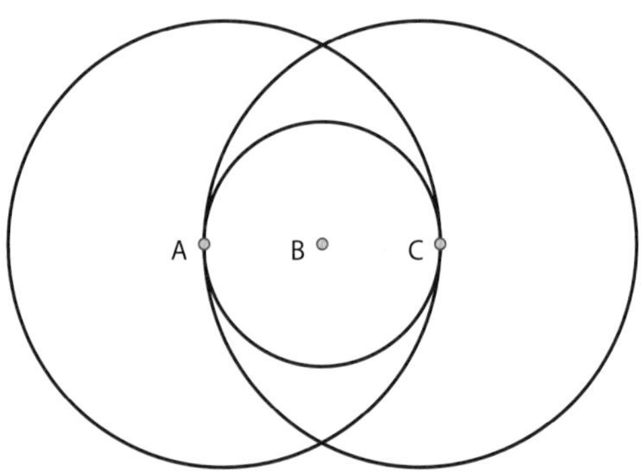

Find the equation of the large circles.

Algebraic Skills

12 The equation of a circle, centre A, is $x^2 + y^2 - 14x - 10y + 49 = 0$.
The equation of a circle, centre B, is $x^2 + y^2 + 16x + 10y + 53 = 0$.
The line AB cuts the circles at C and D as shown.

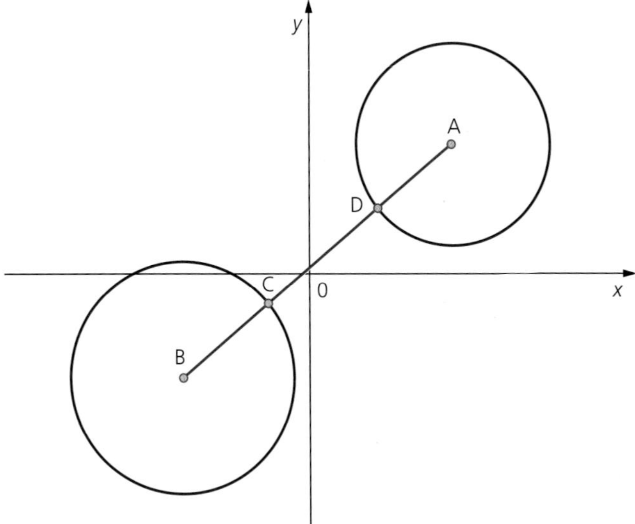

Determine the length of CD. Give your answer correct to one decimal place.

Summary

Circles

1 The equation of a circle with centre (0, 0) and radius r is $x^2 + y^2 = r^2$
2 The equation of a circle with centre (a, b) and radius r is $(x - a)^2 + (y - b)^2 = r^2$
3 The equation $x^2 + y^2 + 2gx + 2fy + c = 0$ is the equation of a circle with centre $(-g, -f)$ and radius $\sqrt{g^2 + f^2 - c}$ provided that $g^2 + f^2 - c > 0$.
4 The equation of the tangent to a circle at the point (a, b) on its circumference is given by $y - b = m_2(x - a)$ where m_1 is the gradient of the radius from the centre of the circle to the point (a, b) and $m_1 m_2 = -1$.
5 A straight line and a circle intersect in two, one or no points. The discriminant can be used to identify how many points of intersection there are:
   * $b^2 - 4ac > 0 \Rightarrow$ two points of intersection
   * $b^2 - 4ac = 0 \Rightarrow$ one point of intersection (i.e. the line is a tangent to the circle)
   * $b^2 - 4ac < 0 \Rightarrow$ no point of intersection.
6 If d is the distance between the centres of two circles with radii R and r, then the two circles
   * do not touch (and the circles are separate) if $d > R + r$
   * touch externally if $d = R + r$.
   * intersect in two points if $d < R + r$.
   * touch internally if $R = d + r$.
   * do not touch (and one circle is enclosed by the other) if $R > d + r$.

CHAPTER 5

Logarithmic and Exponential Expressions

In this chapter we shall look at the logarithmic function, $f(x) = \log_a x$, and the exponential function, $f(x) = a^x$. We shall study their relationship to each other and look at examples of where they arise in real-life contexts. Further work on the graphs of these functions appears in Chapter 11 (Functions).

What I am learning

* Properties of logarithmic and exponential functions and their relationship to each other
* How to simplify expressions using the laws of logarithms
* How to solve logarithmic and exponential equations
* How to use straight line graphs to model the relationships $y = ax^b$ and $y = ab^x$
* How to solve problems involving exponential growth and decay, such as:
  The mass, M grams, of a radioactive sample after a time of t years is given by the formula $M = 50e^{-6t}$.
  a) What was the initial mass of the radioactive sample?
  b) The half-life of the sample is the time taken for half of the radioactive sample to decay. Find the half-life of the sample.

What I should already know/be able to do

* Solve problems involving appreciation/depreciation
* Simplify expressions using the laws of indices
* Evaluate numerical expressions using indices

Quick check!

1 £80 000 is deposited in a bank account with a rate of interest of 5% per annum. How much will be in the account after 3 years?

2 A ball is dropped from a height of 200 centimetres. After each bounce it reaches a height 25% less than its previous height. What is the height of the ball after 5 bounces?

3 Simplify:

a) $a^6 \times a^3$ b) $c^4 \div c^3$ c) $\dfrac{f^6 \times f^{\frac{1}{2}}}{f^{-0.5}}$

d) $(q^2)^3$ e) a^0 f) a^1

4 Evaluate:

a) $0{\cdot}4^3$ b) 3^{-2} c) 7^{-1}

d) $36^{\frac{1}{2}}$ e) $8^{\frac{2}{3}}$

Algebraic Skills

Quick check! – *Solutions*

1 £92 610
2 47·5 cm
3 a) a^9 b) c c) f^7
d) q^6 e) 1 f) a
4 a) 0·064 b) $\frac{1}{9}$ c) $\frac{1}{7}$
d) 6 e) 4

The exponential function

An **exponential function** is one in the form $f(x) = a^x$.

In this function, a is called the **base** and it must be positive, x is the index or **exponent**.

Example

Sketch the graph of the function $f(x) = 2^x$.

SOLUTION

Start by completing this table of values for the function.

x	−3	−2	−1	0	1	2	3	4	5
$y = 2^x$	$\frac{1}{8}$	$\frac{1}{4}$	$\frac{1}{2}$	1	2	4	8	16	32

By plotting the points in the table, you can see what the graph of the function $f(x) = 2^x$ looks like.

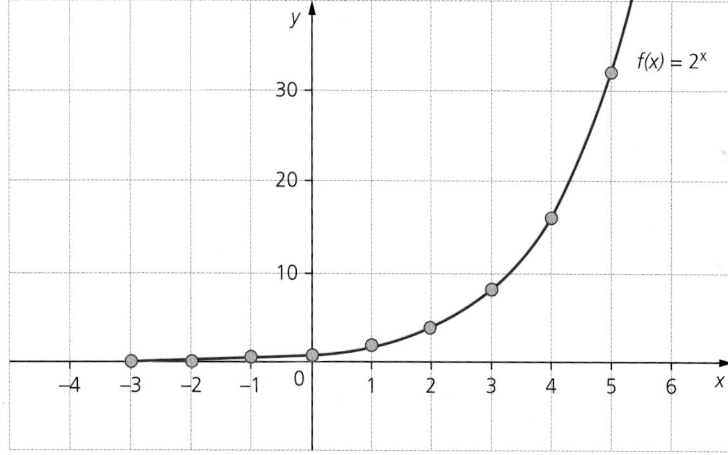

Exercise 5.1

1 a) Complete this table of values for $f(x) = 3^x$.

x	−3	−2	−1	0	1	2	3
$f(x)$							

b) Sketch the graph of $f(x) = 3^x$.

2 a) Complete this table of values for $f(x) = \left(\frac{1}{2}\right)^x$.

x	−3	−2	−1	0	1	2	3
$f(x)$							

b) Sketch the graph of $f(x) = \left(\frac{1}{2}\right)^x$.

3 a) Complete this table of values for $f(x) = \left(\frac{1}{3}\right)^x$.

x	−3	−2	−1	0	1	2	3
$f(x)$							

b) Sketch the graph of $f(x) = \left(\frac{1}{3}\right)^x$.

4 Sketch the graph of $f(x) = 1^x$.

5 For the function $f(x) = 10^x$, evaluate:

a) $f(-2)$ **b)** $f(-1)$ **c)** $f(0)$
d) $f(1)$ **e)** $f(2)$ **f)** $f(3)$

6 For the function $f(x) = \left(\frac{1}{10}\right)^x$, evaluate:

a) $f(-2)$ **b)** $f(-1)$ **c)** $f(0)$
d) $f(1)$ **e)** $f(2)$ **f)** $f(3)$

7 The point A (3, 125) lies on the graph of the function $y = a^x$. Find the value of a.

8 The diagram shows part of the graph whose equation is of the form $y = 6k^x$. ACE

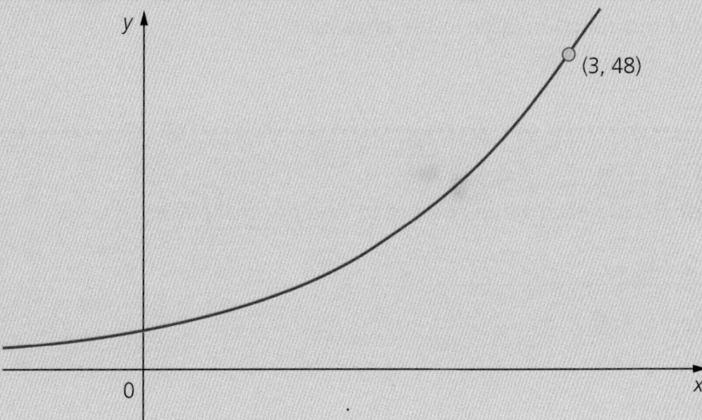

What is the value of k?

Algebraic Skills

All exponential graphs look like the ones you have sketched in the previous exercise, except the graph of $f(x) = 1^x$ which is simply a horizontal line.

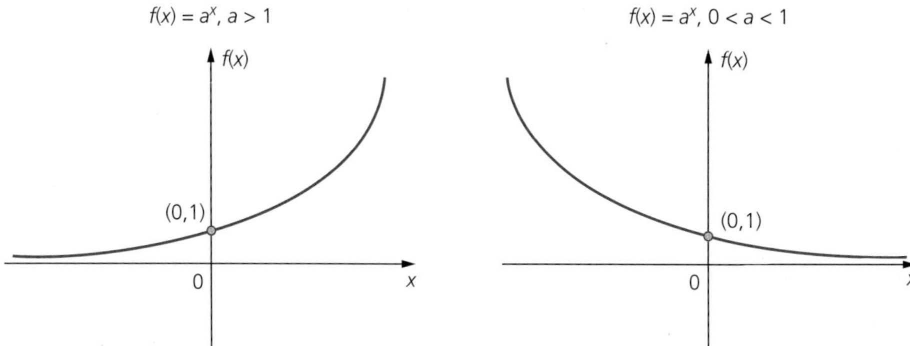

Notice the following:

- a^x is always positive. The graph gets very close to the x-axis but never touches it; the x-axis is an **asymptote** to the curve.
- Since $a^0 = 1$, *all* exponential graphs pass through the point (0,1).
- When $a > 1$, the graph increases, slowly at first but then by ever increasing amounts.
- When $0 < a < 1$, the graph decreases, quickly at first but then by ever decreasing amounts.
- Since $f(x) = \left(\frac{1}{a}\right)^x = \frac{1^x}{a^x} = \frac{1}{a^x} = a^{-x}$, the graph of $f(x) = \left(\frac{1}{a}\right)^x$ is the reflection of the graph of $f(x) = a^x$ in the y-axis.

The natural exponential function

The function $f(x) = e^x$, where e is the irrational number 2·718281 8... is called the **natural exponential function**. This exponential function is very important. It occurs naturally in many areas. As a result, most calculators have an e^x button. We will see some of the applications of this function later in the chapter.

Exercise 5.2

1 a) Complete this table of values for $f(x) = e^x$.
(Use the e^x key on your calculator. Round each value correct to one decimal place.)

x	−3	−2	−1	0	1	2	3
$f(x)$							

b) Sketch the graph of $f(x) = e^x$.

2 Evaluate, correct to three significant figures:

a) e^x when $x = 0{\cdot}7$

b) e^t when $t = 1{\cdot}7$

c) e^{-n} when $n = 2{\cdot}5$

d) e^{2a} when $a = 4$

e) $e^{-0{\cdot}012k}$ when $k = 100$

f) $50e^{-3c}$ when $c = 2$

Algebraic Skills

Exponential growth and decay

Question 1 in the 'Quick check!' is an example of **exponential growth**. Here a quantity increases slowly at first but then by ever increasing amounts.

Example 1

If £80 000 is deposited in a bank account with a rate of interest of 5% per annum, how much will be in the account after 3 years?

SOLUTION

Amount after 1 year $= 1{\cdot}05 \times 80\,000 = £84\,000$

Amount after 2 years $= 1{\cdot}05 \times 84\,000 = £88\,200$

Amount after 3 years $= 1{\cdot}05 \times 88\,200 = £92\,610$

Alternatively, in a single calculation, amount after 3 years $= 1{\cdot}05^3 \times 80\,000 = £92\,610$

A formula for A_n, the amount after n years, is $A_n = 1{\cdot}05^n \times 80\,000$.

Question 2 in the 'Quick check!' is an example of **exponential decay**. Here a quantity decreases quickly at first but then by ever decreasing amounts.

Example 2

A ball is dropped from a height of 200 centimetres. After each bounce it reaches a height 25% less than its previous height. What is the height of the ball after 5 bounces?

SOLUTION

Height after 1 bounce $= 0{\cdot}75 \times 200 = 150\,\text{cm}$

Height after 2 bounces $= 0{\cdot}75 \times 150 = 112{\cdot}5\,\text{cm}$

Height after 3 bounces $= 0{\cdot}75 \times 112{\cdot}5 = 84{\cdot}375\,\text{cm}$

Height after 4 bounces $= 0{\cdot}75 \times 84{\cdot}375 = 63{\cdot}28125\,\text{cm}$

Height after 5 bounces $= 0{\cdot}75 \times 68{\cdot}28125 = 47{\cdot}46\ldots\text{cm} = 47{\cdot}5\,\text{cm}$ to one decimal place

Alternatively, in a single calculation, the height after 5 bounces is $0{\cdot}75^5 \times 200 = 47{\cdot}5\,\text{cm}$ to one decimal place.

A formula for h_n, the height after n bounces, is $h_n = 0{\cdot}75^n \times 200$.

Exercise 5.3

1 The population of a town is 12 000. It is estimated that the population of the town will increase at the rate of 15% per annum.

a) Write down a formula for P_n, the population of the town after n years.
b) Calculate the estimated population after 6 years.

2 The value of a car when new is £25 000. It is estimated that the value of the car will decrease at the rate of 12% per annum.

a) Write down a formula for V_n, the value of the car after n years.
b) Calculate the estimated value of the car after 10 years.

3 The population of the world in 2000 was 6·08 billion. It is estimated that the annual rate of increase is 1·25%.

a) Write down a formula for P_n, the population of the world n years after 2000.
b) Calculate the estimated population in 2016.

4 A 500 millilitre puddle of water is evaporating at a rate of 15% per hour.

a) Write down a formula for W_h, the amount of water in the puddle after h hours.
b) How much water is left in the puddle after 4 hours?

5 Jack borrows £800 from a loan company. He must repay the loan within a year. He can make regular payments throughout the year or a single payment at the end of the year. Interest is charged on any unpaid balance at a rate of 2% per month. Jack chooses to make a single payment at the end of the year. How much will the payment be?

6 A diamond ring was bought a number of years ago for £500. The value of the ring increases by 8% per year. How many years does it take for the ring to double in value?

7 A hospital patient is given a 400 milligram dose of a drug. Each hour, the amount of drug in the patient's body decreases by 30%. When there is less than 100 milligrams of the drug left in the patient's body, it is safe for the patient to be given another dose. How long will it be before the patient can be given another dose?

8 The number of bacteria, N, in a liquid culture is given by the formula $N = 500e^{1.3t}$, where t is the time in hours.

a) How many bacteria are there at time zero?
b) How many bacteria are there after three hours?

9 The mass, m milligram of a radioactive substance is given by the formula $m = 200e^{-0.1t}$, where t represents the time in years.

a) What is the mass of the substance at time zero?
b) What is the mass of the substance after four years?

Logarithmic functions

The inverse of the exponential function $f(x) = a^x$ is the **logarithmic function** $f(x) = \log_a x$.

Read $\log_a x$ as the 'logarithm of x to the base a'.

For example, the inverse of $f(x) = 2^x$ is $f(x) = \log_2 x$.

x	$f(x) = 2^x$
3	8
2	4
1	2
0	1
−1	$\frac{1}{2}$
−2	$\frac{1}{4}$
−3	$\frac{1}{8}$

x	$f(x) = \log_2 x$
8	3
4	2
2	1
1	0
$\frac{1}{2}$	−1
$\frac{1}{4}$	−2
$\frac{1}{8}$	−3

Hence $2^3 = 8 \Leftrightarrow \log_2 8 = 3$

$2^{-2} = \frac{1}{4} \Leftrightarrow \log_2 \frac{1}{4} = -2$ etc.

In general $y = a^x \Leftrightarrow \log_a y = x$

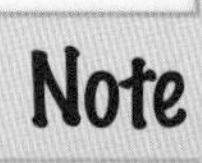

- $a = a^1 \Leftrightarrow \log_a a = 1$
- $1 = a^0 \Leftrightarrow \log_a 1 = 0$
- $\log_a a^x = x$

Algebraic Skills

We can use the values in the tables above to graph the functions $f(x)=2^x$ and $f(x)=\log_2 x$ on the same diagram.

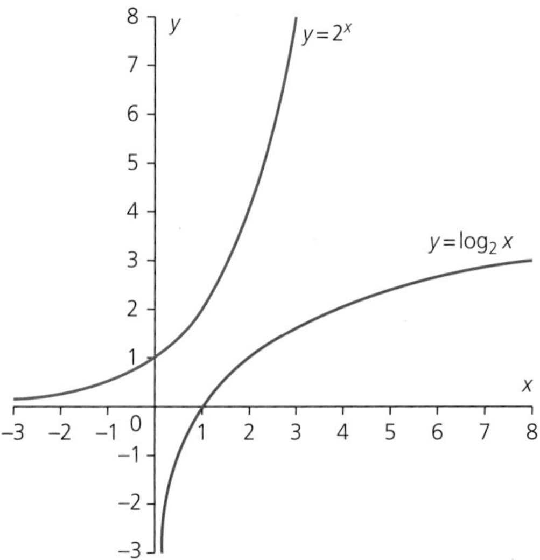

The graphs of $f(x)=\log_2 x$ and $f(x)=2^x$ are reflections of each other in the line $y=x$.

(In Chapter 11 you will see that the graph of any function is the reflection of its inverse in the line $y=x$.)

In general the graphs of $f(x)=\log_a x$ and $f(x)=a^x$ are reflections of each other in the line $y=x$ since the functions are inverses of each other.

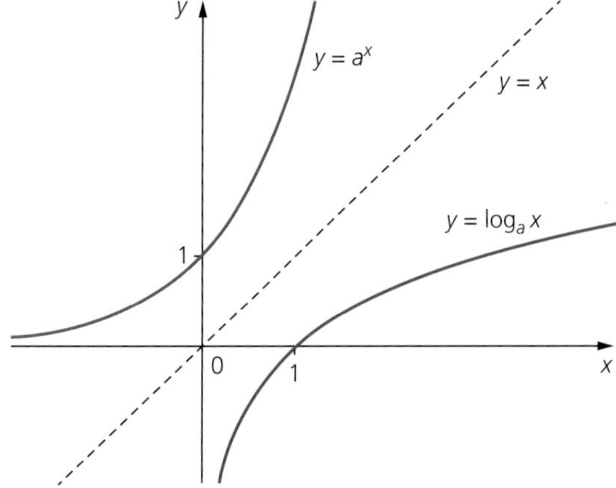

The domain of $f(x)=\log_a x$ is $\{x : x>0,\ x\in R\}$.

Note that since the base, a, of all exponential functions must be positive, then the corresponding bases of all logarithmic functions must be positive.

Example 1

Express $5^3=125$ in logarithmic form.

SOLUTION

$5^3=125 \Rightarrow \log_5 125=3$

Example 2

Solve the equation $\log_x \frac{1}{4} = 2$.

SOLUTION

$$\log_x \frac{1}{4} = 2 \Rightarrow x^2 = \frac{1}{4} \Rightarrow x = \sqrt{\left(\frac{1}{4}\right)} = \frac{1}{2}$$

Example 3

Evaluate $\log_2\left(\frac{1}{32}\right)$.

SOLUTION

Let $\log_2\left(\frac{1}{32}\right) = x \Rightarrow 2^x = \frac{1}{32} = \frac{1}{2^5} = 2^{-5} \Rightarrow x = -5$

Think what power of 2 gives $\frac{1}{32}$.

Exercise 5.4

1 Express in logarithmic form $\left[\text{e.g. } 2^3 = 8 \Rightarrow \log_2 8 = 3\right]$: HPQ

a) $2^4 = 16$ **b)** $10^3 = 1000$ **c)** $3^2 = 9$

d) $8^1 = 8$ **e)** $7^0 = 1$ **f)** $3^{-3} = \frac{1}{27}$

g) $6^{-1} = \frac{1}{6}$ **h)** $10^{-2} = \frac{1}{100}$ **i)** $a^p = q$

j) $m^5 = k$

2 Express in exponential form $\left[\text{e.g. } \log_2 8 = 3 \Rightarrow 2^3 = 8\right]$: HPQ

a) $\log_3 81 = 4$ **b)** $\log_7 49 = 2$ **c)** $\log_6 216 = 3$

d) $\log_3 3 = 1$ **e)** $\log_8 1 = 0$ **f)** $\log_5 \frac{1}{25} = -2$

g) $\log_7 \sqrt{7} = \frac{1}{2}$ **h)** $\log_4 \frac{1}{64} = -3$ **i)** $\log_c d = e$

j) $\log_d f = e$

3 Solve for x:

a) $\log_5 x = 2$ **b)** $\log_2 x = 6$

c) $\log_9 x = \frac{1}{2}$ **d)** $\log_{10} x = -3$

4 Solve for x:

a) $\log_x 81 = 2$ **b)** $\log_x \frac{1}{16} = -2$

c) $\log_x 9 = 4$ **d)** $\log_x 27 = \frac{3}{2}$

5 Evaluate:

a) $\log_2 128$ **b)** $\log_{11} 121$ **c)** $\log_2 \frac{1}{4}$

d) $\log_3 \frac{1}{81}$ **e)** $\log_{\sqrt{5}} 25$ **f)** $\log_9 27$

g) $\log_{10} 1000000$ **h)** $\log_8 \frac{1}{16}$

Logarithms to base 10 and natural logarithms

Two commonly used logarithmic functions are:

- $f(x) = \log_{10} x$, the inverse of $f(x) = 10^x$
- $f(x) = \log_e x$, the inverse of $f(x) = e^x$

These functions arise in so many real-life situations that they have their own keys on scientific calculators so that values can be easily calculated.

The **[LOG]** button is used to evaluate values of $\log_{10} x$.

The second function on the **[LOG]** button is **[10^x]**.

The **[LN]** button is used to evaluate values of $\log_e x$.

The second function on the **[LN]** button is **[e^x]**.

Logarithms to the base e are called **natural logarithms** and are more commonly written as $\ln x$.

Exercise 5.5

1 Use your calculator to write down, correct to three decimal places, the value of:

a) $\log_{10} 2$ **b)** $\log_{10} 3$ **c)** $\log_{10} 5$

d) $\log_{10} 900$ **e)** $\log_{10} \sqrt{10}$ **f)** $\log_{10} 0{\cdot}8$

2 Use your calculator to write down, correct to three decimal places, the value of:

a) $\ln 2$ **b)** $\ln 3$ **c)** $\ln 5$

d) $\ln 900$ **e)** $\ln \sqrt{10}$ **f)** $\ln 0{\cdot}8$

3 a) Complete this table of values for $\log_{10} ab$, $\log_{10} a \times \log_{10} b$ and $\log_{10} a + \log_{10} b$.
Give each value correct to three decimal places.

	$\log_{10} ab$	$\log_{10} a \times \log_{10} b$	$\log_{10} a + \log_{10} b$
$a = 2,\ b = 3$			
$a = 4,\ b = 7$			
$a = 8,\ b = 6$			

b) Make a conjecture based on the values in your table: $\log_{10} ab = \ldots$

4 a) Complete this table of values for $\ln ab$, $\ln a \times \ln b$, $\ln a + \ln b$.
Give each value correct to three decimal places.

	$\ln ab$	$\ln a \times \ln b$	$\ln a + \ln b$
$a = 2,\ b = 3$			
$a = 4,\ b = 7$			
$a = 8,\ b = 6$			

b) Make a conjecture based on the values in your table: $\ln ab = \ldots$

5 a) Complete this table of values for $\log_{10}\frac{a}{b}$, $\frac{\log_{10}a}{\log_{10}b}$ and $\log_{10}a - \log_{10}b$.
Give each value correct to three decimal places.

	$\log_{10}\frac{a}{b}$	$\frac{\log_{10}a}{\log_{10}b}$	$\log_{10}a - \log_{10}b$
$a = 12, b = 4$			
$a = 26, b = 2$			
$a = 15, b = 3$			

b) Make a conjecture based on the values in your table: $\log_{10}\frac{a}{b} = \ldots$

6 a) Complete this table of values for $\ln\frac{a}{b}$, $\frac{\ln a}{\ln b}$ and $\ln a - \ln b$.
Give each value correct to three decimal places.

	$\ln\frac{a}{b}$	$\frac{\ln a}{\ln b}$	$\ln a - \ln b$
$a = 12, b = 4$			
$a = 26, b = 2$			
$a = 15, b = 3$			

b) Make a conjecture based on the values in your table: $\ln\frac{a}{b} = \ldots$

7 a) Complete this table of values for $\log_{10}a^b$, $(\log_{10}a)^b$ and $b\log_{10}a$.
Give each value correct to three decimal places.

	$\log_{10}a^b$	$(\log_{10}a)^b$	$b\log_{10}a$
$a = 5, b = 2$			
$a = 4, b = 3$			
$a = 2, b = 6$			

b) Make a conjecture based on the values in your table: $\log_{10}a^b = \ldots$

8 a) Complete this table of values for $\ln a^b$, $(\ln a)^b$ and $b\ln a$.
Give each value correct to three decimal places.

	$\ln a^b$	$(\ln a)^b$	$b\ln a$
$a = 5, b = 2$			
$a = 4, b = 3$			
$a = 2, b = 6$			

b) Make a conjecture based on the values in your table: $\ln a^b = \ldots$

The laws of logarithms

When you studied indices, you learned the laws of indices:

$a^p \times a^q = a^{p+q}$, $a^p \div a^q = a^{p-q}$, $(a^p)^q = a^{pq}$.

The answers to questions 3–8 in the previous exercise suggest that there are similar laws for logarithms.

There are three laws of logarithms which are true for all bases.

Law 1 $\log_a xy = \log_a x + \log_a y$

Law 2 $\log_a \left(\frac{x}{y}\right) = \log_a x - \log_a y$

Law 3 $\log_a x^n = n\log_a x$

Proof of Law 1

Let $\log_a x = m$ and $\log_a y = n$.

Then $x = a^m$ and $y = a^n$, so $xy = a^{m+n}$

$\Rightarrow \log_a xy = m + n$

$\Rightarrow \log_a xy = \log_a x + \log_a y$

Proof of Law 2

Let $\log_a x = m$ and $\log_a y = n$.

Then $x = a^m$ and $y = a^n$, so $\frac{x}{y} = a^{m-n}$

$\Rightarrow \log_a \frac{x}{y} = m - n$

$\Rightarrow \log_a \frac{x}{y} = \log_a x - \log_a y$

Proof of Law 3

Let $\log_a x = m$.

Then $x = a^m$ so $x^n = a^{mn}$

$\Rightarrow \log_a x^n = mn$

$\Rightarrow \log_a x^n = n\log_a x$

Example 1

Express $\log_3 8 + \log_3 2 - \log_3 4$ as the logarithm of a single number.

SOLUTION

$\log_3 8 + \log_3 2 - \log_3 4$

$= \log_3 \left(\frac{8 \times 2}{4}\right) = \log_3 4$ (Laws 1 and 2)

Algebraic Skills

Example 2

Evaluate $\log_2 3+\log_2 48-2\log_2 3$.

SOLUTION

$\log_2 3+\log_2 48-2\log_2 3$

$=\log_2 3+\log_2 48-\log_2 3^2$ (Law 3)

$=\log_2 3+\log_2 48-\log_2 9$

$=\log_2\left(\frac{3\times 48}{9}\right)$ (Laws 1 and 2)

$=\log_2 16=4$

Exercise 5.6

1 Write each expression as the logarithm of a single number:

a) $\log_4 2+\log_4 3$ **b)** $\log_5 9-\log_5 3$ **c)** $\log_3 4+2\log_3 5$

d) $3\log_5 2+\log_5 6$ **e)** $2\log_7 4+2\log_7 3-\log_7 8$ **f)** $2\log_3 8-5\log_3 2$

g) $\log_{10} 3+\frac{1}{2}\log_{10} 16-\log_{10} 2$ **h)** $2\log_e 8+\log_e 9-\log_e 36$ **i)** $3\ln 6-\frac{2}{3}\ln 27$

2 Solve for x:

a) $\log_3 x=\log_3 4+\log_3 7$ **b)** $\log_2 x=\log_2 18-\log_2 3$

c) $\log_4 x=\log_4 70+\log_4 4-\log_4 14$ **d)** $\log_5 x=2\log_5 3+3\log_5 2$

3 Use the laws of logarithms to evaluate each expression: HPQ

a) $\log_6 9+\log_6 4$ **b)** $\log_5 50-\log_5 2$ **c)** $\log_4 2+\log_4 32$

d) $\log_3 54+\log_3\left(\frac{3}{2}\right)$ **e)** $\log_2 5-\log_2 10$ **f)** $2\log_7 4+3\log_7 2-\log_7 128$

g) $\log_9 24-3\log_9 2$ **h)** $\log_2 3+\frac{1}{2}\log_2 36-2\log_2 3$ **i)** $\log_2 6+3\log_2 2-\frac{1}{2}\log_2 9$

j) $\frac{1}{2}\log_8 16+4\log_8 4-\log_8 2$ **k)** $\frac{2}{3}\log_5 1000-\log_5 4$

4 Prove that $\log_{10} 15=1-\log_{10} 2+\log_{10} 3$.

5 Given $\frac{1}{3}\log_a y=\log_a(x-1)+2\log_a 2$, show that $y=64(x-1)^3$.

6 Given $f=\log_4 6$ and $g=\log_4 5$, express the following in terms of f and g:

a) $\log_4 30$ **b)** $\log_4 1{\cdot}2$ **c)** $\log_4 7776$

7 Express each of the following in terms of $\log_{10} 2$ and $\log_{10} 3$.

a) $\log_{10} 12$ **b)** $\log_{10} 36$.

8 If $\log_e b=2\log_e c+3\log_e d-\frac{1}{2}\log_e f$, express b in terms of c, d and f.

9 Given $\log_3 5=x$ and $\log_3 4=y$, express $\log_3\left(\frac{75}{4}\right)$ in terms of x and y. ACE

→

10 Here is Mike's solution to a problem. ACE

Problem

Express $2\log_2 5-\log_2\left(\frac{4}{5}\right)+\frac{1}{2}\log_2 16$ as the logarithm of a single number.

Mike's solution

$$\begin{aligned}2\log_2 5-\log_2\left(\frac{4}{5}\right)+\frac{1}{2}\log_2 16 &= \log_2 5^2-\log_2\left(\frac{4}{5}\right)+\log_2\left(\frac{16}{2}\right)\\ &= \log_2 25-\log_2\left(\frac{4}{5}\right)+\log_2 8\\ &= \log_2\left(25\times\frac{4}{5}\times 8\right)\\ &= \log_2 160\end{aligned}$$

Identify Mike's mistakes, explain how he made them and correct the solution.

Logarithmic and exponential equations

The laws of logarithms can be used to help solve equations involving logarithms and exponentials.

Example 1

Solve the equation $\log_8(3x+2)-\log_8(2x-3)=1$.

SOLUTION

$$\begin{aligned}\log_8(3x+2)-\log_8(2x-3)=1 &\Rightarrow \log_8\left(\frac{3x+2}{2x-3}\right)=1\\ &\Rightarrow \frac{3x+2}{2x-3}=8^1\\ &\Rightarrow 3x+2=8(2x-3)\\ &\Rightarrow 3x+2=16x-24\\ &\Rightarrow 13x=26\\ &\Rightarrow x=2\end{aligned}$$

Example 2

Solve the equation $2+\log_4 20=\log_4 x$.

SOLUTION

Start by expressing **all** terms as logarithms to base 4.

Use the fact that $\log_a a=1$ to write 2 as $2\log_4 4$.

$$\begin{aligned}2+\log_4 20=\log_4 x &\Rightarrow 2\log_4 4+\log_4 20=\log_4 x\\ &\Rightarrow \log_4 4^2+\log_4 20=\log_4 x\end{aligned}$$

Algebraic Skills

$$\Rightarrow \quad \log_4 16 + \log_4 20 = \log_4 x$$

$$\Rightarrow \quad \log_4(16 \times 20) = \log_4 x$$

$$\Rightarrow \quad \log_4(320) = \log_4 x$$

$$\Rightarrow \quad x = 320$$

Example 3

Solve the equation $5^x = 8$.

SOLUTION

Start to find the solution by taking logarithms to base 10 (or natural logarithms) of both sides of the equation.

$$5^x = 8 \Rightarrow \log_{10} 5^x = \log_{10} 8$$

$$\Rightarrow x\log_{10} 5 = \log_{10} 8$$

$$\Rightarrow x = \frac{\log_{10} 8}{\log_{10} 5} = 1{\cdot}29$$

Exercise 5.7

1 Solve for $x > 0$:

a) $\log_a 4 + \log_a 3x = \log_a 60$ **b)** $2\log_a 3 + \log_a x = \log_a 54$

c) $\log_4 x + \log_4(x+1) = \log_4 2$ **d)** $\log_b(2x+1) - \log_b(x-2) = \log_b 3$

2 Solve for $x > 0$: HPQ

a) $\log_4 x = \log_4 96 - 2$ **b)** $3 + \log_2 x = \log_2 7$

c) $\log_3 x = 3 - \log_3 5$ **d)** $\log_5 x - 3\log_5 2 = 1$

e) $\log_6(x+3) + \log_6(x-2) = 1$ **f)** $\log_3 3x - \log_3(x-2) = 2$

g) $\log_{11}(4x+3) - \log_{11}(2x-3) = 1$ **h)** $\frac{1}{2}\log_5 16 + 2\log_5 x = 2$

3 Solve for $x > 0$:

a) $\log_x 80 - \log_x 5 = 2$ **b)** $2\log_x 5 + \log_x 40 = 3$

c) $\frac{1}{2}\log_x 16 + 3\log_x 2 = 5$ **d)** $2\log_x 6 - \frac{2}{3}\log_x 8 = 2$

4 Solve the following equations, giving your answers correct to two decimal places:

a) $6^x = 40$ **b)** $2^y = 35$

c) $3^a = 5$ **d)** $10^b = 5$

e) $4^{2x-1} = 9$ **f)** $3^{2m+3} = 7$

5 Solve the following equations, giving your answers correct to two decimal places:

a) $p = \log_3 21$ **b)** $q = \log_4 19$

6 Find the coordinates of the points where the following curves cross the **x-axis:** ACE

a) $y = \log_4 x - 2$ **b)** $y = \log_3(x-4) - 1$

c) $y = \log_2(x+1) + 1$

Exponential growth and decay problems

Natural logarithms can be used to solve real-life problems involving exponential growth and decay functions.

Example 1

The mass, M grams, of a radioactive sample after a time of t years is given by the formula $M = 50e^{-6t}$.

a) What was the initial mass of the radioactive sample?

b) The half-life of the sample is the time taken for half of the radioactive sample to decay. Find the half-life of the sample.

SOLUTION

a) The initial mass occurs when $t = 0 \Rightarrow M = 50e^{-6\times 0}$

$= 50e^0$

$= 50$ (since $e^0 = 1$)

Hence the initial mass was 50 grams.

b) The half-life occurs when $M = 25$.

$25 = 50e^{-6t}$

$\Rightarrow \quad 0\cdot 5 = e^{-6t}$

$\Rightarrow \ln 0\cdot 5 = \ln e^{-6t}$ (take natural logarithms of both sides)

$\Rightarrow \ln 0\cdot 5 = -6t \ln e$

$\Rightarrow \ln 0\cdot 5 = -6t$ (since $\ln e = 1$)

$\Rightarrow \quad t = \dfrac{\ln 0\cdot 5}{(-6)}$

$\Rightarrow \quad t = 0\cdot 116$

Hence the half-life is $0\cdot 116$ years (or 42 days).

Sometimes the growth or decay 'constant' needs to be calculated first.

Example 2

A biologist is studying a new strain of bacteria. The initial number of bacteria, B_0, in a petri dish grows to B after t hours according to the formula $B = B_0e^{kt}$. The number of bacteria grows from 100 to 425 in 5 hours.

a) Calculate k, the constant of growth.

b) How many hours will it take for the number of bacteria to reach 1000?

SOLUTION

a) $B = B_0e^{kt} \quad \Rightarrow \quad 425 = 100e^{5k}$ (since $B = 425$, $B_0 = 100$ and $t = 5$)

$\Rightarrow \quad 4\cdot 25 = e^{5k}$

$\Rightarrow \ln 4\cdot 25 = \ln e^{5k}$ (take natural logarithms of both sides)

$\Rightarrow \ln 4\cdot 25 = 5k \ln e$

$\Rightarrow \ln 4\cdot 25 = 5k$ (since $\ln e = 1$)

$\Rightarrow \quad k = \dfrac{\ln 4\cdot 25}{5}$

$\Rightarrow \quad k = 0\cdot 289$

Hence the constant of growth is $0\cdot 289$ and the formula is then $B = B_0e^{0\cdot 289t}$.

b) $B = B_0 e^{0\cdot289t} \Rightarrow 1000 = 100e^{0\cdot289t}$ (since $B = 1000$ and $B_0 = 100$)

$$\Rightarrow \quad 10 = e^{0\cdot289t}$$
$$\Rightarrow \quad \ln 10 = \ln e^{0\cdot289t}$$
$$\Rightarrow \quad \ln 10 = 0\cdot289t$$
$$\Rightarrow \quad t = \frac{\ln 10}{0.289}$$
$$\Rightarrow \quad t = 7\cdot96$$

The time taken to reach 1000 bacteria is almost 8 hours.

Exercise 5.8

All the questions in Exercise 5.8 are ACE questions.

1 A biologist is studying a new strain of bacteria. She starts with 100 bacteria in a dish. The number of bacteria in the dish after t hours is given by $B = 100e^{kt}$. After 5 hours there are 600 bacteria in the dish.

a) Find the value of k correct to three significant figures.

b) Find the number of hours it will take to produce 5000 bacteria.

2 The number of bacteria in a petri dish after t hours is given by $B = B_0 e^{kt}$, where B_0 is the initial number of bacteria.
This strain of bacteria doubles in number every 6·5 hours. There are 1000 of these bacteria in a petri dish at the start of an experiment. How many will there be after two days?

3 Carol invests £5000 in an ISA which gives a return of 4·25% per annum.
The amount of money in the account after t years is given by the formula $A = P \times 1\cdot0425^t$ where £A is the amount of money in the account after t years and £P is the principal (starting amount).
How long will it be before Carol doubles her money?

4 The population, P million, of a country, t years after 2015, is increasing according to the formula $P = 3\cdot47e^{0\cdot0213t}$.

a) What was the country's population in 2015?

b) The government is concerned that if the population exceeds 5 million, there will be a difficulty in feeding the population. In which year will this figure be reached?

5 The last remaining colony of an endangered bird species lives on an island. The initial numbers of birds in the colony, B_0, diminishes to B after time t years according to the rule $B = B_0 e^{kt}$. When naturalists started monitoring the colony, there were 90 birds. After 5 years the colony had diminished to 55 birds. How long will it be before only 2 birds are left?

6 The population of Loganville, x years since January 2000, has increased according to the mathematical model $840500(1\cdot019)^x$. Explain what the numbers 840 500 and 1·019 mean in this model.

7 The area, A_0 square kilometres, covered by a bush fire when it is first measured spreads to A square kilometres after t hours according to the rule $A = A_0 e^{kt}$.

a) If it takes one and a half hours for the area covered by the fire to double, find the value of k correct to three significant figures.

b) A bush fire covers an area of 800 square kilometres. Calculate the area covered after 4 hours if the fire is left unattended.

8 Technetium-99m is a radioactive substance used to diagnose brain, thyroid and kidney diseases. An initial mass, M_0 milligrams, of Technetium-99m nuclei decays to M milligrams after t minutes according to the law $M = M_0 e^{kt}$. Technetium-99m has a half-life of 6 hours.

a) If there are currently 200 milligrams of Technetium-99m, how much will there be after 6 hours?

b) Calculate the value of k correct to three significant figures.

9 Radio isotopes have different half-lives. The number, N_0, of Magnesium-27 nuclei decays to N after t minutes according to the law $N = N_0 e^{kt}$. Magnesium-27 has a half-life of 9·45 minutes. Calculate the value of k correct to two significant figures.

10 The atmospheric pressure at sea level, P_0 hectopascals, diminishes to P_h hectopascals at height h metres above sea level according to the rule $P_h = P_0 e^{kh}$.
Atmospheric pressure at sea level is approximately 1013 hectopascals.
At a height of 1000 metres, the atmospheric pressure has diminished by 12%.

a) Calculate the value of k correct to three significant figures.
b) Calculate the atmospheric pressure at the summit of:
(i) Ben Nevis (height 1344 metres)
(ii) Mount Everest (height 8848 metres).

11 The radioactive element Carbon-14 can be used to estimate the age of organic remains. The number of radioactive nuclei, C_0, of Carbon-14 decays to C_t after t years according to the formula $C_t = C_0 e^{kt}$.

a) The half-life of Carbon-14 is 5730 years. Find the value of the constant k. Give your answer correct to three significant figures.
b) What percentage of Carbon-14 in a sample of bones will remain after 2000 years?

Note *Carbon–14 dating is a way of finding the age of objects of a biological origin up to about 50 000 years old. It can be used to find the age of bone, cloth and plant fibres, and is very helpful to archaeologists. One example is the dating of the famous 'Turin Shroud'. You may be interested to look into this. You can look up a Carbon–14 dating calculator online.*

Experimental data and linear models

Sometimes when conducting an experiment, the results may appear to show that there is an exponential connection between the variables. However, the rapid rise (or decrease) often makes it difficult to interpret the results. We can use logarithms to 'convert' the exponential graphs into linear ones in order to make it easier to find the relationship between the variables.

Linear relationship 1

$y = ax^b \Leftrightarrow$ the graph of $\log_p y$ against $\log_p x$ is a straight line.

Proof

$y = ax^b$

$\Rightarrow \log_p y = \log_p ax^b$ (Take logarithms to base p of both sides)

$\Rightarrow \log_p y = \log_p a + \log_p x^b$ (First law of logarithms)

$\Rightarrow \log_p y = b\log_p x + \log_p a$ (Third law of logarithms)

$\Rightarrow Y = bX + \log_p a$ (where $Y = \log_p y$ and $X = \log_p x$)

This is of the form $Y = mX + c$ (where $m = b$ and $c = \log_p a$) so it represents the equation of a straight line.

Example 1

This table of data was obtained from an experiment.

x	1	2	3	4	5	6	7
y	3·4	10·4	20·8	32·8	49·0	66·5	87·3

a) Show that the variables x and y are related by the formula $y = ax^b$.
b) Find the values of a and b.

SOLUTION

a) Take logarithms to base 10 of x and y.

$\log_{10} x$	0	0·301	0·477	0·602	0·699	0·778	0·845
$\log_{10} y$	0·531	1·017	1·318	1·516	1·690	1·823	1·941

Plot the resulting points in a graph of $\log_{10} y$ against $\log_{10} x$.

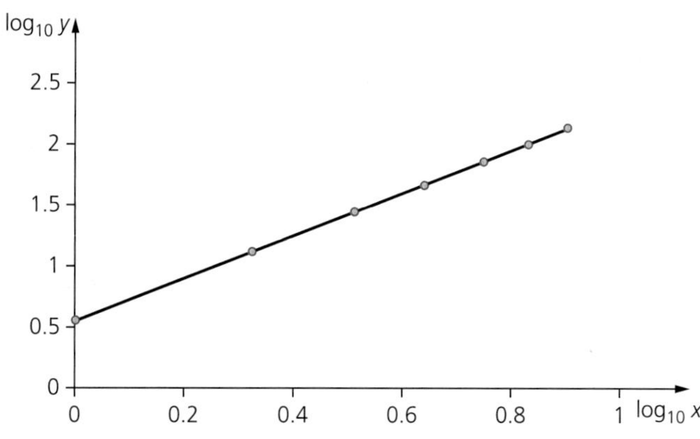

The points lie on a straight line, so x and y are related by the formula $y = ax^b$.

b) The best-fitting line has equation $\log_{10} y = m \log_{10} x + c$

To find m, use two points on the line which are far apart.

$$m = \frac{1{\cdot}941 - 1{\cdot}017}{0{\cdot}845 - 0{\cdot}301} \qquad \text{[Using (0·301, 1·017) and (0·845, 1·941)]}$$

$$= \frac{0{\cdot}924}{0{\cdot}544}$$

$$= 1{\cdot}699$$

$$\cong 1.7$$

To find c, substitute the point (0·845, 1·941) into the above equation.

$1{\cdot}941 = 1{\cdot}7 \times 0{\cdot}845 + c \Rightarrow c = 0{\cdot}505$

The equation of the line is therefore $\log_{10} y = 1{\cdot}7 \log_{10} x + 0{\cdot}505$

$$\Rightarrow \log_{10} y = \log_{10} x^{1{\cdot}7} + \log_{10} 10^{0{\cdot}505}$$

$$\Rightarrow \log_{10} y = \log_{10} x^{1{\cdot}7} + \log_{10} 3{\cdot}2$$

$$\Rightarrow \log_{10} y = \log_{10} 3{\cdot}2x^{1{\cdot}7}$$

$$\Rightarrow \quad y = 3{\cdot}2x^{1{\cdot}7}$$

Hence $a = 3{\cdot}2,\ b = 1{\cdot}7$.

Note Although you could read the y-intercept, c, from the graph above, this will not always be possible, so you can find c by substitution as shown.

Linear relationship 2

$y = ab^x \Leftrightarrow$ the graph of $\log_p y$ against x is a straight line.

Proof

$$y = ab^x$$

$\Rightarrow \log_p y = \log_p ab^x$ (Take logarithms to base p of both sides)

$\Rightarrow \log_p y = \log_p a + \log_p b^x$ (First law of logarithms)

$\Rightarrow \log_p y = x\log_p b + \log_p a$ (Third law of logarithms)

$\Rightarrow \quad Y = x\log_p b + \log_p a$ (where $Y = \log_p y$)

This is of the form $Y = mx + c$ (where $m = \log_p b$ and $c = \log_p a$) so it represents the equation of a straight line.

Example 2

The graph of $\log_{10} y$ against x has been drawn for some experimental data. It is known that the data fits the equation $y = ab^x$ where a and b are constants. Find the values of a and b.

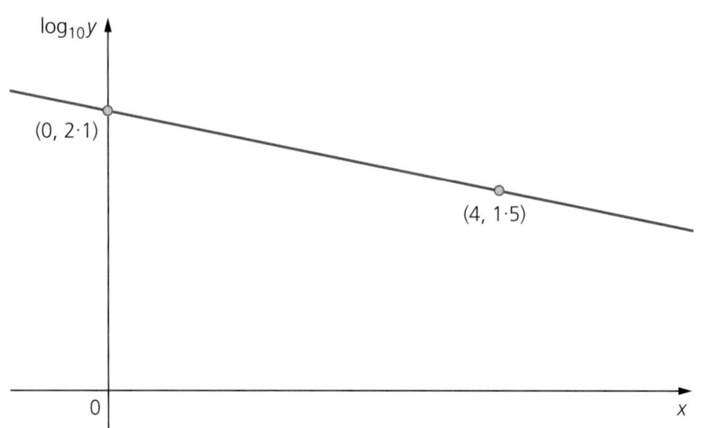

SOLUTION

The straight line has equation $\log_{10} y = mx + c$ (where $m = \log_p b$ and $c = \log_p a$).

$$m = \frac{1{\cdot}5 - 2{\cdot}1}{4 - 0} = \frac{-0{\cdot}6}{4} = -0{\cdot}15 \text{ and } c = 2{\cdot}1.$$

Hence the equation is

$$\log_{10} y = -0{\cdot}15x + 2{\cdot}1$$

$$\Rightarrow \log_{10} y = x\log_{10} 10^{-0\cdot15} + \log_{10} 10^{2\cdot1}$$

$$\Rightarrow \log_{10} y = x\log_{10} 0{\cdot}71 + \log_{10} 126$$

$$\Rightarrow \log_{10} y = \log_{10} 0{\cdot}71^x + \log_{10} 126$$

$$\Rightarrow \log_{10} y = \log_{10}(126 \times 0{\cdot}71^x)$$

$$\Rightarrow \quad y = 126 \times (0{\cdot}71)^x$$

Hence $a = 126$ and $b = 0{\cdot}71$.

Exercise 5.9

1 The results of an experiment led to the graph shown below.

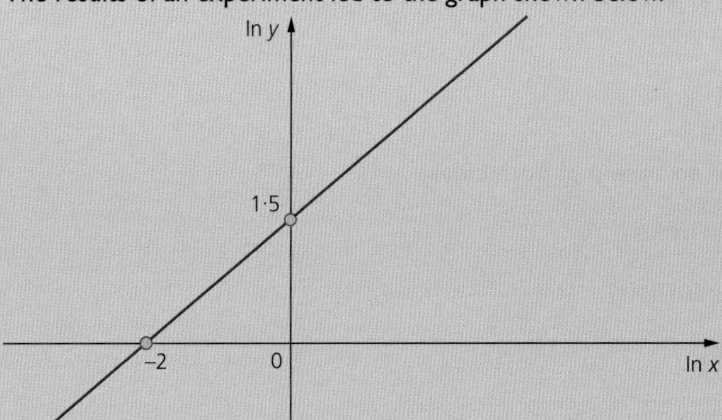

a) Write down the equation of the line in terms of $\ln y$ and $\ln x$.
b) Show that x and y satisfy a relationship of the form $y = ax^b$ and find the values of a and b.

2 Two variables x and y satisfy the relationship $y = 5x^3$.
When $\log_{10} y$ is plotted against $\log_{10} x$ a straight line graph is obtained.
Find the coordinates of the point where this line meets the y-axis.

3 Show that each graph represents a function of the form $y = ax^b$ and determine the values of a and b.

a)

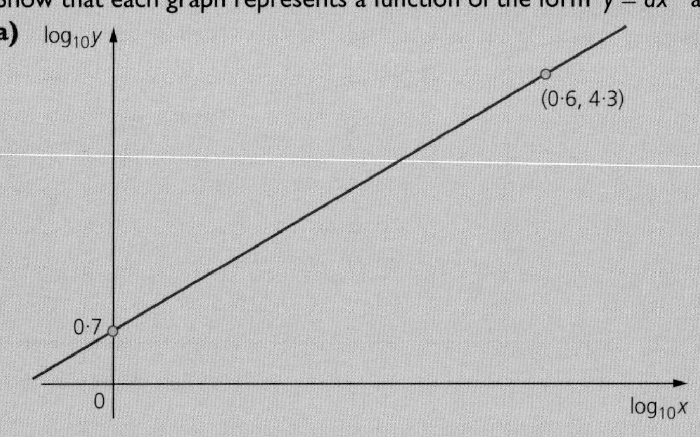

b)

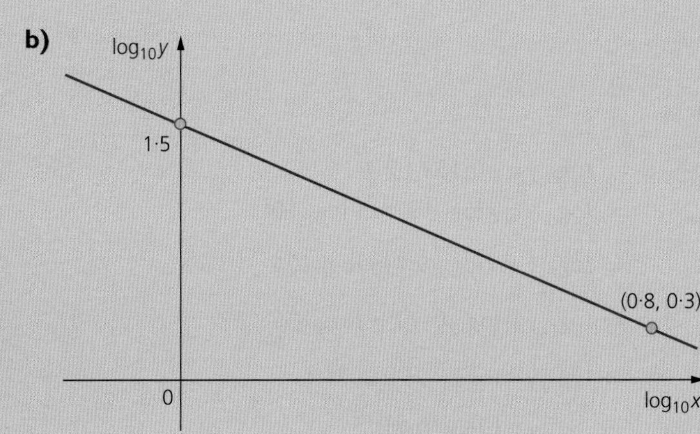

➜

4 Show that each graph represents a function of the form $y = ab^x$ and find the values of a and b.

a)

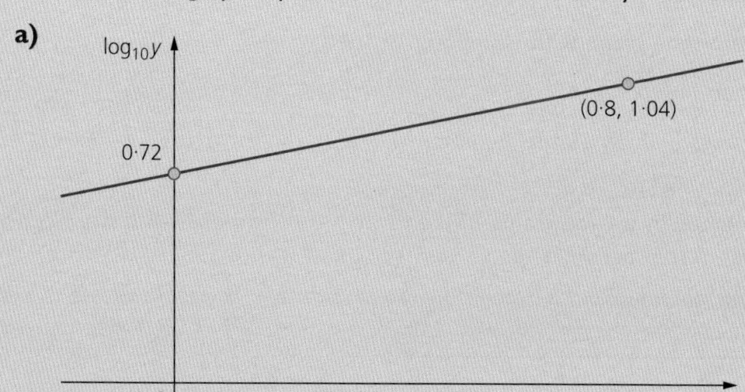

b)

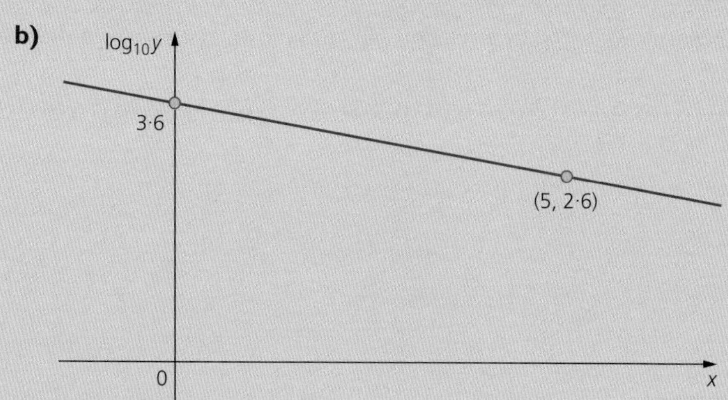

5 This table of data was obtained from an experiment.

x	1·1	2·3	3·1	4·4
y	3·7	18·7	36·2	78·1

a) Show that the variables x and y are related by the formula $y = ax^b$.
b) Find the values of a and b.

6 Repeat question 5 for the data shown in the table below.

x	10	20	30	40
y	1·1	1·5	1·7	2·0

7 This table of data was obtained from an experiment.

x	1	2	3	4
y	8·5	42·5	212·5	1062·5

a) Show that the variables x and y are related by the formula $y = ab^x$.
b) Find the values of a and b.

➜

8 Two variables x and y satisfy the equation $y = 3(4^x)$. ACE

a) Find the value of a if $(a, 6)$ lies on the graph with equation $y = 3(4^x)$.

b) If $\left(-\frac{1}{2}, b\right)$ also lies on the graph, find b.

c) A graph is drawn of $\log_{10} y$ against x. Show that its equation will be of the form $\log_{10} y = Px + Q$ and state the gradient of the line.

9 a) Two variables x and y are connected by a relationship of the form $y = kx^n$ where k and n are constants. Prove that there is a linear relationship between $\log_{10} x$ and $\log_{10} y$.

b) In an experiment some data was obtained and a best-fitting line was drawn. The table shows the data which lies on the best-fitting line.

x	2	4	6	8
y	10·3	33·5	66·7	108·7

The variables x and y in the table are connected by a relationship of the form $y = kx^n$. Find the values of k and n.

Checkout

1 Express $3^5 = 243$ in logarithmic form.

2 Express $\log_6 7 = p$ in exponential form.

3 Express $3\log_{10} 4 - 4\log_{10} 2$ as the logarithm of a single number.

4 Evaluate $2\log_6 2 + \frac{1}{2}\log_6 81$.

5 Solve the equation $\log_{10}(x+1) + \log_{10}(x-1) = \log_{10} 24$.

6 Solve the equation $\log_2 x - \log_2(x-1) = 2$.

7 Solve the equation $5^x = 90$.

8 The concentration, D, of a drug left in a person's system after t hours is modelled by the formula $D = D_0(0\cdot65)^t$ where D_0 is the initial concentration.
If the initial concentration is 120 milligrams, what will the concentration be after 4 hours?

9 A population of bacteria is growing in such a way that the number of bacteria present, N, after t minutes is given by the rule $N = 42e^{0\cdot0134t}$. How long will it be before the population of bacteria doubles?

10 Given that $\log_5 x = d$, show that $\log_{25} x = \frac{1}{2}d$.

11 The diagram shows the graph of $\log_5 y$ against $\log_5 x$ for some experimental data. It is known that the data fits the equation $y = ax^b$ where a and b are constants.

Find the values of a and b.

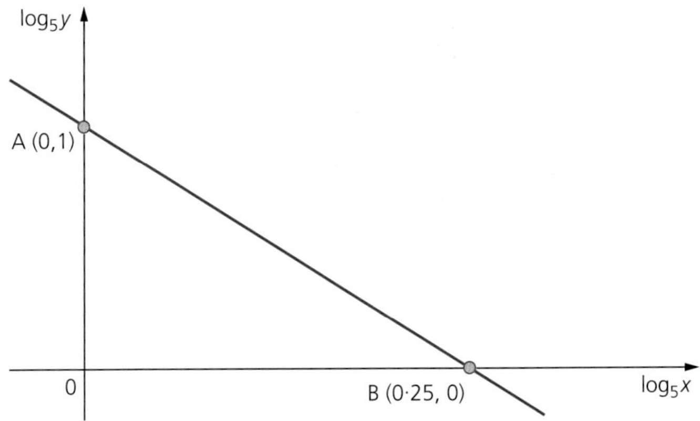

Summary

Logarithmic and Exponential Expressions

1 An exponential function is one in the form $f(x) = a^x$.
a is called the base and it must be positive; x is the index or exponent.

$f(x) = a^x,\ a > 1$

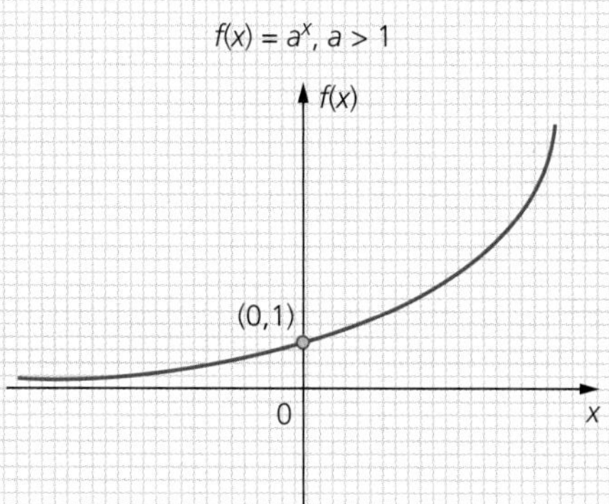

$f(x) = a^x,\ 0 < a < 1$

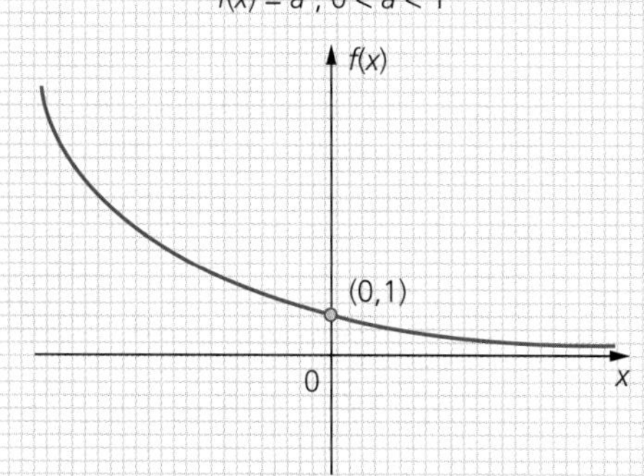

2 The function $f(x) = e^x$, where e is the irrational number 2·7182818..., is called the natural exponential function.

3 The inverse of $f(x) = a^x$ is the logarithmic function $f(x) = \log_a x$.

* $y = a^x \Leftrightarrow \log_a y = x$
* $\log_a 1 = 0$
* $\log_a a = 1$

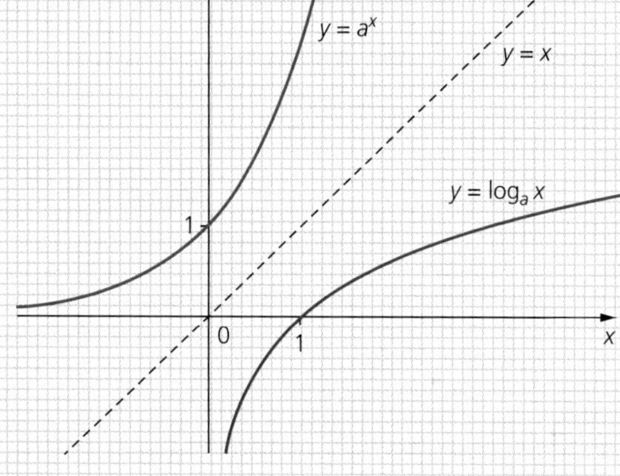

4 Logarithms to the base e, $\log_e x$, are called natural logarithms and are more commonly written as $\ln x$.

5 The laws of logarithms:

Law 1 $\log_a xy = \log_a x + \log_a y$

Law 2 $\log_a \left(\frac{x}{y}\right) = \log_a x - \log_a y$

Law 3 $\log_a x^n = n \log_a x$

6 $y = ax^b \Leftrightarrow$ the graph of $\log_p y$ against $\log_p x$ is a straight line.
$y = ab^x \Leftrightarrow$ the graph of $\log_p y$ against x is a straight line.

CHAPTER

6 Trigonometry – Bridging the Gap

The purpose of this chapter is to remind you of important work you have studied previously in trigonometry, to extend your knowledge of this earlier work, and to bridge the gap between what you already know and the work you will do in trigonometry later in the course. As a result there will be a series of short exercises in which you can practise and improve your skills in trigonometry as well as learning some new ones.

What I am learning

* To understand relationships between angles
* To use exact values
* To solve quadratic trigonometric equations
* To solve equations with multiple angles
* To identify and sketch trigonometric graphs
* To prove trigonometric identities
* To use radians for angle measure
* To solve equations like this without a calculator: $\sqrt{3}\tan x + 1 = 0,\ 0 \leqslant x \leqslant 2\pi$

What I should already know/be able to do

* To use the sine rule and cosine rule and find the area of a triangle
* To solve equations of the type $a\sin x° + b = c,\ 0 \leqslant x \leqslant 360$
* To identify and sketch the graphs of $y = \sin x°$, $y = \cos x°$ and $y = \tan x°$
* To understand the terms amplitude, multiple angle, phase angle and period
* To identify and sketch graphs of the type $y = \sin x° + k$ and $y = \cos x° + k$
* To identify and sketch graphs of the type $y = a\sin bx°$ and $y = a\cos bx°$
* To identify and sketch graphs of the type $y = \sin(x - a)°$ and $y = \cos(x - a)°$
* To prove identities using $\sin^2 x + \cos^2 x = 1$ and $\tan x = \dfrac{\sin x}{\cos x}$
* To factorise quadratic expressions

Quick check!

1 Solve the equation $4\cos x° + 1 = 2, \quad 0 \leqslant x \leqslant 360.$
2 State the period of $y = \sin 3x°$.
3 Part of the graph of $y = a\cos bx°$ is shown below.

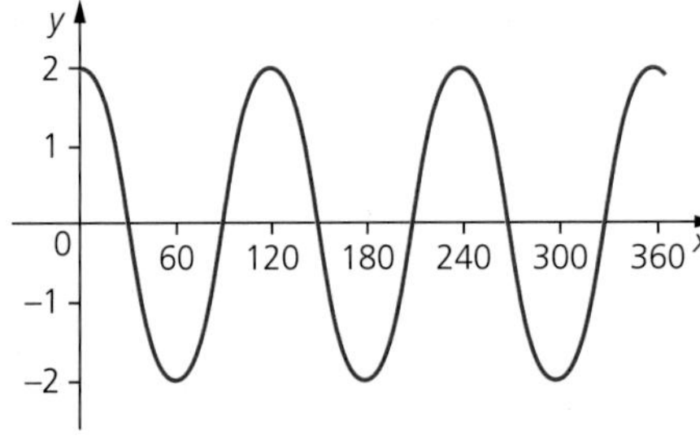

State the values of a and b.

4 Part of the graph of $y = \sin(x - a)^\circ$ is shown below.

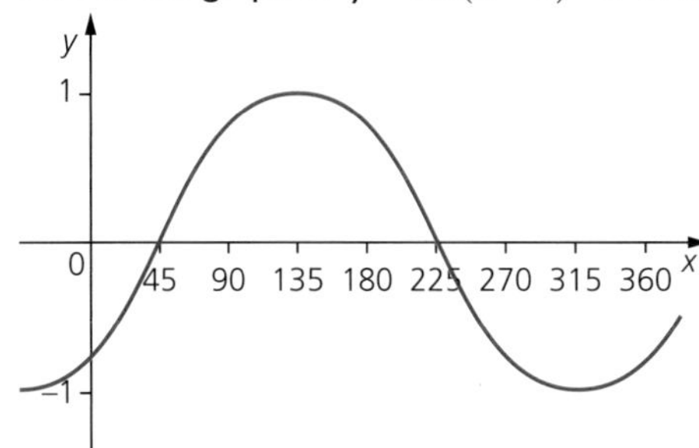

State the value of a.

5 Part of the graph of $y = \sin x^\circ + k$ is shown below.

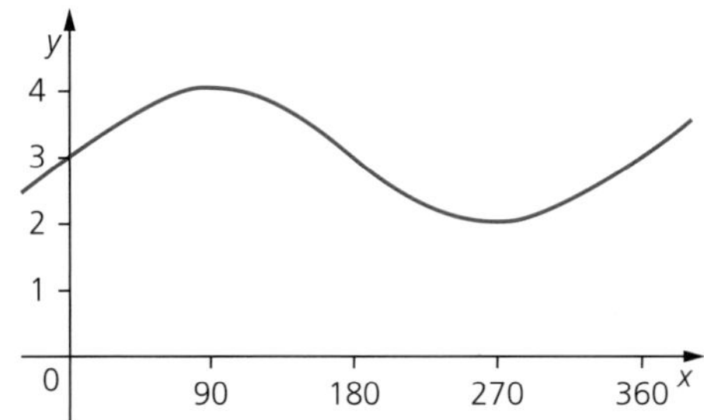

State the value of k.

6 Factorise $2c^2 - 5c - 3 = 0$.

Quick check! – *Solutions*

1	75·5, 284·5	2	120°	3	$a = 2,\ b = 3$
4	$a = 45$	5	$k = 3$	6	$(2c+1)(c-3)$

Relationships between angles

You have already studied how to solve trigonometric equations using the CAST diagram or 'all, sin, tan, cos'. This useful diagram tells us which of the three trigonometric ratios is positive in each quadrant.

This diagram relates angles in the second, third and fourth quadrants to an acute angle in the first quadrant. Hence we can see the following relationships:

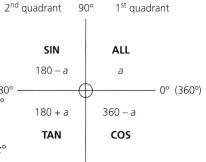

2nd quadrant 90° 1st quadrant

SIN 180 – a | **ALL** a

180° | 0° (360°)

TAN 180 + a | **COS** 360 – a

3rd quadrant 270° 4th quadrant

$\sin(180 - x)^\circ = \sin x^\circ$; $\cos(180 - x)^\circ = -\cos x^\circ$; $\tan(180 - x)^\circ = -\tan x^\circ$

$\sin(180 + x)^\circ = -\sin x^\circ$; $\cos(180 + x)^\circ = -\cos x^\circ$; $\tan(180 + x)^\circ = \tan x^\circ$

$\sin(360 - x)^\circ = -\sin x^\circ$; $\cos(360 - x)^\circ = \cos x^\circ$; $\tan(360 - x)^\circ = -\tan x^\circ$

By considering a right-angled triangle, we can find a trigonometric relationship between an angle and its complement $(90 - x)^\circ$.

We can see that

$\sin x^\circ = \frac{q}{r} = \cos(90 - x)^\circ$ and $\cos x^\circ = \frac{p}{r} = \sin(90 - x)^\circ$

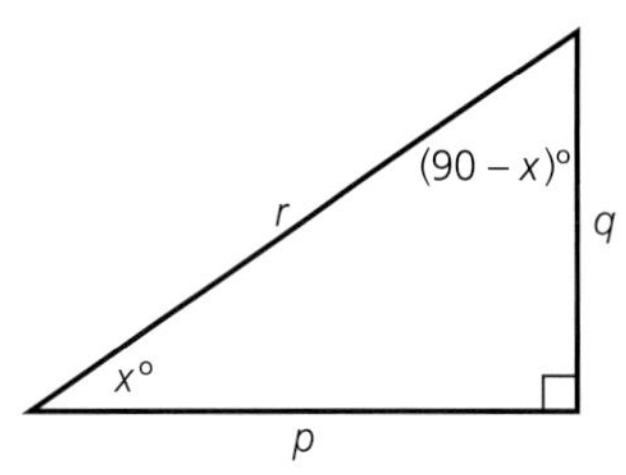

leading to two more useful relationships:

$\sin(90 - x)^\circ = \cos x^\circ$; $\cos(90 - x)^\circ = \sin x^\circ$

Finally, by looking at the chapter on functions and their related graphs, we can find a trigonometric relationship between an angle and its negative $(-x)^\circ$.

Start by considering the graph of $y = \cos x^\circ$.

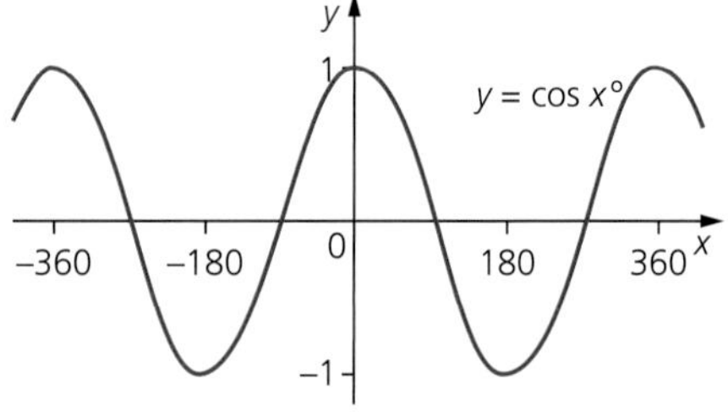

We know that if we reflect the graph of a function $y = f(x)$ in the y-axis then we get the graph of the related function $y = f(-x)$.

We can see that the graph of $y = \cos x^\circ$ is symmetrical about the y-axis, so $\cos(-x)^\circ = \cos x^\circ$.

Now consider the graph of $y = \sin x^\circ$.

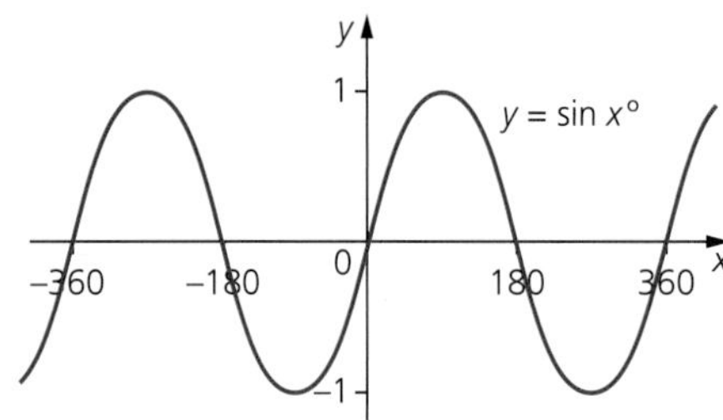

We know that if we give the graph of a function $y = f(x)$ a half-turn rotation about the origin O then we get the graph of the related function $y = -f(-x)$. We can see that the graph of $y = \sin x^\circ$ has half-turn symmetry about O so $\sin x^\circ = -\sin(-x)^\circ$

This leads to two further relationships:

$\sin(-x)^\circ = -\sin x^\circ$; $\cos(-x)^\circ = \cos x^\circ$.

Example

Express the following in terms of the cosine of an acute angle:

a) $\sin 40^\circ$ b) $\cos(-43)^\circ$ c) $\cos 255^\circ$

SOLUTION

a) $\sin 40^\circ = \cos(90 - 40)^\circ = \cos 50^\circ$

b) $\cos(-43)^\circ = \cos 43^\circ$

c) $\cos 255^\circ = \cos(180 + 75)^\circ = -\cos 75^\circ$

Exercise 6.1

(Do **NOT** use a calculator.)

1 Express the following in terms of the sine of an acute angle:

a) $\sin 123^\circ$ **b)** $\sin 215^\circ$ **c)** $\sin 297^\circ$ **d)** $\cos 8^\circ$ **e)** $\sin(-32)^\circ$

2 Express the following in terms of the cosine of an acute angle:

a) $\sin 28^\circ$ **b)** $\cos(-10)^\circ$ **c)** $\cos 125^\circ$ **d)** $\cos 343^\circ$ **e)** $\cos 250^\circ$

3 Simplify the following:

a) $\tan(180 + a)^\circ$ **b)** $\sin(-y)^\circ$ **c)** $\cos(360 - m)^\circ$ **d)** $\cos(90 - b)^\circ$

Exact values

Although you can look up the values of the sine, cosine and tangent of 30°, 45° and 60° on a calculator, the values which appear are approximate. You can find the *exact* values for each of these ratios by considering the diagrams of half of a square and half of an equilateral triangle.

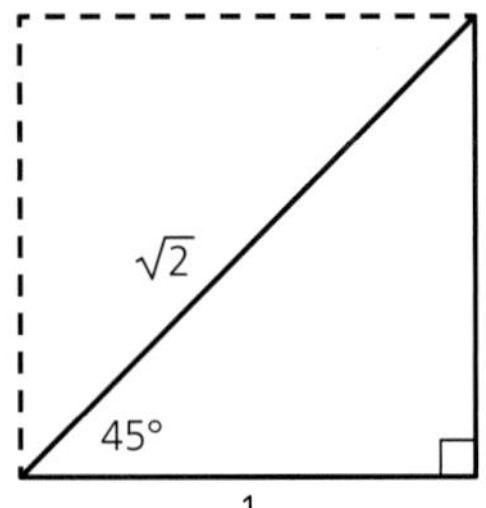

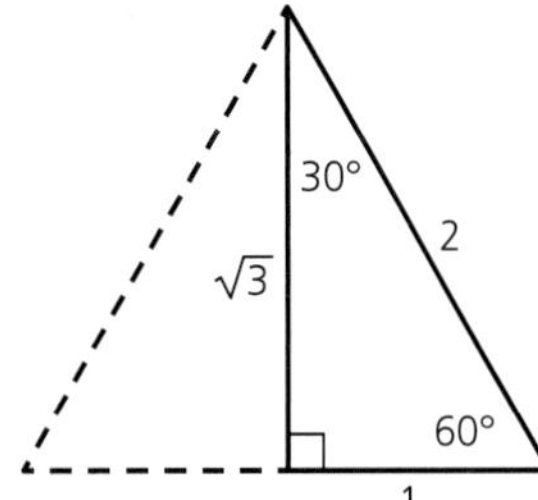

From these diagrams you can deduce the *exact* values of the sine, cosine and tangent of 30°, 45° and 60°. These facts are illustrated in the table below:

	30°	45°	60°
sin	$\frac{1}{2}$	$\frac{1}{\sqrt{2}}$	$\frac{\sqrt{3}}{2}$
cos	$\frac{\sqrt{3}}{2}$	$\frac{1}{\sqrt{2}}$	$\frac{1}{2}$
tan	$\frac{1}{\sqrt{3}}$	1	$\sqrt{3}$

You should memorise the exact values in the table or be able to deduce them from the diagrams. You will be required to attempt questions on the facts in the table without a calculator.

Example 1

Find the exact value of $\sin 225^\circ$.

SOLUTION

225° is in the third quadrant, so $\sin 225^\circ$ is negative.

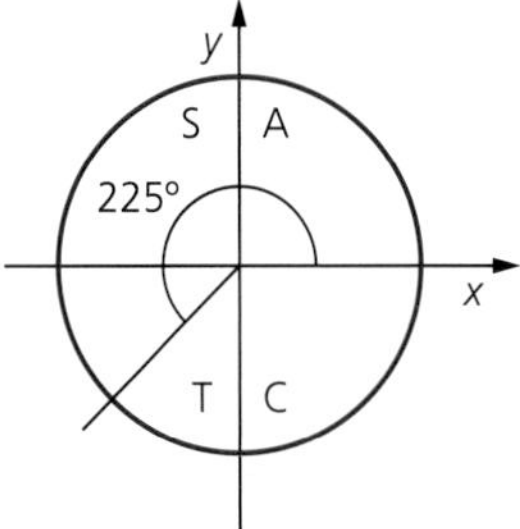

Hence $\sin 225^\circ = \sin(180+45)^\circ = -\sin 45^\circ = -\frac{1}{\sqrt{2}}$

Trigonometric Skills

Example 2

Solve the equation $\tan x° = -\sqrt{3},\ 0 \leqslant x \leqslant 360$.

SOLUTION

Since tangent is negative there are solutions in the second and fourth quadrants.
As $\tan 60° = \sqrt{3}$, the solutions are $(180-60)°$ and $(360-60)°$, that is $120°$ and $300°$.

Other exact values, which should be memorised, are listed below.

$\sin 0° = 0,\quad \sin 90° = 1,\quad \sin 180° = 0,\quad \sin 270° = -1,\quad \sin 360° = 0$

$\cos 0° = 1,\quad \cos 90° = 0,\quad \cos 180° = -1,\quad \cos 270° = 0,\quad \cos 360° = 1$

These values can be checked quickly by reference to the basic sine and cosine graphs.

Exercise 6.2

(Do **NOT** use a calculator.)

1 Write down the exact value of

a) $\sin 150°$ **b)** $\tan 225°$ **c)** $\cos 120°$
d) $\sin 240°$ **e)** $\cos 330°$ **f)** $\tan 150°$
g) $\cos 135°$ **h)** $\cos 210°$ **i)** $\tan 315°$
j) $\sin 300°$

2 Solve the following equations for $0 \leqslant x \leqslant 360$:

a) $\sin x° = -\frac{1}{2}$ **b)** $\cos x° = \frac{\sqrt{3}}{2}$ **c)** $\tan x° = -1$
d) $\sin x° = 0$ **e)** $\cos x° = -1$ **f)** $\cos x° = 0$

3 Solve the following equations for $0 \leq x \leq 360$:

a) $\sqrt{3}\tan x° + 2 = 3$
b) $2\cos x° + \sqrt{3} = 0$

4 Calculate the exact value of

a) $\sin^2 30° + \tan^2 30°$
b) $\dfrac{\sin 60°}{\cos 60°}$

Solving quadratic trigonometric equations

Some trigonometric equations may appear as a quadratic equation in $\sin x°$ or $\cos x°$. When this happens you should try to solve the equation using factorisation.

Example

Solve the equation $10\cos^2 x° - \cos x° - 2 = 0, \quad 0 \leqslant x \leqslant 360$.

SOLUTION

$10\cos^2 x° - \cos x° - 2 = 0 \Rightarrow (5\cos x° + 2)(2\cos x° - 1) = 0$

Hence $\cos x° = -\frac{2}{5}$ or $\cos x° = \frac{1}{2}$

When $\cos x° = -\frac{2}{5}$, $x = 113{\cdot}6$ or $x = 246{\cdot}4$ (correct to one decimal place)

When $\cos x° = \frac{1}{2}$, $x = 60$ or $x = 300$

Hence the solution is $x = 60, 113{\cdot}6, 246{\cdot}4, 300$.

Hint: It may help you to factorise $10\cos^2 x° - \cos x° - 2$ if you replace $\cos x°$ by c and then factorise $10c^2 - c - 2$.

Exercise 6.3

1 Solve the following equations for $0 \leq x \leq 360$:

a) $3\sin^2 x° - \sin x° = 0$

b) $2\cos^2 x° - 5\cos x° - 3 = 0$

c) $9\cos^2 x° - 4 = 0$

d) $4\sin^2 x° + 8\sin x° - 5 = 0$

e) $2\cos^2 x° - 7\cos x° + 3 = 0$

f) $8\sin^2 x° - 2\sin x° = 1$

Solving equations with multiple angles

You may be asked to solve trigonometric equations with multiple angles such as $2x°$ or $3x°$. Extra care must be taken when solving such equations.

Example

Solve the equation $2\cos 2x° - 1 = 0, \quad 0 \leqslant x \leqslant 360$.

SOLUTION

$2\cos 2x° - 1 = 0 \quad \Rightarrow \quad 2\cos 2x° = 1 \quad \Rightarrow \quad \cos 2x° = \frac{1}{2}$

Because of the multiple angle ($2x°$), we need to consider all the solutions in the interval $0 \leqslant 2x \leqslant 720$. Why? Because if we only consider solutions for $2x$ up to 360, when we divide by 2 to find x we will only end up with solutions up to 180.

Hence $\cos 2x° = \frac{1}{2} \quad \Rightarrow \quad 2x = 60,\ 300,\ 60+360,\ 300+360$

$\Rightarrow \quad 2x = 60,\ 300,\ 420,\ 660$

$\Rightarrow \quad x = 30,\ 150,\ 210,\ 330$

The solutions to the above example can be explained graphically. We could solve the equation $\cos 2x° = \frac{1}{2}$ by finding where the graphs of $y = \cos 2x°$ and $y = 0{\cdot}5$ intersect.

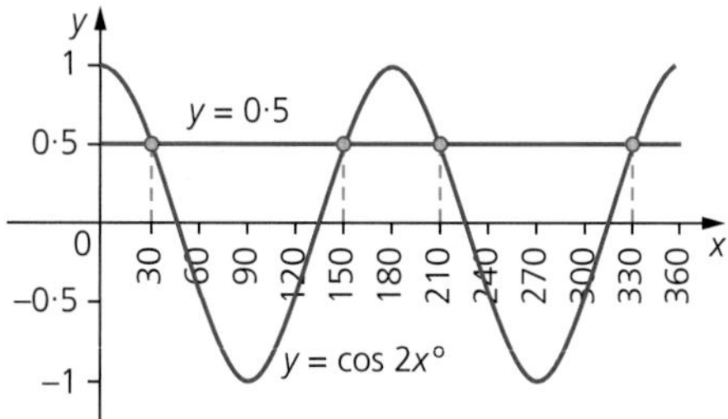

Exercise 6.4

1 Solve the following equations for $0 \leqslant x \leqslant 360$:

a) $\sin 2x° = 1$ **b)** $2\sin 3x° = \sqrt{3}$

c) $\cos 3x° = 0$ **d)** $2\sin 2x° + 1 = 0$

2 Solve the following equations to one decimal place for $0 \leqslant x \leqslant 360$:

a) $\sin 2x° = 0{\cdot}25$ **b)** $3\cos 3x° = 2$

Trigonometric graphs

You should be able to identify and sketch a variety of trigonometric graphs. The ideas you learned when studying functions and their related graphs will be very useful. We have already looked at the graphs of $y = \sin x°$ and $y = \cos x°$. These two graphs will form the starting point for more sine and cosine graphs. You should also be aware of the graph of $y = \tan x°$, shown right.

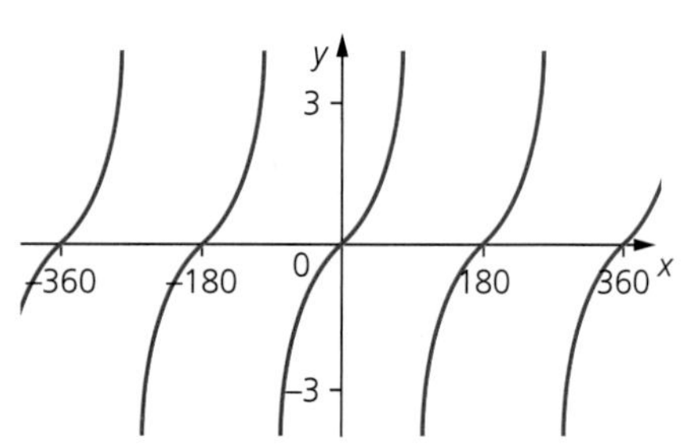

Note that the period of $y = \tan x°$ is 180° as there is a repeating pattern with each cycle having a length of 180°. The period of $y = \tan 2x°$ would be $(180 \div 2) = 90°$.

Trigonometric Skills

Example

Sketch the graph of $y = 3\cos(x - 45)^\circ - 1, \quad 0 \leqslant x \leqslant 360.$

SOLUTION

Start by considering the graph of $y = \cos x^\circ$.

The value 3 is the amplitude of the graph and stretches the graph vertically from −3 to 3.

The value of 45° is the phase angle and indicates that the graph moves 45° to the right.

The value -1 slides the graph parallel to the y-axis downwards by 1 from -4 to 2.

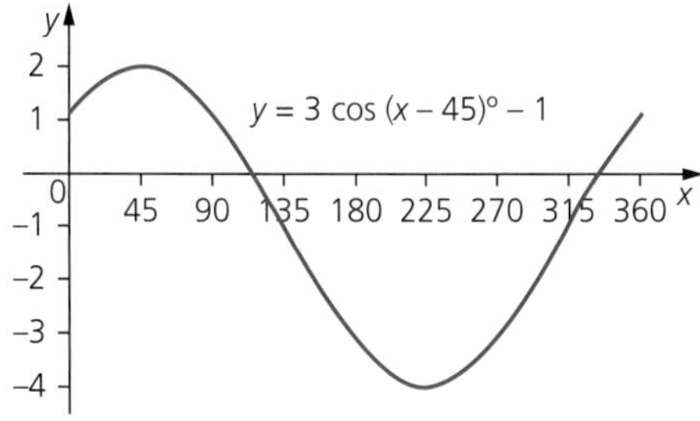

If you are sketching a trigonometric graph, remember to indicate key details, such as a scale on both axes which enables you to see important points, e.g. turning points and points where the graph cuts the x- and y-axes. Remember too that trigonometric graphs are wave functions so try to draw a smooth graph which shows this.

Exercise 6.5

1 Sketch the graph of $y = 3\cos 2x^\circ, \quad 0 \leqslant x \leqslant 360.$

2 Sketch the graph of $y = \sin 2x^\circ + 3, \quad 0 \leqslant x \leqslant 360.$

3 Sketch the graph of $y = 2\sin\,(x + 30)^\circ + 3, \quad 0 \leqslant x \leqslant 360.$

4 Sketch the graph of $y = \tan\frac{1}{2}x^\circ, \quad 0 \leqslant x \leqslant 360.$

5 What is the equation of the graph shown in the diagram below?

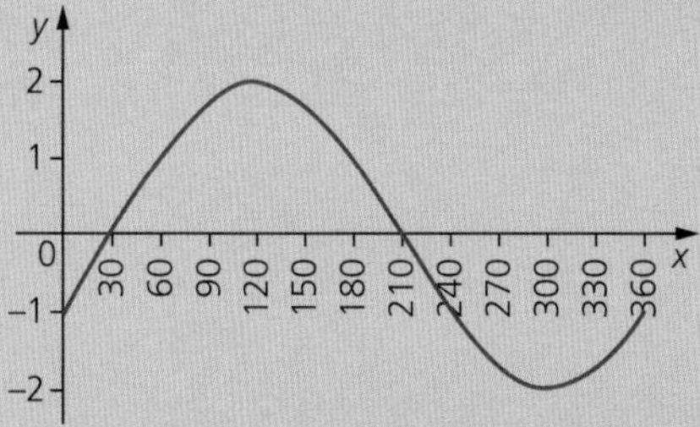

6 What is the equation of the graph shown in the diagram below?

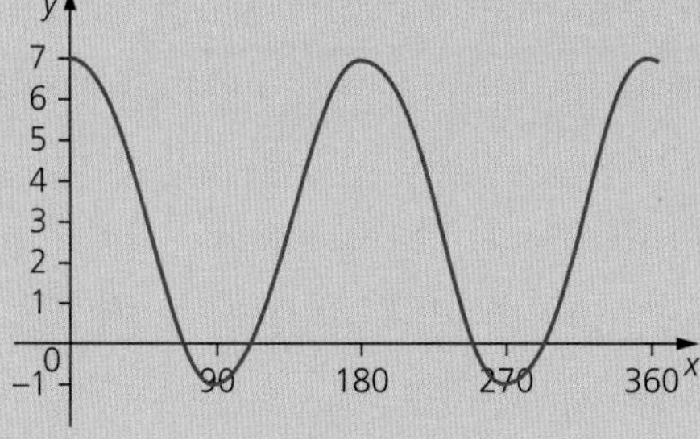

Trigonometric Skills

Trigonometric identities

A **trigonometric identity** is an equation that is true for all values of the variables. You may be asked to verify that a trigonometric identity is true. Such proofs are done in a special way, by starting with one side of the equation and manipulating it until you show that it is equal to the other side. For the following examples, you may use the following formulae (which you should memorise):

$\sin^2 x° + \cos^2 x° = 1$

$\cos^2 x° = 1 - \sin^2 x°$ and $\sin^2 x° = 1 - \cos^2 x°$ (derived from above formula)

$\tan x° = \dfrac{\sin x°}{\cos x°}$

Example

Prove that $\cos^4 x° - \sin^4 x° = 1 - 2\sin^2 x°$.

SOLUTION

Left side $= \cos^4 x° - \sin^4 x°$

$= (\cos^2 x° + \sin^2 x°)(\cos^2 x° - \sin^2 x°)$ (difference of two squares)

$= \cos^2 x° - \sin^2 x°$ (since $\sin^2 x° + \cos^2 x° = 1$)

$= (1 - \sin^2 x°) - \sin^2 x°$

$= 1 - \sin^2 x° - \sin^2 x°$

$= 1 - 2\sin^2 x°$

= Right side

Exercise 6.6

1 Prove the following identities:

a) $\sin^3 x° + \cos^2 x° \sin x° = \sin x°$

b) $\sin x° \cos x° \tan x° = \sin^2 x°$

c) $\cos^4 x° - \sin^4 x° = 2\cos^2 x° - 1$

2 Prove the following identities:

a) $1 - \dfrac{1}{\tan x°} = \dfrac{\sin x° - \cos x°}{\sin x°}$

b) $\dfrac{\cos x° + \sin x°}{\tan x°} = \dfrac{\cos^2 x°}{\sin x°} + \cos x°$

c) $1 + \tan^2 x° = \dfrac{1}{\cos^2 x°}$

Radians

Although we are used to measuring angles in degrees, there is another way of measuring angles, namely in radians. The radian is a measure based on the radius of a circle

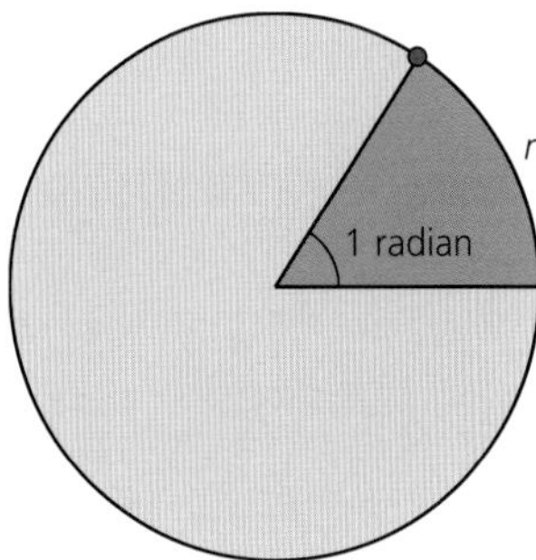

I radian is formed by taking part of the circumference of a circle equal in length to the radius.

As the circumference of a circle is found using the formula $C = 2\pi r$, we can see that there are 2π radians in a complete turn. As there are $360°$ in a complete turn, 2π radians $= 360°$.

Hence π radians $= 180°$.

This is a good starting point if you wish to convert angles from degrees to radians and vice versa.

Example 1

Express I radian in degrees.

SOLUTION

π radians $= 180°$

Hence I radian $= \frac{1}{\pi} \times 180° = 57{\cdot}2957795°$ approximately

Example 2

Express $225°$ in radians. (Do **NOT** use a calculator.)

SOLUTION

$225° = \frac{225}{180} \times \pi$ radians $= \frac{5\pi}{4}$ radians

Example 3

Express $\frac{4\pi}{3}$ radians in degrees. (Do **NOT** use a calculator.)

SOLUTION

$\frac{4\pi}{3}$ radians $= \frac{4}{3} \times 180° = 240°$

Since you can measure angles in radians as well as degrees, when you are asked to solve trigonometric equations you must be careful whether the solution is to be given in degrees $(0 \leqslant x \leqslant 360)$ or radians $(0 \leqslant x \leqslant 2\pi)$.

Example 4

Solve the equation $\sqrt{3}\tan x + 1 = 0, \quad 0 \leqslant x \leqslant 2\pi$. (Do **NOT** use a calculator.)

SOLUTION

$\sqrt{3}\tan x + 1 = 0 \quad \Rightarrow \quad \sqrt{3}\tan x = -1 \quad \Rightarrow \quad \tan x = -\frac{1}{\sqrt{3}}$

Since tangent is negative there are solutions in the second and fourth quadrants.

As $\tan^{-1}\left(\frac{1}{\sqrt{3}}\right) = 30° = \frac{\pi}{6}$, the solutions are $\left(\pi - \frac{\pi}{6}\right)$ and $\left(2\pi - \frac{\pi}{6}\right)$, that is $\frac{5\pi}{6}$ and $\frac{11\pi}{6}$.

Hence $x = \frac{5\pi}{6}, \frac{11\pi}{6}$.

Example 5

Find the solution of the equation $4\sin x + 1 = 0, \; 0 \leqslant x \leqslant 2\pi$.

Give your answer correct to three decimal places.

SOLUTION

$4\sin x + 1 = 0 \quad \Rightarrow \quad 4\sin x = -1 \quad \Rightarrow \quad \sin x = -\frac{1}{4}$

Sine is negative in the third and fourth quadrants.

Put your calculator into radian mode to find that $\sin^{-1}(0{\cdot}25) = 0{\cdot}25268$.

Hence $x = \pi + 0{\cdot}25268 = 3{\cdot}394$ or $x = 2\pi - 0{\cdot}25268 = 6{\cdot}031$ (correct to 3 d.p.).

Exercise 6.7

(Do **NOT** use a calculator except for question 8.)

1 Express in degrees the following angles given in radian measure:

a) $\frac{\pi}{2}$ **b)** $\frac{3\pi}{2}$ **c)** $\frac{\pi}{4}$

d) $\frac{\pi}{6}$ **e)** $\frac{2\pi}{3}$ **f)** $\frac{7\pi}{4}$

g) $\frac{7\pi}{6}$ **h)** $\frac{\pi}{5}$

2 Express in radian measure the following angles given in degrees:

a) 150° **b)** 60° **c)** 135°

d) 300° **e)** 330° **f)** 54°

3 Complete the following table.

	$\frac{\pi}{6}$	$\frac{\pi}{4}$	$\frac{\pi}{3}$
sin			
cos			
tan			

→

4 Find the exact value of:

a) $\sin\frac{2\pi}{3}$

b) $\tan\frac{11\pi}{6}$

c) $\cos\frac{5\pi}{4}$

d) $\sin\left(-\frac{\pi}{4}\right)$

e) $\sin\frac{13\pi}{6}$

5 Solve the following equations for $0 \leqslant x \leqslant 2\pi$:

a) $\sin x = \frac{1}{2}$

b) $\tan x = 1$

c) $\cos x = -\frac{\sqrt{3}}{2}$

d) $\cos x = \frac{1}{2}$

6 What is the equation of the graph shown in the diagram below?

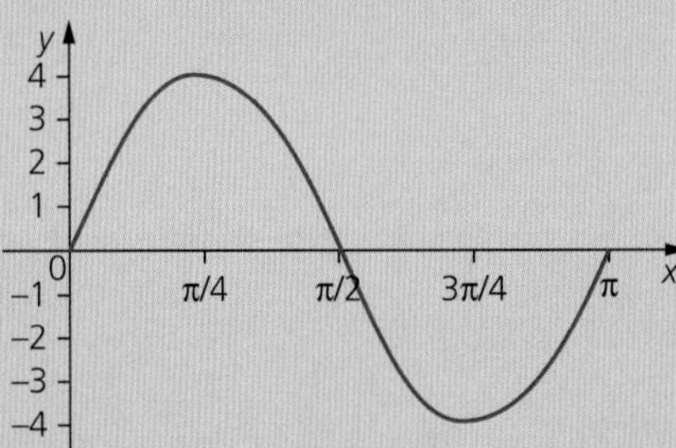

7 Solve the following equations for $0 \leqslant x \leqslant 2\pi$:

a) $2\sin x + \sqrt{3} = 0$

b) $2\cos x + 1 = 2$

c) $\sin 2x = \frac{1}{2}$

d) $2\cos^2 x + \cos x - 1 = 0$

8 Solve the following equations for $0 \leqslant x \leqslant 2\pi$. Give your answers correct to three decimal places.

a) $\cos x = 0{\cdot}7$

b) $5\cos x - 4 = -2$

c) $\sin 2x = 0{\cdot}32$

Three dimensions

Investigation

Find out about the following ideas associated with three-dimensional shapes and try the example given on these ideas.

- Space diagonal
- Angle between a line and a plane
- Angle between two planes

Example

A cuboid ABCDEFGH is shown.

a) Calculate the length of the space diagonal AG.

b) Calculate the size of the angle between the line AG and the plane EFGH.

c) Calculate size of the angle between the planes ABGH and ABCD.

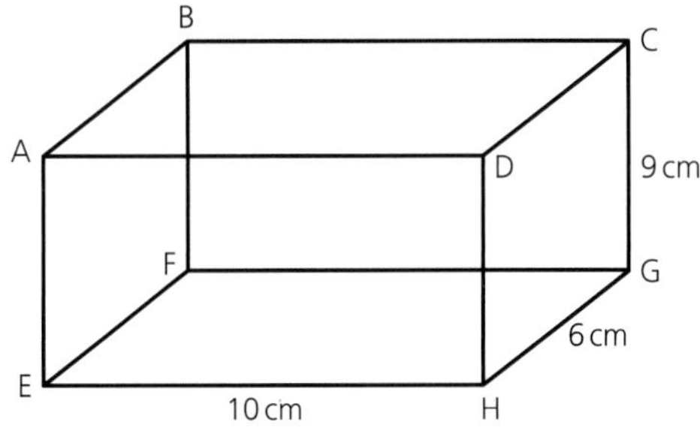

Checkout

(Do **NOT** use a calculator except for question 5.)

1 In triangle ABC, AB = 10 centimetres, AC = 8 centimetres and angle BAC = 30°. Calculate the area of the triangle.

2 What is the exact value of $\sin 420°$?

3 Solve the equation $\cos x° = -\frac{1}{\sqrt{2}}$, $0 \leqslant x \leqslant 360$.

4 What is the period of $y = \tan 2x°$?

5 Solve the equation $6\sin^2 x° - 7\sin x° - 3 = 0$, $0 \leqslant x \leqslant 360$.

6 Solve the equation $\sqrt{2}\sin x° + 1 = 0$, $0 \leqslant x \leqslant 360$.

7 Find the exact value of $\tan^2 60° + \tan^2 45°$.

8 Convert 315° to radians.

Summary

Trigonometry – Bridging the Gap

1 Important relationships between angles include:

$\sin(180 - x)° = \sin x°$, $\cos(180 - x)° = -\cos x°$,

$\cos(90 - x)° = \sin x°$, $\sin(90 - x)° = \cos x°$,

$\sin(-x)° = -\sin x°$, $\cos(-x)° = \cos x°$

2 The exact values of the sine, cosine and tangent of 30°, 45° and 60° are given below:

	30°	45°	60°
sin	$\frac{1}{2}$	$\frac{1}{\sqrt{2}}$	$\frac{\sqrt{3}}{2}$
cos	$\frac{\sqrt{3}}{2}$	$\frac{1}{\sqrt{2}}$	$\frac{1}{2}$
tan	$\frac{1}{\sqrt{3}}$	1	$\sqrt{3}$

3 The graphs of $y = \sin x°$, $y = \cos x°$ and $y = \tan x°$ are shown below.

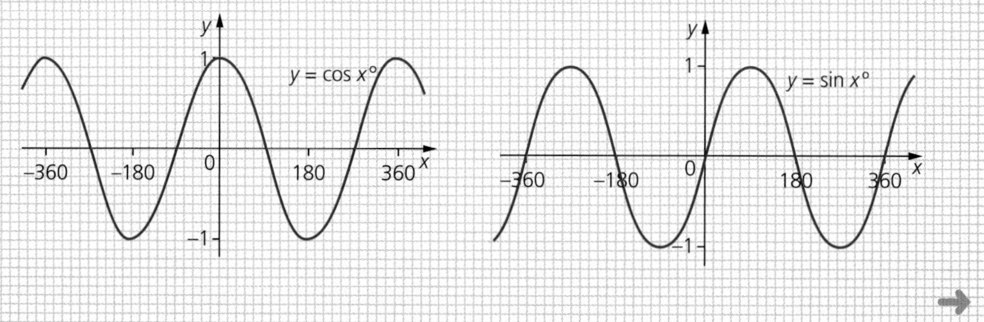

→

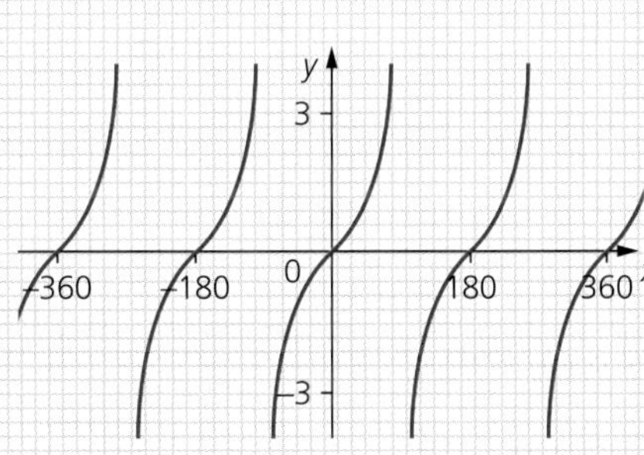

The graph of $y = a \sin bx°$ and $y = a \cos bx°$ have amplitude a and period $\left(\frac{360}{b}\right)°$.

The graph of $y = a \tan bx°$ has period $\left(\frac{180}{b}\right)°$ and undefined amplitude.

4 The angle subtended at the centre of a circle by an arc equal in length to the radius is 1 radian.

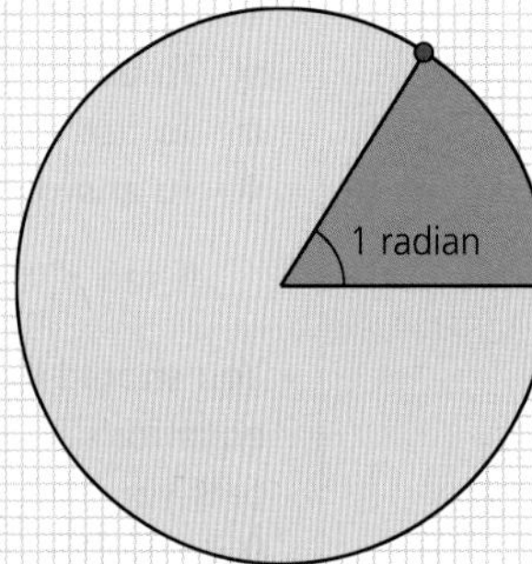

5 π radians = 180°.

CHAPTER

Trigonometry – Compound and Multiple Angles

In this chapter you will study formulae involving compound angles, e.g. sin $(A + B)$, and multiple angles, e.g. sin $2A$.

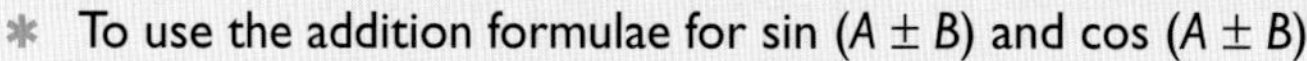

What I am learning

* To use the addition formulae for sin $(A \pm B)$ and cos $(A \pm B)$
* To use the double-angle formulae for sin $2A$ and cos $2A$
* To use the formulae in numerical examples
* To use these formulae to prove trigonometric identities
* To answer questions like this:

  If $\tan x° = \frac{12}{5}$, $0 \leqslant x \leqslant 90$, find the value of $\cos 2x°$.

You should be aware of the distinction between degrees and radians. Consider the two equations $y = \sin x°$ and $y = \sin x$. The fact that there is no degree sign in the second equation tells you that radians are being used to measure angles. Watch out too for intervals such as $0 < x < 360$ (degrees) and $0 < x < 2\pi$ (radians). Keep this in mind as you work through this and subsequent trigonometry chapters.

What I should already know/be able to do

* How to use the Theorem of Pythagoras
* How to carry out the four operations with fractions
* How to simplify surds
* How to express a fraction with a rational denominator
* Know the exact values of the sine and cosine of 0°, 30°, 45°, 60° and 90°
* How to prove trigonometric identities

Quick check!

1 Work out $\frac{24}{25} \times \frac{5}{13}$.

2 Simplify $\sqrt{72}$.

3 Express $\frac{5}{\sqrt{2}}$ as a fraction with a rational denominator.

4 If $\sin x° = \frac{15}{17}$, find the value of $\cos x°$.

Quick check! – *Solutions*

1 $\frac{24}{65}$ 2 $6\sqrt{2}$ 3 $\frac{5\sqrt{2}}{2}$ 4 $\frac{8}{17}$

Addition and double-angle formulae

We shall start by looking at the addition formula for $\sin(\alpha+\beta)$ and $\cos(\alpha+\beta)$ These formulae are called **addition formulae** because the sum $(\alpha+\beta)$ appears in them. These formulae express the sine or cosine of the sum of two angles in terms of the sines and cosines of the individual angles.

$$\sin(\alpha+\beta)=\sin\alpha\cos\beta+\cos\alpha\sin\beta$$

$$\cos(\alpha+\beta)=\cos\alpha\cos\beta-\sin\alpha\sin\beta$$

Proof

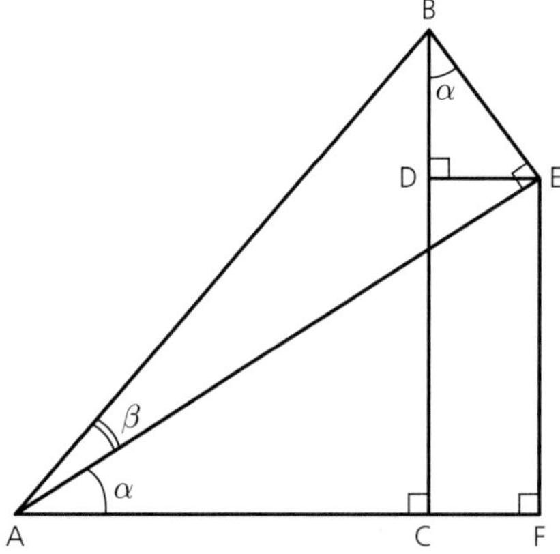

Let AB = 1 unit.
Hence in triangle ABC, AC = $\cos(\alpha+\beta)$ and BC = $\sin(\alpha+\beta)$.

In triangle ABE, BE = $\sin\beta$.
Hence in triangle BDE, BD = $\cos\alpha\sin\beta$ and DE = $\sin\alpha\sin\beta$.

Also in triangle ABE, AE = $\cos\beta$.
Hence in triangle AEF, EF = $\sin\alpha\cos\beta$ and AF = $\cos\alpha\cos\beta$.

As BC = DC + BD = EF + BD, $\sin(\alpha+\beta)=\sin\alpha\cos\beta+\cos\alpha\sin\beta$
As AC = AF − CF = AF − DE, $\cos(\alpha+\beta)=\cos\alpha\cos\beta-\sin\alpha\sin\beta$

By replacing β by $(-\beta)$ in the above formulae, we can find formulae for $\sin(\alpha-\beta)$ and $\cos(\alpha-\beta)$

$$\begin{aligned}\sin(\alpha-\beta)=\sin[\alpha+(-\beta)]&=\sin\alpha\cos(-\beta)+\cos\alpha\sin(-\beta)\\&=\sin\alpha\cos\beta-\cos\alpha\sin\beta\end{aligned}$$

In a similar way we can show that $\cos(\alpha-\beta)=\cos\alpha\cos\beta+\sin\alpha\sin\beta$.

This leads to four addition formulae in trigonometry which will be used in this chapter. Note that the variables, α and β, in the above formulae may change from example to example. All four formulae are in the list of formulae given in assessments in the form shown below.

$$\sin(A\pm B)=\sin A\cos B\pm\cos A\sin B$$

$$\cos(A\pm B)=\cos A\cos B\mp\sin A\sin B$$

Trigonometric Skills

Example 1

If A and B are two acute angles such that $\sin A = \frac{3}{5}$ and $\cos B = \frac{12}{13}$, find the exact value of $\cos(A - B)$.

SOLUTION

We shall be using the formula for cos $(A - B)$ but first we must construct two right-angled triangles, one for A and one for B. We use the Theorem of Pythagoras to find the third side in each triangle and hence find the missing ratios. Note that it will save you time if you are aware of the well-known Pythagorean triples, namely (3, 4, 5), (5, 12, 13), (8, 15, 17), and (7, 24, 25).

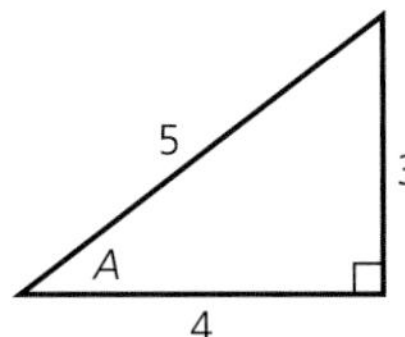

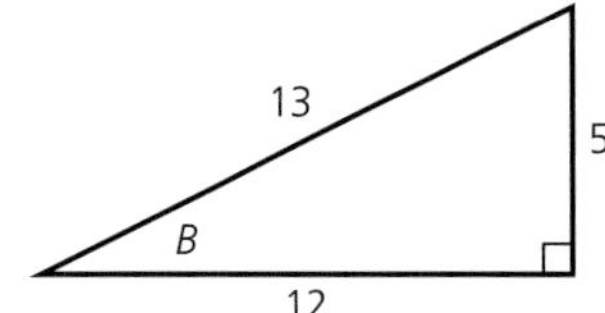

$$\cos(A-B) = \cos A \cos B + \sin A \sin B = \frac{4}{5}\times\frac{12}{13}+\frac{3}{5}\times\frac{5}{13}=\frac{48}{65}+\frac{15}{65}=\frac{63}{65}$$

Hint There was not a problem with signs as both angles were acute. Be careful, however, if one of the ratios is negative. For example, if you are told in an example that an angle C is obtuse then you can use the same method but cos C would be negative.

Example 2

a) Find an expression equal to $\sin(x - 30)°$.

b) Show that the exact value of sin 15° is $\frac{\sqrt{6}-\sqrt{2}}{4}$.

SOLUTION

a) $\sin(x - 30)° = \sin x° \cos 30° - \cos x° \sin 30° = \frac{\sqrt{3}}{2}\sin x° - \frac{1}{2}\cos x°$

b) $\sin 15° = \sin(45 - 30)° = \sin 45° \cos 30° - \cos 45° \sin 30°$

$$= \frac{1}{\sqrt{2}}\times\frac{\sqrt{3}}{2} - \frac{1}{\sqrt{2}}\times\frac{1}{2} = \frac{\sqrt{3}-1}{2\sqrt{2}} = \frac{\sqrt{3}-1}{2\sqrt{2}}\times\frac{\sqrt{2}}{\sqrt{2}} = \frac{\sqrt{6}-\sqrt{2}}{4}$$

Exercise 7.1

(Do **NOT** use a calculator.)

1 Write down expressions for the following:

a) $\sin(p - q)$ **b)** $\cos(x + y)°$ **c)** $\sin(3m + n)$
d) $\cos(c - d)$ **e)** $\cos(4a - 3b)$ **f)** $\sin(z - 2y)°$
g) $\sin(x - a)$ **h)** $\cos(\theta - \omega)$

2 Simplify:

a) $\sin P \cos Q + \cos P \sin Q$ **b)** $\cos 2x \cos y + \sin 2x \sin y$
c) $\sin 57° \cos 33° + \cos 57° \sin 33°$ **d)** $\cos 4x \cos x - \sin 4x \sin x$
e) $\cos 22° \cos 38° - \sin 22° \sin 38°$

3 Using the addition formulae, prove the following identities:

a) $\cos(360 - x)° = \cos x°$ **b)** $\sin(90 - x)° = \cos x°$ →

4 If A and B are two acute angles such that $\sin A = \frac{5}{13}$ and $\cos B = \frac{3}{5}$, find the exact value of $\sin(A + B)$. HPQ

5 If A and B are two acute angles such that $\sin A = \frac{15}{17}$ and $\cos B = \frac{3}{5}$, find the exact value of $\cos(A - B)$.

6 If X and Y are two acute angles such that $\tan X = \frac{4}{3}$ and $\tan Y = \frac{12}{5}$, find the exact value of $\sin(X - Y)$.

7 If A and B are two acute angles such that $\sin A = \frac{1}{\sqrt{3}}$ and $\cos B = \frac{2}{3}$, prove that $\cos(A+B) = \frac{2\sqrt{6} - \sqrt{15}}{9}$.

8 If X and Y are two acute angles such that $\tan X = \frac{3}{4}$ and $\tan Y = \frac{1}{7}$, prove that $\cos(X - Y) = \frac{31\sqrt{2}}{50}$.

9 By expressing 75° as (45 + 30)°, show that $\cos 75° = \frac{\sqrt{3} - 1}{2\sqrt{2}}$.

10 **a)** Find an expression equal to $\cos(x + 30)°$.

b) Show that the exact value of cos 165° is $\frac{-\sqrt{6} - \sqrt{2}}{4}$.

11 If $\sin x° = \frac{12}{13}$, $0 \leq x \leq 90$, and $\cos y° = -\frac{3}{5}$, $90 \leq y \leq 180$, find the exact value of $\sin(x + y)°$.

12 Angle A is an acute angle such that $\cos A = \frac{4}{5}$. Angle B is an obtuse angle such that $\tan B = -\frac{5}{12}$.
Find the exact value of $\sin(A - B)$.

13 On the coordinate diagram shown below, P is the point (12, 5) and Q is the point (8, –6).
Angle POR = a and angle QOR = b. Find the exact value of $\cos(a + b)$.

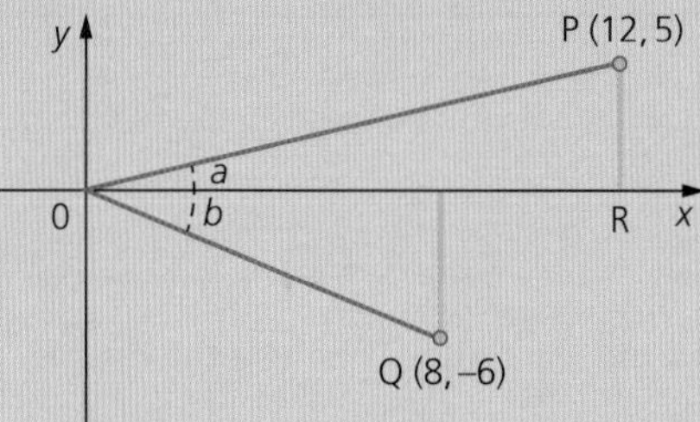

14 In triangle DEF, show that the exact value of $\sin(x + y)$ is $\frac{3\sqrt{10}}{10}$.

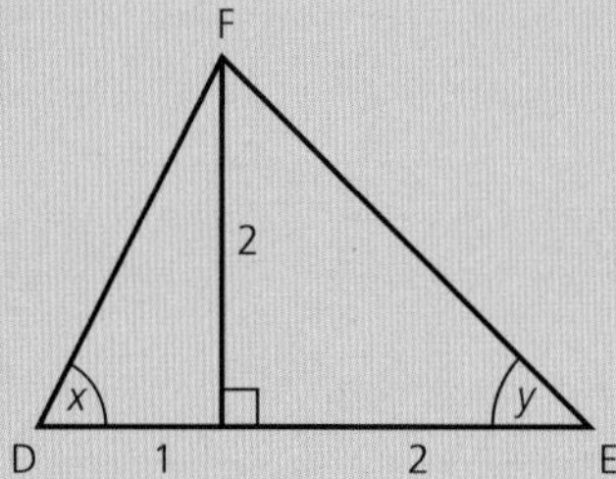

15 Simplify $\cos\alpha\cos\left(\alpha - \frac{\pi}{3}\right) + \sin\alpha\sin\left(\alpha - \frac{\pi}{3}\right)$.

16 In triangle ABC, angle $C = 60°$. What is the value of $\cos A \cos B - \sin A \sin B$? ACE

Trigonometric Skills

Double-angle formulae

Investigation

We shall now consider formulae for $\sin 2A$ and $\cos 2A$. These formulae are called the **double-angle formulae.** We begin by thinking of $\sin 2A$ and $\cos 2A$ as $\sin(A + A)$ and $\cos(A + A)$ respectively and then using the addition formulae from the previous section. Later on in the chapter we shall look at other formulae for multiple angles, namely $\sin 3A$ and $\cos 3A$

$$\sin 2A = \sin(A+A) = \sin A\cos A + \cos A\sin A = 2\sin A\cos A$$

$$\cos 2A = \cos(A+A) = \cos A\cos A - \sin A\sin A = \cos^2 A - \sin^2 A$$

The formula for $\cos 2A$ can be given in two other more useful forms by replacing $\sin^2 A$ by $1 - \cos^2 A$ for one formula and $\cos^2 A$ by $1 - \sin^2 A$ for another.

$$\cos 2A = \cos^2 A - \sin^2 A = \cos^2 A - (1 - \cos^2 A) = 2\cos^2 A - 1$$
$$\cos 2A = \cos^2 A - \sin^2 A = (1 - \sin^2 A) - \sin^2 A = 1 - 2\sin^2 A$$

All these formulae are in the list of formulae given in assessments in the form shown below.

$$\sin 2A = 2\sin A\cos A$$
$$\begin{aligned}\cos 2A &= \cos^2 A - \sin^2 A\\ &= 2\cos^2 A - 1\\ &= 1 - 2\sin^2 A\end{aligned}$$

Example 1

If $\tan x° = \frac{12}{5}$, $0 \leqslant x \leqslant 90$, find the value of $\cos 2x°$.

SOLUTION

Construct a right-angled triangle and use the Theorem of Pythagoras to find the third side. Then use the double-angle formulae.

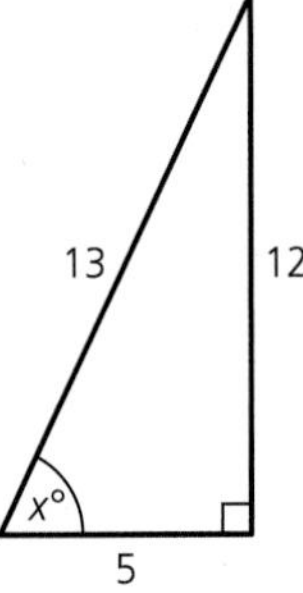

$$\begin{aligned}\cos 2x° = \cos^2 x° - \sin^2 x° &= \left(\frac{5}{13}\right)^2 - \left(\frac{12}{13}\right)^2\\ &= \frac{25}{169} - \frac{144}{169}\\ &= -\frac{119}{169}\end{aligned}$$

Trigonometric Skills

Example 2

If A is an acute angle such that $\sin A = \frac{4}{5}$ find the exact values of:

a) $\sin 2A$ b) $\cos 2A$ c) $\tan 2A$

SOLUTION

Construct a right-angled triangle and use the Theorem of Pythagoras to find the third side. Then use the double-angle formulae.

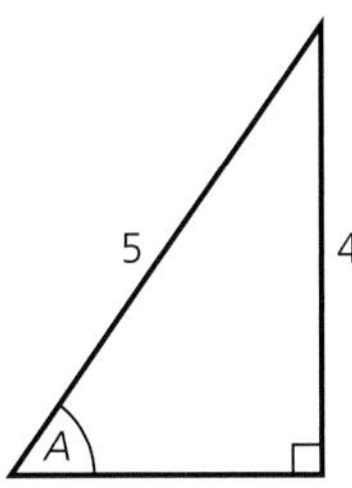

a) $\sin 2A = 2\sin A \cos A = 2 \times \frac{4}{5} \times \frac{3}{5} = \frac{24}{25}$

b) $\cos 2A = \cos^2 A - \sin^2 A = \left(\frac{3}{5}\right)^2 - \left(\frac{4}{5}\right)^2 = \frac{9}{25} - \frac{16}{25} = -\frac{7}{25}$

c) $\tan 2A = \frac{\sin 2A}{\cos 2A} = \frac{24/25}{-7/25} = -\frac{24}{7}$

Exercise 7.2

(Do **NOT** use a calculator.)

1 Write down expressions for the following:

a) $\sin 2C$ **b)** $\sin 4A$ **c)** $\sin 6X$
d) $\sin 10p$ **e)** $\sin A$

2 Write down three expressions for each of the following:

a) $\cos 6B$ **b)** $\cos 2y°$ **c)** $\cos Q$
d) $\cos 4E$ **e)** $\cos 12A$

3 Simplify:

a) $2 \sin Y \cos Y$ **b)** $\cos^2 F - \sin^2 F$ **c)** $1 - 2\sin^2 2A$
d) $2 \sin 2z \cos 2z$ **e)** $2\cos^2 3p - 1$ **f)** $2 \sin 15° \cos 15°$
g) $2\sin\frac{\pi}{4}\cos\frac{\pi}{4}$ **h)** $\cos^2 30° - \sin^2 30°$ **i)** $2\cos^2 15° - 1$

4 If α is an acute angle such that $\sin\alpha = \frac{3}{5}$, find the exact value of $\sin 2\alpha$.

5 If A is an acute angle such that $\cos A = \frac{12}{13}$, find the exact value of the following:

a) $\sin 2A$ **b)** $\cos 2A$ **c)** $\tan 2A$

6 If P is an acute angle such that $\tan P = \frac{\sqrt{11}}{3}$, find the exact value of $\cos 2P$.

7 Given that $\sin\alpha° = \frac{15}{17}$, where $0 < \alpha < 90$, find the exact value of $\sin 2\alpha°$.

8 Given that $\sin X° = \frac{2}{3}$, where $0 < X < 90$, find the exact value of $\sin 2X°$.

➜

9 **a)** Express $\cos^2 A$ in terms of $\cos 2A$.
b) Express $\sin^2 A$ in terms of $\cos 2A$.

Remember These two formulae may be useful when you study integration.

10 If $\cos 2a° = \frac{7}{25}$, $0 \leqslant a \leqslant 90$, find the exact value of:
a) $\cos a°$ **b)** $\sin a°$

11 If $\sin \beta° = \frac{3}{5}$, $0 \leqslant \beta \leqslant 90$, find the exact value of:
a) $\sin 2\beta°$ **b)** $\sin 4\beta°$

12 If P is an obtuse angle such that $\sin P = \frac{1}{\sqrt{5}}$, find the exact value of $\cos 2P$.

13 If $\tan A° = -\frac{1}{2}$, $90 \leqslant A \leqslant 180$, find the exact value of $\cos 2A°$.

14 Find the exact value of:
a) $\sin D$
b) $\sin 2D$
c) $\cos 2D$

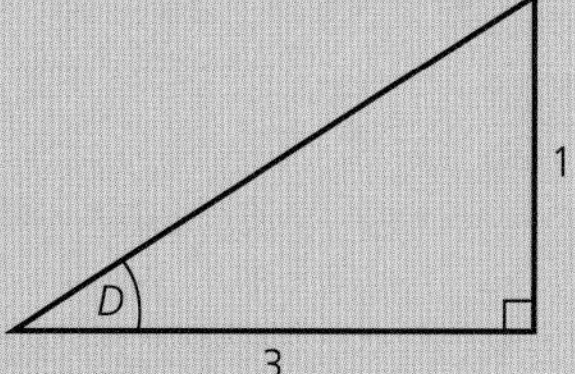

15 Express $3 \cos 2x - \cos x - 2$ as a quadratic expression in $\cos x$. 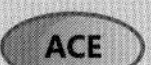

Trigonometric identities

You studied trigonometric identities in the previous chapter (Trigonometry – Bridging the Gap). You will still be able to use the identities from that chapter: $\sin^2 x + \cos^2 x = 1$ and $\tan x = \frac{\sin x}{\cos x}$. However, now that you know the addition and double-angle formulae, you can tackle some more complex identities.

Example

By writing $3x$ as $(2x + x)$ and expanding, prove that $\sin 3x = 3 \sin x - 4 \sin^3 x$.

SOLUTION

Left side $= \sin 3x$
$= \sin (2x + x)$
$= \sin 2x \cos x + \cos 2x \sin x$
$= (2 \sin x \cos x) \cos x + (1 - 2 \sin^2 x) \sin x$
$= 2 \sin x \cos^2 x + \sin x - 2 \sin^3 x$
$= 2 \sin x (1 - \sin^2 x) + \sin x - 2 \sin^3 x$
$= 2 \sin x - 2 \sin^3 x + \sin x - 2 \sin^3 x$
$= 3 \sin x - 4 \sin^3 x$
= Right side.

Trigonometric Skills

Exercise 7.3

All the questions in Exercise 7.3 are ACE questions.

1 Prove the following identities:

a) $\sin(A + B) + \sin(A - B) = 2\sin A\cos B$

b) $\cos(A + B) + \cos(A - B) = 2\cos A\cos B$

c) $\sin\left(A - \frac{\pi}{6}\right) = \frac{1}{2}\left(\sqrt{3}\sin A - \cos A\right)$

2 Prove the following identities:

a) $\tan 5A + \tan 3A = \frac{\sin 8A}{\cos 5A\cos 3A}$

b) $\tan P + \tan Q = \frac{\sin(P+Q)}{\cos P\cos Q}$

3 Prove that $\frac{1+\tan^2 x}{1-\tan^2 x} = \frac{1}{\cos 2x}$.

4 A is the point with coordinates $[\cos(\alpha - \beta), \sin(\alpha - \beta)]$ and B is the point with coordinates $[\cos(\alpha + \beta), \sin(\alpha + \beta)]$, where α is not a multiple of $\frac{\pi}{2}$. Prove that the gradient of AB equals $-\frac{1}{\tan\alpha}$.

5 By writing $3x$ as $(2x + x)$ and expanding, prove that $\cos 3x = 4\cos^3 x - 3\cos x$.

More formulae

Investigation

You know formulae for $\sin(A + B)$ and $\cos(A + B)$. In this investigation, you will find a formula for $\tan(A + B)$. You can then find two more formulae and try an example involving one of the formulae.

$$\tan(A + B) = \frac{\sin(A+B)}{\cos(A+B)} = \frac{\sin A\cos B + \cos A\sin B}{\cos A\cos B - \sin A\sin B}$$

Now divide the numerator and denominator of the fraction by $\cos A\cos B$.

$$\tan(A+B) = \frac{\frac{\sin A\cos B}{\cos A\cos B} + \frac{\cos A\sin B}{\cos A\cos B}}{\frac{\cos A\cos B}{\cos A\cos B} - \frac{\sin A\sin B}{\cos A\cos B}} = \frac{\tan A + \tan B}{1 - \tan A\tan B}.$$

The formula for $\tan(A + B)$ is then $\tan(A + B) = \frac{\tan A + \tan B}{1 - \tan A\tan B}$.

Hence find formulae for $\tan(A - B)$ and $\tan 2A$.

Try the following example.

Example

Prove that $\tan 75° = \frac{\sqrt{3}+1}{\sqrt{3}-1}$.

Trigonometric Skills

Checkout

(Do **NOT** use a calculator.)

1 Simplify cos 65° cos 25° – sin 65° sin 25°.

2 a) Find an expression equal to cos$(x - 45)°$.

b) Show that the exact value of cos15° is $\frac{1+\sqrt{3}}{2\sqrt{2}}$.

3 If A and B are two acute angles such that $\sin A = \frac{5}{13}$ and $\sin B = \frac{3}{5}$, find the exact value of $\sin(A + B)$.

4 If A is an acute angle such that $\tan A = \frac{1}{\sqrt{2}}$, find the exact value of the following:

a) sin $2A$ b) cos $2A$ c) tan $2A$

5 Prove that $\cos A - \cos\left(A + \frac{\pi}{3}\right) + \cos\left(A + \frac{2\pi}{3}\right) = 0$.

Summary

Trigonometry – Compound and Multiple Angles

1 The addition formulae:
$\sin(A \pm B) = \sin A \cos B \pm \cos A \sin B$
$\cos(A \pm B) = \cos A \cos B \mp \sin A \sin B$

2 The double-angle formulae:
$\sin 2A = 2\sin A \cos A$
$\cos 2A = \cos^2 A - \sin^2 A$
$= 2\cos^2 A - 1$
$= 1 - 2\sin^2 A$

3 Know how to use the above formulae to solve numerical problems and prove identities.

CHAPTER 8

Trigonometric Equations 1

In the first of two chapters on trigonometric equations, we shall study equations which involve the double-angle formulae and can be solved by factorising quadratic trigonometric expressions.

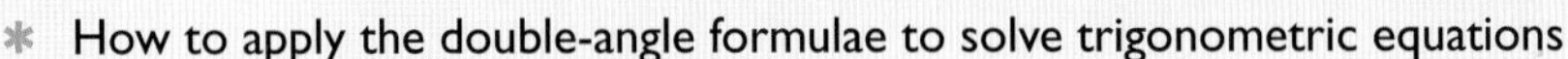

What I am learning

* How to apply the double-angle formulae to solve trigonometric equations
* How to solve equations like this:
  $2\cos 2x - 4\cos x - 1 = 0,\ 0 \leqslant x \leqslant 2\pi$

What I should already know/be able to do

* How to use the double-angle formulae for $\sin 2A$ and $\cos 2A$
* How to solve quadratic trigonometric equations in both degrees and radians
* How to solve quadratic equations using the quadratic formula $x = \dfrac{-b \pm \sqrt{b^2 - 4ac}}{2a}$

Quick check!

1. Solve the equation $2\sin x + 1 = 0,\ 0 \leqslant x \leqslant 2\pi$.
2. Express $\cos 2x° - 3\sin x° - 2$ as a quadratic expression in $\sin x$.
3. Solve the equation $2\sin^2 x° + 3\sin x° + 1 = 0,\ 0 \leqslant x \leqslant 360$.
4. Solve the equation $x^2 - 4x + 1 = 0$, giving your answers correct to one decimal place.

Quick check! – *Solutions*

1. $\dfrac{7\pi}{6}, \dfrac{11\pi}{6}$
2. $-2\sin^2 x° - 3\sin x° - 1$
3. $x = 210,\ 270,\ 330$
4. $x = 0{\cdot}3,\ 3{\cdot}7$

Trigonometric equations

Many trigonometric equations containing $\sin 2x$ or $\cos 2x$ can be solved by replacing $\sin 2x$ or $\cos 2x$ by one of the double-angle formulae in order to form a quadratic trigonometric equation in $\sin x$ or $\cos x$. The resulting quadratic equation can then be solved using factorisation or the quadratic formula.

Example 1

Solve the equation $5\sin 2x° - \cos x° = 0,\ 0 \leqslant x \leqslant 360$.

SOLUTION

In this equation we can replace $\sin 2x°$ with $2\sin x° \cos x°$ and then continue to solve the equation by factorisation (using a common factor).

$$5\sin 2x° - \cos x° = 0$$
$$\Rightarrow 5(2\sin x° \cos x°) - \cos x° = 0$$
$$\Rightarrow 10\sin x° \cos x° - \cos x° = 0$$
$$\Rightarrow \cos x°(10\sin x° - 1) = 0$$
$$\Rightarrow \cos x° = 0 \text{ or } \sin x° = \frac{1}{10}$$
$$\Rightarrow x = 5{\cdot}7,\ 90,\ 174{\cdot}3,\ 270$$

Example 2

Solve the equation $2\cos 2x - 4\cos x - 1 = 0,\ 0 \leqslant x \leqslant 2\pi$.

SOLUTION

In this equation we can start by replacing $\cos 2x$ with a double-angle formula. However, there are *three* possible formulae for $\cos 2x$, so which one should we choose?

The choice depends on whether the other trigonometric term in the equation is $\sin x$ or $\cos x$. In the equation $2\cos 2x - 4\cos x - 1 = 0$, we can replace $\cos 2x$ with $2\cos^2 x - 1$ so that we can form a quadratic equation in $\cos x$. For an equation such as $2\cos 2x - 4\sin x - 1 = 0$, we would replace $\cos 2x$ with $1 - 2\sin^2 x$ so that we could form a quadratic equation in $\sin x$. We usually choose from these two formulae for $\cos 2x$ and do not use the formula $\cos 2x = \cos^2 x - \sin^2 x$.

$$2\cos 2x - 4\cos x - 1 = 0$$
$$\Rightarrow 2(2\cos^2 x - 1) - 4\cos x - 1 = 0$$
$$\Rightarrow 4\cos^2 x - 2 - 4\cos x - 1 = 0$$
$$\Rightarrow 4\cos^2 x - 4\cos x - 3 = 0$$
$$\Rightarrow (2\cos x + 1)(2\cos x - 3) = 0$$
$$\Rightarrow \cos x = -\frac{1}{2} \text{ or } \cos x = \frac{3}{2}$$
$$\Rightarrow x = \frac{2\pi}{3}, \frac{4\pi}{3}$$

$\cos x = \frac{3}{2}$ has no solution.

Exercise 8.1

1 Solve the following equations for $0 \leqslant x \leqslant 360$:

a) $\sin 2x° - \cos x° = 0$ b) $\sin 2x° + \sin x° = 0$ c) $3\sin 2x° + 2\cos x° = 0$

2 Solve the equation $\cos 2x° - 3\cos x° + 2 = 0$, $0 \leqslant x \leqslant 360$. HPQ

3 Solve the following equations for $0 \leqslant x \leqslant 360$:

a) $2\cos 2x° - 4\cos x° - 1 = 0$ b) $\cos 2x° - 4\sin x° + 5 = 0$ c) $4\cos 2x° - 2\sin x° - 1 = 0$

d) $\cos 2x° + 5\cos x° - 2 = 0$ e) $\cos 2x° + 3\cos x° + 2 = 0$ f) $6\cos 2x° - 11\cos x° + 8 = 0$

g) $\sin 2x° - 4\sin x° = 0$ h) $3\sin 2x° + 4\cos x° = 0$ i) $2\cos 2x° + \sin x° + 1 = 0$

4 Solve the following equations for $0 \leqslant x \leqslant 360$:

a) $\cos 2x° - \sin x° + 1 = 0$

b) $3\cos 2x° + 2\cos x° - 3 = 0$

Hint You will need to use the quadratic formula.

5 Solve the following equations for $0 \leqslant x \leqslant 2\pi$:

a) $\sin 2x - 2\cos x = 0$ b) $\cos 2x + \cos x = 0$ c) $2\cos 2x + 2\sin x = 0$

6 Solve the following equations for $0 \leqslant x \leqslant 2\pi$, giving your answers correct to two decimal places:

a) $3\cos 2x - 4\cos x - 2 = 0$

b) $2\cos 2x - \cos x = 0$

Hint You will need to use the quadratic formula.

7 Solve the equation $2\sin 2x° - 1 = 0$, $0 \leqslant x \leqslant 360$.

8 Solve the equation $(\sin\theta + \cos\theta)^2 = 2$, $0 \leqslant \theta \leqslant 2\pi$.

9 Given that $(\sin\alpha + \cos\beta)^2 + (\cos\alpha + \sin\beta)^2 = 3$, find two possible values of angle $(\alpha + \beta)$ between 0 and 2π. ACE

Hint You do not need to use the double-angle formula to solve the equation in Q7.

Checkout

1 Solve the equation $5\sin 2x° - \sin x° = 0$, $0 \leqslant x \leqslant 360$.

2 Solve the equation $6\cos 2x° - 5\cos x° + 4 = 0$, $0 \leqslant x \leqslant 360$.

Summary

Trigonometric Equations 1

1 To solve equations such as

* $\sin 2x - \cos x = 0$, substitute $2\sin x \cos x$ for $\sin 2x$
* $2\cos 2x - 4\cos x - 1 = 0$, substitute $2\cos^2 x - 1$ for $\cos 2x$
* $\cos 2x - 4\sin x + 5 = 0$, substitute $1 - 2\sin^2 x$ for $\cos 2x$

CHAPTER 9 The Wave Function

Functions such as $f(x) = a\sin x$ and $f(x) = b\cos x$ can be described as wave functions. When we add together a sine and cosine function with the same period, the new function $f(x) = a\sin x + b\cos x$ is also a wave function. As a result we can express the sum of the two functions as a single trigonometric function. By doing this we can solve many problems in trigonometry.

What I am learning

* How to solve equations of the type $k\sin\alpha = a$ and $k\cos\alpha = b$
* How to express $a\sin x + b\cos x$ in the forms $k\cos(x \pm \alpha)$ and $k\sin(x \pm \alpha)$
* How to find the maximum and minimum values of $a\sin x + b\cos x$
* How to sketch the graph of $y = a\sin x + b\cos x$
* How to express functions such as $f(x) = 3\sin x° - 4\cos x°$ in the form $f(x) = k\sin(x + \alpha)°$, where $k > 0$ and $0 < \alpha < 360$.

What I should already know/be able to do

* Use the addition formulae for $\sin(A \pm B)$ and $\cos(A \pm B)$
* Use the identities $\sin^2 x + \cos^2 x = 1$ and $\tan x = \dfrac{\sin x}{\cos x}$
* Use the CAST diagram to find the quadrant of an angle
* Sketch graphs of the form $y = k\sin(x - \alpha)$ and $= k\cos(x - \alpha)$

Quick check!

1 Write down an expression for $\cos(x - \alpha)$.

2 If $\sin x° = \frac{3}{5}$, $0 \leqslant x \leqslant 360$, and $\cos x° = -\frac{4}{5}$, $0 \leqslant x \leqslant 360$, find the value of x.

3 Sketch the graph of $y = 4\cos(x - 45)°$, $0 \leqslant x \leqslant 360$.

Quick check! – *Solutions*

1 $\cos x \cos\alpha + \sin x \sin\alpha$

2 $x = 143{\cdot}1$

3

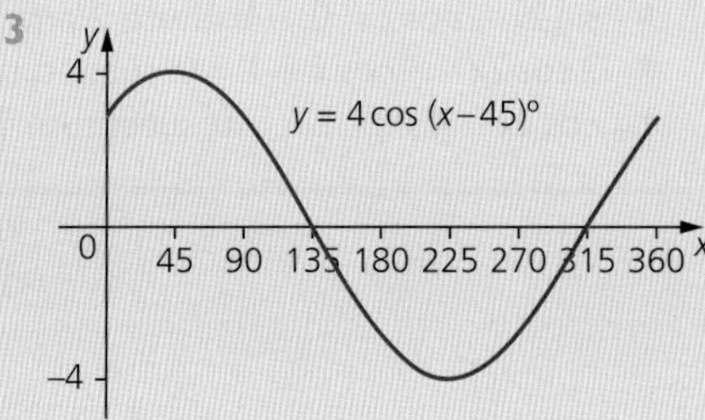

Trigonometric Skills

Introduction

The two most basic wave functions are $f(x) = \sin x$ and $f(x) = \cos x$. You are familiar with their graphs. Suppose you add these two functions together to form a new function $f(x) = \sin x + \cos x$. What would the graph of this function look like? If you have a graphing calculator check what this graph looks like.

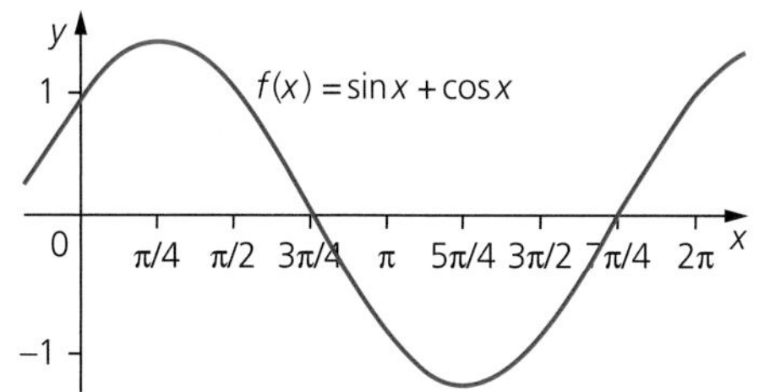

You can see that the amplitude has changed (in fact it has increased) and that there is a phase shift. This graph also shows a wave function. The graph appears to be a function of the form $f(x) = k\cos(x - \alpha)$.

In fact it is the graph of the function $f(x) = \sqrt{2}\cos\left(x - \frac{\pi}{4}\right)$.

You will study functions of this type in this chapter.

Solving equations of the type $k \sin \alpha = a$ and $k \cos \alpha = b$

It is an essential part of this chapter that you are able to solve simultaneous equations of the type $k\sin\alpha = a$ and $k\cos\alpha = b$. Unlike simultaneous equations you may have solved before, you solve for each variable separately (no substitution is required) using the identities $\sin^2 x + \cos^2 x = 1$ and $\tan x = \frac{\sin x}{\cos x}$.

Example

Solve the pair of equations $\begin{cases} k\cos\alpha° = 8 \\ k\sin\alpha° = -6 \end{cases}$ for $k > 0$ and $0 < \alpha < 360$.

SOLUTION

To find k, start by squaring both equations and then add them:

$k^2\cos^2\alpha° = 64$ and $k^2\sin^2\alpha° = 36$

$\Rightarrow k^2\cos^2\alpha° + k^2\sin^2\alpha° = 64 + 36 = 100$

$\Rightarrow k^2(\cos^2\alpha° + \sin^2\alpha°) = 100$

$\Rightarrow k^2 = 100$ (because $\cos^2\alpha° + \sin^2\alpha° = 1$)

$\Rightarrow k = 10$

To find α, divide the equations, putting the equation involving sine in the numerator:

$\frac{k\sin\alpha°}{k\cos\alpha°} = \frac{-6}{8} \Rightarrow \tan\alpha° = -\frac{6}{8}$ $\left(\text{because } \tan x = \frac{\sin x}{\cos x}\right)$

You know that cosine is + (from $k\cos\alpha° = 8$) and sine is − (from $k\sin\alpha° = -6$), so α is in the fourth quadrant (using the CAST diagram).

S	A ✓
✓ T	✓✓ C

Hence $\tan\alpha° = -\frac{6}{8} \quad \Rightarrow \quad \alpha = 323{\cdot}1$

In this type of example, $\alpha°$ is called the **auxiliary angle**.

Remember that, in common with other simultaneous equations, you can check both solutions by substituting them into the original equations.

Exercise 9.1

(Do **NOT** use a calculator for question 2.)

1 Solve the following pairs of equations where $k > 0$ and $0 < \alpha < 360$:

a) $k\sin\alpha° = 1$ and $k\cos\alpha° = 1$

b) $k\sin\alpha° = 3$ and $k\cos\alpha° = 4$

c) $k\sin\alpha° = 2$ and $k\cos\alpha° = -1$

d) $k\sin\alpha° = -5$ and $k\cos\alpha° = 12$

e) $k\sin\alpha° = \sqrt{2}$ and $k\cos\alpha° = 1$

f) $k\sin\alpha° = -1$ and $k\cos\alpha° = -3$

2 Solve the following pairs of equations where $k > 0$ and $0 < \alpha < 2\pi$:

a) $k\sin\alpha° = 1$ and $k\cos\alpha° = \sqrt{3}$

b) $k\sin\alpha° = -2$ and $k\cos\alpha° = 2$

Expressing *a* sin *x* + *b* cos *x* in the form *k* cos(*x* ± *α*) or *k* sin(*x* ± *α*)

When you are given a function such as $a\sin x + b\cos x$, it can be expressed in four different but equivalent forms: $k\cos(x+\alpha)$, $k\cos(x-\alpha)$, $k\sin(x+\alpha)$ or $k\sin(x-\alpha)$. It is very helpful to solve problems and draw graphs when functions such as $a\sin x + b\cos x$ are written as a single function rather than as the sum of two separate functions. In order to do this, you must use the addition formulae.

Example 1

Express $\cos x° - 3\sin x°$ in the form $k\sin(x+\alpha)°$, where $k > 0$ and $0 < \alpha < 360$.

SOLUTION

Start by referring to the addition formula for $\sin(A+B)$:

$\cos x° - 3\sin x° = k\sin(x+\alpha)°$ becomes $\cos x° - 3\sin x° = k(\sin x° \cos\alpha° + \cos x° \sin\alpha°)$

$\Rightarrow \cos x° - 3\sin x° = k\sin x° \cos\alpha° + k\cos x° \sin\alpha°$

Now equate coefficients of $\cos x°$ (terms in red) and $\sin x°$ (terms in green), leading to $k\sin\alpha° = 1$ and $k\cos\alpha° = -3$.

Next, use the method from the previous section to find k and α:

$k^2 = 1^2 + (-3)^2 = 1 + 9 = 10 \Rightarrow k = \sqrt{10}$ and $\tan\alpha° = \dfrac{k\sin\alpha°}{k\cos\alpha°} = \dfrac{1}{-3}$

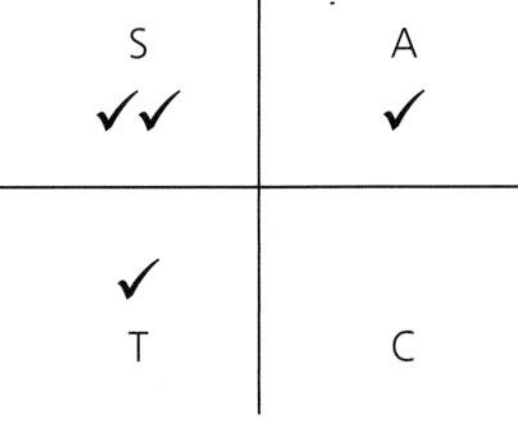

Check the signs to see that sine is + and cosine is –, meaning that α is in the second quadrant.

Hence $\tan\alpha° = -\dfrac{1}{3} \Rightarrow \alpha = 161{\cdot}6$

and so $\cos x° - 3\sin x° = \sqrt{10}\sin(x + 161{\cdot}6)°$.

Be careful when you are equating coefficients. You may not be able to colour the different parts of the equation, but you could underline one pair.

Example 2

Express $3\sin x° - 4\cos x°$ in the form $k\cos(x+\alpha)°$ where $k > 0$ and $0 < \alpha < 360$.

SOLUTION

$3\sin x° - 4\cos x° = k\cos(x+\alpha)° = k\cos x° \cos\alpha° - k\sin x° \sin\alpha°$

Hence $k\sin\alpha° = -3$ and $k\cos\alpha° = -4$

$k = \sqrt{(-3)^2 + (-4)^2} = \sqrt{9+16} = \sqrt{25} = 5$ and $\tan\alpha° = \dfrac{-3}{-4}$

As sine and cosine are both negative, $\tan\alpha° = \dfrac{k\sin\alpha°}{k\cos\alpha°} = \dfrac{3}{4} \Rightarrow \alpha = 216{\cdot}9$.

Hence $3\sin x° - 4\cos x° = 5\cos(x + 216{\cdot}9)°$

Exercise 9.2

(Do **NOT** use a calculator for question 5.)

1 Express the following in the form $k\cos(x-\alpha)^\circ$, where $k>0$ and $0<\alpha<360$: HPQ

a) $\sin x^\circ - \cos x^\circ$ c) $6\cos x^\circ - 4\sin x^\circ$ b) $4\sin x^\circ - 3\cos x^\circ$ d) $2\sin x^\circ - 2\cos x^\circ$

2 Express the following in the form $k\cos(x+\alpha)^\circ$, where $k>0$ and $0<\alpha<360$:

a) $\sqrt{5}\cos x^\circ + \sin x^\circ$ c) $-\cos x^\circ - 4\sin x^\circ$ b) $\sqrt{3}\cos x^\circ - 7\sin x^\circ$ d) $-24\sin x^\circ + 7\cos x$

3 Express the following in the form $k\sin(x+\alpha)^\circ$, where $k>0$ and $0<\alpha<360$:

a) $2\cos x^\circ - \sin x^\circ$ c) $\sqrt{8}\cos x^\circ - \sin x^\circ$ b) $15\cos x^\circ + 8\sin x^\circ$ d) $-2\sin x^\circ + 3\cos x^\circ$

4 Express the following in the form $k\sin(x-\alpha)^\circ$, where $k>0$ and $0<\alpha<360$:

a) $\sin x^\circ - \sqrt{15}\cos x^\circ$ c) $-\cos x^\circ + 3\sin x^\circ$ b) $4\sin x^\circ - 2\cos x^\circ$ d) $5\cos x^\circ + 4\sin x^\circ$

5 Express the following in the form $k\cos(x-\alpha)$, where $k>0$ and $0<\alpha<2\pi$:

a) $\cos x - \sqrt{3}\sin x$ b) $4\cos x - 4\sin x$

6 Express $9\sin x - 12\cos x$ in the form $k\sin(x-\alpha)$, where $k>0$ and $0<\alpha<2\pi$.

Maximum and minimum values

You can use k to find the maximum and minimum values of the function $a\sin x + b\cos x$ and the auxiliary angle to find the corresponding values of x and the zeros of the function. These facts will be particularly useful if you are asked to sketch graphs.

In assessments you will normally be told which of the four forms, $k\cos(x+\alpha)$, $k\cos(x-\alpha)$, $k\sin(x+\alpha)$ or $k\sin(x-\alpha)$, to use. If you are not told such information, you can choose any one of the four with $k\cos(x-\alpha)$ being recommended as it is simplest to get the signs for the tangent ratio when calculating α.

There are further suggestions as to which form is most suitable in the investigation at the end of the next chapter.

Example

Find the maximum and minimum values of the function $f(x)=\sqrt{5}\sin x^\circ + 2\cos x^\circ$, the corresponding values of x and the zeros of the function in the interval $0 \leqslant x \leqslant 360$.

SOLUTION

We shall express $\sqrt{5}\sin x^\circ + 2\cos x^\circ$ in the form $k\cos(x-\alpha)^\circ$ and then use the following key facts (from consideration of the graph of $y=\cos x^\circ$) to complete the question:

* $\cos x^\circ$ has a maximum value of 1 at 0 and 360
* $\cos x^\circ$ has a minimum value of -1 at 180
* $\cos x^\circ$ has zeros (the values of x such that $\cos x = 0$) at 90 and 270

$\sqrt{5}\sin x^\circ + 2\cos x^\circ = k\cos(x-\alpha)^\circ = k\cos x^\circ \cos\alpha^\circ + k\sin x^\circ \sin\alpha^\circ$

Hence $k\sin\alpha^\circ = \sqrt{5}$ and $k\cos\alpha^\circ = 2$

$k=\sqrt{\left(\sqrt{5}\right)^2+2^2}=\sqrt{5+4}=\sqrt{9}=3$ and $\tan\alpha^\circ = \dfrac{k\sin\alpha^\circ}{k\cos\alpha^\circ}=\dfrac{\sqrt{5}}{2}$

As sine and cosine are both positive, $\tan\alpha^\circ = \dfrac{\sqrt{5}}{2} \Rightarrow \alpha = 48{\cdot}2$

Hence $\sqrt{5}\sin x^\circ + 2\cos x^\circ = 3\cos(x-48{\cdot}2)^\circ$

The maximum value of the function is therefore 3.

It occurs when $x-48{\cdot}2=0 \Rightarrow x=48{\cdot}2$

The minimum value of the function is -3.

It occurs when $x-48{\cdot}2=180 \Rightarrow x=180+48{\cdot}2=228{\cdot}2$

The zeros occur when $x-48{\cdot}2=90,\ 270 \Rightarrow x=138{\cdot}2,\ 318{\cdot}2$

Hint

If you are asked to find the maximum and minimum values and the zeros of a sine function, remember that:

- sin x° has a maximum value of 1 at 90
- sin x° has a minimum value of –1 at 270
- sin x° has zeros at 0, 180, 360.

Exercise 9.3

1 Find the maximum and minimum values of the function $f(x) = 4\cos(x - 25)°$, the corresponding values of x and the zeros of the function in the interval $0 \leqslant x \leqslant 360$.

2 Find the maximum and minimum values of the function $f(x) = \sqrt{10}\cos(x - 17)°$, the corresponding values of x and the zeros of the function in the interval $0 \leqslant x \leqslant 360$.

3 **a)** Express $\sqrt{3}\sin x° - 5\cos x°$ in the form $k\sin(x - \alpha)°$, where $k > 0$ and $0 < \alpha < 360$.

b) Hence find the maximum and minimum values of the function $f(x) = \sqrt{3}\sin x° - 5\cos x°$, the corresponding values of x and the zeros of the function in the interval $0 \leqslant x \leqslant 360$.

4 Find the maximum and minimum values of the following functions, the corresponding values of x and the zeros of the functions in the interval $0 \leqslant x \leqslant 360$:

a) $f(x) = \sqrt{2}\sin x° + 3\cos x°$ **b)** $f(x) = -2\sin x° - 4\cos x°$ **c)** $f(x) = 6\sin x° - 10\cos x°$

5 Find the maximum and minimum values of the function $f(x) = \sin x - \cos x$, the corresponding values of x and the zeros of the function in the interval $0 \leqslant x \leqslant 2\pi$.

Sketching the graph of y = *a* sin x + *b* cos x

Example

Sketch the graph of $y = \sqrt{5}\sin x° + 2\cos x°$ in the interval $0 \leqslant x \leqslant 360$.

SOLUTION

This is the same function as in the previous section so we can use the information from there to draw the graph.

$y = \sqrt{5}\sin x° + 2\cos x° = 3\cos(x - 48{\cdot}2)°$

We found that the graph lies between –3 and 3 with a maximum turning point at (48·2, 3) and a minimum turning point at (228·2, –3). From the zeros of the function, we can see that the graph crosses the *x*-axis at (138·2, 0) and (318·2, 0).

We can also find where the graph crosses the *y*-axis by putting $x = 0$ into the equation $y = \sqrt{5}\sin x° + 2\cos x°$ (it is simpler to use the original equation to find the *y*-intercept). We obtain (0, 2).

We can also find the right-hand end point of the graph by putting $x = 360$ in the equation $y = \sqrt{5}\sin x° + 2\cos x°$. We obtain (360, 2).

We can now sketch the graph, annotating all the key data.

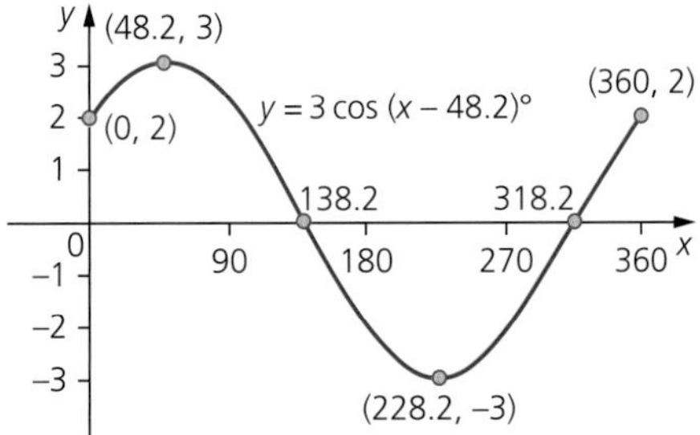

Exercise 9.4

1 Use your answers to question 4 in Exercise 9.3 to sketch the graphs of:

a) $y = \sqrt{2}\sin x° + 3\cos x°,\ 0 \leqslant x \leqslant 360$

b) $y = -2\sin x° - 4\cos x°,\ 0 \leqslant x \leqslant 360$

c) $y = 6\sin x° - 10\cos x°,\ 0 \leqslant x \leqslant 360$

2 **a)** Express $\sin x° + 4\cos x°$ in the form $k\cos(x - \alpha)°$ where $k > 0$ and $0 < \alpha < 360$.

b) Find the maximum and minimum values of $\sin x° + 4\cos x°$ and determine the values of x, in the interval $0 \leqslant x \leqslant 360$, at which these maximum and minimum values occur.

c) Find where the graph of $y = \sin x° + 4\cos x°$ crosses the y-axis and hence sketch the graph of $y = \sin x° + 3\cos x°$, where $0 \leqslant x \leqslant 360$.

3 Use the answer to question 5 in Exercise 9.3 to sketch the graph of $y = \sin x - \cos x$ in the interval $0 \leqslant x \leqslant 2\pi$.

Checkout

1 Express $2\cos x° - 3\sin x°$ in the form $k\cos(x + \alpha)°$ where $k > 0$ and $0 < \alpha < 360$.

2 Express $\sqrt{3}\cos x - \sin x$ in the form $k\sin(x + \alpha)$ where $k > 0$ and $0 < \alpha < 2\pi$.

3 a) Express $7\sin x° - \cos x°$ in the form $k\sin(x - \alpha)°$ where $k > 0$ and $0 < \alpha < 360$.

b) Hence find the maximum and minimum values of the function $f(x) = 7\sin x° - \cos x°$, the corresponding values of x and the zeros of the function in the interval $0 \leqslant x \leqslant 360$.

c) Find where the graph of $y = 7\ \sin x° - \cos x°$ crosses the y-axis and hence sketch the graph of $y = 7\sin x° - \cos x°$, where $0 \leqslant x \leqslant 360$.

Summary

The Wave Function

1 Functions such as $a \sin x + b \cos x$ can be expressed in any of the four forms $k\cos(x \pm \alpha)$ and $k\sin(x \pm \alpha)$, where $k = \sqrt{a^2 + b^2},\ k > 0$ and $\tan \alpha = \dfrac{k\sin\alpha}{k\cos\alpha}$.

2 The maximum and minimum values of functions expressed in any of the four forms $k\cos(x \pm \alpha)$ and $k\sin(x \pm \alpha)$ and k and $-k$ respectively.

CHAPTER

Trigonometric Equations 2

In the second of two chapters on trigonometric equations, we shall study equations which involve expressions of the form $a \sin x + b \cos x$.

What I am learning

- How to solve equations of the form $a \sin x + b \cos x = c$
- How to solve equations of the form $a \sin px + b \cos qx = c$
- How to answer questions like this:
  - a) Express $6 \cos 2x° - 4 \sin 2x°$ in the form $k \cos(2x - \alpha)°$, where $k > 0$ and $0 < \alpha < 360$.
  - b) Hence solve the equation $6 \cos 2x° - 4 \sin 2x° - 3 = 0, 0 \leqslant x \leqslant 360$.

What I should already know/be able to do

- Express $a \sin x + b \cos x$ in the forms $k \cos(x \pm \alpha)$ and $k \sin(x \pm \alpha)$
- Find the maximum and minimum values of $a \sin x + b \cos x$
- Sketch the graph of $y = a \sin x + b \cos x$

Quick check!

1 Express $3 \cos x° + 4 \sin x°$ in the form $k \cos(x - \alpha)°$, where $k > 0$ and $0 < \alpha < 360$.

2 Find the maximum and minimum values of $3 \cos x° + 4 \sin x°$, the corresponding values of x and the zeros of the function in the interval $0 < x < 360$.

3 Sketch the graph of $3 \cos x° + 4 \sin x°, 0 < x < 360$.

Quick check! – *Solutions*

1 $3 \cos x° + 4 \sin x° = 5 \cos (x - 53{\cdot}1)°$

2 Maximum value = 5 when $x = 53{\cdot}1$; minimum value = −5 when $x = 233{\cdot}1$; zeros when $x = 143{\cdot}1$ and $323{\cdot}1$

3

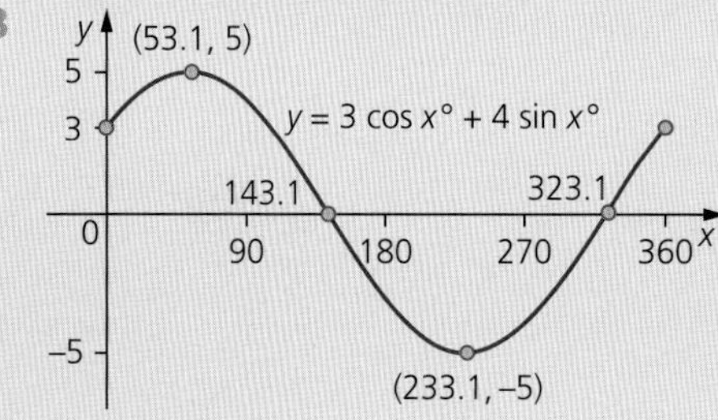

Solving equations of the form $a \sin x + b \cos x = c$

We shall look at how to solve equations of the form $a \sin x + b \cos x = c$. Before we can do this, however, $a \sin x + b \cos x = c$ must be expressed in one of the forms $k \cos(x \pm \alpha)$ or $k \sin(x \pm \alpha)$. As a result questions on this type of equation often occur in two (or more) parts.

Example

a) Express $\sin x^\circ + 5 \cos x^\circ$ in the form $k \cos(x - \alpha)^\circ$, where $k > 0$ and $0 < \alpha < 360$.
b) Hence solve the equation $\sin x^\circ + 5 \cos x^\circ = 2$ for $0 < x < 360$.

SOLUTION

a) $\sin x^\circ + 5 \cos x^\circ = k \cos(x - \alpha)^\circ = k \cos x^\circ \cos \alpha^\circ + k \sin x^\circ \sin \alpha^\circ$
Hence $k \sin \alpha^\circ = 1$ and $k \cos \alpha^\circ = 5$.

$k = \sqrt{1^2 + 5^2} = \sqrt{1 + 25} = \sqrt{26}$ and $\tan \alpha^\circ \ \dfrac{k \sin \alpha^\circ}{k \cos \alpha^\circ} = \dfrac{1}{5}$

As sine and cosine are both positive, $\tan \alpha^\circ = \dfrac{1}{5} \Rightarrow \alpha = 11 \cdot 3$

S	A
✓	✓✓
T	✓ C

Hence $\sin x^\circ + 5 \cos x^\circ = \sqrt{26} \cos(x - 11{\cdot}3)^\circ$.

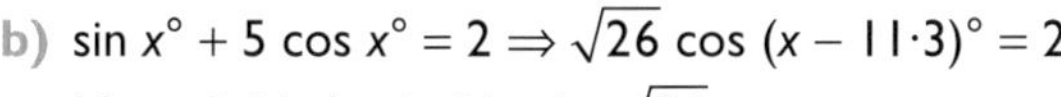

b) $\sin x^\circ + 5 \cos x^\circ = 2 \Rightarrow \sqrt{26} \cos(x - 11{\cdot}3)^\circ = 2$
Now divide both sides by $\sqrt{26}$:

$\cos(x - 11{\cdot}3)^\circ = \dfrac{2}{\sqrt{26}}$

There are two solutions in the first and fourth quadrants as cosine is positive, so $x - 11{\cdot}3 = 66{\cdot}9$ or $293{\cdot}1$.
Hence $x = 78{\cdot}2$ or $304{\cdot}4$.

Exercise 10.1

1 Solve the equation $4 \cos(x - 28)^\circ = 3$, $0 \leqslant x \leqslant 360$.

2 Solve the equation $7 \sin(x + 70)^\circ = 5$, $0 \leqslant x \leqslant 360$.

3 **a)** Express $2 \sin x^\circ + 4 \cos x^\circ$ in the form $k \sin(x + \alpha)^\circ$, where $k > 0$ and $0 < \alpha < 360$.
b) Hence solve the equation $2 \sin x^\circ + 4 \cos x^\circ = 2$ for $0 \leqslant x \leqslant 360$.

4 **a)** Express $\cos x^\circ + 3 \sin x^\circ$ in the form $k \cos(x - \alpha)^\circ$, where $k > 0$ and $0 < \alpha < 360$. HPQ
b) Hence solve the equation $\cos x^\circ + 3 \sin x^\circ = 1$ for $0 \leqslant x \leqslant 360$.

5 **a)** Express $\sqrt{2} \sin x^\circ - 3 \cos x^\circ$ in the form $k \sin(x - \alpha)^\circ$, where $k > 0$ and $0 < \alpha < 360$.
b) Hence solve the equation $\sqrt{2} \sin x^\circ - 3 \cos x^\circ = 1$ for $0 \leqslant x \leqslant 360$.

6 **a)** Express $-\sin x^\circ - 2 \cos x^\circ$ in the form $k \cos(x + \alpha)^\circ$, where $k > 0$ and $0 < \alpha < 360$.
b) Hence solve the equation $-\sin x^\circ - 2 \cos x^\circ = 2$ for $0 \leqslant x \leqslant 360$.

7 **a)** Express $6 \sin x^\circ - 8 \cos x^\circ$ in the form $k \sin(x - \alpha)^\circ$, where $k > 0$ and $0 < \alpha < 360$.
b) Hence solve the equation $6 \sin x^\circ - 8 \cos x^\circ = 9$ for $0 \leqslant x \leqslant 360$.

8 Solve the equation $11 \cos x^\circ + 60 \sin x^\circ = 48$ for $0 \leqslant x \leqslant 360$.

9 By using the form $k \cos(x - \alpha)$, find the exact solutions of the following equations in the interval $0 \leqslant x \leqslant 2\pi$:
a) $\cos x + \sin x = 1$
b) $\sqrt{3} \cos x + \sin x = 1$

10 Solve the following equation giving your answer correct to three decimal places: ACE
$24 \sin x + 7 \cos x = 14$, $0 < x < 2\pi$

Solving equations of the form $a \sin px + b \cos px = c$

We can extend the ideas already used to solve equations where multiple angles are involved. This has many practical applications, e.g. the height of the water in a harbour depending on the tides, the motion of an object attached to a spring, the frequency of sound waves, etc. These areas are worth further investigation. Study the following examples carefully.

Example 1

a) Express $6 \cos 2x° - 4 \sin 2x°$ in the form $k \cos(2x + \alpha)°$, where $k > 0$ and $0 < \alpha < 360$.
b) Hence solve the equation $6 \cos 2x° - 4 \sin 2x° - 3 = 0$, $0 \leqslant x < 360$.

SOLUTION

a) $6\cos 2x° - 4\sin 2x° = k\cos(2x+\alpha)° = k\cos 2x° \cos\alpha° - k\sin 2x° \sin\alpha°$
Hence $k \sin \alpha° = 4$ and $k \cos \alpha° = 6$

$k = \sqrt{4^2+6^2} = \sqrt{16+36} = \sqrt{52}$ and $\tan\alpha° = \frac{k\sin\alpha°}{k\cos\alpha°} = \frac{4}{6}$

As sine and cosine are both positive, $\tan\alpha° = \frac{4}{6} \Rightarrow \alpha = 33{\cdot}7$

Hence $6\cos 2x° - 4\sin 2x° = \sqrt{52}\cos(2x+33{\cdot}7)°$

b) $6\cos 2x° - 4\sin 2x° - 3 = 0 \Rightarrow \sqrt{52}\cos(2x+33{\cdot}7)° - 3 = 0$

Hence $\sqrt{52}\cos(2x+33{\cdot}7)° = 3 \Rightarrow \cos(2x+33{\cdot}7)° = \frac{3}{\sqrt{52}}$

Hence $2x + 33{\cdot}7 = 65{\cdot}4, 294{\cdot}6, 425{\cdot}4, 654{\cdot}6$
Hence $x = 15{\cdot}9, 130{\cdot}4, 195{\cdot}9, 310{\cdot}4$

Now we shall look at a practical example from a real-life situation.

Example 2

Due to tidal variations, the depth of water in a harbour is given by the formula

$$D(t) = 4 + 2(\cos 30t° - 3 \sin 30t°)$$

where $D(t)$ is the depth of water in metres and t is the time in hours after midnight on a Monday night.

a) Express $\cos 30t° - 3 \sin 30t°$ in the form $k \cos(30t + \alpha)°$ where $k > 0$ and $0 < \alpha < 360$.
b) A boat needs at least a depth of 9 metres of water to leave the harbour. What is the earliest time on Tuesday that the boat can leave the harbour?

SOLUTION

a) $\cos 30t° - 3\sin 30t° = k\cos(30t+\alpha)° = k\cos 30t° \cos\alpha° - k\sin 30t° \sin\alpha°$
Hence $k \sin \alpha° = 3$ and $k \cos \alpha° = 1$

$k = \sqrt{3^2+1^2} = \sqrt{10}$ and $\tan \alpha° = \frac{k\sin\alpha°}{k\cos\alpha°} = \frac{3}{1}$

As sine and cosine are positive, $\tan \alpha° = 3 \Rightarrow \alpha = 71{\cdot}565$
Hence $\cos 30t° - 3\sin 30t° = \sqrt{10}\cos(30t+71{\cdot}565)°$

b) Solve the equation $4 + 2(\cos 30t° - 3 \sin 30t°) = 9$. Using the solution to part (a), this becomes
$4 + 2\sqrt{10}\cos(30t+71{\cdot}565)° = 9$.
This leads to $2\sqrt{10}\cos(30t + 71{\cdot}565)° = 5 \Rightarrow \cos(30t+71{\cdot}565)° = \frac{5}{2\sqrt{10}}$.
As the cosine is positive, there are two solutions in the first and fourth quadrants.
The earliest time occurs when
$30t + 71{\cdot}565 = 37{\cdot}761$ or $30t + 71{\cdot}565 = 360 - 37{\cdot}761 = 322{\cdot}239 \Rightarrow t = -1{\cdot}127$ or $t = 8{\cdot}356$.
The negative answer is before midnight, so the earliest time the boat can leave is 8·356 hours after midnight, that is at 0822 on Tuesday morning.

Exercise 10.2

1 The number of hours, h, of daylight in a city on a given day is given by the formula

$$h=\frac{1}{3}\left[18+36\sin\left(\frac{360x}{365}\right)^{\circ}\right]$$

where x is the number of days after the 21st April.

a) The summer solstice is the day with the most hours of daylight. How many hours of daylight will there be on the summer solstice?

b) How many days after the 21st April will the summer solstice occur?

2 **a)** Express $4\cos 3x^{\circ} + 3\sin 3x^{\circ}$ in the form $k\cos(3x - \alpha)^{\circ}$, where $k > 0$ and $0 \leqslant x \leqslant 360$. HPQ

b) Hence solve the equation $4\cos 3x^{\circ} + 3\sin 3x^{\circ} = -2$, $0 \leqslant x \leqslant 360$.

3 **a)** Express $5\cos 2x^{\circ} - 2\sin 2x^{\circ}$ in the form $k\cos(2x + \alpha)^{\circ}$, where $k > 0$ and $0 \leqslant x \leqslant 360$.

b) Hence solve the equation $5\cos 2x^{\circ} - 2\sin 2x^{\circ} = 4$, $0 \leqslant x \leqslant 360$.

4 The frequency, f cycles per second, of a fire alarm in a college is given by the formula $f = 750 + 120\sin 180t^{\circ} + 120\sqrt{3}\cos 180t^{\circ}$ where t seconds is the length of time for which the alarm has been switched on. ACE

It is known that when the frequency drops below 550 cycles per second the fire alarm will be inaudible to some people in the building.

Will the fire alarm ever be inaudible to some people in the building? Justify your answer.

5 The height, h centimetres, of the water above the mean sea level in a harbour t hours after midnight one Wednesday is given by the formula $h = 80(2\cos 30t^{\circ} + \sin 30t^{\circ})$.

a) Express h in the form $k\cos(30t^{\circ} - \alpha)$.

b) Find the times of high tide and low tide.

c) Find the times on Thursday when the tide was 60 centimetres above mean sea level.

Which formula?

Investigation

Suppose you are asked to solve the equation $4\sin x^{\circ} - 3\cos x^{\circ} = 3{\cdot}5$, $0 \leqslant x \leqslant 360$, and you start by expressing $4\sin x^{\circ} - 3\cos x^{\circ}$ in the form $k\cos(x + \alpha)^{\circ}$.

Check that $4\sin x^{\circ} - 3\cos x^{\circ} = 5\cos(x + 233{\cdot}1)^{\circ}$.

If you continue to solve $5\cos(x + 233{\cdot}1)^{\circ} = 3{\cdot}5$, you should find that $x = -187{\cdot}5$ or $81{\cdot}3$. One of these solutions ($-187{\cdot}5$) is outside the required interval. It can happen sometimes that you get a solution which is less than zero or greater than 360. To find the corresponding solution in the interval $0 \leqslant x \leqslant 360$, simply add or subtract 360.

Therefore the solutions to the above equation are $x = 81{\cdot}3$ or $-187{\cdot}5 + 360 = 172{\cdot}5$.

In order to avoid this happening it would have been better to choose the formula from $k\cos(x \pm \alpha)$ or $k\sin(x \pm \alpha)$ which ensures that α is an acute angle, although in assessments you are usually told the required form.

The following ideas will help you to make α an acute angle when asked to solve an equation and not given a starting point.

- For expressions such as $3\sin x + 4\cos x$, use $k\sin(x + \alpha)$.
- For expressions such as $3\sin x - 4\cos x$, use $k\sin(x - \alpha)$.
- For expressions such as $3\cos x + 4\sin x$, use $k\cos(x - \alpha)$.
- For expressions such as $3\cos x - 4\sin x$, use $k\cos(x + \alpha)$.

Investigate why these four ideas lead to α being an acute angle.

Investigate how to make α an acute angle for an expression such as $-3\sin x - 4\cos x$.

It is worth noting that the form $k\cos(x - \alpha)$ is a simple form if you quickly need to express an expression of the form $a\sin x + b\cos x$ in one of the forms $k\cos(x \pm \alpha)$ or $k\sin(x \pm \alpha)$. The quadrant for α can be found by inspection in this case. Simply choose the quadrant in which the point with coordinates (b, a) lies.

For example to express 3 sin $x°$ – 4 cos $x°$ in the form k cos(x – α)°, you can see that $k=\sqrt{3^2+4^2}=5$ and $\tan\alpha=-\frac{3}{4}$ with α in the second quadrant as this is the quadrant for the point (–4, 3). Hence α = 143·1 and 3 sin $x°$ – 4 cos $x°$ = 5 cos(x – 143·1)°

Investigate why this works for k cos(x – α).

Now try the following example:

Example

Choose the expression from $k\cos(x \pm \alpha)°$ or $k\sin(x \pm \alpha)°$ which makes α an acute angle for the expression 6 sin $x°$ – cos $x°$ and use this expression to solve the equation 6 sin $x°$ – cos $x°$ = 3, $0 \leqslant x \leqslant 360$.

Checkout

1 a) Express 12 sin $x°$ – 16 cos $x°$ in the form $k\sin(x-\alpha)°$ where $k > 0$ and $0 \leqslant \alpha \leqslant 360$.
  b) Hence solve the equation 12 sin $x°$ – 16 cos $x°$ = 10, $0 \leqslant \alpha \leqslant 360$.

2 a) Express $\sqrt{6}\cos 2x° - 3\sin 2x°$ in the form $k\cos(2x+\alpha)°$ where $k > 0$ and $0 \leqslant \alpha \leqslant 360$.
  b) Hence solve the equation $\sqrt{6}\cos 2x° - 3\sin 2x° = 1$, $0 \leqslant \alpha \leqslant 360$.

Summary

Trigonometric Equations 2

1 Equations of the type 2 sin $x°$ + 7 cos $x°$ = 3 can be solved by expressing 2 sin $x°$ + 7 cos $x°$ in any of the four forms $k\cos(x \pm \alpha)°$ and $k\sin(x \pm \alpha)°$.

2 Equations of the type 3 sin $2x°$ + 4 cos $2x°$ = 1 can be solved by expressing 3 sin $2x°$ + 4 cos $2x°$ in any of the four forms $k\cos(2x \pm \alpha)°$ and $k\sin(2x \pm \alpha)°$.

CHAPTER 11

Functions

In this chapter you will study how to sketch the graphs of functions and look at composite and inverse functions.

What I am learning

- To understand the meaning of the terms domain, range and one–one correspondence
- To find the domain and range of a function
- To complete the square on a non-unitary quadratic expression
- To draw the graph of functions related to a given graph
- To sketch related exponential and logarithmic functions
- To find the formula for the composition of two functions
- To know the conditions for a function to have an inverse
- To sketch the graph of an inverse function
- To find a formula for an inverse function
- How to solve problems like this:
  A function f is given by the formula $f(x) = x^2 + 3$ where x is a member of the set of positive real numbers.
  a) State the range of $f(x)$.
  b) Find a formula for $f^{-1}(x)$.
  c) State the domain of $f^{-1}(x)$.
  d) State the range of $f^{-1}(x)$.

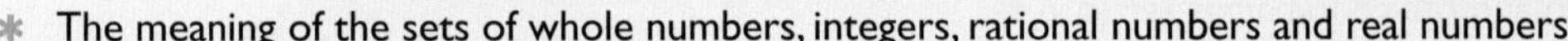

What I should already know/be able to do

- The meaning of the sets of whole numbers, integers, rational numbers and real numbers
- How to use functional notation
- How to complete the square
- How to sketch the graph of a quadratic function
- How to solve quadratic inequalities
- The graphs of the basic logarithmic and exponential functions
- The laws of logarithms
- The graphs of basic trigonometric functions

Quick check!

1 If $f(x) = 3x^2 - 6x + 2$, find the value of $f(-2)$.
2 Sketch the graph of the parabola $y = x^2$.
3 Express $x^2 + 6x + 3$ in the form $(x+p)^2 + q$.
4 Write down the turning point of the parabola with equation $y = x^2 + 6x + 3$.
5 Is the turning point of the parabola $y = x^2 + 6x + 3$ a maximum or a minimum?
6 Sketch the graph of the quadratic function $y = x^2 + 6x + 8$.
7 Solve the inequality $x^2 + 6x + 8 < 0$.
8 Express $\log_{10} 5 + \log_{10} 8$ as the logarithm of a single number.

Quick check! – *Solutions*

1 26

2

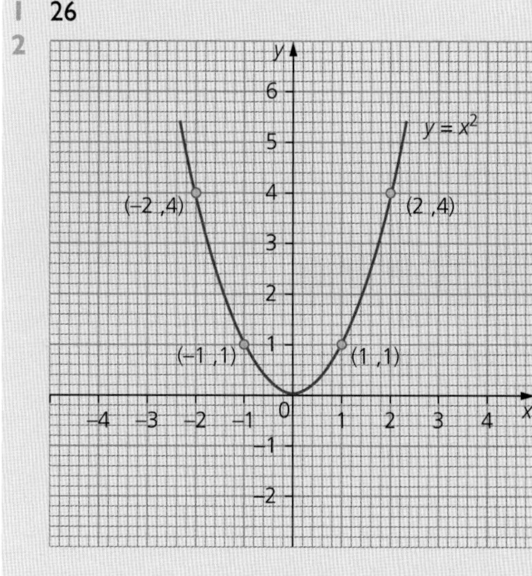

3 $(x+3)^2-6$

4 (−3, −6)

5 A minimum turning point

6

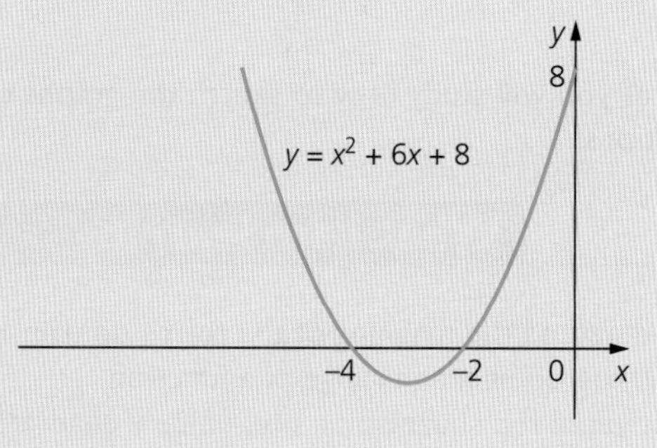

7 $-4 < x < -2$

8 $\log_{10} 40$

The domain and range of a function

A function is a special type of relationship between two sets of numbers.
It can be illustrated in an arrow diagram.

The **domain** of a function is a set of values put into the function (the x values).
The **range** of a function is the set of values coming out of the function (the y values). The **codomain** of a function is a set of values that includes the range, but may also include additional values beyond the range. The range is a subset of the codomain.

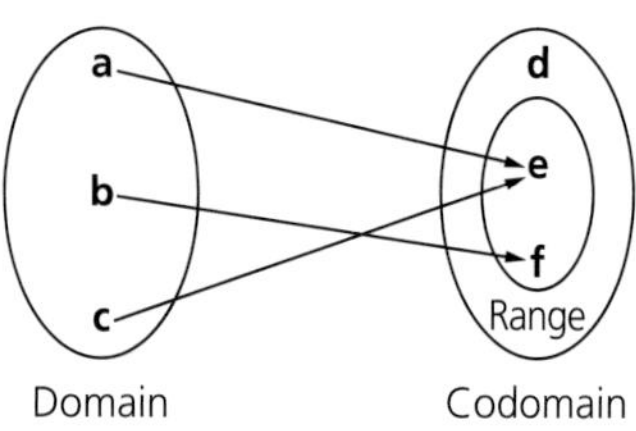

The arrow diagram here shows a function. It is a function because every member of the domain has exactly one image in the range. For this function the domain is the set {a, b, c}, the range is set {e, f} and the codomain is set {d, e, f}.

A special type of function is a one–one correspondence. An example is shown in the lower arrow diagram.

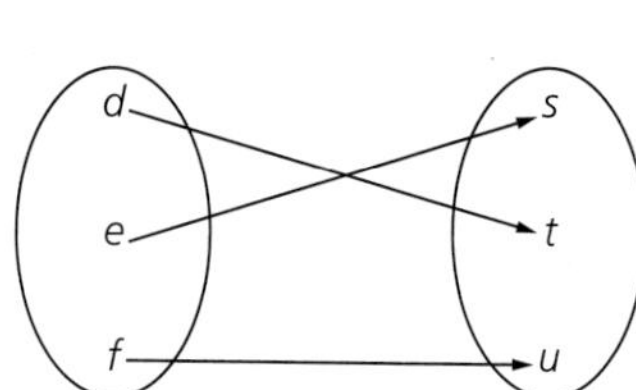

In this case the domain of the function is the set $\{d, e, f\}$ and the range is the set $\{s, t, u\}$. In a one–one correspondence all the members of the first set are paired off with a member of the second set. If the arrows are reversed another one–one correspondence is formed.

In most of the examples we shall study in this chapter the domain for each function will be the set of real numbers, R.

However, there will be important exceptions which we shall now investigate. The two most common exceptions are shown below.

1 Functions involving division (as division by zero is impossible).
2 Functions involving square roots (as the square root of a negative number is impossible).

Example 1

A function is given by $f(x) = \dfrac{4}{x+5}$. What is the largest possible domain of f?

SOLUTION

It is possible to find an image for every real number using this function with one exception because division by zero is impossible. If $x = -5$ there would be no related member in the range; therefore a suitable domain is $\{x : x \in R,\ x \neq -5\}$.

Hint The form of the solution $\{x : x \in R,\ x \neq -5\}$ is called set-builder notation and is a very complete way of stating the domain of the function. It means that x is a member of the set of all real numbers except for –5.

Example 2

A function is given by $f(x) = \sqrt{x-2}$. What is the largest possible domain of f?

SOLUTION

Because we cannot find the square root of a negative number, $x - 2 \geqslant 0$. Therefore a suitable domain is $\{x : x \in R,\ x \geqslant 2\}$.

Note If there are missing parts in the domain of a function, this will be visible when you look at the graph of the function. As an illustration, consider the graph of $y = \tan x°$ which you looked at earlier in trigonometry and part of which is shown below.

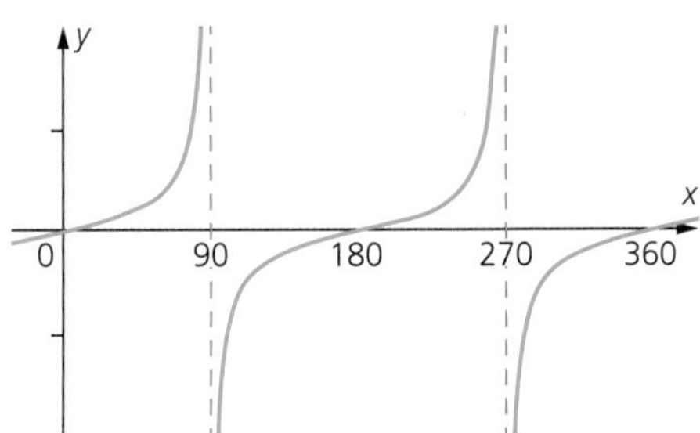

As we cannot find the values of $\tan 90°$, $\tan 270°$ and so on, we can see that there is a break in the continuity of the graph at these points.

Example 3

What is the range of the function $y = 2\sin x°$?

SOLUTION

Consider the graph of $y = 2\sin x°$ shown.

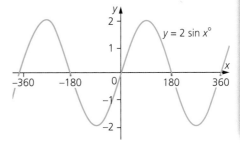

We can see that there are no solutions (y-values) less than –2 or greater than 2; therefore the range is $\{y : y \in R,\ -2 \leqslant y \leqslant 2\}$.

When you study a graph, remember that it is the graph of a function if the graph goes all the way across the page; for example $y = x^2$. It is a one–one correspondence if the graph goes all the way across the page *and* is never at the same height twice, for example $y = x^3$.

Exercise 11.1

1 Which two of the following functions are one–one correspondences?
$y = 1 - x^2$, $y = -x - 5$, $y = (x+2)^2$, $y = \cos x$, $y = 3 - x^3$

2 Find the largest possible domain for each of the following functions:

a) $f(x) = \sqrt{x}$ **b)** $f(x) = \frac{1}{x}$

c) $f(x) = \sqrt{2x - 4}$ **d)** $f(x) = \sqrt{(x-1)}$

e) $f(x) = \frac{2}{x-4}$ **f)** $f(x) = -\frac{5}{3x+9}$

g) $f(x) = \sqrt{(1-2x)}$ **h)** $f(x) = \frac{x}{5+x}$

3 State the range of the following functions:

a) $y = 3\sin 2x°$

b) $y = x^2$

c) $y = x^2 - 2$

d) $y = \cos(x - 45)°$

Note It may help to do a quick sketch of the graphs first.

4 Find the largest possible domain for each of the following functions:

a) $f(x) = \frac{5}{x^2 - 13x - 48}$ **b)** $f(x) = \sqrt{(x^2 - 2x - 15)}$ 

Completing the square

You should already know how to express a quadratic expression in the form $(x+p)^2 + q$.

This process is known as completing the square. If you are given the equation of a quadratic function in the form $y = ax^2 + bx + c$ it will help you to sketch the graph of the function (which is a parabola) if you express the equation in the form $y = a(x+p)^2 + q$.

In this form, the coordinates of the turning point are $(-p,\ q)$.

If the x^2 term is positive there will be a minimum turning point; if the x^2 term is negative there will be a maximum turning point.

Example 1

a) Express $2x^2 + 12x + 4$ in the form $a(x+p)^2 + q$.
b) Write down the coordinates of the turning point of the parabola with equation $y = 2x^2 + 12x + 4$.

SOLUTION

a) $2x^2 + 12x + 4 = 2(x^2 + 6x) + 4 = 2(x^2 + 6x + 9) - 18 + 4 = 2(x+3)^2 - 14$
b) $(-3, -14)$

Example 2

a) Express $25 - 8x - x^2$ in the form $q - (x+p)^2$.
b) Write down the coordinates of the maximum turning point of the parabola with equation $y = 25 - 8x - x^2$.

SOLUTION

a) $25 - 8x - x^2 = 25 - (x^2 + 8x) = 25 - [(x^2 + 8x + 16) - 16] = 41 - (x+4)^2$
b) $(-4, 41)$

When you complete the square in a quadratic expression, you can check that your answer is correct by squaring the bracket and collecting like terms.

Example 3

Find the roots of the equation $x^2+8x+2=0$ by completing the square.

SOLUTION

$x^2+8x+2=0$

$\Rightarrow x^2+8x=-2$

$\Rightarrow x^2+8x+16=-2+16$

$\Rightarrow (x+4)^2=14$

$\Rightarrow x+4=\pm\sqrt{14}$

$\Rightarrow x=-4\pm\sqrt{14}$

Exercise 11.2

1 Express each of the following in the form $a(x+p)^2+q$:

a) $2x^2+4x+1$ b) $2x^2-16x+5$

c) $2x^2-8x+8$ d) $4x^2+24x-9$

e) $3x^2+12x-2$ f) $2x^2-20x+80$

g) $2x^2-6x+1$

2 Express each of the following in the form $q-(x+p)^2$:

a) $10-2x-x^2$ b) $15-6x-x^2$

c) $18+10x-x^2$ d) $7-6x-x^2$

e) $25+12x-x^2$

3 Use the answer to question 2(a) to sketch the graph of $y=10-2x-x^2$.

4 Express each of the following in the form $q-a(x+p)^2$:

a) $14-12x-2x^2$ b) $11-8x-2x^2$

c) $6+6x-3x^2$ d) $7+10x-5x^2$

e) $23-12x-2x^2$ f) $15+24x-3x^2$

5 Solve the following equations by completing the square:

a) $x^2-8x-15=0$

b) $2x^2+4x+1=0$

6 Solve the equation $ax^2+bx+c=0$ by completing the square. 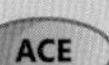

Algebraic & Trigonometric Skills

Graphs of related functions

We have already looked at how to draw the graphs of certain functions if we know the graph of a related function. We have seen how our knowledge of the graph of the most basic parabola, $y = x^2$, enables us to sketch the graph of related parabolas. We know that the graph of say $y = (x-2)^2 + 5$ is just the graph of $y = x^2$ moved 2 to the right and 5 up.

We have also looked at how our knowledge of the most basic trigonometric graphs, $y = \sin x$ and $y = \cos x$, enables us to draw the graphs of related trigonometric graphs. We know that the graph of say $y = 2\sin x$ stretches the graph of $y = \sin x$ vertically; that the graph of $y = \sin x + 2$ moves the graph of $y = \sin x$ up 2 units; that the graph of $y = \sin 2x$ compresses the graph of $y = \sin x$ horizontally; that the graph of $y = \sin(x - \pi)$ moves the graph of $y = \sin x$ by π radians to the right, and so on.

In this section we shall have a very detailed look at how, given the graph of a function $y = f(x)$, we can draw the graph of a related function.

If you are given the graph of a function, $y = f(x)$, the following transformations describe how to sketch the graph of related functions.

$y = -f(x)$	reflect $y = f(x)$ in the x-axis
$y = f(-x)$	reflect $y = f(x)$ in the y-axis
$y = -f(-x)$	give $y = f(x)$ a half turn rotation about the origin
$y = f(x) + a$	slide $y = f(x)$ a units up (parallel to the y-axis)
$y = f(x - a)$	slide $y = f(x)$ a units to the right (parallel to the x-axis)
$y = af(x)$	stretch $y = f(x)$ parallel to the y-axis by a scale factor of a
$y = f\left(\frac{x}{a}\right)$	stretch $y = f(x)$ parallel to the x-axis by a scale factor of a
$y = f'(x)$	the graph of the derivative of $y = f(x)$

Note The final related graph in this list will be studied later in calculus as part of the differentiation topic.

Example 1

The graph of a function $y = f(x)$ is shown below.

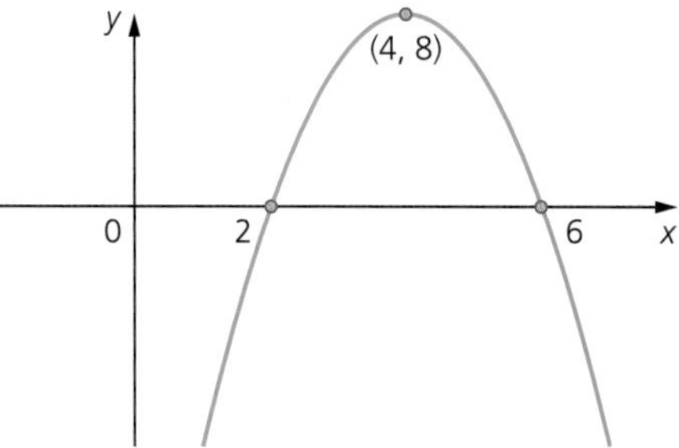

Sketch the following graphs:

a) $y = -f(x)$
b) $y = f(-x)$
c) $y = -f(-x)$
d) $y = f(x) - 3$
e) $y = f(x+3)$
f) $y = 2f(x)$
g) $y = f(2x)$
h) $y = f\left(\frac{x}{2}\right)$

SOLUTION

a) For $y = -f(x)$ reflect $y = f(x)$ in the x-axis.

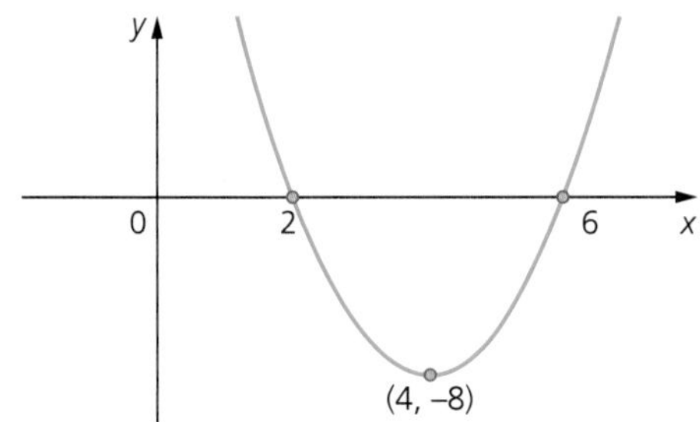

b) For $y = f(-x)$ reflect $y = f(x)$ in the y-axis.

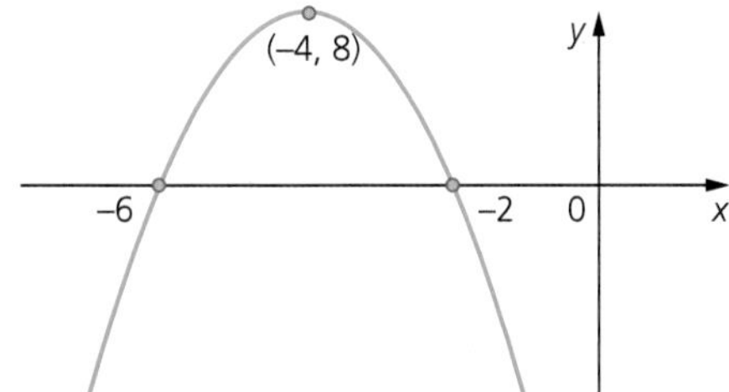

c) For $y = -f(-x)$ give $y = f(x)$ a half turn rotation about the origin.

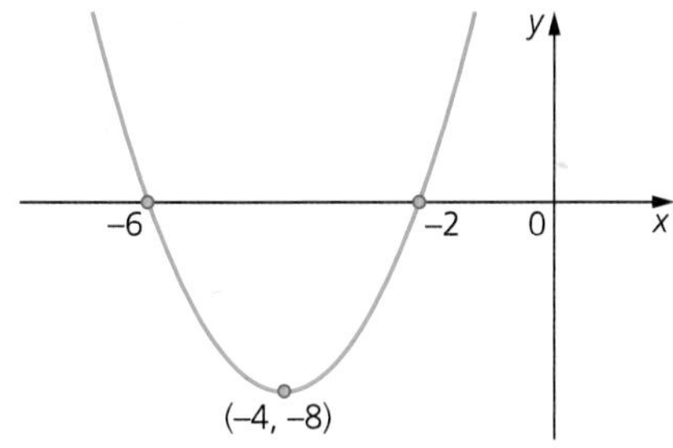

d) For $y = f(x) - 3$ slide $y = f(x)$ 3 units down (parallel to the y-axis).

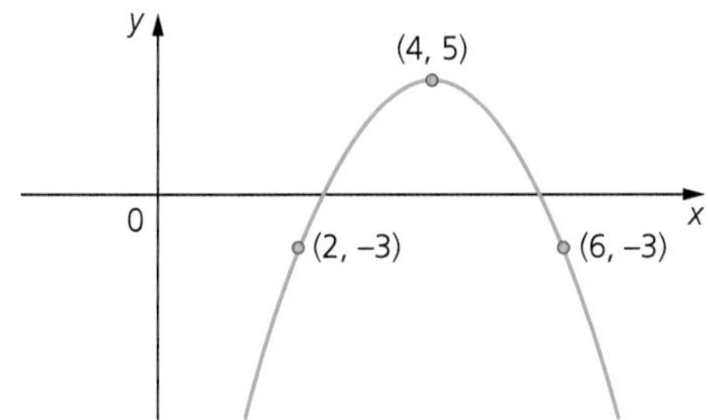

e) For $y = f(x+3)$ slide $y = f(x)$ 3 units to the left (parallel to the x-axis).

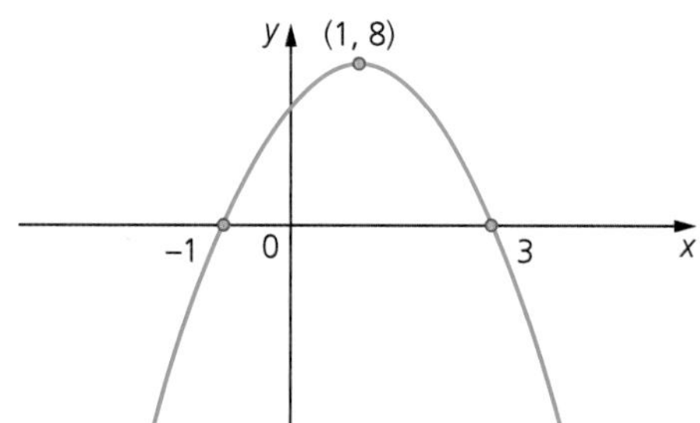

f) For $y = 2f(x)$ stretch $y = f(x)$ parallel to the y-axis by a scale factor of 2.

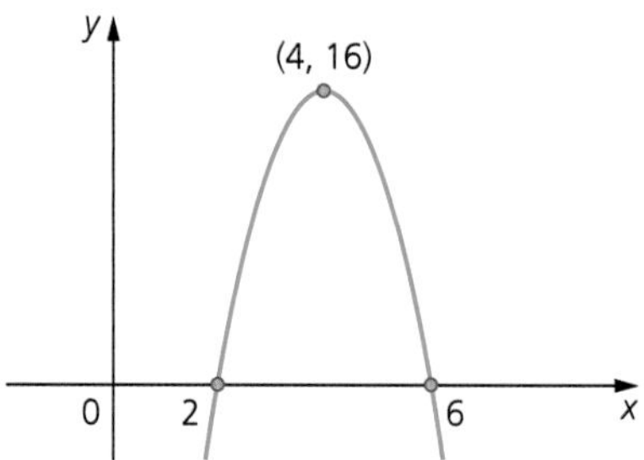

g) For $y = f(2x)$ compress $y = f(x)$ parallel to the x-axis by a scale factor of 2.

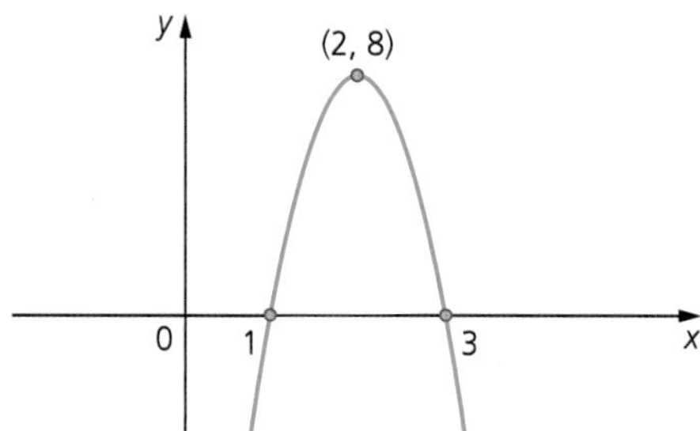

h) For $= f\left(\frac{x}{2}\right)$ stretch $y = f(x)$ parallel to the x-axis by a scale factor of 2.

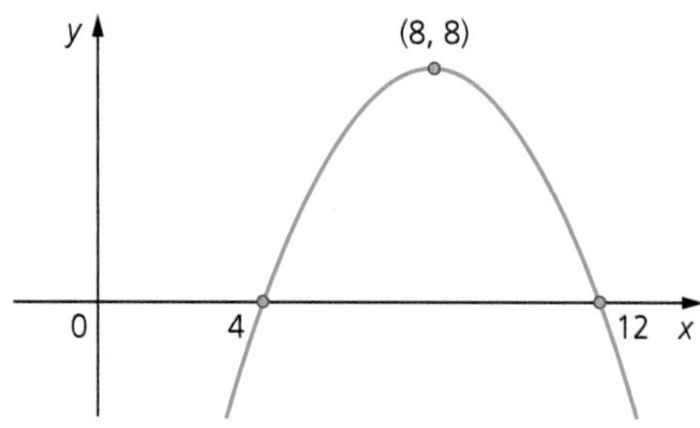

Sometimes you will be given a composition of transformations to carry out on a function, i.e. more than one transformation.

Example 2

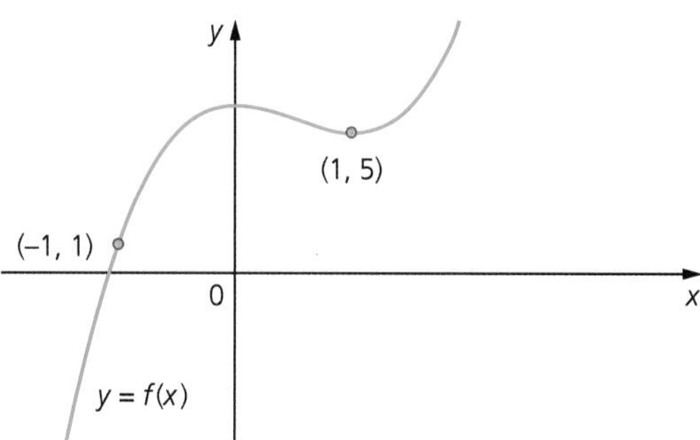

The diagram on the right shows a sketch of the function $y=f(x)$.
Sketch the graph of $y=3-f(x)$.

SOLUTION

To draw the graph of $y=3-f(x)$ think of it as $y=-f(x)+3$, then reflect the graph of $y=f(x)$ in the x-axis, followed by moving it up 3 units in the direction of the y-axis. You should check that $(-1, 1) \rightarrow (-1, -1) \rightarrow (-1, 2)$ and $(1, 5) \rightarrow (1, -5) \rightarrow (1, -2)$.

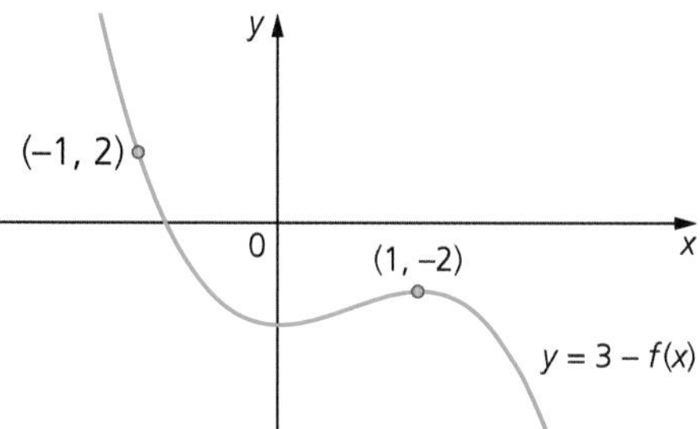

Hint In the above example you could copy the original diagram, show the reflection of the original graph in the x-axis followed by the final graph after moving the reflection 3 units upwards. Always indicate clearly your final solution with a label or a key, or on a separate diagram. Always remember to label the x-axis and y-axis and to include the coordinates of the points used to find the solution.

Exercise 11.3

1 On the same diagram, sketch and label the graphs of:

a) $y=x^2$ b) $y=-x^2$.

c) $y=2x^2$ d) $y=\frac{1}{2}x^2$

2 Sketch the graph of $y=4-x^2$ showing where the graph crosses the x- and y-axes.

3 This diagram shows the sketch of the function $y=f(x)$.
On separate diagrams sketch the graphs of:

a) $y=2-f(x)$

b) $y=f(x-2)-4$

4 Sketch the graph of $y=-\frac{1}{2}\sin x°$, $0 \leqslant x \leqslant 360$.

5 This diagram shows the sketch of the function $y=f(x)$.
On separate diagrams sketch the graphs of:

a) $y=-3-f(x)$

b) $y=f(x+4)+5$

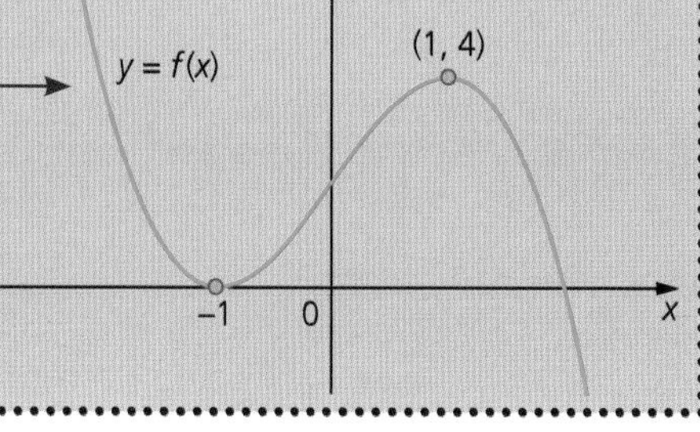

The exponential function

We looked at exponential functions earlier in Chapter 5. An **exponential function** is one in the form $f(x) = a^x$.

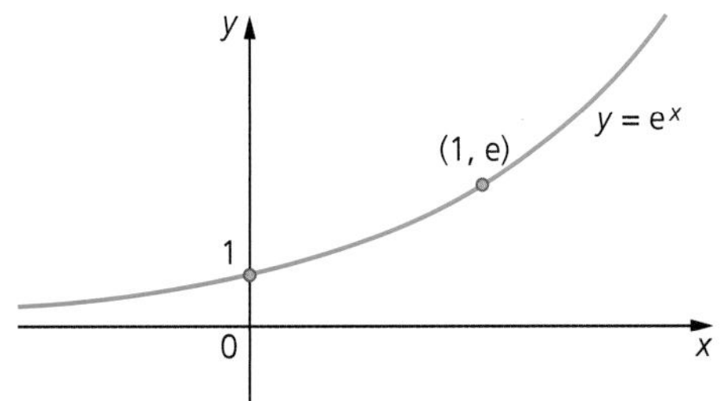

In that chapter you met the number called e. It is approximately equal to 2·718 and is very important in mathematics. Logarithms to the base e are called **natural logarithms** and instead of being written in the form $\log_e x$ are often written in the form $\ln x$.

The graph of the function $f(x) = e^x$ is shown opposite. This graph, in common with all graphs in the form $f(x) = a^x$, passes through the point (0, 1). Note that the graph of the function $f(x) = e^x$ will also pass through the point (1, e).

Example 1

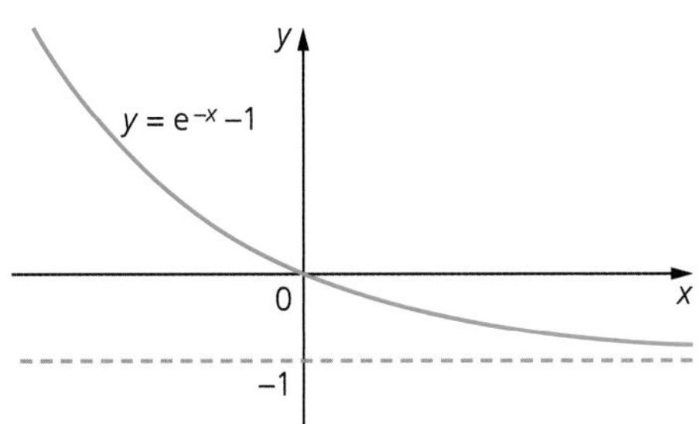

Sketch the graph of the function $y = e^{-x} - 1$.

SOLUTION

Reflect the graph of $y = e^x$ in the y-axis then slide 1 unit down (parallel to the y-axis).

The graph approaches the dotted line which has equation $y = -1$ without ever touching it. It is called the **asymptote** and should be shown on the graph. In the graph of $y = e^x$ the x-axis is the asymptote.

Example 2

The diagram shows the sketch of the function $y = 3^x$.

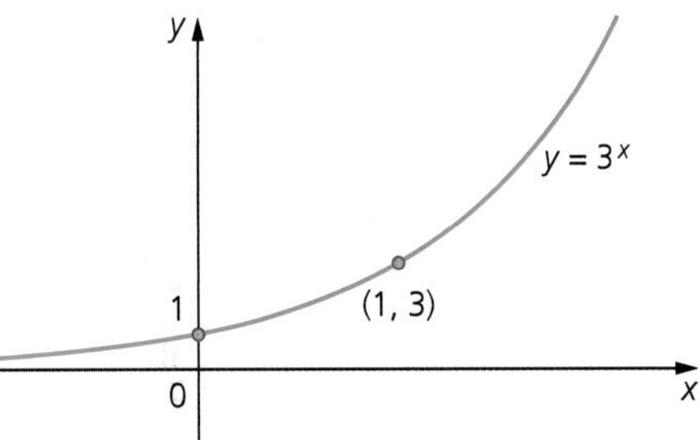

Sketch the graph of the function $y = 3^{2x}$.

SOLUTION

$y = 3^{2x} = (3^2)^x = 9^x$. Check that the graph of $y = 9^x$ passes through the points (0, 1) and (1, 9).

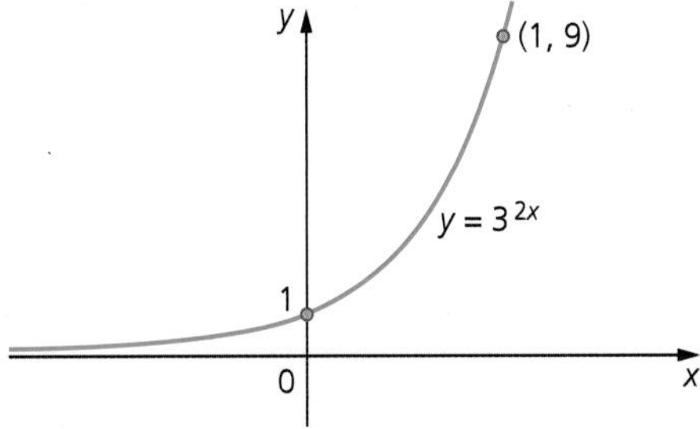

Exercise 11.4

1 On separate diagrams sketch the graphs of the following functions:

a) $y = -e^x$ **b)** $y = e^x + 2$ **c)** $y = 2 - e^x$

2 On separate diagrams sketch the graphs of the following functions:

a) $y = 3^x - 2$ **b)** $y = 3^{-x}$

3 On the same diagram sketch the graphs of:

a) $y = 2^x$ **b)** $y = 2^{3x}$

4 The diagram opposite shows part of the graph of $y = 4^x$.

a) The points $(0, p)$ and $(1, q)$ lie on the graph. Write down the values of p and q.

b) Copy the graph and on it sketch the graph of $y = 4^{2x}$.

c) Find the coordinates of the point where the graph of $y = 4^{2x}$ intersects the line $x = 1$.

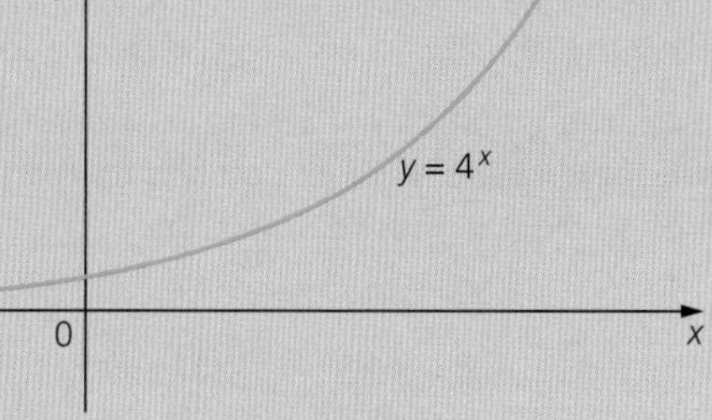

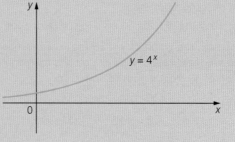

5 The diagram below shows part of the graph of $y = ae^{0.5x}$.

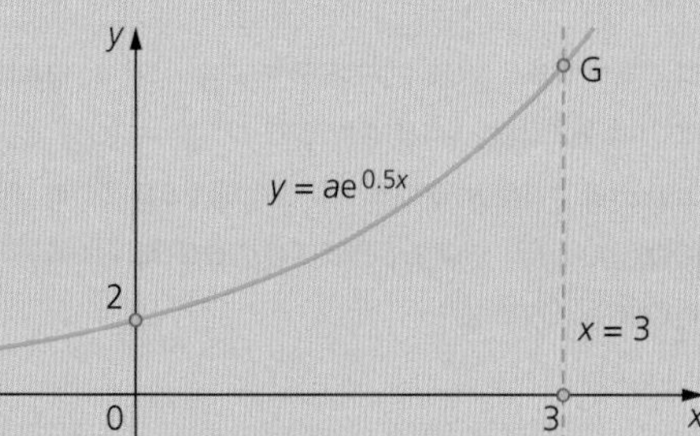

a) Find the value of a.

b) The line with equation $x = 3$ intersects the graph at point G. Find the coordinates of G.

The logarithmic function

We know that the inverse function of $f(x) = a^x$ is $f(x) = \log_a x$.

The graph of $y = \log_a x$ is obtained by reflecting the graph of $y = a^x$ in the line $y = x$.

Remember, when dealing with logarithms, that for all bases a, $\log 1 = 0$ and $\log a = 1$.

Remember too that in the important case where $f(x) = 10^x$, the inverse function is $\log_{10} x$.

The graph of $y = \log_{10} x$ is shown opposite. Note that the y-axis is an asymptote to this graph.

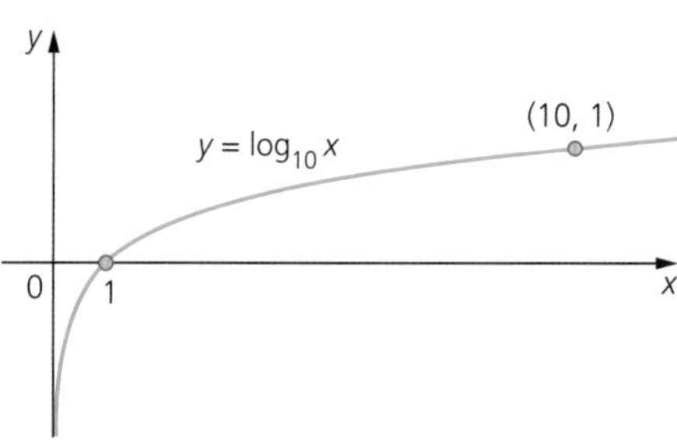

Example 1

Sketch the graph of the function $y = \log_{10}(x - 2)$.

SOLUTION

To sketch the graph of $y = \log_{10}(x - 2)$, slide the graph of $y = \log_{10} x$ along 2 units to the right parallel to the x-axis.

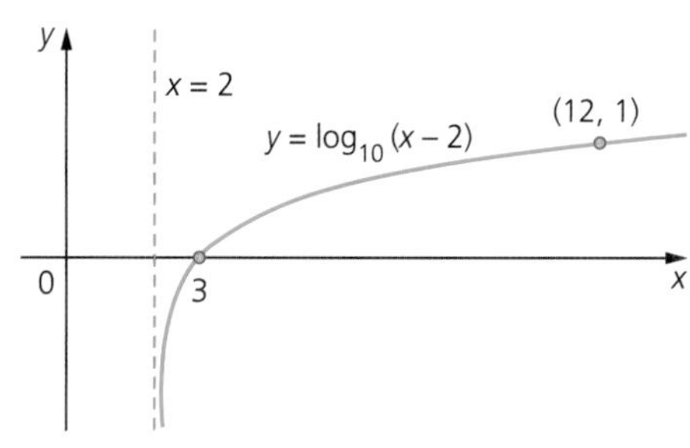

Example 2

The diagram opposite shows the graph of $y = \log_2 x$.
Sketch the graph of $y = \log_2 8x$.

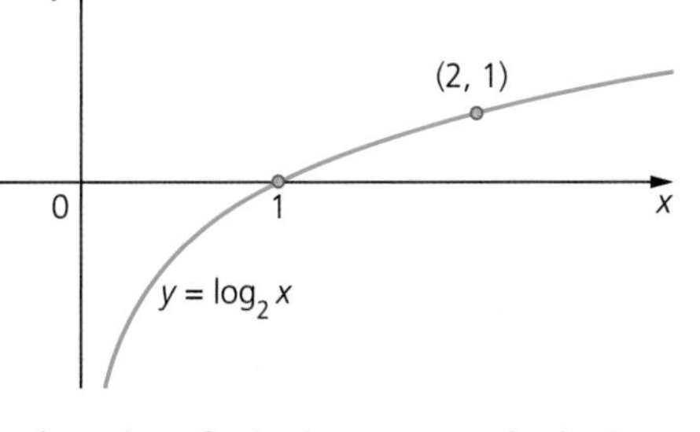

SOLUTION

The difficulty here is deciding how to start. Use the first law of logarithms and proceed from there.

$\log_2 8x = \log_2 8 + \log_2 x = 3 + \log_2 x$ (since $\log_2 8 = \log_2 (2)^3 = 3$)

To sketch the graph of $y = 3 + \log_2 x$, remember that $y = f(x) + a$ means that we should slide $y = f(x)$ a units up (parallel to the y-axis). Hence the graph of $y = \log_2 8x$ is the same as the basic graph of $y = \log_2 x$ moved 3 units up.

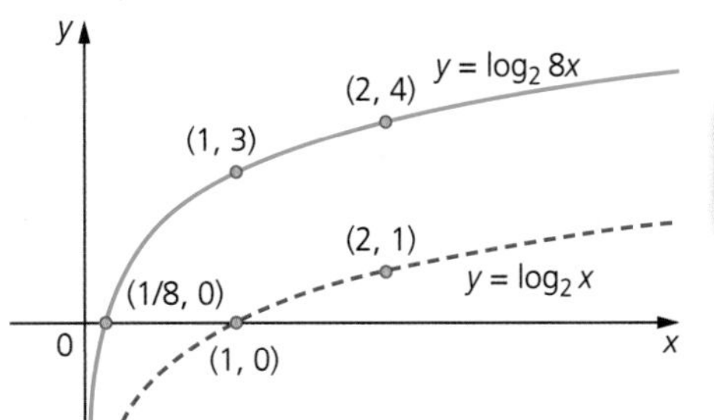

Hint You can use your knowledge of logarithms to find where the graph of $y = \log_2 8x$ crosses the x-axis. It crosses the x-axis where $y = 0$, so solve the equation $\log_2 8x = 0$.

$\log_2 8x = 0 \Rightarrow 3 + \log_2 x = 0 \Rightarrow \log_2 x = -3 \Rightarrow x = \frac{1}{8}$. Why? Because $2^{-3} = \frac{1}{8}$.

Hence the graph crosses the x-axis at the point $\left(\frac{1}{8}, 0\right)$.

Example 3

The diagram opposite shows the graph of $y = \log_a (x - b)$.
Find the values of a and b.

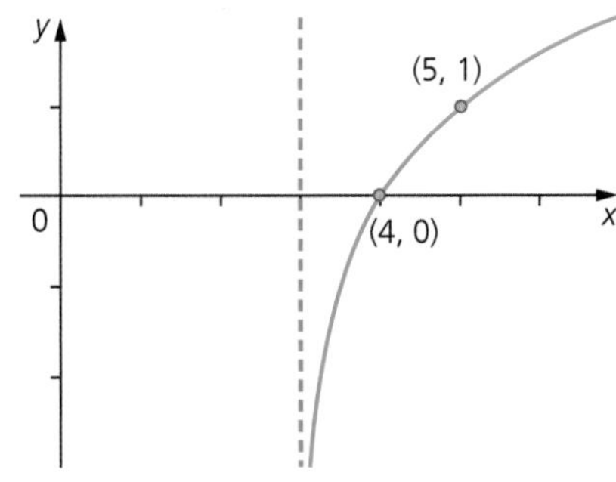

SOLUTION

We know that, for any base a, the point $(1, 0)$ lies on the graph of $y = \log_a x$. As this graph passes through $(4, 0)$, we have a situation where the basic graph has been moved 3 units to the right. From our work on related graphs, we see that the equation of the graph must be $y = \log_a (x - 3)$ leading to $b = 3$. Now substitute $(5, 1)$ into this equation, giving $1 = \log_a (5 - 3)$. Hence $1 = \log_a 2 \Rightarrow a = 2$. The equation of the graph is $y = \log_2 (x - 3)$.

Hint Substitute the coordinates of *both* points into your solution to check that they work.

Note that other graphs may arise where the laws of logarithms will prove helpful. For example, for the graph of $y = \log_2 \frac{1}{x}$ you could think of $y = \log_2 \frac{1}{x} = \log_2 1 - \log_2 x = -\log_2 x$ and then reflect the graph of $y = \log_2 x$ in the x-axis.

Exercise 11.5

1 Refer to the graph of $y = \log_2 x$ shown in Example 2 and sketch the graphs of the following functions on separate diagrams:

a) $y = \log_2(-x)$ **b)** $y = \log_2 x - 4$ **c)** $y = \log_2(x+1)$

2 **a)** Sketch the graph of $y = \log_2 16x$.

b) Find the coordinates of the point where the graph of $y = \log_2 16x$ crosses the x-axis.

3 Sketch the graphs of the following functions on separate diagrams:

a) $y = \log_2 \frac{2}{x}$ **b)** $y = 2\log_2 x$ **c)** $y = \log_2 \sqrt{x}$

4 The diagram below shows the graph of $y = \log_a(x - b)$. HPQ

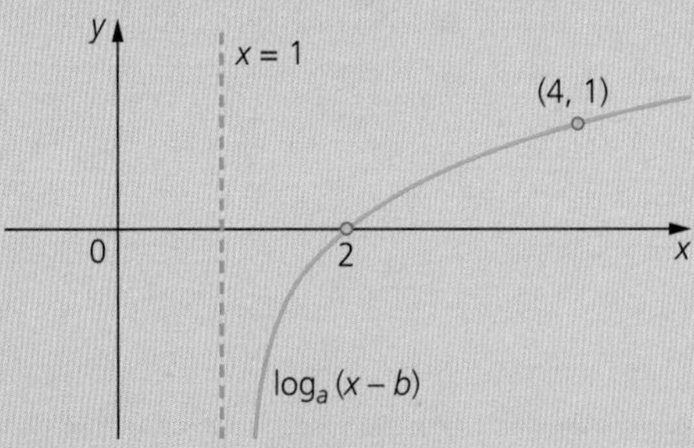

Find the values of a and b.

5 The diagram below shows a sketch of the graph of $y = a\log_2(x - b)$.

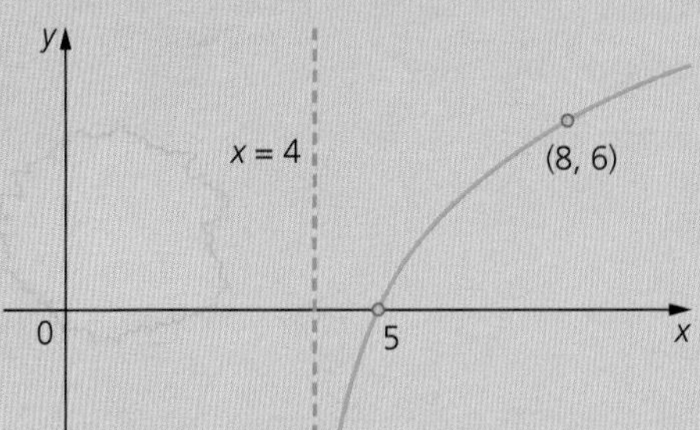

Find the values of a and b.

6 The diagram shows a sketch of part of the graph of $y = \log_6 x$.

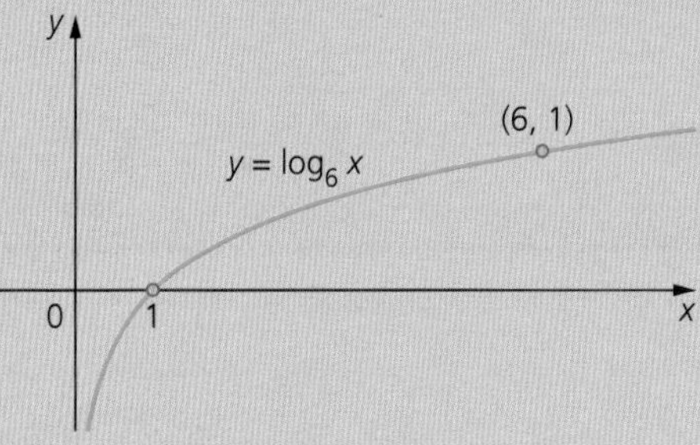

a) Sketch the graph of $y = \log_6 x + 1$.

b) Find the coordinates of the point where the graph crosses the x-axis.

c) On a new diagram, sketch the graph of $y = \log_6 \frac{36}{x}$.

→

Algebraic & Trigonometric Skills

7 A sketch of part of the graph of $y = \log_7(x+b)$ is shown.

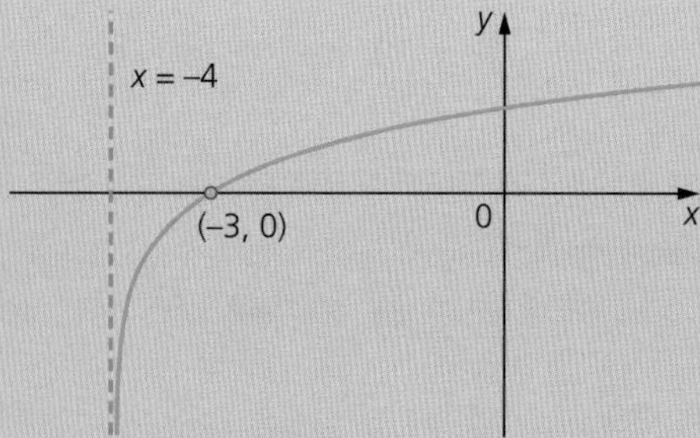

Find the value of b.

8 The diagram below shows part of the graph of $y = \log_3 x$.

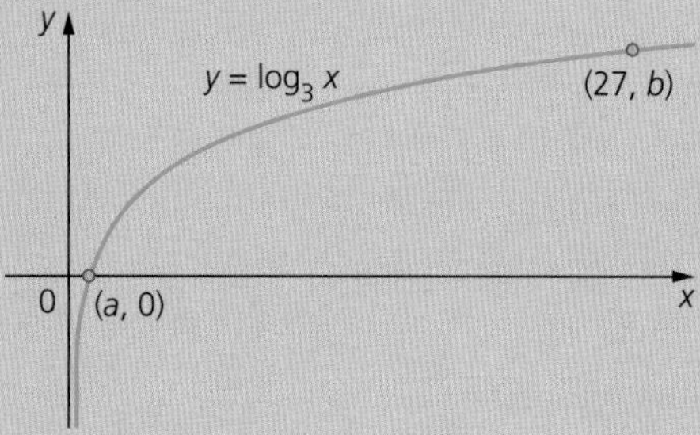

a) Find the values of a and b.
b) Sketch the graph of $y = \log_3(x-4)+2$.

9 A function f is in the form $f(x) = \log_m(x-n)$.
The graph of $y = f(x)$ is shown in the diagram.

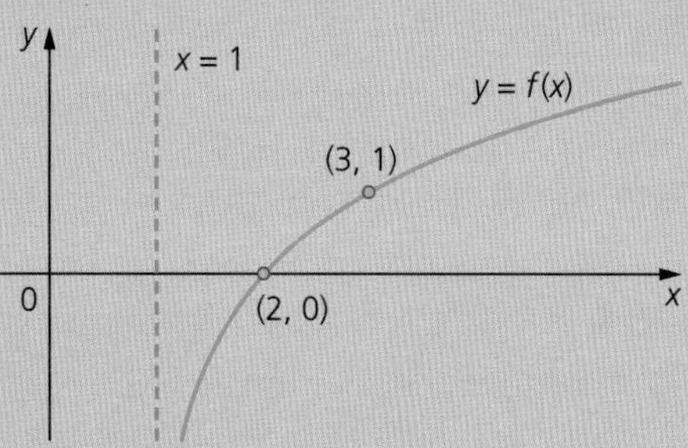

a) Find the values of m and n.
b) State the domain of f.

Composition of functions

A **composition of functions** occurs when we apply one function to the result of another. For example suppose we have two functions given by $f(x) = 3x + 2$ and $g(x) = 7 - x$. We might be asked to calculate $f(g(3))$. This means we must apply function $f(x)$ to the result of $g(3)$. Hence $f(g(3)) = f(7-3) = f(4) = 3 \times 4 + 2 = 14$.

We can find a formula for the composite function.

Algebraic & Trigonometric Skills

Example 1

If $f(x) = 3x + 2$ and $g(x) = 7 - x$, find a formula for a) $f(g(x))$ b) $g(f(x))$.

SOLUTION

a) $f(g(x)) = f(7 - x) = 3(7 - x) + 2 = 21 - 3x + 2 = 23 - 3x$

b) $g(f(x)) = g(3x + 2) = 7 - (3x + 2) = 7 - 3x - 2 = 5 - 3x$

Use the formula for $f(g(x))$ to confirm that $f(g(3)) = 14$. Use the formula for $g(f(x))$ to show that $g(f(3)) = -4$.

Note that the order of applying the functions is vital because $f(g(x)) \neq g(f(x))$ in this case. Remember that $f(g(x))$ means 'f after g'.

In most of the examples in the next exercise, the domain and range of both functions will be the set of real numbers, R. However, if a function has a restriction on its domain, such as the domain of the function $f(x) = \sqrt{x}$ which is $x \geq 0$, then this must be considered for the domain of any composite function involving $f(x)$.

Example 2

If $f(x) = \sqrt{x}$ and $g(x) = 2x^2$, find a formula for $g(f(x))$ and a suitable domain for $g(f(x))$.

SOLUTION

$g(f(x)) = g\left(\sqrt{x}\right) = 2\left(\sqrt{x}\right)^2 = 2x$

Now the domain of $f(x) = \sqrt{x}$ is $x \geqslant 0$ and the domain of $g(x) = 2x^2$ is R, so the domain of $g(f(x))$ must be $x \geqslant 0$ even though '$2x$' would normally have a domain of R.

The phrase 'in a suitable domain' is often used in examples. This is letting you know that, although there may be restrictions on the domain of one of the functions, you can simply concentrate on getting a formula for the composition of functions without having to worry about the domain.

Exercise 11.6

1 Functions f and g are defined on R by $f(x) = 2x - 4$ and $g(x) = 3x + 2$. Calculate:

a) $f(g(3))$ **b)** $f(g(5))$ **c)** $f(g(-2))$

d) $g(f(3))$ **e)** $g(f(-1))$

2 Functions f and g are defined on R by $f(x) = 2x - 4$ and $g(x) = x^2 + 1$. Find formulae for: HPQ

a) $f(g(x))$ **b)** $g(f(x))$ **c)** $f(f(x))$

d) $g(g(x))$

3 Two functions are defined by $f(x) = 4 - x$ and $g(x) = \frac{2}{x}$, $x \neq 0$.

a) Find $h(x)$ where $h(x) = f(g(x))$.

b) If $k(x) = \frac{2}{1 - x}$, $x \neq 1$, find $h(k(x))$ in its simplest form.

4 Three functions f, g and h are defined on suitable domains by $f(x) = 2x + 1$, $g(x) = \frac{1}{x - 2}$, $h(x) = 3x - 6$. Find formulae for:

a) $f(h(x))$ **b)** $h(f(x))$ **c)** $f(g(x))$

d) $g(g(x))$ **e)** $h(g(x))$

5 On a suitable domain, functions f and g are defined on R by:

$$f(x)=\frac{1}{x-3}, \qquad g(x)=\frac{1}{x}+3$$

Find $f(g(x))$ in its simplest form.

6 The functions $f(x)$ and $g(x)$ are defined on suitable domains by $f(x)=\sin x°$ and $g(x)=2x$.

a) Find expressions for **(i)** $f(g(x))$ **(ii)** $g(f(x))$

b) Solve the equation $2f(g(x))+g(f(x))=0, \quad 0\le x\le 360$.

7 The diagram below illustrates three functions f, g and h.

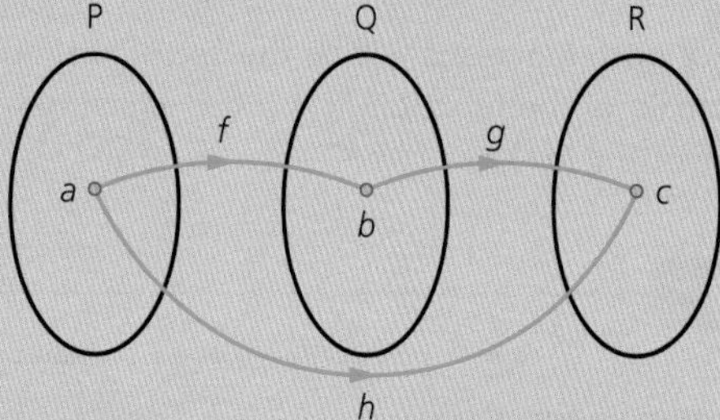

The functions f and g are defined by $f(x)=3x-1$ and $g(x)=x^2+2$.

The function h is such that whenever $f(a)=b$ and $g(b)=c$, then $h(a)=c$.

a) If $a=4$, find the values of b and c.

b) Find a formula for $h(x)$ in terms of x.

8 Functions $f(x)=x+2$ and $g(x)=x^2+5$ are defined on the set of real numbers.

a) Find $h(x)$ where $h(x)=g(f(x))$.

b) **(i)** Write down the coordinates of the minimum turning point of $y=h(x)$.

(ii) Hence state the range of the function h.

9 a) The function f is defined by $f(x)=x^3-3x^2-4x+12$. The function g is defined by $g(x)=x+2$ ACE

Show that $f(g(x))=x^3+3x^2-4x$.

b) Factorise fully $f(g(x))$.

c) The function k is such that $k(x)=\frac{1}{f(g(x))}$. For what values of x is the function k not defined?

10 Functions $f(x)=\sin x$, $g(x)=\cos x$, $h(x)=x-\frac{\pi}{3}$ and $k(x)=x-\frac{\pi}{6}$ are defined on a suitable set of real numbers. ACE

a) Find expressions for:

(i) $f(h(x))$

(ii) $g(k(x))$

b) **(i)** Show that $f(h(x))=\frac{1}{2}\sin x-\frac{\sqrt{3}}{2}\cos x$.

(ii) Find a similar expression for $g(k(x))$ and hence solve the equation

$$f(h(x))-g(k(x))=\frac{\sqrt{3}}{2}, \quad 0\le x\le 2\pi$$

Inverse functions

What is an inverse function?

The inverse of a function $f(x)$ is denoted by $f^{-1}(x)$. An inverse function goes in the reverse direction. Consider the function $f(x)=2x+4$. To use this function we multiply values of x by 2 and then add 4. The reverse process is to subtract 4 then divide by 2, so the inverse function of $f(x)=2x+4$ is $f^{-1}(x)=\frac{1}{2}(x-4)$. Note that the inverse function returns to the original value, e.g. check that $f(5)=14$ and that $f^{-1}(14)=5$ as an example.

Example

If $f(x)=2x+4$ and $f^{-1}(x)=\frac{1}{2}(x-4)$, find an expression for $f(f^{-1}(x))$.

SOLUTION

$$f(f^{-1}(x))=f\left(\frac{1}{2}(x-4)\right)=2\left(\frac{1}{2}(x-4)\right)+4=x-4+4=x$$

This is an important result as we can see that when we apply a function followed by its inverse to a particular value we return to the original value.

Do all functions have inverses?

Think of the function $f(x)=x^2$. The value of $f(-2)=4$.

The inverse function appears to be $f^{-1}(x)=\sqrt{x}$, yet $\sqrt{4}=-2$ or 2. Therefore there is a problem and $f(x)=x^2$ does not have an inverse. In order that it does have an inverse we need to restrict the domain so that $f(x)=x^2,\ x\geq 0$.

A function only has an inverse if each member of the domain has a unique image in the range, in other words it is a one–one correspondence. Its graph will go all the way across the page *and* never be at the same height twice.

How do we find a formula for the inverse of a function?

Given the formula for a function, we can find a formula for the inverse function by changing the subject of a formula.

Example

A function is given by $f(x)=4x-5$. Find the inverse function $f^{-1}(x)$.

SOLUTION

Let $y=f(x)$ then $x=f^{-1}(y)$.

$$y=4x-5 \Rightarrow 4x=y+5 \Rightarrow x=\frac{y+5}{4}$$

$$\Rightarrow f^{-1}(y)=\frac{y+5}{4}$$

Hence $f^{-1}(x)=\frac{x+5}{4}$

Hint

You should check your solution by substituting a simple value for x in f (x). For example check that f(3) = 7 and then $f^{-1}(7)$ = 3 to verify your solution.

Exercise 11.7

1 Show that $f(x)=4x-1$ and $g(x)=\frac{1}{4}(x+1)$ are inverse functions.

2 The following functions are defined on R. Find a formula for the inverse function $f^{-1}(x)$ in each case.

a) $f(x)=5x$ **b)** $f(x)=4x-3$ **c)** $f(x)=8-3x$ **d)** $f(x)=\frac{1}{x}$

e) $f(x)=2x^3$ **f)** $f(x)=2-5x$ **g)** $f(x)=2+6x$

3 The function $f(x)=3x^3-4$ is defined of the set of real numbers R.
a) Find a formula for the inverse function $f^{-1}(x)$.
b) Evaluate $f^{-1}(20)$.

4 Two functions are defined by $f(x)=\frac{2(x+3)}{5}$ and $g(x)=\frac{5x-6}{2}$.
By finding an expression for $f(g(x))$ state the relationship between $f(x)$ and $g(x)$.

5 A function f is given by the formula $f(x)=x^2+3$ where x is a member of the set of positive real numbers.
a) Find a formula for $f^{-1}(x)$.
b) State the domain of $f^{-1}(x)$.

6 **a)** Sketch the graph of the function $f(x)=2x+4$.
b) Find a formula for $f^{-1}(x)$ and sketch its graph on the same diagram.
c) What transformation maps one graph onto the other?

7 A function is defined by $f(x)=2^x$.
a) Write down the inverse function $f^{-1}(x)$.
b) Evaluate $f^{-1}\left(\frac{1}{32}\right)$.

8 A function f is defined by $f(x)=\sqrt[3]{\frac{1}{8}(x-5)}$ where x is a member of the set of real numbers and g is the inverse function of f.
a) Obtain a formula for $g(x)$.
b) Evaluate $g'(f(69))$. ACE

The graph of an inverse function

Every point (x, y) on a function becomes the point (y, x) on the inverse function; in other words, the coordinates are swapped around.

The point (y, x) is the reflection of the point (x, y) in the line $y = x$, hence the graph of $y=f^{-1}(x)$ is obtained by reflecting the graph of $y = f(x)$ in the line $y = x$.

The diagram below shows the graph of the function $f(x)=4^x+2$.

Sketch the graph of the inverse of this function.

SOLUTION

Under reflection in the line $y = x$: $(0, 3) \rightarrow (3, 0)$, $(1, 6) \rightarrow (6, 1)$ and the asymptote $y = 2 \rightarrow x = 2$.

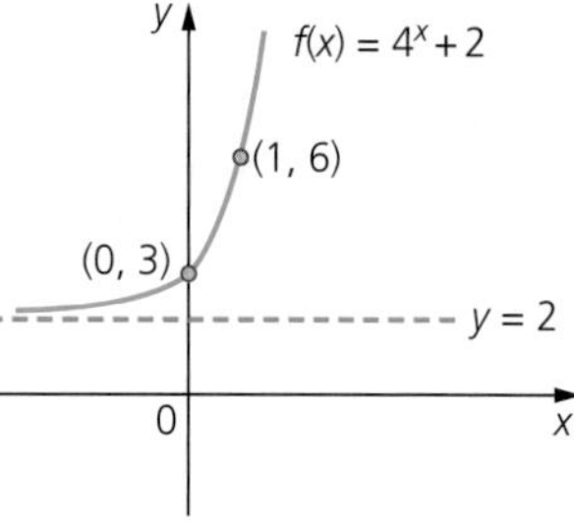

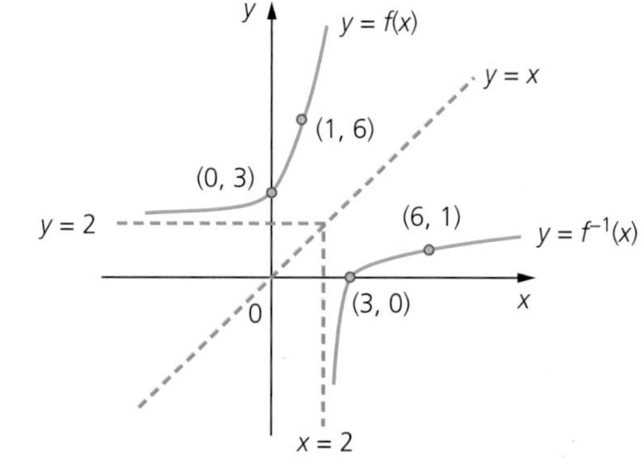

Exercise 11.8

Copy the graph of each of these functions. Sketch the graph of $y = f^{-1}(x)$ on the same diagram in each case.

1

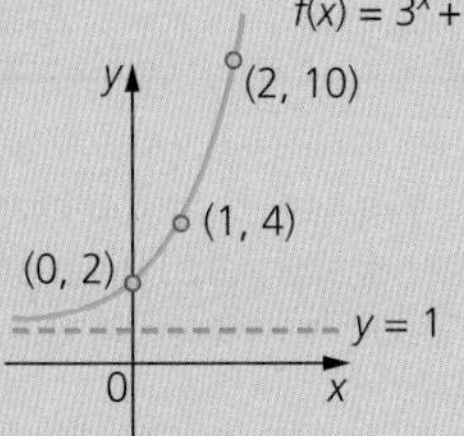

2

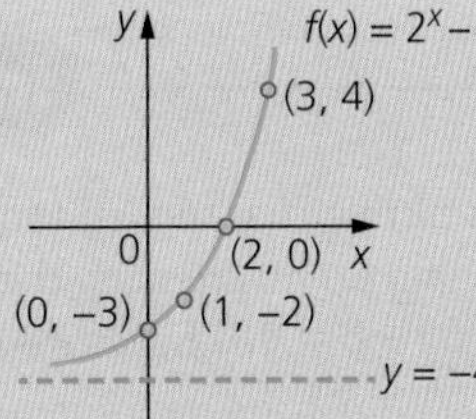

3

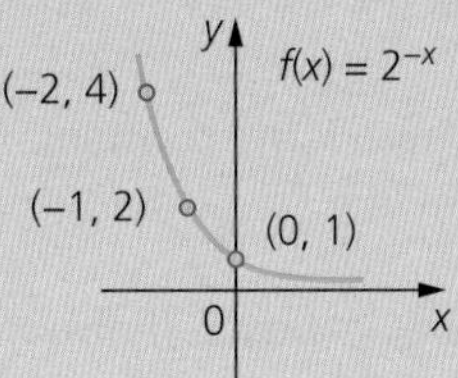

4

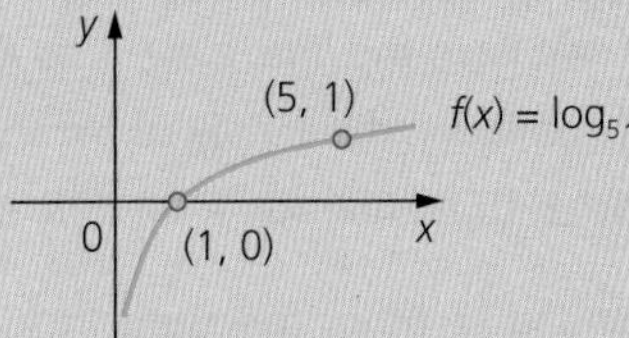

5

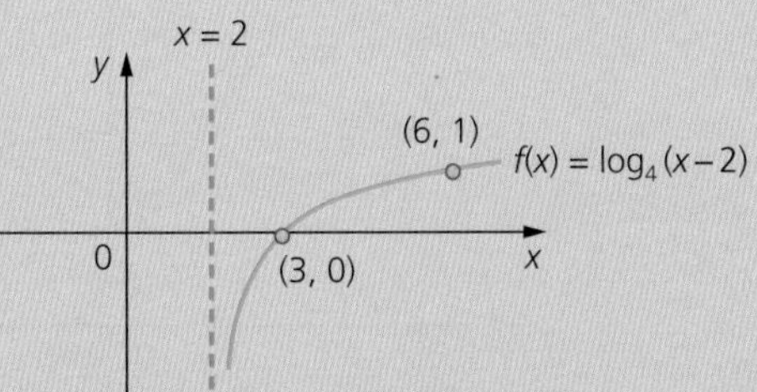

6

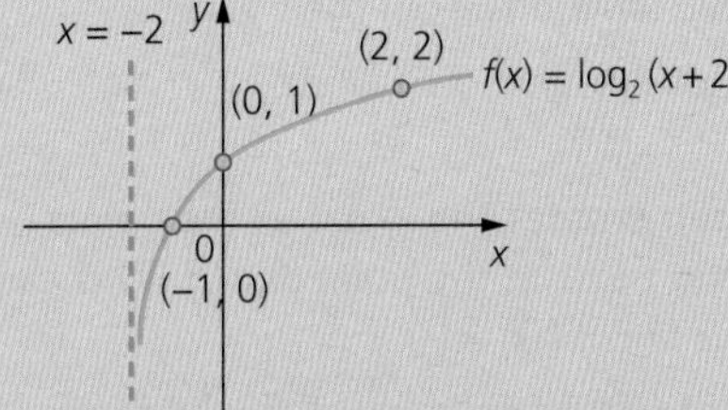

7

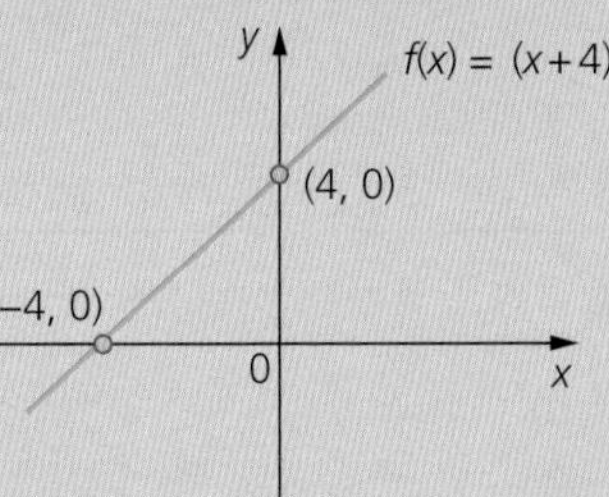

8

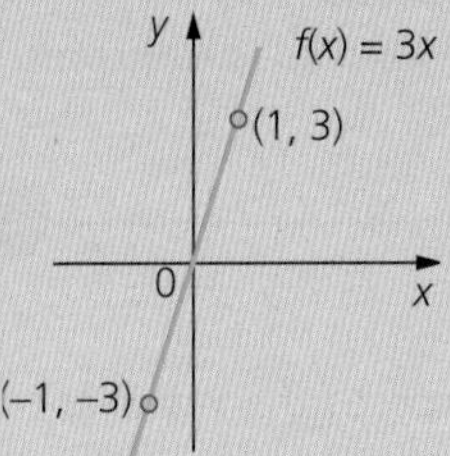

9

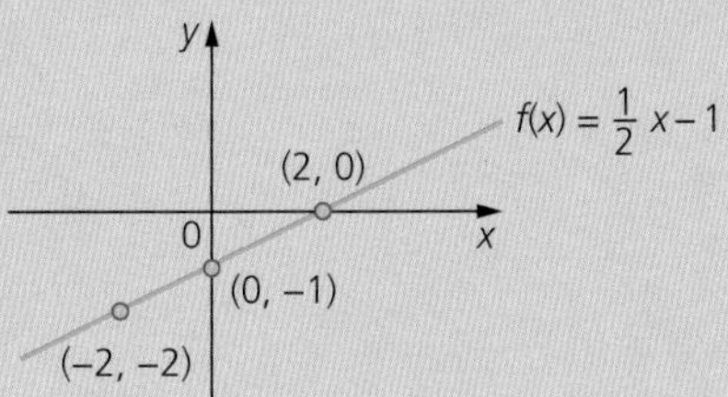

10

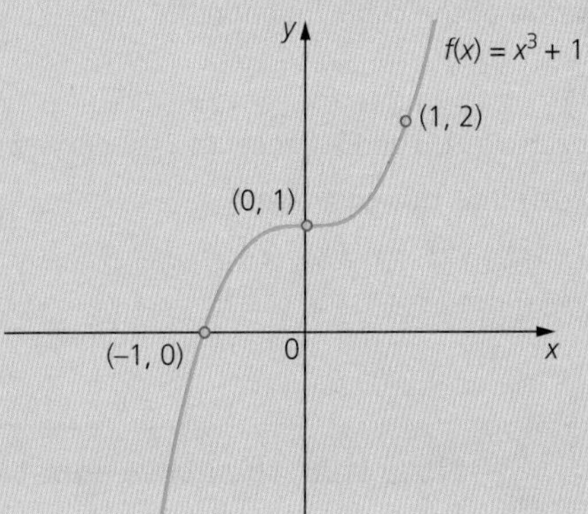

Algebraic & Trigonometric Skills

Families of graphs

Investigation

In the Quick check at the start of this chapter we looked at the graph of $y = x^2 + 6x + 8$. We saw that the graph was a parabola with a minimum turning point, crossing the *x*-axis at the points where $x = -2$ and $x = -4$. These points are the roots of the equation $x^2 + 6x + 8 = 0$. Therefore the equation of the parabola could also be written in the form $y = (x+2)(x+4)$.

In fact there is a whole family of related parabolas, with a minimum turning point, crossing the *x*-axis at the points where $x = -2$ and $x = -4$. All will have the line $x = -3$ as an axis of symmetry.

We can find a general formula for this family of parabolas, namely $y = k(x+2)(x+4)$, where *k* is a constant.

Investigate what happens to the graph for $k > 1$ and $k < 1$.

These ideas can be extended to other functions including cubic functions which we met in Chapter 3 (Polynomial Expressions and Equations) and can help us to find the equations of quadratic and cubic functions from their graphs.

Inspect the graph of the function $f(x) = 2x^3 + 5x^2 - 23x + 10$ shown opposite.

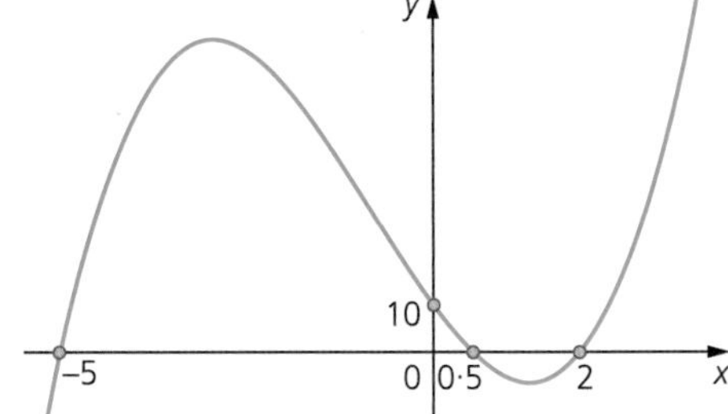

Note that the graph crosses the *x*-axis at the points $(-5, 0)$, $(0{\cdot}5, 0)$ and $(2, 0)$. It crosses the *y*-axis at the point $(0, 10)$. This can be found by replacing *x* by 0 to find $f(0) = 10$.

There is a series of related polynomial graphs passing through $(-5, 0)$, $(0{\cdot}5, 0)$ and $(2, 0)$. They have equation $f(x) = k(2x^3 + 5x^2 - 23x + 10)$ or $f(x) = k(x-2)(2x-1)(x+5)$ where *k* is a constant.

Example

The graph of a cubic function crosses the *x*-axis at the points $(-2, 0)$, $(1, 0)$ and $(3, 0)$.

The graph crosses the *y*-axis at the point $(0, 24)$.

Find the equation of the cubic function.

SOLUTION

The roots occur at -2, 1 and 3, hence $f(x) = k(x+2)(x-1)(x-3)$.

Substitute $(0, 24)$ into this equation:

$24 = k \times 2 \times (-1) \times (-3) \Rightarrow 6k = 24 \Rightarrow k = 4$

Hence the equation is $f(x) = 4(x+2)(x-1)(x-3)$.

Hint

Note that the above equation could be given in the form $f(x) = 4x^3 - 8x^2 - 20x + 24$ by expanding the brackets. It is not necessary to do this but check that you can expand the brackets accurately. It will be a good test of your algebra skills.

Exercise 11.9

1 The graph of a quadratic function $y = f(x)$ crosses the x-axis at the points $(-3, 0)$ and $(5, 0)$. The graph crosses the y-axis at the point $(0, -45)$. Find the equation of the quadratic function.

2 The graph of a cubic function $y = f(x)$ crosses the x-axis at the points $(-1, 0)$, $(1, 0)$ and $(3, 0)$. The graph crosses the y-axis at the point $(0, -3)$. Find the equation of the cubic function.

3 The graph of a cubic function $y = f(x)$ crosses the x-axis at the point $(0, 0)$. The x-axis is a tangent to the graph at the point $(4, 0)$. The graph passes through the point $(5, -10)$. Find the equation of the cubic function.

4 The graph of a cubic function $y = f(x)$ crosses the x-axis at the point $(6, 0)$. The x-axis is a tangent to the graph at the point $(-2, 0)$. The graph crosses the y-axis at the point $(0, -72)$. Find the equation of the cubic function.

Checkout

1 A function is given by $f(x) = \frac{1}{3x-1}$. What is the largest possible domain of f?

2 Express $2x^2 - 16x - 2$ in the form $a(x+p)^2 + q$.

3 The diagram below shows the sketch of the function $y = f(x)$.

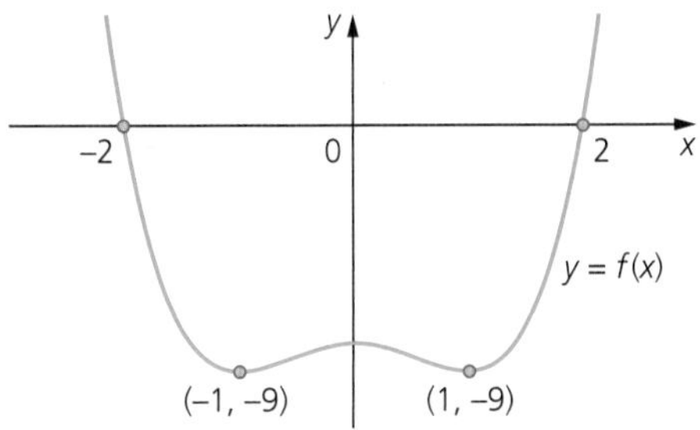

Sketch the graph of $y = -4 - f(x)$.

4 By referring back to the graph of $y = \log_2 x$ shown on page 140, sketch the graph of $y = \log_2 4x$.

5 The diagram below shows the graph of $y = \log_a(x - b)$.

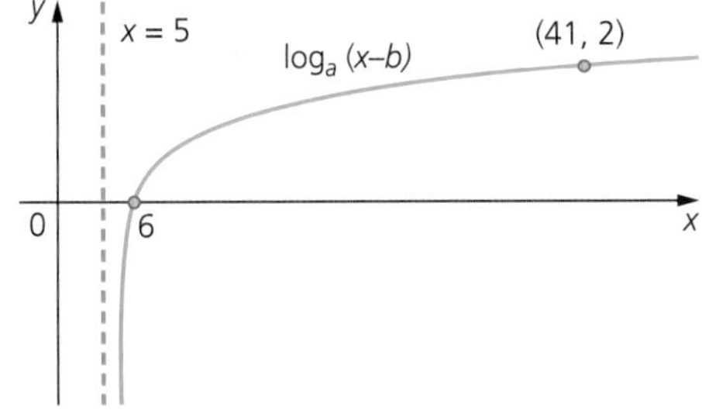

Find the values of a and b.

6 If $f(x)=5x-2$ and $g(x)=2-3x$, find a formula for a) $f(g(x))$ b) $g(f(x))$.

7 Functions f and g are given by $f(x)=2x-3$ and $g(x)=x^2+2$.

a) (i) Find $u(x)$ where $u(x)=f(g(x))$.

(ii) Find $v(x)$ where $v(x)=g(f(x))$.

b) Find the value of a such that $v(a)=2u(a)-15$.

8 The function $k(x)=7-4x$ is defined on the set of real numbers R. Find an expression for the inverse function $k^{-1}(x)$.

9 a) Two functions are defined by $f(x)=x^2+p$, $g(x)=2x+1$, where p is a constant.

(i) Find $f(g(x))$.

(ii) Find $g(f(x))$.

b) Show that the expression $f(g(x))-g(f(x))$ simplifies to $2x^2+4x-p$.

c) Find the value of p such that $2x^2+4x-p=0$ has equal roots.

10 A cubic curve crosses the x-axis at the points $(1,0)$, $(2,0)$ and $(3,0)$. The curve crosses the y-axis at the point $(0,-24)$. Find the equation of the curve.

11 The diagram opposite shows the graph of the function $f(x) = 2\log_3 x$. Copy the diagram. Sketch the graph of $y=f^{-1}(x)$ on the same diagram.

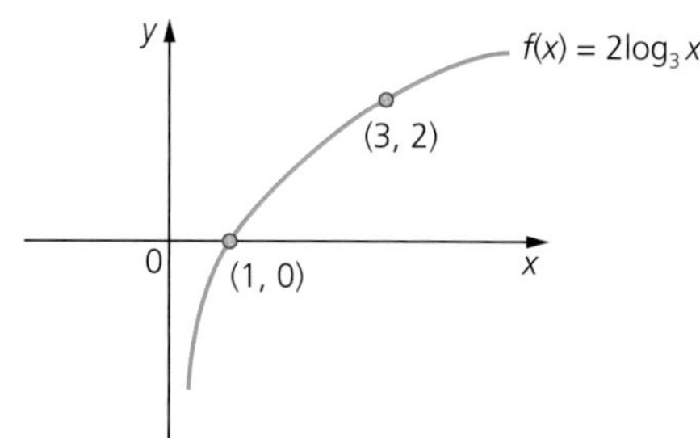

Summary

Functions

You should now:

1 know the meaning of the terms domain, range, codomain, function, one–one correspondence, composite function and inverse function, and the notation $f^{-1}(x)$.

2 be able to find a suitable domain and range of a given function.

3 be able to complete the square on a quadratic expression, e.g. to express $2x^2+8x+1$ in the form $a(x-b)^2+c$.

4 be able, given the graph of a function, to draw the graph of related functions using the information below.

$y=-f(x)$	reflect $y=f(x)$ in the x-axis
$y=f(-x)$	reflect $y=f(x)$ in the y-axis
$y=-f(-x)$	give $y=f(x)$ a half turn rotation about the origin
$y=f(x)+a$	slide $y=f(x)$ a units up (parallel to the y-axis)
$y=f(x-a)$	slide $y=f(x)$ a units to the right (parallel to the x-axis)
$y=af(x)$	stretch $y=f(x)$ parallel to the y-axis by a scale factor of a
$y=f\left(\frac{x}{a}\right)$	stretch $y=f(x)$ parallel to the x-axis by a scale factor of a
$y=f^{-1}(x)$	reflect in $y=x$

5 be able, given the graph of an exponential or logarithmic function, to draw the graph of related functions.

6 be able to find an expression for the composition of two functions, e.g. given that $f(x)=2x+2$ and $g(x)=3x+1$, find expressions for $f(g(x))$ and $g(f(x))$.

7 know the condition for a function to have an inverse and be able to find the inverse of a given function, e.g. given that $f(x)=2x+2$, find $f^{-1}(x)$.

CHAPTER

12 Vectors

A vector is a geometric quantity with magnitude (or length) and direction. In this chapter you will extend your current knowledge about vectors to include study of the scalar product.

What I am learning

* To use position vectors in two and three dimensions
* To use the distance formula in three dimensions
* To use the three unit vectors **i, j** and **k**
* To determine whether or not three points in space are collinear
* To find the ratio in which one point divides the line joining another two points
* To use the section formula
* To use vector pathways in three dimensions
* To use the distributive law for vectors
* To use the scalar product in the form $\mathbf{a.b} = |\mathbf{a}||\mathbf{b}|\cos\theta$
* To use the scalar product in the form $\mathbf{a.b} = a_1b_1 + a_2b_2 + a_3b_3$
* To know that if two vectors are perpendicular, then $\mathbf{a.b} = 0$
* To calculate the angle between two vectors
* To answer questions like this:
  A is the point (3, –5, 0), B is the point (–5, 2, 4) and C is the point (–1, 3, –7).
  Calculate the size of angle ABC.

What I should already know/be able to do

* Find the coordinates of the midpoint of a line
* Understand the converse of the Theorem of Pythagoras
* Understand the meaning of the components of a vector in two and three dimensions
* Find the magnitude of a vector in two and three dimensions
* Understand negative and zero vectors
* Add and subtract vectors
* Multiply a vector by a scalar
* Use directed line segments
* Understand coordinates in three dimensions
* Use vector pathways in two dimensions

Quick check!

1. Find the midpoint of the line joining A(3, –4) and B(5, 8).
2. A triangle has sides of length 53 centimetres, 45 centimetres and 28 centimetres. Is the triangle right-angled?
3. Calculate the magnitude of the vector with components $\begin{pmatrix} 4 \\ 12 \\ -3 \end{pmatrix}$.

4 Two vectors **u** and **v** have components $\begin{pmatrix} -8 \\ -2 \\ 1 \end{pmatrix}$ and $\begin{pmatrix} 4 \\ 1 \\ -3 \end{pmatrix}$ respectively.
Find the components of $3\mathbf{u} - 4\mathbf{v}$.

5 The diagram opposite shows a trapezium QPSR in which QP is parallel to RS.
If $\overrightarrow{SR}$ represents the vector **a**, $\overrightarrow{SP}$ represents the vector **b** and $\overrightarrow{QR}$ represents the vector **c**, express $\overrightarrow{QP}$ in terms of **a, b** and **c.**

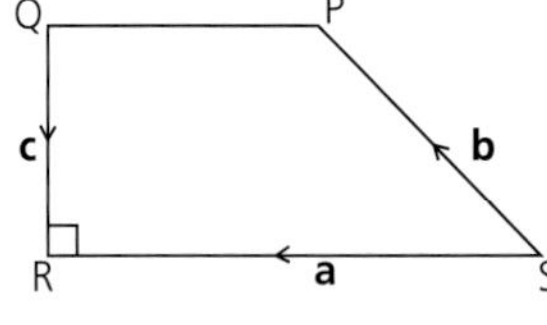

6 An aeroplane travels due south at a speed of 250 kilometres per hour.
At the same time there is wind blowing due west at 40 kilometres per hour.
a) Calculate the resultant velocity of the aeroplane.
b) Calculate the three-figure bearing of the direction of the flight of the aeroplane.

7 The diagram below shows a cuboid OABCDEFG.

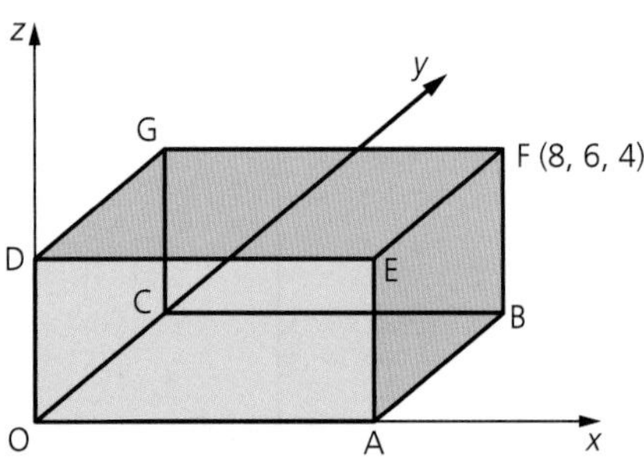

a) Write down the coordinates of points B, G and E.
b) M is the midpoint of GE. Write down the coordinates of M.
c) Find the coordinates of the vector $\overrightarrow{MB}$.
d) Calculate the magnitude of $\overrightarrow{MB}$.

Quick check! – *Solutions*

1 (4, 2)
2 Yes, since $53^2 = 45^2 + 28^2$
3 13
4 $\begin{pmatrix} -40 \\ -10 \\ 15 \end{pmatrix}$
5 $\overrightarrow{QP} = \mathbf{c} - \mathbf{a} + \mathbf{b}$
6 a) 253 km/h
b) 189°
7 a) B (8, 6, 0), G (0, 6, 4), E (8, 0, 4)
b) (4, 3, 4)
c) $\begin{pmatrix} 4 \\ 3 \\ -4 \end{pmatrix}$
d) $\sqrt{41}$

Position vectors

A position vector shows how to arrive at a point from the origin O.
If a point A has coordinates (*x*, *y*, *z*), then point A can be represented by the position vector $\mathbf{a} = \begin{pmatrix} x \\ y \\ z \end{pmatrix}$ where $\mathbf{a} = \overrightarrow{OA}$.

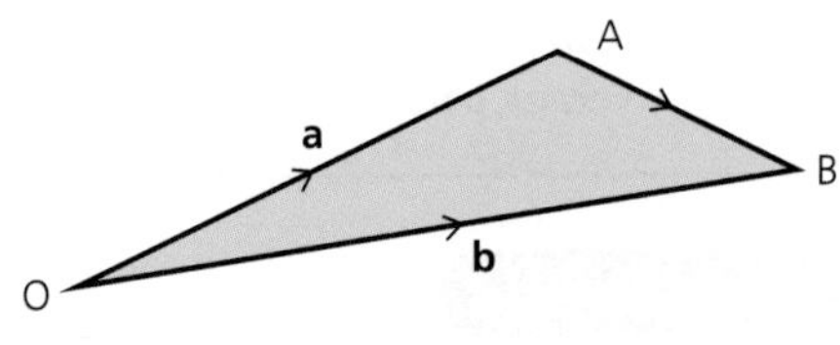

If you know the coordinates of two points, A and B, you can use position vectors to find the components of the vector $\overrightarrow{AB}$ by considering a pathway from A to B via the origin:

$$\begin{aligned} \overrightarrow{AB} &= \overrightarrow{AO} + \overrightarrow{OB} \\ &= -\overrightarrow{OA} + \overrightarrow{OB} \\ &= \overrightarrow{OB} - \overrightarrow{OA} \\ &= \mathbf{b} - \mathbf{a} \end{aligned}$$

Geometric Skills

Example

A is the point (3, –2, 5) and B is the point (5, –1, 9).

a) Find the components of the vector $\overrightarrow{AB}$

b) Find the magnitude of vector $\overrightarrow{AB}$

SOLUTION

a) $\overrightarrow{AB} = \mathbf{b} - \mathbf{a} = \begin{pmatrix} 5 \\ -1 \\ 9 \end{pmatrix} - \begin{pmatrix} 3 \\ -2 \\ 5 \end{pmatrix} = \begin{pmatrix} 2 \\ 1 \\ 4 \end{pmatrix}$

b) $|\overrightarrow{AB}| = \sqrt{(2^2 + 1^2 + 4^2)} = \sqrt{21}$

Exercise 12.1

1 P is the point (2, –1, 3).

a) Write down the components of the position vector **p**.

b) Find the magnitude of the vector $\overrightarrow{OP}$.

2 Three points D, E and F have coordinates (–4, 0, –2), (5, 2, –3) and (–1, 6, 4) respectively.
Find the components of:

a) $\overrightarrow{DE}$ **b)** $\overrightarrow{DF}$ **c)** $\overrightarrow{ED}$

d) $\overrightarrow{EF}$ **e)** $\overrightarrow{FD}$ **f)** $\overrightarrow{FE}$

3 A is the point (5, 1, –6); B is the point (10, –2, –2).

a) Find the components of the vector $\overrightarrow{AB}$.

b) Find the magnitude of vector $\overrightarrow{AB}$. Express your answer as a surd in its simplest form.

4 C is the point (2, 3, –1); D is the point (–1, 7, –13).
Calculate the length of vector $\overrightarrow{CD}$.

Note that for the points A (x_1, y_1, z_1) and B (x_2, y_2, z_2), $\overrightarrow{AB} = \mathbf{b} - \mathbf{a} = \begin{pmatrix} x_2 - x_1 \\ y_2 - y_1 \\ z_2 - z_1 \end{pmatrix}$

and the distance between the points is given by $d = \sqrt{(x_2 - x_1)^2 + (y_2 - y_1)^2 + (z_2 - z_1)^2}$.
This is the three-dimensional version of the **distance formula**.

Example

Calculate the distance between the points P(2, –7, 1) and Q(–1, 0, –4).

Method 1

$$d = \sqrt{(x_2 - x_1)^2 + (y_2 - y_1)^2 + (z_2 - z_1)^2}$$

$$\Rightarrow d = \sqrt{(-1-2)^2 + (0+7)^2 + (-4-1)^2}$$

$$= \sqrt{(-3)^2 + 7^2 + (-5)^2} = \sqrt{9 + 49 + 25} = \sqrt{83}$$

Method 2

$$\overrightarrow{PQ} = \mathbf{q} - \mathbf{p} = \begin{pmatrix} -1 \\ 0 \\ -4 \end{pmatrix} - \begin{pmatrix} 2 \\ -7 \\ 1 \end{pmatrix} = \begin{pmatrix} -3 \\ 7 \\ -5 \end{pmatrix}$$

$$\Rightarrow d = \sqrt{(-3)^2 + 7^2 + (-5)^2} = \sqrt{9 + 49 + 25} = \sqrt{83}$$

Exercise 12.1 (continued)

5 Calculate the distance between the following pairs of points:

a) A(−5, −2, 3) and B (−1, 2, −4)

b) C (−1, 0, 4) and D (6, −3, 2)

c) E(4, −2, 1) and F (3, 0, −3)

d) G (−2, 6, −3) and H (1, −4, 3)

e) J(6, 1, 16) and K (3, −3, 9)

f) L (4, −5, −2) and M (−1, −3, −6)

g) O (0, 0, 0) and P (−2, 3, 7)

6 A triangle has vertices R (6, −6, 1), S (−6, −12, 5) and T (12, −2, 13). Show that triangle RST is isosceles.

7 Use the distance formula to show that QRST is a parallelogram where Q is the point (1, 3, 7), R is the point (5, 6, 8), S is the point (−2, 4, 3) and T is the point (−6, 1, 2).

8 Triangle ABC has vertices A (9, −3, 5), B (11, −4, 2) and C (12, −8, 4). Prove that triangle ABC is right-angled.

Unit vectors

A unit vector is any vector which has a length of 1 unit.

Three important unit vectors are **i**, **j** and **k**. These are three vectors, each of length 1 unit, in the direction of the *x*-, *y*- and *z*-axes respectively.

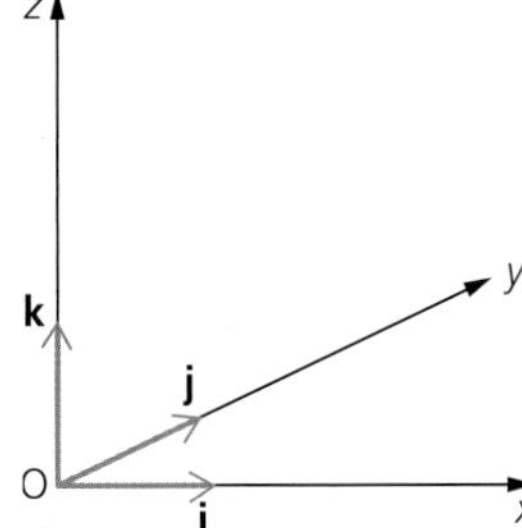

Hence $\mathbf{i} = \begin{pmatrix} 1 \\ 0 \\ 0 \end{pmatrix}$, $\mathbf{j} = \begin{pmatrix} 0 \\ 1 \\ 0 \end{pmatrix}$ and $\mathbf{k} = \begin{pmatrix} 0 \\ 0 \\ 1 \end{pmatrix}$.

If a point P has coordinates (a, b, c), then the vector

$\overrightarrow{OP} = \mathbf{p} = a\mathbf{i} + b\mathbf{j} + c\mathbf{k}$ and has components $\begin{pmatrix} a \\ b \\ c \end{pmatrix}$.

Example 1

Find the length of vector $\mathbf{v} = 2\mathbf{i} - 2\mathbf{j} + 8\mathbf{k}$.

SOLUTION

The vector $\mathbf{v} = 2\mathbf{i} - 2\mathbf{j} + 8\mathbf{k}$ has components $\begin{pmatrix} 2 \\ -2 \\ 8 \end{pmatrix}$.

Hence $|\mathbf{v}| = \sqrt{2^2 + (-2)^2 + 8^2} = \sqrt{4 + 4 + 64} = \sqrt{72} = 6\sqrt{2}$

Hint

If you were asked to find a unit vector in the direction of vector **v**, use the fact that $|\mathbf{v}| = 6\sqrt{2}$. In other words **v** is $6\sqrt{2}$ times greater than a unit vector. As a result the unit vector in the direction of vector **v** has components $\frac{1}{6\sqrt{2}}\begin{pmatrix} 2 \\ -2 \\ 8 \end{pmatrix}$.

Example 2

A unit vector is defined by $\frac{1}{2}\mathbf{i} + \frac{1}{3}\mathbf{j} + a\mathbf{k}$. Find the values of a.

SOLUTION

$$\left(\frac{1}{2}\right)^2 + \left(\frac{1}{3}\right)^2 + a^2 = 1 \Rightarrow a^2 = 1 - \frac{1}{4} - \frac{1}{9} \Rightarrow a^2 = \frac{36}{36} - \frac{9}{36} - \frac{4}{36} = \frac{23}{36} \Rightarrow a = \pm\sqrt{\frac{23}{36}} = \pm\frac{\sqrt{23}}{6}$$

Exercise 12.2

1 Write down the components of the following vectors:

a) $\mathbf{u} = 3\mathbf{i} - 2\mathbf{j} + \mathbf{k}$ b) $\mathbf{v} = 4\mathbf{i} + 3\mathbf{j} - 5\mathbf{k}$ c) $\mathbf{w} = -4\mathbf{i} - 2\mathbf{j} + 3\mathbf{k}$ d) $\mathbf{x} = 3\mathbf{i} - \mathbf{k}$

2 Find the lengths of **u**, **v**, **w** and **x** in question 1.

3 a) Express in component form:

i) $\mathbf{p} = 3\mathbf{u} + 2\mathbf{v} + \mathbf{w}$ ii) $\mathbf{q} = \mathbf{u} - 4\mathbf{v} - \mathbf{x}$

b) Calculate the magnitudes of vectors $\mathbf{p} + \mathbf{q}$ and $\mathbf{p} - \mathbf{q}$.

4 Refer to the diagram in question 6 of Quick check!

a) Express $\overrightarrow{OF}$ in terms of **i**, **j** and **k**.

b) Express $\overrightarrow{GN}$ in terms of **i**, **j** and **k** where N is the midpoint of OA.

5 If $\mathbf{a} = 2\mathbf{i} - \mathbf{j} + 6\mathbf{k}$ and $\mathbf{b} = 5\mathbf{i} + 2\mathbf{j} - 3\mathbf{k}$, find the length of the vector $4\mathbf{a} - \mathbf{b}$.

6 Find the components of a unit vector parallel to $\begin{pmatrix} -1 \\ 1 \\ 2 \end{pmatrix}$. HPQ

7 Find a unit vector parallel to:

a) $\begin{pmatrix} 3 \\ 0 \\ 4 \end{pmatrix}$ b) $\begin{pmatrix} 2 \\ -3 \\ 1 \end{pmatrix}$ c) $\begin{pmatrix} 6 \\ -3 \\ 2 \end{pmatrix}$ d) $\begin{pmatrix} -4 \\ 12 \\ -3 \end{pmatrix}$

8 The vector $\mathbf{u} = \frac{1}{2}\mathbf{i} - \frac{1}{2}\mathbf{j} + m\mathbf{k}$ is a unit vector. Find the values of m.

9 The vector $\mathbf{u} = \frac{1}{4}\mathbf{i} - \frac{1}{3}\mathbf{j} + m\mathbf{k}$ is a unit vector. Find the values of m.

10 The sides of a triangle are represented by the vectors $\mathbf{p} = 4\mathbf{i} + \mathbf{j} - 2\mathbf{k}$, $\mathbf{q} = 3\mathbf{i} - 2\mathbf{j} + \mathbf{k}$ and $\mathbf{r} = -\mathbf{i} + 5\mathbf{j} + 3\mathbf{k}$. Prove that the triangle is right-angled.

Collinear points

When a series of points lie on the same straight line, the points are said to be **collinear**. You have already studied collinear points in Chapter 1 on the straight line. You can show that three points A, B and C are collinear by proving that the gradients of, say, AB and BC are equal (which means that the lines are parallel) and then show they are collinear because the point B lies on both line segments. It is a common point.

You can use a similar approach for points in three dimensions using vectors. Here you show that the vectors are parallel if one is a scalar multiple of the other.

Remember that, in general, vectors **u** and $k\mathbf{u}$ are vectors in the same direction such that the length of vector $k\mathbf{u}$ is k times the length of vector **u**.

Example

D, E and F have coordinates (4, 6, 5), (5, 2, 7) and (7, –6, 11) respectively.

a) Prove that D, E and F are collinear.

b) Find the ratio in which point E divides DF.

SOLUTION

a) $\overrightarrow{DE} = \mathbf{e} - \mathbf{d} = \begin{pmatrix} 5 \\ 2 \\ 7 \end{pmatrix} - \begin{pmatrix} 4 \\ 6 \\ 5 \end{pmatrix} = \begin{pmatrix} 1 \\ -4 \\ 2 \end{pmatrix}$ and $\overrightarrow{EF} = \mathbf{f} - \mathbf{e} = \begin{pmatrix} 7 \\ -6 \\ 11 \end{pmatrix} - \begin{pmatrix} 5 \\ 2 \\ 7 \end{pmatrix} = \begin{pmatrix} 2 \\ -8 \\ 4 \end{pmatrix}$

$\overrightarrow{DE} = \frac{1}{2}\overrightarrow{EF}$ so DE is parallel to EF with point E in common. Hence D, E and F are collinear.

b) The ratio in which point E divides DF is 1:2.

Hint

When we were asked to show that D, E and F were collinear, we could have chosen any two from six possible directed line segments to prove this, namely $\overrightarrow{DE}$, $\overrightarrow{DF}$, $\overrightarrow{ED}$, $\overrightarrow{EF}$, $\overrightarrow{FD}$ or $\overrightarrow{FE}$. The reason that $\overrightarrow{DE}$ and $\overrightarrow{EF}$ were chosen is that we were asked for the ratio in which point E divides DF. By choosing these two directed line segments, we can quickly find the solution to part (b).

Exercise 12.3

1 A is the point (1, –2, 5), B is (5, 0, 1) and C is (13, 4, –7).
Show that A, B and C are collinear and find the ratio in which B divides AC.

2 D is the point (–1, 2, 1), E is (3, 4, –1) and F is (11, 8, –5).
Show that D, E and F are collinear and find the ratio in which point E divides DF.

3 G is the point (4, 2, 10), K is (6, –2, 8) and H is (7, –4, 7).
Show that G, H and K are collinear and find the ratio in which K divides GH. HPQ

4 L is the point (–4, –3, –2), M is (–2, –2, –3) and N is (2, 0, –5).
Show that L, M and N are collinear and find the ratio in which M divides LN.

5 P is the point (4, –3, –6), Q is (6, –1, –4) and R is (13, 6, 3).
Show that P, Q and R are collinear and find the ratio in which Q divides PR.

6 S is the point (0, –1, 4), T is (–1, 0, 3) and U is (–5, 4, –1).
Show that S, T and U are collinear and find the ratio in which T divides SU.

7 X is the point (–12, –9, 5), Y is (–3, –3, 14) and Z is (3, 1, 20).
Show that X, Y and Z are collinear and find the ratio in which Y divides XZ.

8 A is the point (3, –2, 4), C is (7, 2, 16) and E is (4, –1, 7).
Show that A, C and E are collinear and find the ratio in which E divides AC.

The section formula

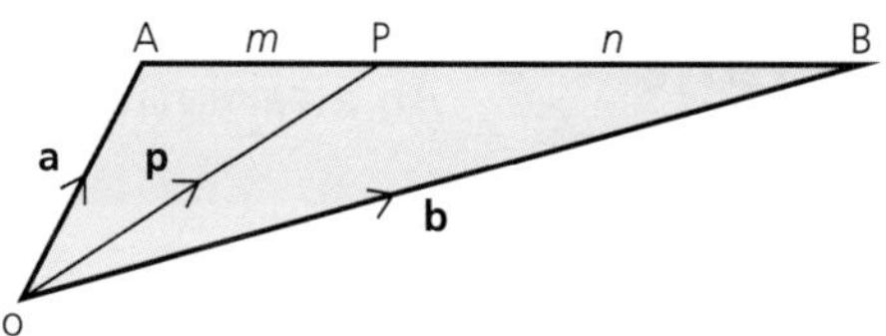

When a point P divides a line AB in the ratio $m:n$, we can use the **section formula** to find **p**, the position vector of P. If we know the coordinates of A and B, we can then find the coordinates of P.

We can derive the section formula by considering a vector pathway in the following diagram.

$$\mathbf{p} = \overrightarrow{OP} = \overrightarrow{OA} + \overrightarrow{AP} = \mathbf{a} + \frac{m}{m+n}\overrightarrow{AB} = \mathbf{a} + \frac{m}{m+n}(\mathbf{b}-\mathbf{a}) = \frac{m\mathbf{a}+n\mathbf{a}+m\mathbf{b}-m\mathbf{a}}{m+n} = \frac{1}{m+n}(m\mathbf{b}+n\mathbf{a})$$

This can be summarised as the section formula:

$$\mathbf{p} = \frac{1}{m+n}(m\mathbf{b}+n\mathbf{a})$$

Example 1

Express the position vector of P which divides the line CD in the ratio 3:5 in terms of **c** and **d** (the position vectors of points C and D).

SOLUTION

$$\mathbf{p} = \frac{1}{m+n}(m\mathbf{d}+n\mathbf{c}) = \frac{1}{3+5}(3\mathbf{d}+5\mathbf{c}) = \frac{1}{8}(3\mathbf{d}+5\mathbf{c}).$$

Example 2

A point P divides the line joining A (8, 3, 0) and B (–2, 8, 15) in the ratio 2:3.

Find the coordinates of P.

SOLUTION

Use the section formula:

$$\mathbf{p} = \frac{1}{m+n}(m\mathbf{b}+n\mathbf{a}) = \frac{1}{2+3}\left[2\begin{pmatrix}-2\\8\\15\end{pmatrix} + 3\begin{pmatrix}8\\3\\0\end{pmatrix}\right] = \frac{1}{5}\left[\begin{pmatrix}-4\\16\\30\end{pmatrix} + \begin{pmatrix}24\\9\\0\end{pmatrix}\right] = \frac{1}{5}\begin{pmatrix}20\\25\\30\end{pmatrix} = \begin{pmatrix}4\\5\\6\end{pmatrix}$$

Hence P has coordinates (4, 5, 6)

In practice, it is probably simpler to use a sketch with crossing lines for the section formula. Check the following working carefully.

A (8, 3, 0)   B (–2, 8, 15)

2 : 3

$$\text{P is } \left(\frac{2\times(-2)+(3\times 8)}{5}, \frac{(2\times 8)+(3\times 3)}{5}, \frac{(2\times 15)+(3\times 0)}{5}\right) = (4, 5, 6).$$

Note An alternative method of finding the coordinates of P is shown below.

x_A to x_B is 8 to −2 $(=-10)$. Point P lies $\frac{2}{5}$ of the way, so $x_P = 8+\frac{2}{5}\times(-10) = 8-4 = 4$.

Use this method to confirm that $y_P = 5$ and $z_P = 6$.

Using this method is a good way to check an answer calculated using the section formula.

Note A special case of the section formula occurs when P is the midpoint of AB. In this case P divides AB in the ratio 1:1 and therefore $\mathbf{p} = \frac{1}{2}(\mathbf{a} + \mathbf{b})$. This should remind you of how you found the midpoint of a straight line which you met earlier.

Exercise 12.4

1 Draw a straight line AB divided into five equal parts by the points C, D, E and F. Write down the value of each of the following ratios:

a) AD:DB **b)** AF:FB **c)** CD:DB **d)** AD:DF **e)** AC:CB

2 Find the midpoint of the line joining A (−3, −4, 7) and B (5, −6, −1).

3 Find the coordinates of P which divides the line AB where: HPQ

a) A is (3, 4, 5) and B is (7, 12, 9) in the ratio 3:1
b) A is (2, 0, −5) and B is (8, 12, 1) in the ratio 1:2
c) A is (9, 3, −8) and B is (14, −7, 7) in the ratio 3:2
d) A is (−7, 1, 2) and B is (−4, 10, −4) in the ratio 2:1
e) A is (1, 4, 7) and B is (9, 4, −9) in the ratio 3:5
f) A is (−3, −1, −6) and B is (4, 13, −13) in the ratio 4:3

4 Express in terms of **p** and **q** (the position vectors of points P and Q) the position vector of:

a) R where R divides PQ in the ratio 1:4
b) S where S divides PQ in the ratio 5:4
c) T where T divides PQ in the ratio 3:7

5 Triangle ABC has vertices A (6, 2), B (8, −6) and C (16, −2).
D is the midpoint of BC and P divides AD in the ratio 2:1.
E is the midpoint of AC and Q divides BE in the ratio 2:1.
F is the midpoint of AB and R divides CF in the ratio 2:1.

a) Find the coordinates of P, Q and R.
b) Make two comments about the medians of this triangle.
c) What name is given to the point of intersection of the medians of a triangle?

6 The points C (4, −2, 0), D (10, 4, −6) and E (13, x, y) are collinear.

a) State the ratio in which D divides CE.
b) State the values of x and y.

Hint Do not use the section formula.

7 The points C (−3, 5, 6), D (1, −3, 2) and E (9, p, q) are collinear.
State the values of p and q.

8 KLMN is a parallelogram with vertices K (−1, −6, 2), L (7, −2, −10), M (5, 12, −10) and N (−3, 8, 2). ACE
P is the midpoint of KL and Q divides NP in the ratio 2:1.
Show that K, Q and M are collinear and find the ratio in which Q divides KM.

Vector pathways in three dimensions

You have already studied vector pathways in two dimensions and should be able to solve problems such as the one given below.

Example 1

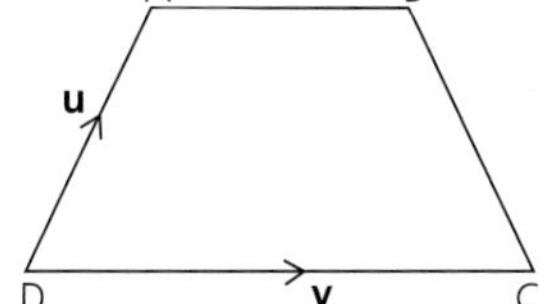

ABCD is a trapezium in which AB is parallel to DC.

The vector $\overrightarrow{DA}$ is represented by **u**. The vector $\overrightarrow{DC}$ is represented by **v**. AB is half the length of DC.

a) Express $\overrightarrow{AB}$ in terms of **v**.

b) Express $\overrightarrow{CB}$ in terms of **u** and **v**.

SOLUTION

a) $\overrightarrow{AB} = \frac{1}{2}\overrightarrow{DC} = \frac{1}{2}\mathbf{v}$

b) $\overrightarrow{CB} = \overrightarrow{CD} + \overrightarrow{DA} + \overrightarrow{AB} = -\mathbf{v} + \mathbf{u} + \frac{1}{2}\mathbf{v} = \mathbf{u} - \frac{1}{2}\mathbf{v}$

We shall now extend the ideas used in that question to vector pathways in three dimensions. You will need to use directed line segments such as $\overrightarrow{AB}$ and remember that vectors in the same direction as the arrow are positive and vectors in the opposite direction to the arrow are negative. Remember that if $\overrightarrow{AB} = \mathbf{u}$, then $\overrightarrow{BA} = -\mathbf{u}$.

Before we start, you should be aware that a parallelepiped is a prism with six faces, each of which is a parallelogram.

Example 2

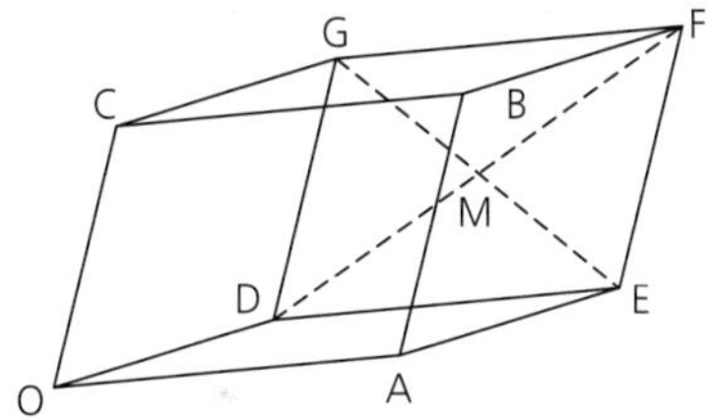

OABC, DEFG is a parallelepiped with O (0, 0, 0) A (6, 2, 3) D (3, 8, 3) and C (2, 4, 7)

Find the coordinates of M, the point of intersection of GE and DF.

SOLUTION

M is the midpoint of GE (or DF), so we will find the coordinates of G and E.

$$\overrightarrow{OE} = \overrightarrow{OA} + \overrightarrow{AE} = \overrightarrow{OA} + \overrightarrow{OD} = \begin{pmatrix} 6 \\ 2 \\ 3 \end{pmatrix} + \begin{pmatrix} 3 \\ 8 \\ 3 \end{pmatrix} = \begin{pmatrix} 9 \\ 10 \\ 6 \end{pmatrix} = \mathbf{e}$$

$$\overrightarrow{OG} = \overrightarrow{OD} + \overrightarrow{DG} = \overrightarrow{OD} + \overrightarrow{OC} = \begin{pmatrix} 3 \\ 8 \\ 3 \end{pmatrix} + \begin{pmatrix} 2 \\ 4 \\ 7 \end{pmatrix} = \begin{pmatrix} 5 \\ 12 \\ 10 \end{pmatrix} = \mathbf{g}$$

$$\mathbf{m} = \frac{1}{2}(\mathbf{e} + \mathbf{g}) = \frac{1}{2}\left[\begin{pmatrix} 9 \\ 10 \\ 6 \end{pmatrix} + \begin{pmatrix} 5 \\ 12 \\ 10 \end{pmatrix}\right] = \begin{pmatrix} 7 \\ 11 \\ 8 \end{pmatrix}$$

Hence M is the point (7, 11, 8).

Exercise 12.5

1 a) In the diagram, $\overrightarrow{OP}$, $\overrightarrow{PQ}$ and $\overrightarrow{QR}$ represent vectors $\mathbf{u}$, $\mathbf{v}$ and $\mathbf{w}$, respectively. OP is equal and parallel to RS.
Find the vector represented by $\overrightarrow{OS}$ in terms of $\mathbf{u}$, $\mathbf{v}$ and $\mathbf{w}$.

b) If OS is parallel to PQ and OS = 2PQ, prove that $2\mathbf{u} = \mathbf{v} - \mathbf{w}$.

2 In the cuboid ABCD, EFGH, $\overrightarrow{AB} = \mathbf{x}$, $\overrightarrow{AD} = \mathbf{y}$ and $\overrightarrow{EA} = \mathbf{z}$.

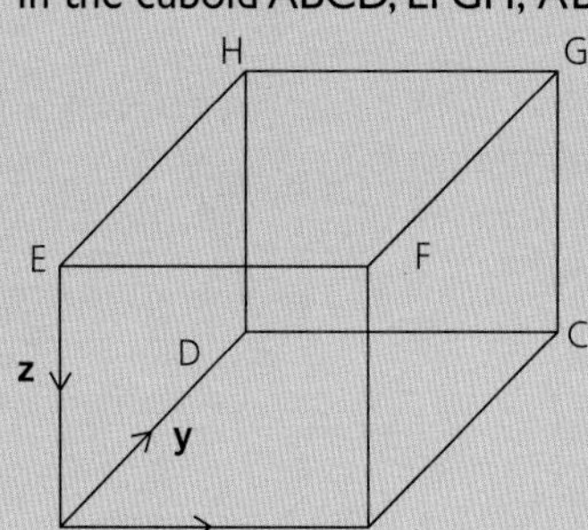

Find the vector represented by $\overrightarrow{HB}$ in terms of $\mathbf{x}$, $\mathbf{y}$ and $\mathbf{z}$.

3 The diagram shows a triangular prism CDE, FGH, $\overrightarrow{CD} = \mathbf{u}$, $\overrightarrow{CE} = \mathbf{v}$, $\overrightarrow{CF} = \mathbf{w}$.

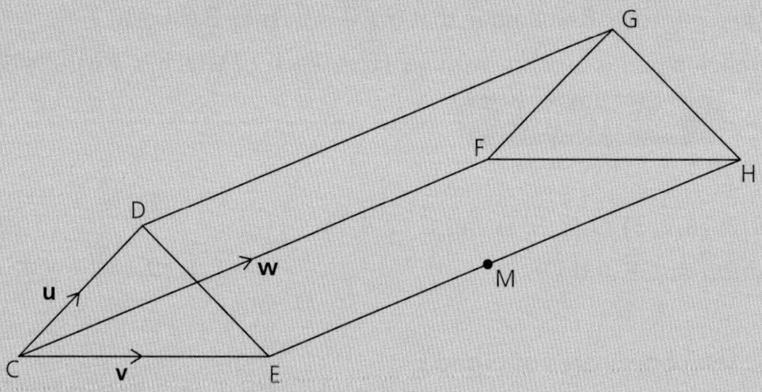

a) Express $\overrightarrow{DE}$ in terms of $\mathbf{v}$ and $\mathbf{u}$.

b) If M is the midpoint of EH, express $\overrightarrow{MG}$ in terms of $\mathbf{u}$, $\mathbf{v}$ and $\mathbf{w}$.

4 Three vectors can be expressed as follows:

$\overrightarrow{KL} = 2\mathbf{i} - \mathbf{j} + 3\mathbf{k}$

$\overrightarrow{LM} = -4\mathbf{i} + 2\mathbf{j} - 6\mathbf{k}$

$\overrightarrow{MN} = -2\mathbf{i} - 4\mathbf{j} + \mathbf{k}$

a) Find $\overrightarrow{KN}$.

b) Hence, or otherwise, find $\overrightarrow{MK}$. HPQ

5 OADB, CEFG is a parallelepiped.

$\overrightarrow{OA} = \mathbf{i} + 3\mathbf{j} + 2\mathbf{k}$, $\overrightarrow{OB} = 4\mathbf{i} + \mathbf{j}$, $\overrightarrow{OC} = 6\mathbf{i} + 3\mathbf{j}$.

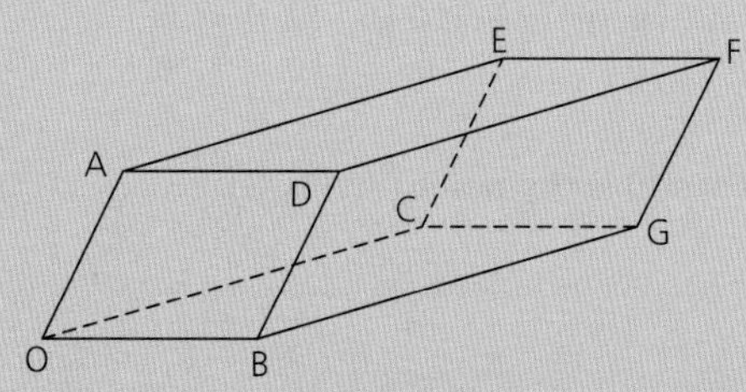

Find the components of:

a) $\overrightarrow{OG}$ b) $\overrightarrow{OF}$

c) $\overrightarrow{CF}$ d) $\overrightarrow{ED}$

e) $\overrightarrow{GE}$ f) $\overrightarrow{BE}$

g) $\overrightarrow{AG}$ h) $\overrightarrow{OH}$, where H is the midpoint of BC.

➜

Geometric Skills

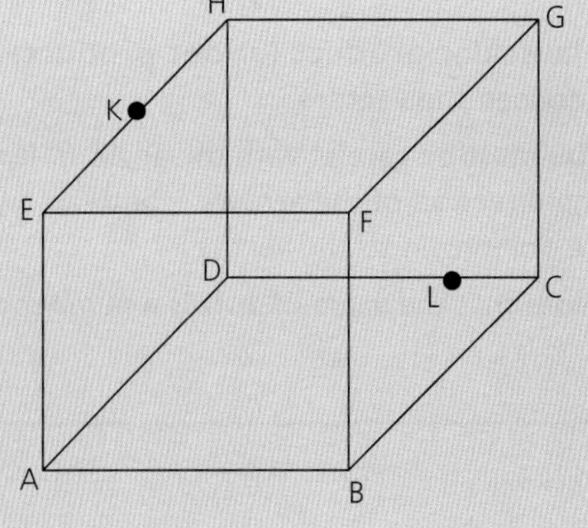

6 ABCD, EFGH is a cuboid.

K is the midpoint of EH and L divides DC in the ratio 2:1

Relative to suitable axes, $\overrightarrow{BC} = 4\mathbf{i} + 2\mathbf{j} + 2\mathbf{k}$, $\overrightarrow{BA} = -3\mathbf{i} + 6\mathbf{j} + 3\mathbf{k}$, $\overrightarrow{BF} = -6\mathbf{i} - 18\mathbf{j} + 30\mathbf{k}$

Find the components of

a) $\overrightarrow{BK}$

b) $\overrightarrow{BL}$

c) $\overrightarrow{KL}$

7 V, ABCD is a right-pyramid with a rectangular base.

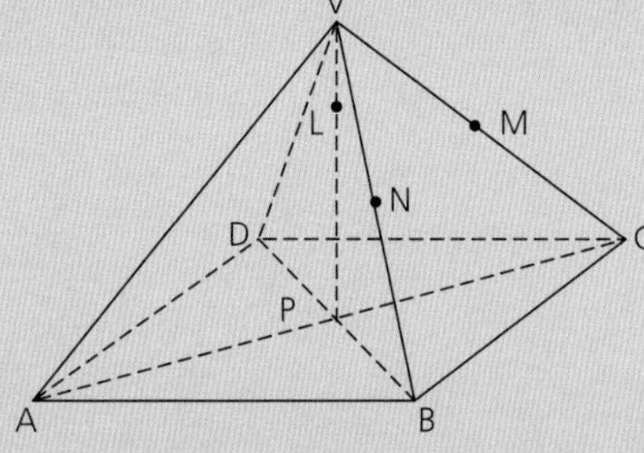

$$\overrightarrow{AV} = \begin{pmatrix} 18 \\ 14 \\ 2 \end{pmatrix}, \overrightarrow{AD} = \begin{pmatrix} -4 \\ 16 \\ 8 \end{pmatrix}, \overrightarrow{AB} = \begin{pmatrix} 8 \\ -4 \\ 12 \end{pmatrix}$$

P is the centre of the base.
M is the midpoint of VC.
N is the midpoint of VB.
L is three-quarters of the way up PV.
Find the components of

a) $\overrightarrow{AM}$

b) $\overrightarrow{DN}$

c) $\overrightarrow{CL}$.

8 O, ABCDE is a pentagonal pyramid.

AC and BD intersect at G.

In the following equations, $\overrightarrow{PQ}$ represents a vector somewhere within this diagram.

Solve each equation for $\overrightarrow{PQ}$.

a) $\overrightarrow{AG} + \overrightarrow{GD} + \overrightarrow{PQ} = \overrightarrow{AO}$

b) $\overrightarrow{BC} + \overrightarrow{PQ} + \overrightarrow{GE} = \overrightarrow{BA} + \overrightarrow{AO} + \overrightarrow{OE}$ ACE

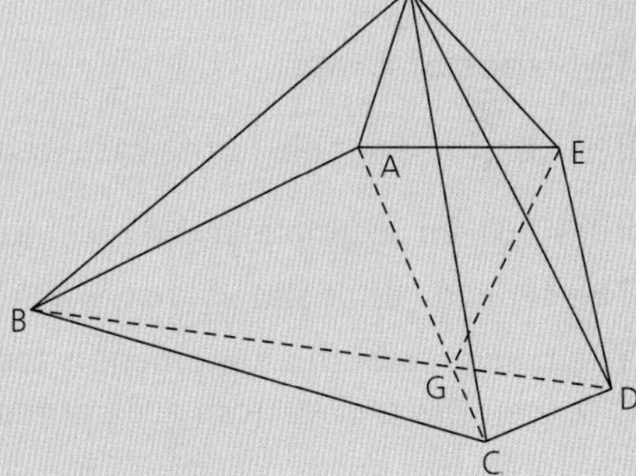

Geometric Skills

The scalar product

The **scalar product** (or **dot product**) of two vectors is given by the formula $\mathbf{a}.\mathbf{b} = |\mathbf{a}||\mathbf{b}|\cos\theta$, where θ is the angle between the vectors.

You must be careful with the angle θ. It must be the angle between the positive direction of the vectors so always check the direction of the arrows – both arrows should be pointing out from the vertex of the angle or both vectors should be pointing in to the vertex.

Note that the value of $\mathbf{a}.\mathbf{b}$ is a number and not a vector, hence the reason it is called the scalar product.

Example

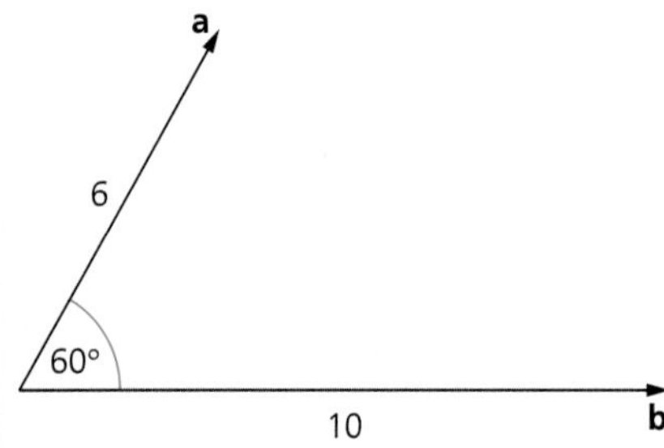

Evaluate $\mathbf{a}.\mathbf{b}$.

SOLUTION

$$\begin{aligned}\mathbf{a}.\mathbf{b} &= |\mathbf{a}||\mathbf{b}|\cos\theta \\ &= 6 \times 10 \times \cos 60^\circ \\ &= 6 \times 10 \times 0.5 \\ &= 30\end{aligned}$$

Two special cases

If $\theta = 0°$, for example in the case $\mathbf{a}.\mathbf{a} = |\mathbf{a}||\mathbf{a}|\cos 0°$, then as $\cos 0° = 1$, $\mathbf{a}.\mathbf{a} = |\mathbf{a}|^2$.

If $\theta = 90°$, for example in the case $\mathbf{a}.\mathbf{b} = |\mathbf{a}||\mathbf{b}|\cos 90°$, then as $\cos 90° = 0$, $\mathbf{a}.\mathbf{b} = 0$.
The second result shows that, when two vectors **a** and **b** are perpendicular, then $\mathbf{a}.\mathbf{b} = 0$.
The converse of this statement is true and is a very important result: if the scalar product of two vectors is 0, then the two vectors are perpendicular.

Exercise 12.6

1 Evaluate **u.v** for each diagram below:

a)

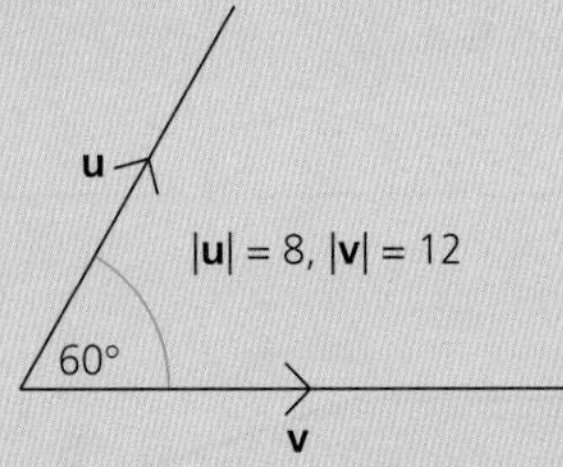

d)

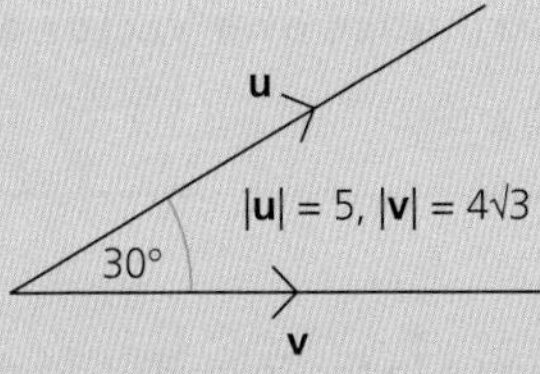

b)

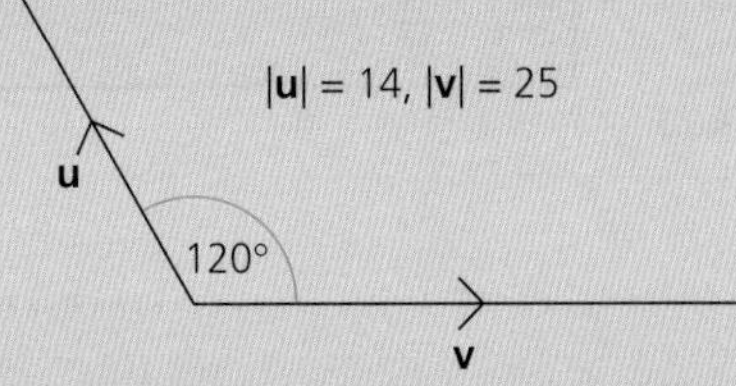

e)

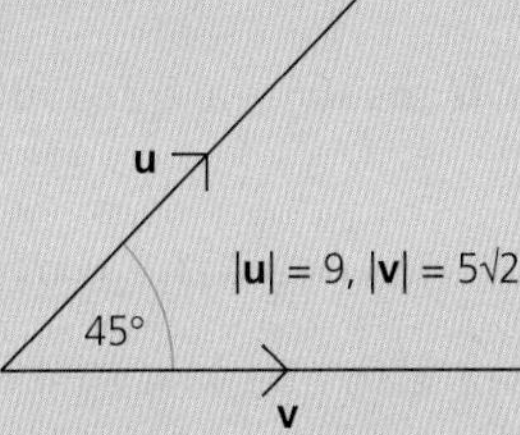

c)

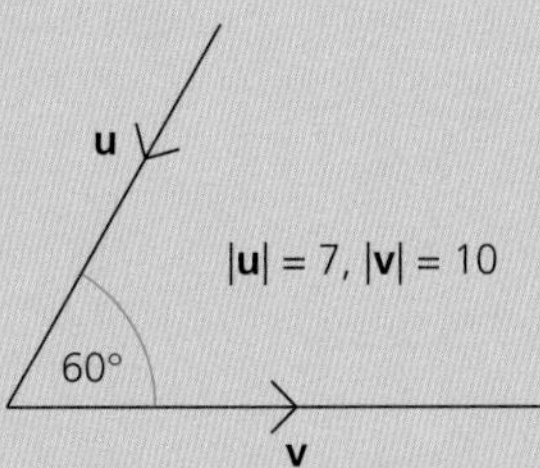

f)

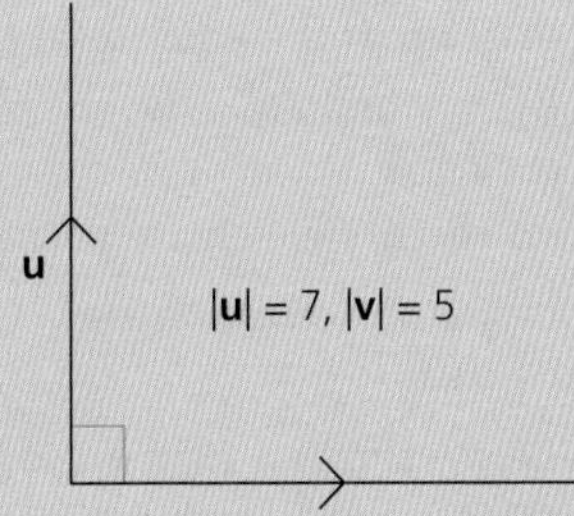

2 PQRS is a rectangle with PQ = 12 units and QR = 5 units.

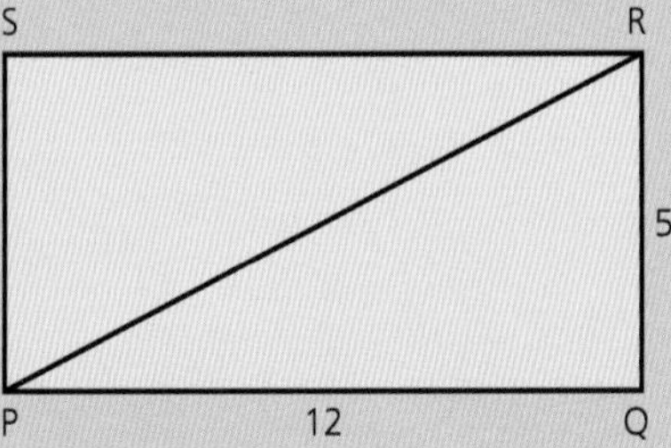

Evaluate:

a) $\overrightarrow{PQ}.\overrightarrow{PR}$ **b)** $\overrightarrow{SP}.\overrightarrow{PR}$ **c)** $\overrightarrow{RQ}.\overrightarrow{RS}$

3 ABC is an equilateral triangle with sides of length 8 units. Evaluate:

a) $\overrightarrow{BA}.\overrightarrow{BC}$

b) $\overrightarrow{AB}.\overrightarrow{AC}$

c) $\overrightarrow{CA}.\overrightarrow{BC}$.

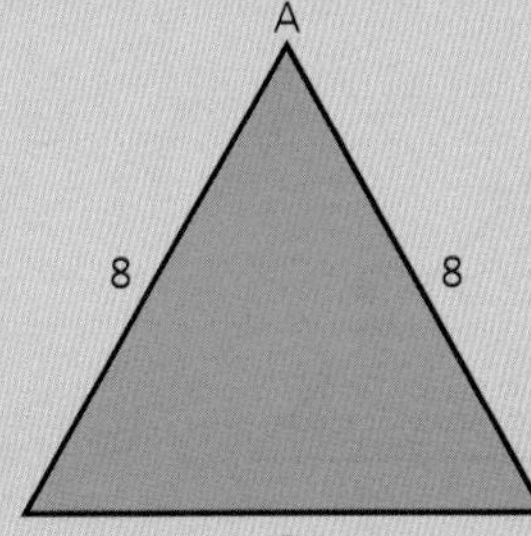

Two other results involving the scalar product will occur in examples.

The scalar product is **commutative**, i.e. $\mathbf{a.b} = \mathbf{b.a}$.

The scalar product is **distributive over vector addition**, i.e. $\mathbf{a.(b+c)} = \mathbf{a.b} + \mathbf{a.c}$.

Example

Vectors **a**, **b** and **c** are shown in the following diagram. Angle HEF = 30°.
Given that $|\mathbf{a}| = 8$ and $|\mathbf{b}| = 6$, find the exact value of $\mathbf{a}.(\mathbf{b}+\mathbf{c})$.

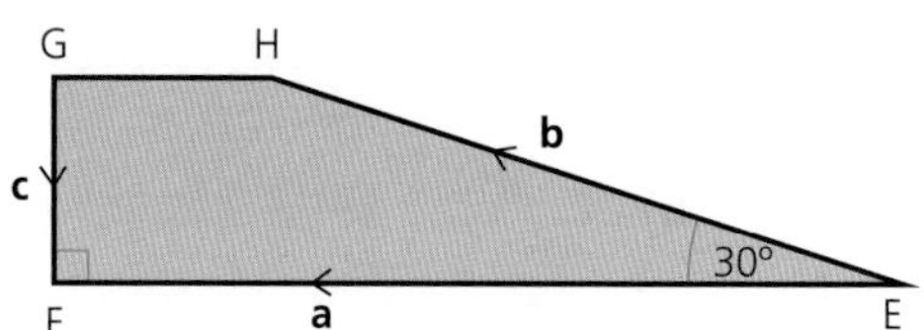

SOLUTION

$\mathbf{a}.(\mathbf{b}+\mathbf{c}) = \mathbf{a}.\mathbf{b} + \mathbf{a}.\mathbf{c} = |\mathbf{a}||\mathbf{b}|\cos 30° + |\mathbf{a}||\mathbf{c}|\cos 90° = 8 \times 6 \times \frac{\sqrt{3}}{2} + 0 = 24\sqrt{3}$

Exercise 12.6 (continued)

4 Find the value of $\mathbf{a}.(\mathbf{b}+\mathbf{a})$ where $|\mathbf{a}| = 5$, $|\mathbf{b}| = 4$ and the angle between **a** and **b** is 60°. HPQ

5 If $|\mathbf{u}| = 7$ and $|\mathbf{v}| = 3$, evaluate $(\mathbf{u}+\mathbf{v}).(\mathbf{u}-\mathbf{v})$.

6 Refer to the diagram of the equilateral triangle in question 3.
Let $\overrightarrow{BA} = \mathbf{u}$, $\overrightarrow{BC} = \mathbf{v}$ and $\overrightarrow{AC} = \mathbf{w}$.

a) Evaluate $\mathbf{u}.(\mathbf{v}+\mathbf{w})$.

b) Identify two vectors which are perpendicular.

7 Refer to the diagram in question 1(a).
Evaluate $\mathbf{u}\cdot(\mathbf{u}+\mathbf{v})$.

8 The diagram below shows a right-angled isosceles triangle whose sides represent the vectors **p**, **q** and **r**. The two equal sides have length 4 units.

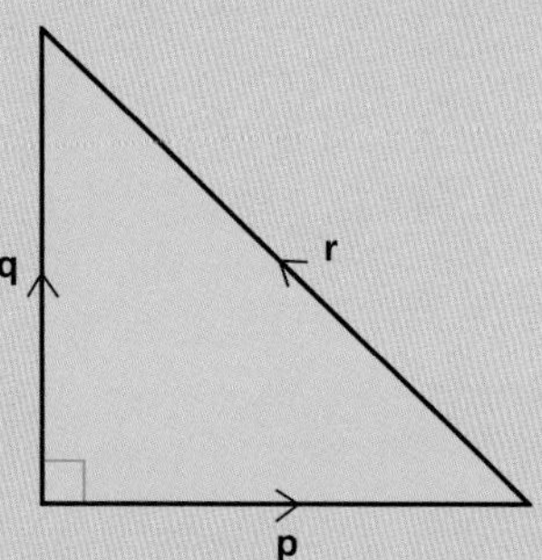

Evaluate $\mathbf{q}.(\mathbf{p}+\mathbf{q}+\mathbf{r})$.

9 Vectors **a**, **b** and **c** are shown in the following diagram. Angle PSR = 60°.

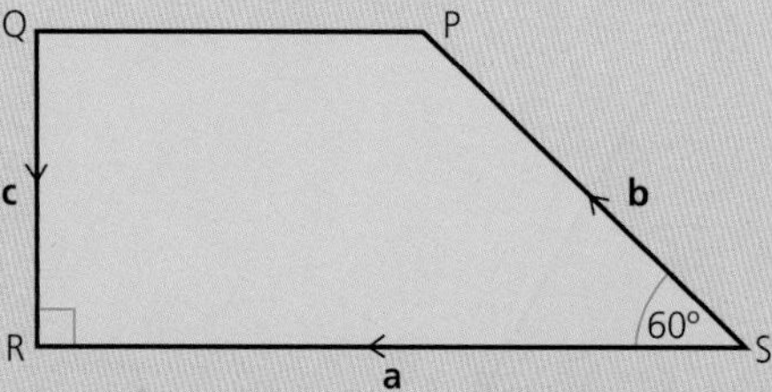

Given that $|\mathbf{a}| = 6$ and $|\mathbf{b}| = 5$:

a) evaluate $\mathbf{a}.(\mathbf{b}+\mathbf{c})$.

b) find $|\mathbf{b}+\mathbf{c}|$.

➜

Geometric Skills

10 In the diagram below, **a**, **b** and **c** are unit vectors and $0 < \theta < \pi$ and $0 < \phi < \pi$. ACE

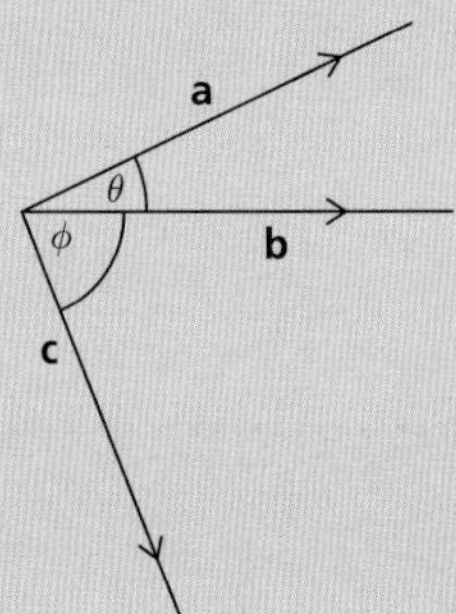

If $\mathbf{a.b} = \frac{4}{5}$ and $\mathbf{b.c} = \frac{5}{13}$, show, without evaluating θ and ϕ, that $\mathbf{a.c} = -\frac{16}{65}$.

11 In the diagram below VOABC is a pyramid whose base OABC is a rhombus in which OA = 1 unit. ACE

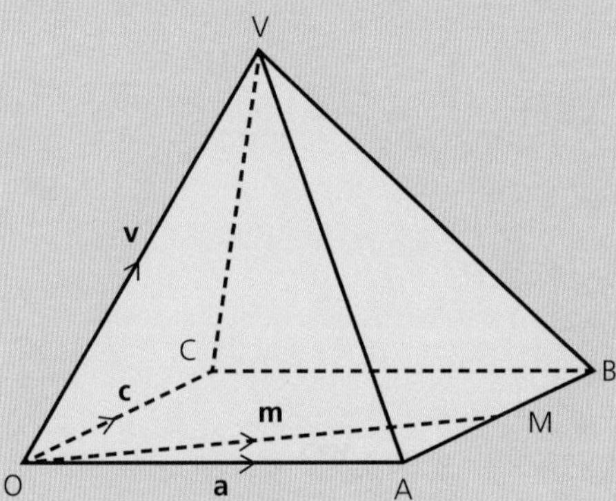

The faces OAV and OCV are equilateral triangles.
$\overrightarrow{OA}$, $\overrightarrow{OC}$ and $\overrightarrow{OV}$ represent the vectors **a**, **c** and **v** respectively.

a) Evaluate **v.c**.

b) M is the midpoint of AB and $\overrightarrow{OM}$ represents the vector **m**. Evaluate **v.m**.

The scalar product in components

The scalar product can also be worked out when vectors are in component form using the following formula:

$$\mathbf{a.b} = a_1b_1 + a_2b_2 + a_3b_3 \quad \text{where } \mathbf{a} = \begin{pmatrix} a_1 \\ a_2 \\ a_3 \end{pmatrix} \text{ and } \mathbf{b} = \begin{pmatrix} b_1 \\ b_2 \\ b_3 \end{pmatrix}.$$

Example 1

Find the value of **a.b** where $\mathbf{a} = 2\mathbf{i} - 3\mathbf{j} + 5\mathbf{k}$ and $\mathbf{b} = 4\mathbf{i} - 3\mathbf{j} + 3\mathbf{k}$.

SOLUTION

$$\mathbf{a} = 2\mathbf{i} - 3\mathbf{j} + 5\mathbf{k} = \begin{pmatrix} 2 \\ -3 \\ 5 \end{pmatrix} \text{ and } \mathbf{b} = 4\mathbf{i} - 3\mathbf{j} + 3\mathbf{k} = \begin{pmatrix} 4 \\ -3 \\ 3 \end{pmatrix}$$

$$\mathbf{a.b} = (2\times 4) + [(-3)\times(-3)] + (5\times 3) = 8 + 9 + 15 = 32$$

Geometric Skills

Example 2

For what value of k are the vectors $\mathbf{u} = \begin{pmatrix} 3 \\ 2 \\ k \end{pmatrix}$ and $\mathbf{v} = \begin{pmatrix} -4 \\ -9 \\ 3 \end{pmatrix}$ perpendicular?

SOLUTION

$\mathbf{u}$ and $\mathbf{v}$ are perpendicular if $\mathbf{u}.\mathbf{v} = 0$.

$$[3\times(-4)]+[2\times(-9)]+(k\times 3)=0 \Rightarrow -12+(-18)+3k=0 \Rightarrow k=10$$

Exercise 12.7

1 If $\mathbf{a} = \begin{pmatrix} 4 \\ 2 \\ 5 \end{pmatrix}$, $\mathbf{b} = \begin{pmatrix} 4 \\ -1 \\ -2 \end{pmatrix}$, $\mathbf{c} = \begin{pmatrix} 7 \\ 0 \\ -1 \end{pmatrix}$ and $\mathbf{d} = \begin{pmatrix} -3 \\ 2 \\ -6 \end{pmatrix}$, evaluate the following:

a) **a.b** **b)** **a.c** **c)** **a.d** **d)** **b.c** **e)** **b.d** **f)** **c.d**

2 Evaluate $\mathbf{u}.\mathbf{v}$ if:

a) $\mathbf{u} = 3\mathbf{i} - \mathbf{j} + 5\mathbf{k}$ and $\mathbf{v} = 4\mathbf{i} - 3\mathbf{j} - \mathbf{k}$

b) $\mathbf{u} = -3\mathbf{i} + 4\mathbf{j} - 2\mathbf{k}$ and $\mathbf{v} = \mathbf{i} - 4\mathbf{k}$ HPQ

c) $\mathbf{u} = 3\mathbf{i} - \mathbf{j} + 5\mathbf{k}$ and $\mathbf{v} = 2\mathbf{i} - \mathbf{j} - 3\mathbf{k}$

d) $\mathbf{u} = -4\mathbf{i} + 2\mathbf{k}$ and $\mathbf{v} = 4\mathbf{i} - \mathbf{j} + \mathbf{k}$

e) $\mathbf{u} = \mathbf{i} - 2\mathbf{j} + 3\mathbf{k}$ and $\mathbf{v} = -4\mathbf{i} + 5\mathbf{j} - 4\mathbf{k}$

3 For what value of m are the vectors $\begin{pmatrix} 5 \\ m \\ -3 \end{pmatrix}$ and $\begin{pmatrix} 2 \\ 4 \\ 6 \end{pmatrix}$ perpendicular?

4 Find the value of k if the vectors $\begin{pmatrix} k+3 \\ 5 \\ -1 \end{pmatrix}$ and $\begin{pmatrix} 2 \\ -8 \\ -10 \end{pmatrix}$ are perpendicular. HPQ

5 A is the point (2, –7, 1), B is the point (3, –2, –8) and C is the point (–2, 1, –3).

a) Find the components of $\overrightarrow{AB}$.

b) Find the components of $\overrightarrow{AC}$.

c) Evaluate $\overrightarrow{AB}.\overrightarrow{AC}$.

6 P is the point (10, –6, 2), Q is (10, 12, 10), R is (–2, 4, 14) and S is (–2, 22, 22).
Show that PS is perpendicular to QR.

7 S, T, U and V are the points (2, 6, 4), (4, 9, 10), (3, 5, 8) and (4, 7, 13) respectively.

a) Find the components of $\overrightarrow{ST}$ and $\overrightarrow{UV}$.

b) The vector $\begin{pmatrix} a \\ b \\ 1 \end{pmatrix}$ is perpendicular to both $\overrightarrow{ST}$ and $\overrightarrow{UV}$. Find a and b.

c) Find a vector of unit length parallel to $\overrightarrow{ST}$

8 ABCD is a quadrilateral with vertices A (8, –3, 7), B (–1, 9, 10), C (–2, 13, 1) and D (7, 1, –2).

a) Find the components of $\overrightarrow{AB}$ and hence prove that ABCD is a parallelogram.

b) If the point P divides AB in the ratio 2 : 1, calculate the coordinates of P.

c) Show that PC is perpendicular to BD.

9 D and E are the points (–2, –2, 4) and (4, –8, –2) respectively. The point F divides DE in the ratio 5 : 1.

a) Find the coordinates of F.

b) If G is the point (p, –8, –4) and FG is perpendicular to DE, find p.

10 H and K are the points with coordinates (4, –1, 5) and (7, –5, 1) respectively.

a) If the point M divides HK in the ratio 1 : k, write down the coordinates of M in terms of k.

b) Given that OM is perpendicular to HK, find the value of k.

The angle between two vectors

We can use the two forms of the scalar product to calculate the angle between any two vectors when they are given in component form.

Remember that $\mathbf{a}.\mathbf{b} = |\mathbf{a}||\mathbf{b}|\cos\theta \Rightarrow \cos\theta = \dfrac{\mathbf{a}.\mathbf{b}}{|\mathbf{a}||\mathbf{b}|}$.

Example 1

Calculate the angle between the vectors **u** and **v** where **u** = 2**i** – **j** + 3**k** and **v** = –4**i** + 3**j** – 12**k**.

SOLUTION

$$\mathbf{u} = \begin{pmatrix} 2 \\ -1 \\ 3 \end{pmatrix} \text{ and } \mathbf{v} = \begin{pmatrix} -4 \\ 3 \\ -12 \end{pmatrix}$$

$$\mathbf{u}.\mathbf{v} = [2\times(-4)] + [(-1)\times 3] + [3\times(-12)] = (-8)+(-3)+(-36) = -47$$

$$|\mathbf{u}| = \sqrt{2^2+(-1)^2+3^2} = \sqrt{4+1+9} = \sqrt{14}$$

$$|\mathbf{v}| = \sqrt{(-4)^2+3^2+(-12)^2} = \sqrt{16+9+144} = \sqrt{169} = 13$$

Let θ be the required angle.

$$\cos\theta = \frac{\mathbf{u}.\mathbf{v}}{|\mathbf{u}||\mathbf{v}|} = \frac{-47}{\sqrt{14}\times 13} = -0{\cdot}966\ldots \Rightarrow \theta = 165{\cdot}1^\circ.$$

Example 2

A is the point (3, –5, 0), B is the point (–5, 2, 4) and C is the point (–1, 3, –7).

Calculate the size of angle ABC.

SOLUTION

As the vertex of the required angle is B, find the components of $\overrightarrow{BA}$ and $\overrightarrow{BC}$.

$$\overrightarrow{BA} = \mathbf{a} - \mathbf{b} = \begin{pmatrix} 3 \\ -5 \\ 0 \end{pmatrix} - \begin{pmatrix} -5 \\ 2 \\ 4 \end{pmatrix} = \begin{pmatrix} 8 \\ -7 \\ -4 \end{pmatrix}$$

$$\overrightarrow{BC} = \mathbf{c} - \mathbf{b} = \begin{pmatrix} -1 \\ 3 \\ -7 \end{pmatrix} - \begin{pmatrix} -5 \\ 2 \\ 4 \end{pmatrix} = \begin{pmatrix} 4 \\ 1 \\ -11 \end{pmatrix}$$

$$\overrightarrow{BA}.\overrightarrow{BC} = (8\times 4) + [(-7)\times 1] + [-4\times(-11)] = 32 + (-7) + 44 = 69$$

$$\left|\overrightarrow{BA}\right| = \sqrt{8^2+(-7)^2+(-4)^2} = \sqrt{64+49+16} = \sqrt{129}$$

$$\left|\overrightarrow{BC}\right| = \sqrt{4^2+1^2+(-11)^2} = \sqrt{16+1+121} = \sqrt{138}$$

Hence $\cos A\hat{B}C = \dfrac{\overrightarrow{BA}.\overrightarrow{BC}}{|\overrightarrow{BA}||\overrightarrow{BC}|} = \dfrac{69}{\sqrt{129}\times\sqrt{138}} = 0{\cdot}517\ldots \Rightarrow A\hat{B}C = 58{\cdot}9^\circ$

Geometric Skills

Exercise 12.8

1 Calculate the angle between each of the following pairs of vectors:

a) $\mathbf{u} = \begin{pmatrix} 3 \\ -5 \\ 2 \end{pmatrix}$ and $\mathbf{v} = \begin{pmatrix} -1 \\ 4 \\ -6 \end{pmatrix}$ **b)** $\mathbf{a} = \begin{pmatrix} 2 \\ 5 \\ 2 \end{pmatrix}$ and $\mathbf{b} = \begin{pmatrix} 3 \\ 0 \\ 8 \end{pmatrix}$

c) $\mathbf{m} = \begin{pmatrix} -4 \\ -2 \\ -3 \end{pmatrix}$ and $\mathbf{n} = \begin{pmatrix} -5 \\ 7 \\ -1 \end{pmatrix}$ **d)** $\mathbf{x} = \begin{pmatrix} -6 \\ 8 \\ 24 \end{pmatrix}$ and $\mathbf{y} = \begin{pmatrix} 8 \\ 12 \\ -9 \end{pmatrix}$.

2 Calculate the angle between the vectors **p** and **q** where $\mathbf{p} = 2\mathbf{i} - 2\mathbf{j} + 6\mathbf{k}$ and $\mathbf{q} = 5\mathbf{i} + 9\mathbf{j} + 13\mathbf{k}$.

3 Calculate the angle between the vectors **v** and **w** where $\mathbf{v} = 4\mathbf{i} - 2\mathbf{j} + 5\mathbf{k}$ and $\mathbf{w} = 6\mathbf{i} - 2\mathbf{j} - 3\mathbf{k}$.

4 A is the point (6, –2, 4), B is the point (3, –2, –1) and C is the point (–4, 0, –2). HPQ
Calculate the size of angle ABC.

5 P is the point (–6, 8, 3), Q is the point (4, –2, –1) and R is the point (–5, –4, 6).
Calculate the size of angle QPR.

6 D, F and E are the points (2, –1, 1), (6, –3, 5) and (8, –4, 7) respectively.
a) Show that D, F and E are collinear and find the ratio in which F divides DE.
b) P is the point (*a*, 2, 4) and DP is perpendicular to EP. Calculate the value of *a*.
c) Show that triangle DPF is isosceles and calculate the size of angle DPF.

7 The diagram below shows a cuboid OABCPQRS.

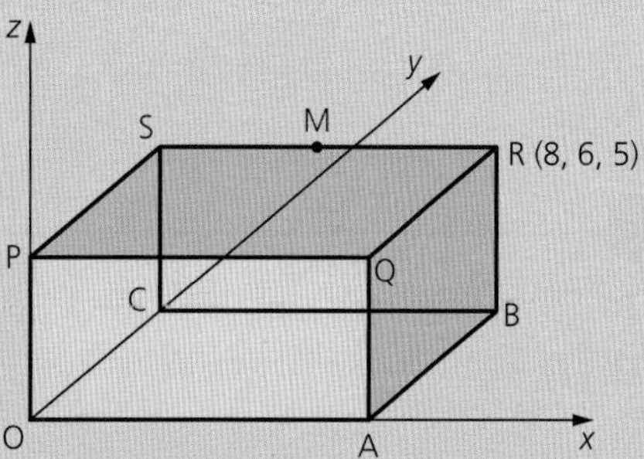

R is the point (8, 6, 5). M is the midpoint of RS.
a) State the coordinates of the points M and Q.
b) Calculate the size of angle RMQ.

8 The diagram shows a cuboid OPQRSTUV.

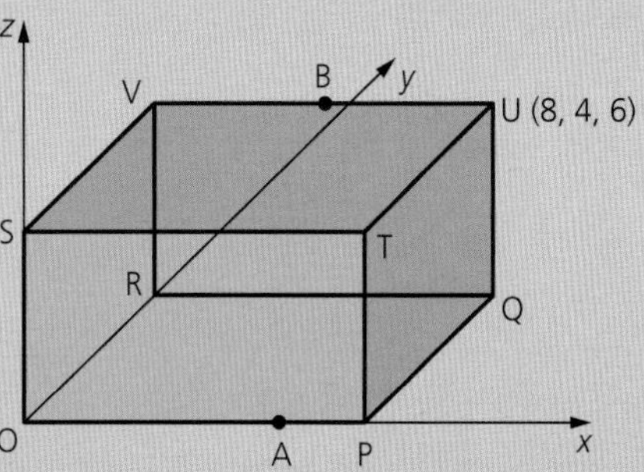

U is the point with coordinates (8, 4, 6). Point A divides OP in the ratio 3:1. B is the midpoint of VU.
a) State the coordinates of A and B.
b) Write down the components of $\overrightarrow{UA}$ and $\overrightarrow{UB}$.
c) Find the size of angle AUB.

➜

Geometric Skills

9 P, Q and R are the points (2, 3, 4), (3, 3, 3) and (5, 6, 10) respectively.
S is the point on PR dividing PR in the ratio 1:2.
a) Find the coordinates of S.
b) Find the size of angle PQS.

10 The diagram below shows a square-based pyramid of height 9 units.

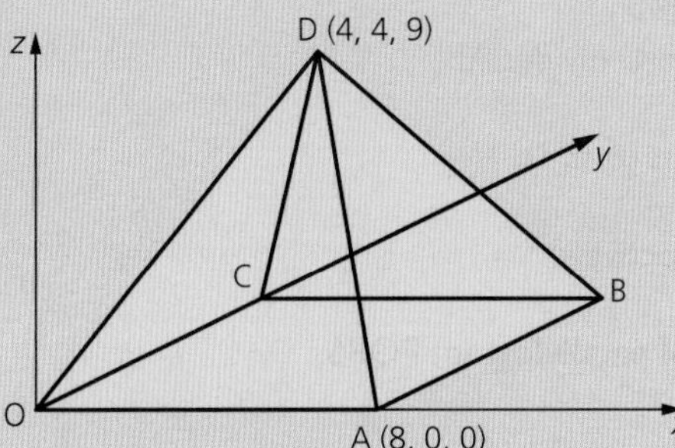

Square OABC has side of length 8 units.
The coordinates of A and D are (8, 0, 0) and (4, 4, 9) respectively. C lies on the *y*-axis.
a) Write down the coordinates of B.
b) Determine the components of $\overrightarrow{DA}$ and $\overrightarrow{DB}$.
c) Calculate the size of angle ADB.

11 X, Y and Z are three collinear points such that $\overrightarrow{XY} = \frac{5}{4}\overrightarrow{XZ}$.
X is the point (–3, 5, 1) and Z is the point (5, 9, –3).
a) Find the coordinates of Y.
b) If W is the point (8, –2, 4), calculate the size of angle XWY.

12 A, B and C are the points (–3, 2, 1), (–2, 0, 3) and (0, 4, –1) respectively. ACE
a) Show that $\cos A\hat{B}C$ equals $\frac{7}{9}$.
b) Hence, or otherwise, prove that the area of triangle ABC is $4\sqrt{2}$ square units.

Checkout

1 Calculate the distance between the points (5, 4, 2) and (6, –6, 4).
2 Find the length of the vector $\mathbf{v} = 3\mathbf{i} - \mathbf{j} + 4\mathbf{k}$.
3 If $\mathbf{p} = 5\mathbf{i} - \mathbf{j} + 2\mathbf{k}$ and $\mathbf{q} = \mathbf{i} + 2\mathbf{j} - \mathbf{k}$, find the length of $2\mathbf{p} - 3\mathbf{q}$.
4 PQR is a triangle such that $\overrightarrow{PQ}$ and $\overrightarrow{RQ}$ have components $\begin{pmatrix} 5 \\ 6 \\ -5 \end{pmatrix}$ and $\begin{pmatrix} 5 \\ -4 \\ -6 \end{pmatrix}$.
If a parallelogram PQRS is completed, what are the components of $\overrightarrow{SQ}$?
5 A, B and C are the points (4, –3, 5), (6, 3, 1) and (9, 12, –5) respectively.
Show that A, B and C are collinear and find the ratio in which B divides AC.
6 C and D have coordinates (4, 2, 1) and (14, 7, –19) respectively.
Find the coordinates of point E which divides CD in the ratio 3:2.
7 If **i**, **j** and **k** are unit vectors along mutually perpendicular axes, find the value of $(\mathbf{i} + 2\mathbf{j}).(\mathbf{j} + 2\mathbf{k})$.
8 Evaluate $\mathbf{u}.\mathbf{v}$ if $\mathbf{u} = 2\mathbf{i} - 4\mathbf{j} + \mathbf{k}$ and $\mathbf{v} = 2\mathbf{i} - 5\mathbf{j} + 8\mathbf{k}$.

9 Three vectors can be expressed as follows:
$\overrightarrow{AB} = 5\mathbf{i} + 2\mathbf{j} - \mathbf{k}$
$\overrightarrow{BC} = -7\mathbf{i} - 2\mathbf{k}$
$\overrightarrow{CD} = 3\mathbf{i} - 5\mathbf{j} + 6\mathbf{k}$

Find the components of vector $\overrightarrow{DA}$.

10 A, B and C are the points (0, 10, 10), (8, 2, 2) and (5, 5, 5) respectively.
a) Prove that A, B and C are collinear and find the ratio in which C divides AB.
b) If O is the origin, prove that OC bisects angle AOB.

11 R is the point (−2, 6, 1), S is the point (2, −2, −3) and T is the point (6, 0, 1).
Calculate the size of angle RST.

12 P, Q and R have coordinates (5, −1, 6), (6, 3, 8) and (2, 5, −3) respectively.
a) Find the coordinates of S such that PQRS is a parallelogram.
b) Calculate the size of the acute angle between the diagonals of parallelogram PQRS.

Summary

Vectors

You should now:

1 know that the distance between two points A (x_1, y_1, z_1) and B (x_2, y_2, z_2) is given by the distance formula $d = \sqrt{(x_2 - x_1)^2 + (y_2 - y_1)^2 + (z_2 - z_1)^2}$.

2 understand three important unit vectors (vectors of length 1 unit) are **i, j** and **k**. These are three vectors in the positive direction of the x-, y- and z-axes respectively.

3 know that if three points A, B and C are such that $\overrightarrow{AB} = k\overrightarrow{BC}$, then A, B and C are collinear (common point and same direction) and you should be able to find the ratio in which B divides AC.

4 be able to use the section formula to find the coordinates of a point P which divides a line AB in a given ratio.

5 be able to solve problems involving vector pathways in three dimensions.

6 understand and be able to use the scalar product $\mathbf{a}.\mathbf{b} = |\mathbf{a}||\mathbf{b}|\cos\theta$, including use of the distributive law.

7 be able to use the scalar product in its component form, i.e. $\mathbf{a}.\mathbf{b} = a_1b_1 + a_2b_2 + a_3b_3$, where $\mathbf{a} = \begin{pmatrix} a_1 \\ a_2 \\ a_3 \end{pmatrix}$ and $\mathbf{b} = \begin{pmatrix} b_1 \\ b_2 \\ b_3 \end{pmatrix}$.

8 be able to use the scalar product in the form $\cos\theta = \dfrac{\mathbf{a}.\mathbf{b}}{|\mathbf{a}||\mathbf{b}|}$ to find the size of an angle.

9 know that for $\mathbf{a}, \mathbf{b} \neq 0$, $\mathbf{a}.\mathbf{b} = 0 \Leftrightarrow \mathbf{a}$ is perpendicular to $\mathbf{b}$.

CHAPTER 13

Differentiating Functions

Problems involving rate of change and the gradient of curves are studied in a branch of mathematics called **differential calculus.** This chapter is an introduction to differential calculus in which we'll look at how to differentiate a range of algebraic and trigonometric functions.

What I am learning

- To know that the derivative of a function is a measure of the
  - rate of change of the function
  - gradient of the graph of the function
- To differentiate algebraic functions which can be reduced to expressions involving powers of x
- To differentiate $k\sin x$ and $k\cos x$
- To differentiate composite functions using the chain rule
- To solve problems like:
  A small rocket is fired into the air. The motion of the rocket is given by the equation $h(t) = 36t - 3t^2$, where $h(t)$ metres is its height after t seconds.
  Find the speed of the rocket after 2 seconds.

What I should already know/be able to do

- Find the gradient of a straight line
- Expand brackets and simplify
- Express a quotient as a sum of terms
- Work with indices
- Work with radians

Quick check!

1 Find the gradient of the line joining the points P (1, –5) and Q (4, 7).

2 Expand the brackets and simplify:

a) $(3x+4)(x^2-2)$ b) $(2y-5)^2$ c) $(a+1)(a-4)(a+3)$

3 Express each quotient as a sum of terms:

a) $\dfrac{x^4+3x^2-1}{x^2}$ b) $\dfrac{n^2+5}{2n}$

4 Find the exact value of:

a) 3^{-2} b) 7^{-1} c) 12^0

d) $8^{\frac{1}{3}}$ e) $9^{\frac{3}{2}}$ f) $16^{-\frac{3}{4}}$

5 Express in the form ax^n:

a) $\dfrac{1}{x^4}$ b) $\dfrac{5}{x^3}$ c) $\dfrac{1}{2x}$ d) $\dfrac{4}{3x^2}$

6 Express in the form $x^{\frac{m}{n}}$:

a) $\sqrt[3]{x^2}$ b) $\sqrt{x}$ c) $\dfrac{1}{\sqrt[4]{x^7}}$ d) $\dfrac{1}{\sqrt{x^5}}$

7 Convert to degrees:
a) π radians b) $\frac{\pi}{2}$ radians c) $\frac{2\pi}{3}$ radians d) $\frac{5\pi}{6}$ radians

Quick check! – *Solutions*

1 4

2 a) $3x^3+4x^2-6x-8$ b) $4y^2-20y+25$ c) $a^3-13a-12$

3 a) x^2+3-x^{-2} b) $\frac{1}{2}n+\frac{5}{2}n^{-1}$

4 a) $\frac{1}{9}$ b) $\frac{1}{7}$ c) 1
d) 2 e) 27 f) $\frac{1}{8}$

5 a) x^{-4} b) $5x^{-3}$ c) $\frac{1}{2}x^{-1}$ d) $\frac{4}{3}x^{-2}$

6 a) $x^{\frac{2}{3}}$ b) $x^{\frac{1}{2}}$ c) $x^{-\frac{7}{4}}$ d) $x^{-\frac{5}{2}}$

7 a) 180° b) 90° c) 120° d) 150°

Introductory problem

A small rocket is fired into the air. The motion of the rocket is given by the equation $h(t) = 36t - 3t^2$, where $h(t)$ metres is its height after t seconds.

Find the speed of the rocket after 2 seconds.

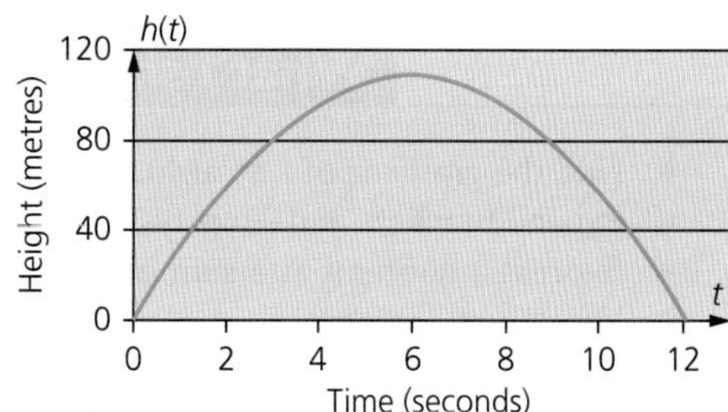

The required speed (i.e. the rate of change of the rocket's height with respect to time travelled) is given by the gradient of the curve at the point where $t = 2$.

In this chapter we will consider how to find the gradient of curves like this one.

The gradient of a curve

The gradient of a straight line is the same at all points on the line.

However, the gradient of a curve depends on where you are on the curve.

For example, the gradient of the curve $h(t) = 36t - 3t^2$ is

- positive at the point (2, 60)
- zero at the point (6, 108)
- negative at the point (9, 81)

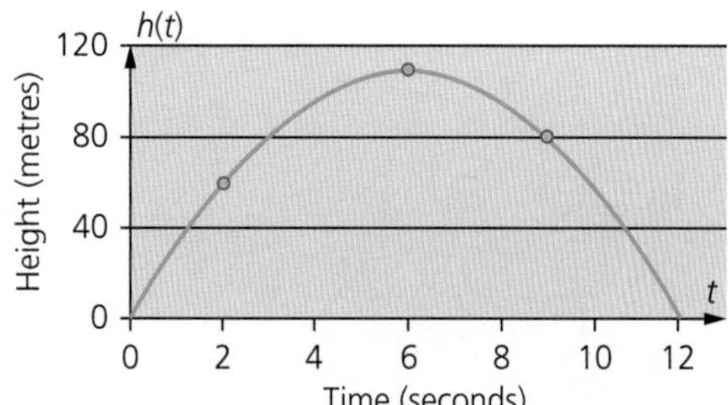

Calculus Skills

The gradient (or rate of change) at point P on the curve is defined as the gradient of the tangent to the curve at the point P.

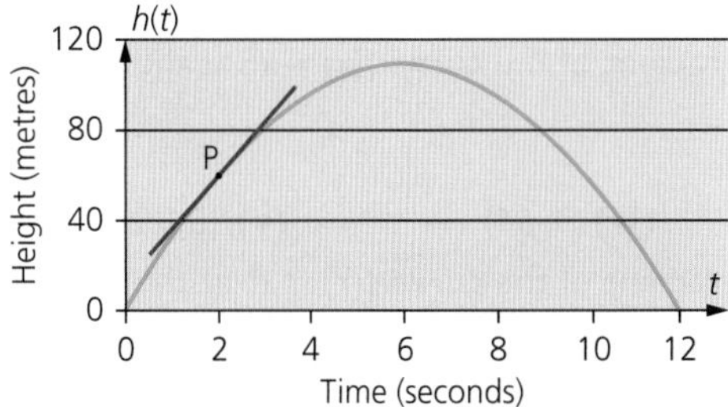

It is difficult to *accurately* draw the tangent to a curve and therefore to *measure* the gradient of a curve at a particular point.

Calculating the gradient of a curve

The method described below can be used to *calculate* the gradient of a curve at a particular point.

If P is a point on the curve $y = f(x)$, and Q is another point on the curve near to P, then the gradient of the chord PQ gives an approximation for the gradient of the tangent to the curve at the point P.

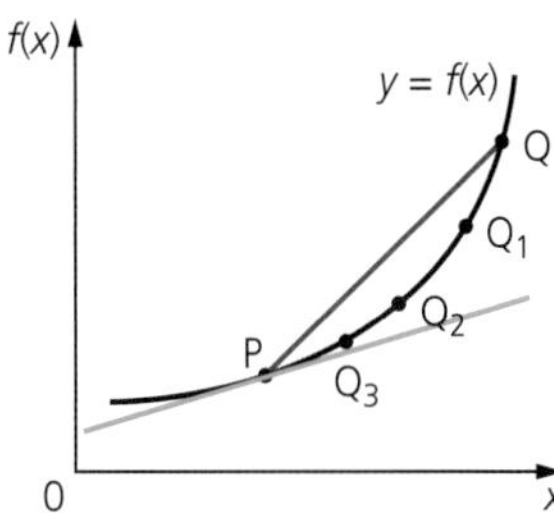

As Q moves nearer to P, say to points Q_1, Q_2, Q_3, then the gradient of the chords PQ_1, PQ_2, PQ_3, give better and better approximations for the gradient of the tangent at P and therefore the gradient of the curve at P.

Example

Find the gradient of the curve $f(x) = x^2$ at the point P (3, 9).

SOLUTION

Let Q be the point $(3{\cdot}5, 3{\cdot}5^2)$, $Q_1(3{\cdot}1, 3{\cdot}1^2)$, $Q_2(3{\cdot}01, 3{\cdot}01^2)$ and $Q_3(3.001, 3.001^2)$.

Then $m_{PQ} = \dfrac{3{\cdot}5^2 - 9}{3{\cdot}5 - 3} = \dfrac{3{\cdot}25}{0{\cdot}5} = 6{\cdot}5$

$$m_{PQ_1} = \frac{3{\cdot}1^2 - 9}{3{\cdot}1 - 3} = \frac{0{\cdot}61}{0{\cdot}1} = 6{\cdot}1$$

$$m_{PQ_2} = \frac{3{\cdot}01^2 - 9}{3{\cdot}01 - 3} = \frac{0{\cdot}0601}{0{\cdot}01} = 6{\cdot}01$$

$$m_{PQ_3} = \frac{3{\cdot}001^2 - 9}{3{\cdot}001 - 3} = \frac{0{\cdot}006001}{0{\cdot}001} = 6{\cdot}001$$

As Q moves nearer to P (3, 9), the gradient of the chord gets nearer and nearer to 6.

The gradient of the tangent and therefore the gradient of the curve $f(x) = x^2$ at the point (3, 9) is 6.

Exercise 13.1

1 **a)** Find the gradient of the curve $f(x) = x^2$ at the point:
(i) (1, 1) **(ii)** (2, 4) **(iii)** (4, 16) **(iv)** (5, 25)
b) Use your answers to (a) to write down an expression for the gradient of the curve $f(x) = x^2$ at the point P(x, y).

2 **a)** Find the gradient of the curve $f(x) = x^3$ at the point:
(i) (1, 1) **(ii)** (2, 8) **(iii)** (3, 27) **(iv)** (4, 64) **(v)** (5, 125)
b) Use your answers to (a) to write down an expression for the gradient of the curve $f(x) = x^3$ at the point P(x, y).

3 **a)** Find the gradient of the curve $f(x) = x^4$ at the point:
(i) (1, 1) **(ii)** (2, 16) **(iii)** (3, 81) **(iv)** (4, 256) **(v)** (5, 625)
b) Use your answers to (a) to write down an expression for the gradient of the curve $f(x) = x^4$ at the point P(x, y).

4 Complete the table below using the results to questions 1, 2 and 3.

f(x)	x	x^2	x^3	x^4	x^5	x^n
Gradient of f(x) at the point (x, y)						

The gradient function

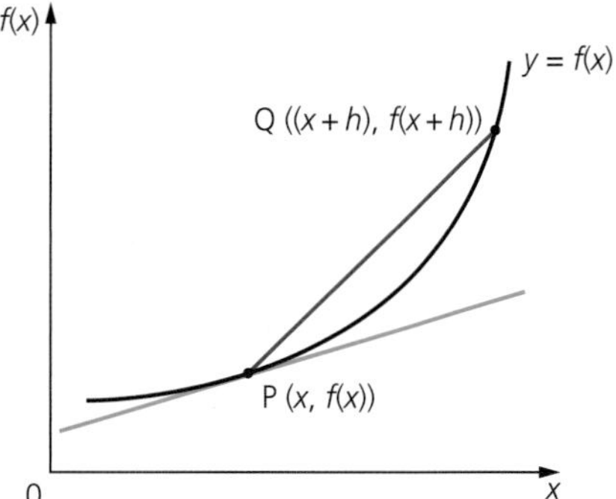

The gradient of $f(x)$ at P = the gradient of PQ as Q → P

$$= \underset{Q\to P}{\text{limit}} \frac{f(x+h) - f(x)}{h}$$

The gradient function is denoted by $f'(x)$, where $f'(x) = \lim_{h\to 0} \frac{f(x+h) - f(x)}{h}$.

The answers to the questions in Exercise 13.1 suggest that the gradient function for the curve $f(x) = x^n$ is $f'(x) = nx^{n-1}$.

Example

Use the formula $f'(x) = \lim_{h\to 0} \frac{f(x+h) - f(x)}{h}$ to prove that if $f(x) = x^2$ then $f'(x) = 2x$.

SOLUTION

$$f'(x) = \lim_{h\to 0} \frac{f(x+h) - f(x)}{h}$$

$$= \lim_{h\to 0} \frac{(x+h)^2 - x^2}{h}$$

$$= \lim_{h\to 0} \frac{x^2 + 2xh + h^2 - x^2}{h}$$

$$= \lim_{h\to 0} \frac{2xh + h^2}{h}$$

$$= \lim_{h\to 0} 2x + h$$

$$= 2x$$

Exercise 13.2

Use the formula $f'(x)=\lim\limits_{h\to 0}\frac{f(x+h)-f(x)}{h}$ to prove that:

1 If $f(x)=5x^2$ then $f'(x)=10x$.

2 If $f(x)=x$ then $f'(x)=1$.

3 If $f(x)=4x$ then $f'(x)=4$.

4 If $f(x)=x^3$ then $f'(x)=3x^2$. → **Hint** $(x+h)^3=x^3+3x^2h+3xh^2+h^3$

5 If $f(x)=2x^3$ then $f'(x)=6x^2$.

6 If $f(x)=x^4$ then $f'(x)=4x^3$. → **Hint** $(x+h)^4=x^4+4x^3h+6x^2h^2+4xh^3+h^4$

7 If $f(x)=\frac{1}{x}$ then $f'(x)=\frac{-1}{x^2}$.

8 If $f(x)=\frac{1}{x^2}$ then $f'(x)=\frac{-2}{x^3}$.

The derivative of $f(x)$

The gradient function, $f'(x)$, is called the **derivative** of $f(x)$.

The process of deriving $f'(x)$ from $f(x)$ is called **differentiation**.

Using the formula $f'(x)=\lim\limits_{h\to 0}\frac{f(x+h)-f(x)}{h}$ to derive $f'(x)$ from $f(x)$ is called **differentiating from first principles**.

Differentiating functions from first principles can be time-consuming and cumbersome, so we will use certain rules for differentiating without proof.

The derivative of $f(x) = ax^n$

If $f(x)=ax^n$ then $f'(x)=anx^{n-1}$, where a is a constant and n is a whole number.

Example

Find the derivative of each of the following functions.

a) $f(x)=x^9$ b) $g(x)=4x^5$ c) $h(x)=8$

SOLUTION

a) $f'(x)=9x^8$ b) $g'(x)=20x^4$ c) $h(x)=8x^0 \Rightarrow h'(x)=0$

Exercise 13.3

Find the derivative of each of the following functions:

1 $f(x)=x^6$	2 $g(x)=x^{20}$	3 $V(x)=x$	4 $r(s)=1$
5 $h(x)=2x^7$	6 $r(x)=-3x^2$	7 $C(n)=4n$	8 $s(u)=5$
9 $f(p)=\frac{1}{2}p^4$	10 $g(t)=\frac{4}{5}t^{10}$	11 $A(x)=\frac{1}{4}x^6$	12 $P(a)=\frac{5}{12}a^8$

Key points

The value of $f'(x)$ when $x = a$ is denoted by $f'(a)$.
The value $f'(a)$ is a measure of:

- the rate of change of $f(x)$ at $x = a$
- the gradient of the curve $y = f(x)$ at the point $(a, f(a))$
- the gradient of the tangent to the curve $y = f(x)$ at the point $(a, f(a))$.

Example

For $f(t) = 2t^3$, find the value of:

a) $f'(4)$
b) the derivative of f at $t = 5$
c) the gradient of f at $t = -2$
d) the rate of change of f at $t = \frac{1}{3}$

SOLUTION

$f'(t) = 6t^2 \Rightarrow$

a) $f'(4) = 6 \times 4^2 = 96$
b) $f'(5) = 6 \times 5^2 = 150$
c) $f'(-2) = 6 \times (-2)^2 = 24$
d) $f'\left(\frac{1}{3}\right) = 6 \times \left(\frac{1}{3}\right)^2 = \frac{2}{3}$

Exercise 13.4

1 For $f(x) = x^4$, find the value of:
 a) the derivative of f at $x = 2$
 b) $f'(3)$
 c) the gradient of f at $x = -1$
 d) the rate of change of f at $x = \frac{1}{2}$

2 Find the rate of change of $s(t) = t^5$ at $t = 2$.

3 Find the gradient of the tangent to the curve $g(x) = 4x^3$ at the point $\left(\frac{1}{4}, \frac{1}{16}\right)$.

4 Find the gradient of the curve $A(x) = \frac{1}{3}x^2$ at the point $(-6, 12)$. HPQ

5 If $C(n) = n^3$, find two possible values for a given that $C'(a) = 75$. ACE

6 Find the coordinates of the point on the curve $f(x) = \frac{1}{2}x^4$ at which the gradient is 16. ACE

7 Prove that the gradient of the curve $f(x) = 3x^5$ is never negative. ACE

The derivative of a sum or product of terms

- If $f(x) = g(x) + h(x) + \dots$ then $f'(x) = g'(x) + h'(x) + \dots$.
- To find the derivative of a product of terms, first express it as a sum of terms and then differentiate term by term.

Example

Find the derivative of each of the following functions:

a) $f(x)=2x^5-3x^4+7x-2$

b) $g(t)=(t+3)(2t-1)$

SOLUTION

a) $f'(x)=10x^4-12x^3+7$

b) $g(t)=2t^2+5t-3 \Rightarrow g'(t)=4t+5$

Exercise 13.5

Find the derivative of each of the following functions:

1 $f(x)=x^4-2x^3+4x^2-5x+3$

2 $g(x)=7+5x-\frac{2}{3}x^3$

3 $h(x)=(3x-2)(x+4)$

4 $f(t)=(1-t)(5-t)$

5 $g(n)=(n+6)^2$

6 $A(r)=(2r-3)^2$

7 $V(t)=7t(2-t)$

8 $m(x)=(x^2+4)(2x+1)$ HPQ

9 $f(p)=(p+1)(p+3)(p+5)$

10 $S(d)=(d+2)^3$

11 Given that $P(x)=(x-1)(x^3+1)$, find $P'(2)$.

12 Find the gradient of the curve $f(x)=3x(x+1)$ at the point $(-2, 6)$.

13 Find the rate of change of $V(h)=h(1-h)^2$ at $h=3$.

14 A small rocket is fired into the air. The motion of the rocket is given by the equation $h(t) = 36t - 3t^2$, where $h(t)$ metres is its height after t seconds. Find the speed of the rocket after 2 seconds. ACE

15 Find the gradient of the tangent to the curve $g(x)=(x-1)^3$ at the point $(0,-1)$.

16 Does the curve $g(x)=2x(5-x)$ slope up or down at the point $(3,12)$? Explain your answer. ACE

17 If $f(x)=x^3+2x$ find two possible values for a given that $f'(a)=50$. ACE

18 Find the coordinates of the point on the curve $f(x)=5x^2-3x$ at which the gradient is 7.

19 Find the coordinates of the point on the curve $g(x)=(x-7)^2$ at which the gradient is -2.

Differentiating functions involving rational powers of *x*

The rule for differentiating $f(x)=ax^n$ also applies when n is a rational number.
That is, $f(x)=ax^n \Rightarrow f'(x)=anx^{n-1}$, where a is a constant and n is a rational number.

Example

Find the derivative of each of the following functions:

a) $f(x)=2x^{-5}$

b) $g(x)=x^{\frac{4}{3}}$

c) $v(t)=8t^{\frac{3}{4}}$

SOLUTION

a) $f'(x)=2\times -5x^{-6}=-10x^{-6}$

b) $g'(x)=\frac{4}{3}x^{\frac{1}{3}}=\frac{4x^{\frac{1}{3}}}{3}$

c) $v'(t)=8\times\frac{3}{4}t^{-\frac{1}{4}}=6t^{-\frac{1}{4}}$

Calculus Skills

Exercise 13.6

Find the derivative of each of the following functions:

1 $f(x)=x^{-2}$ 2 $f(x)=3x^{-7}$ 3 $g(x)=\frac{1}{10}x^{-30}$ 4 $g(x)=x^{\frac{5}{2}}$ 5 $h(x)=2x^{\frac{7}{4}}$

6 $f(a)=\frac{1}{3}a^{\frac{6}{5}}$ 7 $A(h)=h^{\frac{4}{7}}$ 8 $C(n)=3n^{\frac{5}{6}}$ 9 $f(t)=t^{-\frac{1}{5}}$ 10 $s(u)=4u^{-\frac{5}{4}}$

Reminders $\frac{1}{x^n}=x^{-n}$ $\sqrt[n]{x^m}=x^{\frac{m}{n}}$

Example

Find the derivative of each of the following functions:

a) $g(x)=\frac{1}{x^4}$ b) $f(x)=\sqrt[3]{x^4}$ c) $f(t)=\sqrt[4]{t}$ d) $P(n)=\frac{1}{\sqrt{n^5}}$

SOLUTION

a) $g(x)=x^{-4} \Rightarrow g'(x)=-4x^{-5}=-\frac{4}{x^5}$

b) $f(x)=x^{\frac{4}{3}} \Rightarrow f'(x)=\frac{4}{3}x^{\frac{1}{3}}=\frac{4\sqrt[3]{x}}{3}$

c) $f(t)=t^{\frac{1}{4}} \Rightarrow f'(t)=\frac{1}{4}t^{-\frac{3}{4}}=\frac{1}{4t^{\frac{3}{4}}}=\frac{1}{4\sqrt[4]{t^3}}$

d) $P(n)=n^{-\frac{5}{2}} \Rightarrow f'(n)=-\frac{5}{2}n^{-\frac{7}{2}}=-\frac{5}{2n^{\frac{7}{2}}}=-\frac{5}{2\sqrt{n^7}}$

Exercise 13.7

Find the derivative of each of the following functions.

1 $f(x)=\frac{1}{x^3}$ 2 $g(x)=\frac{1}{x^5}$ 3 $h(x)=\sqrt[4]{x^9}$ 4 $f(t)=\sqrt{t^5}$

5 $m(n)=\sqrt[3]{n^2}$ 6 $g(t)=\sqrt{t}$ 7 $g(u)=\frac{1}{\sqrt[3]{u^7}}$ 8 $m(a)=\frac{1}{\sqrt[5]{a^2}}$

9 Given that $f(x)=\frac{1}{x^2}$, find $f'(2)$. HPQ

10 Find the gradient of the curve $f(x)=\sqrt{x^3}$ at the point (4, 8). HPQ

11 Find the gradient of the tangent to the curve $f(x)=\frac{1}{x}$ at the point $\left(3,\frac{1}{3}\right)$.

12 Find the rate of change of $h(t)=\frac{1}{\sqrt{t}}$ at $t=4$.

Example

Find the derivative of each of the following functions:

a) $f(p)=\frac{1}{3p^2}$ b) $h(t)=\frac{t}{5}-\frac{4}{t}$

c) $g(s)=\sqrt{s}(s-\sqrt{s})$ d) $C(n)=\left(n+\frac{1}{n}\right)\left(2n-\frac{1}{n}\right)$

SOLUTION

a) $f(p) = \frac{1}{3}p^{-2} \Rightarrow f'(p) = -\frac{2}{3}p^{-3} = -\frac{2}{3p^3}$

b) $h(t) = \frac{1}{5}t - 4t^{-1} \Rightarrow h'(t) = \frac{1}{5} + 4t^{-2} = \frac{1}{5} + \frac{4}{t^2}$

c) $g(s) = s^{\frac{1}{2}}(s - s^{\frac{1}{2}}) = s^{\frac{3}{2}} - s \Rightarrow g'(s) = \frac{3}{2}s^{\frac{1}{2}} - 1 = \frac{3\sqrt{s}}{2} - 1$

d) $C(n) = 2n^2 + 1 - \frac{1}{n^2} = 2n^2 + 1 - n^{-2} \Rightarrow C'(n) = 4n + 2n^{-3} = 4n + \frac{2}{n^3}$

Exercise 13.8

Find the derivative of each of the following functions:

1 $h(t) = \frac{1}{4t^8}$
2 $f(p) = \frac{4}{p^8}$
3 $g(t) = \frac{5}{2t^6}$
4 $h(x) = 2\sqrt{x^5}$
5 $r(s) = 6\sqrt[3]{s^2}$
6 $v(x) = 7\sqrt{x}$
7 $q(r) = \frac{10}{\sqrt{r}}$
8 $m(a) = \frac{4}{5\sqrt{a^3}}$
9 $h(t) = 3t^2 + \frac{1}{t}$
10 $r(u) = 2\sqrt{u^5} - \frac{3}{4u^4}$
11 $k(x) = 6\sqrt[3]{x^4} + \frac{6}{\sqrt{x}}$
12 $u(t) = t\sqrt{t}(2+t)$
13 $v(u) = \left(\sqrt{u} - 3\right)^2$
14 $f(x) = \left(x + \frac{2}{x}\right)\left(x + \frac{3}{x}\right)$
15 $h(c) = \left(\frac{1}{c^2} + 2c\right)^2$
16 $g(p) = \left(\sqrt{p} + \frac{1}{\sqrt{p}}\right)\left(\frac{3}{\sqrt{p}} - \sqrt{p}\right)$

The derivative of a rational function

If $f(x) = \frac{g(x)}{h(x)}$ then rearrange $f(x)$ into a sum of terms and differentiate term by term.

Example

Find the derivative of each of the following functions:

a) $f(x) = \frac{x^3 + 4x - 1}{x}$

b) $g(t) = \frac{2t - 1}{\sqrt{t}}$

SOLUTION

a) $f(x) = \frac{x^3}{x} + \frac{4x}{x} - \frac{1}{x} = x^2 + 4 - x^{-1} \Rightarrow f'(x) = 2x + x^{-2} = 2x + \frac{1}{x^2}$

b) $g(t) = \frac{2t}{t^{\frac{1}{2}}} - \frac{1}{t^{\frac{1}{2}}} = 2t^{\frac{1}{2}} - t^{-\frac{1}{2}} \Rightarrow g'(t) = t^{-\frac{1}{2}} + \frac{1}{2}t^{-\frac{3}{2}} = \frac{1}{t^{\frac{1}{2}}} + \frac{1}{2t^{\frac{3}{2}}} = \frac{1}{\sqrt{t}} + \frac{1}{2\sqrt{t^3}}$

Exercise 13.9

Find the derivative of each of the following functions:

1 $f(x)=\dfrac{x^4-x+2}{x}$

2 $g(x)=\dfrac{2x^3+x^2-3}{x^3}$

3 $h(x)=\dfrac{1-4x}{x^2}$

4 $k(x)=\dfrac{(x+3)(2-x)}{x}$ HPQ

5 $B(n)=\dfrac{(2n-3)(n+1)}{3n}$

6 $g(t)=\dfrac{(t-4)^2}{2t^2}$

7 $f(t)=\dfrac{t^2+6t}{\sqrt{t}}$ HPQ

8 $r(s)=\dfrac{1-2s}{s\sqrt{s}}$

9 $h(t)=\dfrac{t^2+2t+3}{\sqrt[3]{t}}$

Another notation for the derivative

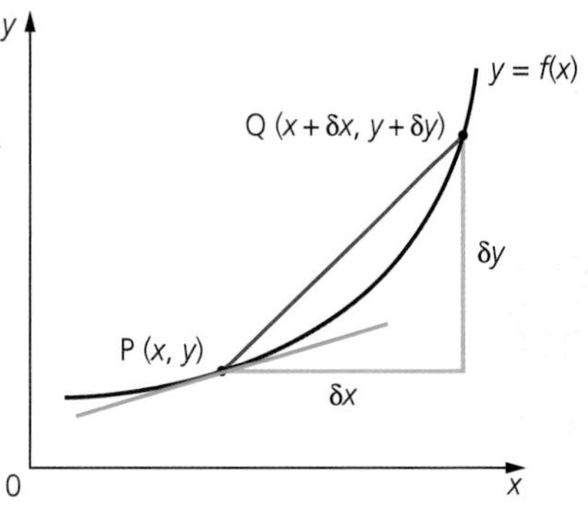

Instead of writing the derivative as $f'(x)$, **Leibniz notation** can be used.

If P has coordinates (x, y) and Q has coordinates $(x+\delta x, y+\delta y)$, where δx and δy denote small changes in x and y respectively, then

$$m_{PQ}=\frac{(y+\delta y)-y}{(x+\delta x)-x}=\frac{\delta y}{\delta x} \text{ and } f'(x)=\lim_{\delta x\to 0}\frac{\delta y}{\delta x} \text{ which is denoted by } \frac{dy}{dx}.$$

Equivalent notations for the derivative: $f'(x)$, $\dfrac{dy}{dx}$, $\dfrac{d}{dx}(f(x))$.

For example, $f(x)=x^2 \Rightarrow f'(x)=2x$

$$y=x^2 \Rightarrow \frac{dy}{dx}=2x$$

$$\frac{d}{dx}(x^2)=2x$$

Example 1

Find the derivative of $y=2x^3-5x^2+7x-4$.

SOLUTION

$$\frac{dy}{dx}=6x^2-10x+7$$

Example 2

Find $\dfrac{d}{dt}\left(2t+\dfrac{1}{2t}\right)$.

SOLUTION

$$\frac{d}{dt}\left(2t+\frac{1}{2}t^{-1}\right)=2-\frac{1}{2}t^{-2}=2-\frac{1}{2t^2}$$

Example 3

Differentiate $p = 10\sqrt{s^3}$ with respect to s.

SOLUTION

$$p = 10s^{\frac{3}{2}} \Rightarrow \frac{dp}{ds} = 10 \times \frac{3}{2}s^{\frac{1}{2}} = 15\sqrt{s}$$

Example 4

Find the rate of change of the surface area, $A = 4\pi r^2$, of a sphere with respect to its radius, when the radius is 3 units.

SOLUTION

$$A = 4\pi r^2 \Rightarrow \frac{dA}{dr} = 8\pi r \quad \text{when } r = 3,\ \frac{dA}{dr} = 24\pi.$$

Exercise 13.10

1 Differentiate each of the following with respect to the relevant variable:

a) $2x^5 + 9x - 6$ **b)** $t - \frac{1}{t^3}$ **c)** $2\sqrt{u} + 9\sqrt[3]{u}$ **d)** $(3p-2)(p+4)$

e) $(4n+5)^2$ **f)** $\sqrt{a}(a-4)$ **g)** $\frac{5r^3 + r^2 - 2}{r^2}$ **h)** $\frac{(\sqrt{x}-3)^2}{\sqrt{x}}$

2 Given that $T = 3v^2(2+v)$, find the derivative of T at $v = 0 \cdot 5$. HPQ

3 Given that $A = n^2\left(4 - \frac{1}{n^3}\right)$, find the rate of change of A at $n = -1$.

4 The distance s metres travelled in t seconds by a falling object is given by the formula $s = 5t^2$.
Find the speed of the object after 3 seconds. ACE

5 Find the gradient of the tangent to the curve $y = 4x + x^3$ at the point $(2, 16)$.

6 Find the gradient of the curve $y = 3\sqrt{x}$ at the point (4, 6).

7 Find the coordinates of the points on the curve $y = x^3 - 3x^2 - 5x + 10$ at which the gradient is 4.

8 Find the coordinates of the points on the curve $y = \frac{20}{x}$ at which the gradient is -5.

9 A tangent to the curve $y = x^2 - 6x + 1$ is parallel to the x-axis. ACE
Find the coordinates of the point of contact of the tangent and the curve.

10 Prove that the gradient of the curve $y = \frac{8}{x}$ is always negative. ACE

11 Prove that the gradient of the curve $y = x^3 - 3x^2 + 3x - 1$ is never negative. ACE

The derivative of sin x

The diagram shows part of the graph of $y = \sin x$ with tangents drawn at $x = 0, \frac{\pi}{2}, \pi, \frac{3\pi}{2}$ and 2π.

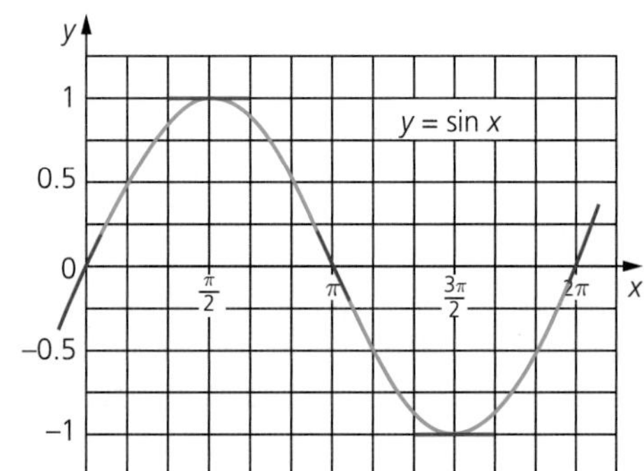

The gradients of these and other tangents have been found and plotted in the lower diagram.

This can be done manually or by using a graph drawing package.

The resulting curve is the graph of $y = \text{gradient of } \sin x$.

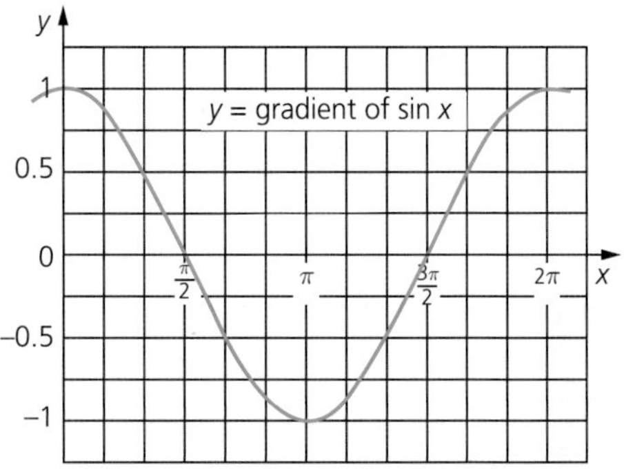

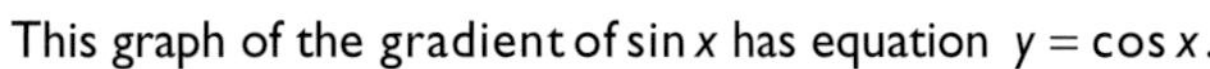

This graph of the gradient of $\sin x$ has equation $y = \cos x$.

This suggests that $\frac{d}{dx}(\sin x) = \cos x$, or in functional notation

$f(x) = \sin x \Rightarrow f'(x) = \cos x$

This can be confirmed by differentiating $f(x) = \sin x$ from first principles:

$$f'(x) = \lim_{h\to 0} \frac{f(x+h) - f(x)}{h}$$

$$= \lim_{h\to 0} \frac{\sin(x+h) - \sin x}{h}$$

$$= \lim_{h\to 0} \frac{\sin x \cos h + \cos x \sin h - \sin x}{h}$$

$$= \lim_{h\to 0} \frac{\sin x(\cos h - 1) + \cos x \sin h}{h}$$

$$= \sin x \lim_{h\to 0} \frac{(\cos h - 1)}{h} + \cos x \lim_{h\to 0} \frac{\sin h}{h}$$

h radians	$\frac{(\cos h - 1)}{h}$	$\frac{\sin h}{h}$
0·1	–0·05	0·998
0·01	–0·005	0·99998
0·001	–0·0005	0·9999998

$$= \sin x \times 0 + \cos x \times 1 \text{ since } \lim_{h\to 0} \frac{(\cos h - 1)}{h} = 0 \text{ and } \lim_{h\to 0} \frac{\sin h}{h} = 1$$

Hence $f'(x) = \cos x$.

Note

When h is in degrees, $\lim_{h\to 0} \frac{\sin h}{h} \neq 1$. Hence $\frac{d}{dx}(\sin x) = \cos x$ is only true when the angle is in radians.

Calculus Skills

The derivative of cos x

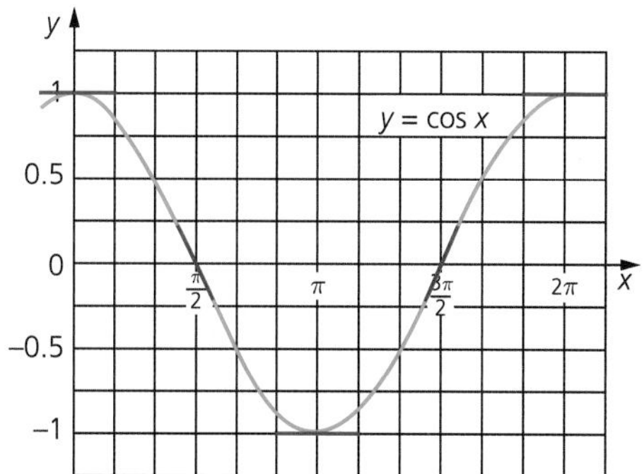

When the gradients of the tangents to the graph of $y = \cos x$ are found and plotted in a diagram, the resulting curve showing the gradient of $\cos x$ has equation $y = -\sin x$.

This suggests that $\frac{d}{dx}(\cos x) = -\sin x$, or in functional notation

$f(x) = \cos x \Rightarrow f'(x) = -\sin x$

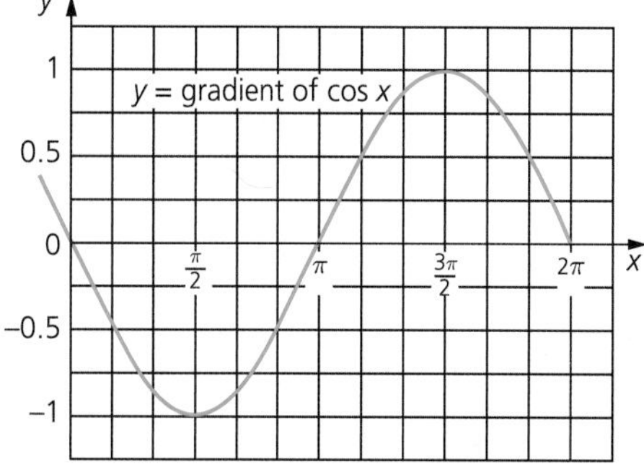

This can be confirmed by differentiating $f(x) = \cos x$ from first principles:

$$f'(x) = \lim_{h \to 0} \frac{f(x+h) - f(x)}{h}$$

$$= \lim_{h \to 0} \frac{\cos(x+h) - \cos x}{h}$$

$$= \lim_{h \to 0} \frac{\cos x \cos h - \sin x \sin h - \cos x}{h}$$

$$= \lim_{h \to 0} \frac{\cos x(\cos h - 1) - \sin x \sin h}{h}$$

$$= \cos x \lim_{h \to 0} \frac{(\cos h - 1)}{h} - \sin x \lim_{h \to 0} \frac{\sin h}{h}$$

$$= \cos x \times 0 - \sin x \times 1$$

$$= -\sin x$$

Note Again $\frac{d}{dx}(\cos x) = -\sin x$ is only true when the angle is in radians.

Example

Find the derivative of each of the following:

a) $f(x) = 3\sin x$

b) $v = t^2 + 5\cos t$

SOLUTIONS

a) $f'(x) = 3\cos x$

b) $\frac{dv}{dt} = 2t - 5\sin t$

Exercise 13.11

Find the derivative of each of the following:

1 $f(x) = 4\sin x$ 2 $g(x) = 2\cos x$ 3 $h(t) = -\frac{1}{3}\sin t$ 4 $f(\theta) = -6\cos\theta$

5 $y = \sin x - 3\cos x$ 6 $s = \frac{1}{2}\cos r + \frac{3}{4}\sin r$ 7 $A = \sqrt{b} - \sin b$ 8 $M = 2q^3 + \frac{2}{3}\cos q$

9 $v = 8\sin t - 4\cos t + \sqrt[3]{t^2}$ 10 $P = \cos\theta + 10\sin\theta - \frac{1}{\theta^2}$

11 Given that $f(x) = \sqrt{2}\sin x$, find $f'\left(\frac{\pi}{4}\right)$. HPQ

12 Find the rate of change of $L = 5\cos\theta$ at $\theta = \frac{3\pi}{2}$. HPQ

13 Find the gradient of the graph of the function $f(x) = \sin x + \cos x$ at: HPQ

a) $x = 0$ b) $x = \frac{\pi}{4}$ c) $x = \frac{\pi}{2}$ d) $x = \pi$

The chain rule for differentiation

Exercise 13.12

All questions in Exercise 13.12 are ACE questions.

Show the following:

1 If $y = (2x-1)^2$ then $\frac{dy}{dx} = 4(2x-1)$.

2 If $y = (2x-1)^3$ then $\frac{dy}{dx} = 6(2x-1)^2$. → Hint $(2x-1)^3 = 8x^3 - 12x^2 + 6x - 1$

3 If $y = (2x-1)^4$ then $\frac{dy}{dx} = 8(2x-1)^3$. → Hint $(2x-1)^4 = 16x^4 - 32x^3 + 24x^2 - 8x + 1$

4 If $y = (x^2+2)^2$ then $\frac{dy}{dx} = 4x(x^2+2)$.

5 If $y = (x^2+2)^3$ then $\frac{dy}{dx} = 6x(x^2+2)^2$. → Hint $(x^2+2)^3 = x^6 + 6x^4 + 12x^2 + 8$

6 If $y = (x^3+1)^2$ then $\frac{dy}{dx} = 6x^2(x^3+1)$.

7 If $y = (x^3+1)^3$ then $\frac{dy}{dx} = 9x^2(x^3+1)^2$. → Hint $(x^3+1)^3 = x^9 + 3x^6 + 3x^3 + 1$

In Exercise 13.12 you have been differentiating composite functions.

For example:

In question 3, $y = (2x-1)^4$ is equivalent to $y = u^4$ where $u = 2x - 1$:

$$\frac{dy}{dx} = 8(2x-1)^3 = 4(2x-1)^3 \times 2 = 4u^3 \times 2 = \frac{dy}{du} \times \frac{du}{dx}$$

In question 5, $y = (x^2+2)^3$ is equivalent to $y = u^3$ where $u = x^2 + 2$:

$$\frac{dy}{dx} = 6x(x^2+2)^2 = 3(x^2+2)^2 \times 2x = 3u^2 \times 2x = \frac{dy}{du} \times \frac{du}{dx}$$

In question 6, $y=(x^3+1)^2$ is equivalent to $y=u^2$ where $u=x^3+1$:

$$\frac{dy}{dx}=6x^2(x^3+1)=2(x^3+1)\times 3x^2=2u\times 3x^2=\frac{dy}{du}\times\frac{du}{dx}$$

If $y=f(x)$ is a composite function such that y is a function of u and u is a function of x then $\frac{dy}{dx}=\frac{dy}{du}\times\frac{du}{dx}$.

This is called the **chain rule** for differentiation.

In functional notation, if $F(x)=f(g(x))$ then $F'(x)=f'(g(x))\times g'(x)$.

Examples

Differentiate:

a) $y=(2x+5)^3$ b) $v=\sqrt{1-4t}$ c) $f(x)=\dfrac{1}{x^2+3x}$

SOLUTIONS

a) $\frac{dy}{dx}=3(2x+5)^2\times 2=6(2x+5)^2$ $[y=u^3,\quad u=2x+5]$

b) $v=(1-4t)^{\frac{1}{2}} \Rightarrow \frac{dv}{dt}=\frac{1}{2}(1-4t)^{-\frac{1}{2}}\times -4=-\frac{2}{(1-4t)^{\frac{1}{2}}}=-\frac{2}{\sqrt{1-4t}}$ $[v=u^{\frac{1}{2}},\quad u=1-4t]$

c) $f(x)=(x^2+3x)^{-1} \Rightarrow f'(x)=-(x^2+3x)^{-2}\times(2x+3)=-\frac{2x+3}{(x^2+3x)^2}$ $[f=g^{-1},\quad g=x^2+3x]$

Exercise 13.13

Find the derivative of each of the following.

1 $f(x)=(x+2)^6$
2 $g(x)=(3x-1)^4$
3 $h(x)=(5-2x)^3$
4 $P(x)=(4-x)^7$
5 $y=(x^2+5)^3$
6 $s=(3-r^2)^4$
7 $A=(b^3-2)^5$
8 $M=(1+q^4)^3$
9 $f(x)=(x^2+3x-2)^4$
10 $g(n)=(n^3+n)^8$
11 $h(t)=(t^2-5t+6)^{10}$
12 $C(p)=(2+p-3p^2)^9$ HPQ
13 $y=(8x-1)^{\frac{1}{2}}$
14 $m=(6k+5)^{\frac{1}{3}}$
15 $V=(2c+9)^{-3}$
16 $E=(7-w)^{-5}$
17 $f(x)=\sqrt{10x+3}$
18 $s(t)=\sqrt{5-2t}$
19 $n(c)=\sqrt{c^2+9}$ HPQ
20 $g(z)=\sqrt[3]{6z-z^3}$
21 $y=\dfrac{1}{(7x+2)^2}$
22 $A=\dfrac{2}{(r^2-4)^3}$
23 $p=\dfrac{1}{8-y}$ HPQ
24 $F=\dfrac{4}{g^3+9g}$
25 $g(x)=\dfrac{1}{\sqrt{2x+1}}$
26 $h(t)=\dfrac{3}{\sqrt{3-4t}}$

27 Given that $g(t)=\dfrac{2}{(t^2+t+2)^2}$, find $g'(-2)$.

28 Find the gradient of the curve $f(x)=\left(\frac{1}{2}x-1\right)^3$ at the point (8, 27).

29 Find the rate of change of $L(u)=\sqrt{25-u^2}$ at $u=3$. HPQ

30 Find the gradient of the tangent to the curve $g(x)=\dfrac{20}{1+x^2}$ at the point (3, 2). HPQ

The chain rule and trigonometric functions

The chain rule can also be applied to composite trigonometric functions.

$$\frac{d}{dx}(\sin(ax+b)) = \cos(ax+b)\times a = a\cos(ax+b) \qquad [y=\sin u, \quad u=ax+b]$$

$$\frac{d}{dx}(\cos(ax+b)) = -\sin(ax+b)\times a = -a\sin(ax+b) \qquad [y=\cos u, \quad u=ax+b]$$

$$\frac{d}{dx}(\sin^n x) = \frac{d}{dx}(\sin x)^n = n(\sin x)^{n-1}\times \cos x = n\sin^{n-1}x\cos x \qquad [y=u^n, \quad u=\sin x]$$

$$\frac{d}{dx}(\cos^n x) = \frac{d}{dx}(\cos x)^n = n(\cos x)^{n-1}\times(-\sin x) = -n\cos^{n-1}x\sin x \qquad [y=u^n, \quad u=\cos x]$$

Examples

Differentiate:

1 $y=\sin(4x+1)$ 2 $f(x)=\cos^3 x$

SOLUTIONS

1 $\frac{dy}{dx} = \cos(4x+1)\times 4 = 4\cos(4x+1)$ $[y=\sin u, \quad u=4x+1]$

2 $f'(x) = 3\cos^2 x\times(-\sin x) = -3\cos^2 x\sin x$ $[f=g^3; \quad g=\cos x]$

Exercise 13.14

Find the derivative of each of the following.

1 $f(x)=\sin 2x$ **2** $y=3\sin 4x$ **3** $g(x)=\sin(3x-2)$ **4** $s=10\sin\left(\frac{1}{2}t+3\right)$

5 $f(x)=\cos 3x$ **6** $y=2\cos 5x$ **7** $h(t)=\cos(1-2t)$ HPQ **8** $p=6\sin\left(\frac{1}{3}n+2\right)$

9 $g(x)=\sin^3 x$ **10** $A=\sin^4\theta$ HPQ **11** $h(u)=\cos^2 u$ **12** $m=\cos^5\theta$

13 $f(x)=\sin x^3$ **14** $f(x)=\frac{1}{\sin^3 x}$ **15** $y=\sqrt{\sin x}$ HPQ **16** $y=\sin\sqrt{x}$ HPQ

17 $f(x)=\cos x^2$ **18** $f(x)=\frac{1}{\cos x}$ **19** $y=\frac{1}{\sqrt{\cos x}}$ **20** $y=(1-\cos x)^2$

21 Given that $f(x)=3\sin(2x+\pi)$, find $f'\left(\frac{\pi}{3}\right)$.

22 Find the rate of change of $y=\cos^4\theta$ at $\theta=\frac{\pi}{6}$. HPQ

23 Find the gradient of the graph of the function $f(t)=\cos\frac{t}{2}+\sin(2\pi-t)$ at $t=\pi$. HPQ

24 Given that $x° = \frac{\pi x}{180}$ radians, find the derivative of: **a)** $f(x)=\sin x°$ **b)** $g(x)=\cos x°$ ACE

Checkout

1 Find the derivative of each of the following:

a) $y=(2x^2+3)(x-1)$ b) $f(x)=(5x+2)^2$ c) $g(x)=\frac{5}{x^2}+4\sqrt{x^3}$

d) $s=\frac{3t^4-5t^2-7}{t^2}$ e) $f(n)=\frac{1}{3n}$ f) $u=\frac{v^2-1}{\sqrt{v}}$

2 Differentiate each of the following:

a) $f(x)=(x^2+4)^3$ b) $y=(3\sin x+1)^4$ c) $k(x)=\sqrt{1+\cos x}$

d) $h=\frac{2}{1-5t}$ e) $g(x)=\frac{1}{\sqrt{3-2x^2}}$ f) $f(\theta)=\sin(6\theta+1)$

g) $y=\sin 2x-3\cos 4x$ h) $g(\theta)=4\cos^3\theta$ i) $s=\sin^2 t-\cos^2 t$

3 Find the value of $f'(16)$ given that $f(x)=\sqrt[4]{x}-\frac{1}{\sqrt[4]{x}}$.

4 Find the value of $f'(0)$ given that $f(\theta)=3\sin 4\theta$.

5 If $P(n)=\frac{1}{3}n^3-n^2$ find two possible values for a given that $P'(a)=3$.

6 Find the rate of change of $s(t)=t^3-5t^2+2t-7$ at $t=5$.

7 Find the rate of change of $f(x)=(x^3-x+1)^5$ at $x=-1$.

8 A missile is fired into the air.
The height, h metres, of the missile t seconds after firing is given by the formula $h=72t-4{\cdot}9t^2$.
Find the speed of the missile after 5 seconds.

9 The point P(3, 2) lies on the curve with equation $y=x^2-5x+8$. What is the gradient of the tangent to the curve at P?

10 Find the gradient of the curve $f(x)=x(x^3+9)$ at $x=-1$.

11 Find the gradient of the curve $g(x)=\sqrt{2x+1}$ at $x=4$.

12 Find the coordinates of the point on the curve $y=8-3x^2$ at which the gradient is 12.

13 Prove that the rate of change of $f(\theta)=\sin^4\theta+\sin 4\theta+4\sin\theta$ at $\theta=\frac{\pi}{4}$ is $2\sqrt{2}-3$.

14 Prove that the gradient of the curve $y=x^3+6x^2+12x+3$ is never negative.

Calculus Skills

Summary

Differentiating Functions

1 $f'(x)$ is called the derivative of $f(x)$.

2 $f(x) = ax^n \Rightarrow f'(x) = anx^{n-1}$, where a is a constant and n is a rational number.

3 $f'(x) = \lim_{h \to 0} \dfrac{f(x+h) - f(x)}{h}$.

4 The value $f'(a)$ is
* the rate of change of $f(x)$ at $x = a$
* the gradient of the curve $y = f(x)$ at the point $(a, f(a))$
* the gradient of the tangent to the curve $y = f(x)$ at the point $(a, f(a))$.

5 If $f(x) = g(x) + h(x) + \ldots$ then $f'(x) = g'(x) + h'(x) + \ldots$.

6 To find the derivative of a product or quotient of terms, first express it as a sum of terms and then differentiate term by term.

7 Equivalent notations for the derivative are $f'(x)$, $\dfrac{dy}{dx}$, $\dfrac{d}{dx}(f(x))$.

8 $\dfrac{d}{dx}(k \sin x) = k \cos x$ and $\dfrac{d}{dx}(k \cos x) = -k \sin x$, where k is a constant and x is in radians.

9 The chain rule for differentiating composite functions:
$F(x) = f(g(x)) \Rightarrow F'(x) = f'(g(x)) \times g'(x)$ or $\dfrac{dy}{dx} = \dfrac{dy}{du} \times \dfrac{du}{dx}$

Calculus Skills

CHAPTER

14 Using Differentiation to Investigate the Nature and Properties of Functions

In this chapter we will look at how to use derivatives to find equations of tangents, to determine the gradient of curves and to sketch graphs of functions.

What I am learning

- To determine the equation of the tangent to a curve at a given point
- To determine where a function is strictly increasing or strictly decreasing
- To sketch the graph of an algebraic function by determining its stationary point(s) and nature, intersection with axes and behaviour for large $\pm$ values of x
- To solve problems like:
  Find the equation of the tangent to the curve $y = (x - 3)^2$ which has gradient 4.

What I should already know/be able to do

- To determine the equation of a straight line
- To determine the gradient of the tangent to a curve at a given point
- To solve a quadratic inequation
- To solve a cubic equation

Quick check!

1 Find the equation of the straight line through the point $(2, -1)$ with gradient 3.

2 Find the gradient of the tangent to the curve $y = x^3 + 2x^2 - 3x + 5$ at the point $(-1, 9)$.

3 Solve $x^2 + 3x - 4 > 0$.

4 Solve $x^3 - 2x^2 - 5x + 6 = 0$.

Quick check! – *Solutions*

1 $y = 3x - 7$ 2 -4 3 $x < -4$ or $x > 1$ 4 $x = -2$ or $x = 1$ or $x = 3$

Equations of tangents

To find the equation of the tangent to the curve $y = f(x)$ at some point $P(a, b)$ on the curve, use $y - b = m(x - a)$ with the gradient $m = f'(a)$.

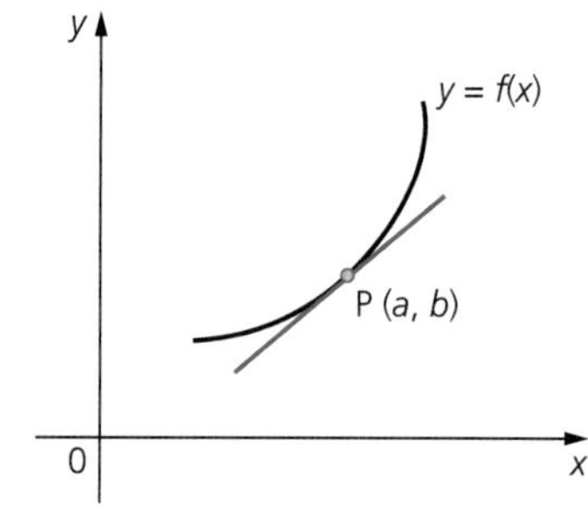

Example

Find the equation of the tangent to the curve $y = x^3 - 2x + 1$ at the point (2, 5).

SOLUTION

$\frac{dy}{dx} = 3x^2 - 2$

At $x = 2$, $\frac{dy}{dx} = 3(2)^2 - 2 = 10$.

So the gradient of the tangent at the point (2, 5) is 10.

The equation of the tangent is $y - 5 = 10(x - 2)$

$\Rightarrow y = 10x - 15$.

Exercise 14.1

Find the equations of the tangents to the curves:

1 $y = x^2 - 3x - 1$ at $(4, 3)$
2 $y = 5x - x^3$ at $(1, 4)$
3 $y = (x-1)(2x-7)$ at $(2, -3)$
4 $y = 4\sqrt{x}$ at $x = 9$ HPQ
5 $y = \frac{1}{x^4}$ at $x = -1$
6 $y = \frac{x+8}{x}$ at $x = 2$

7 Show that the tangents to the curve $y = \frac{1}{2}x^3$ at the points given by $x = 2$ and $x = -2$ are parallel. Find the coordinates of the points where these tangents cut the x- and y-axes.

8 The gradient of the tangent to the curve $y = 8 + 4x - x^2$ is 6. Find the coordinates of the point of contact of the tangent.

9 The gradient of two tangents to the curve $y = x^3 + 2x$ is 50. Find the coordinates of the point of contact of each tangent.

10 Find the equation of the tangent to the curve $y = x^2 + x$ which has gradient 7.

11 Find the equation of the tangent to the curve $y = (x-3)^2$ which has gradient 4. ACE

12 The tangent at P to the curve with equation $y = x^2 + 5x + 7$ is parallel to the line with equation $x + y = 1$. Find the coordinates of P.

13 Find the equations of the tangents to the curve $y = (x-1)(x^2+1)$ at the points where it crosses the x- and y-axes.

14 The tangents at A and B to the curve with equation $y = \frac{1}{3}x^3 - 2x^2 + 3x - 1$ are parallel to the x-axis. Find the coordinates of A and B. ACE

15 The line with equation $y = x - 1$ is a tangent to the curve with equation $y = x^2 + bx + c$ at the point $(3, 2)$. Find the values of b and c. ACE

Find the equations of the tangents to the curves:

16 $y = \left(\frac{1}{3}x - 1\right)^3$ at $(9, 8)$
17 $y = \sqrt{x^2 + 16}$ at $(3, 5)$
18 $y = 2 - \sin x$ at $(\pi, 2)$
19 $y = \frac{4}{4-x}$ at $x = 2$
20 $y = \cos 3x$ at $x = \frac{\pi}{6}$
21 $y = \cos^2 x$ at $x = \frac{\pi}{4}$

Increasing and decreasing functions

The curve $y = f(x)$ shown below has:

- a positive gradient (is rising) when $x < a$ and $x > b$
- a negative gradient (is falling) when $a < x < b$.

We say that when $f(x)$ has

- a positive gradient, it is **increasing**, i.e. if $f'(x) > 0$ then $f(x)$ is increasing
- a negative gradient, it is **decreasing**, i.e. if $f'(x) < 0$ then $f(x)$ is decreasing.

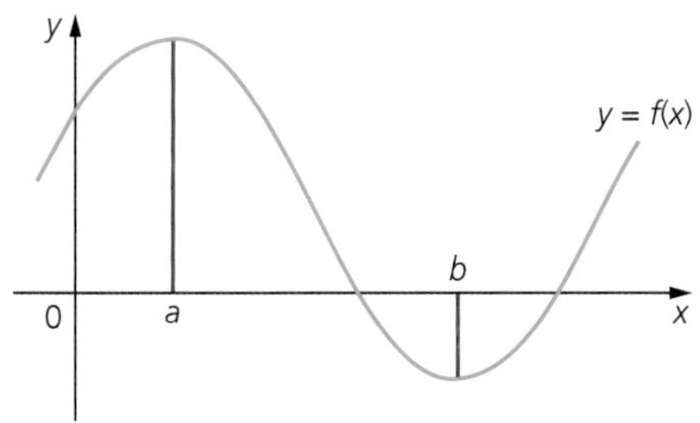

Example 1

Find the interval for which the function $f(x) = x^2 + x - 2$ is increasing.

SOLUTION

$f'(x) = 2x + 1$

The function is increasing when $f'(x) > 0$

i.e. when $2x + 1 > 0$

$$2x > -1$$

$$x > -\frac{1}{2}$$

Example 2

Find the intervals for which $y = x^3 + 4x^2 - 3x + 2$ is increasing and decreasing.

SOLUTION

$$\frac{dy}{dx} = 3x^2 + 8x - 3$$

Increasing when $\frac{dy}{dx} > 0$

i.e. when $3x^2 + 8x - 3 > 0$

$$(x + 3)(3x - 1) > 0$$

To solve this inequation, sketch the graph of $\frac{dy}{dx} = 3x^2 + 8x - 3$. It crosses the x-axis at $(-3, 0)$ and $\left(\frac{1}{3}, 0\right)$ and it has a minimum turning point as the x^2 term is positive.

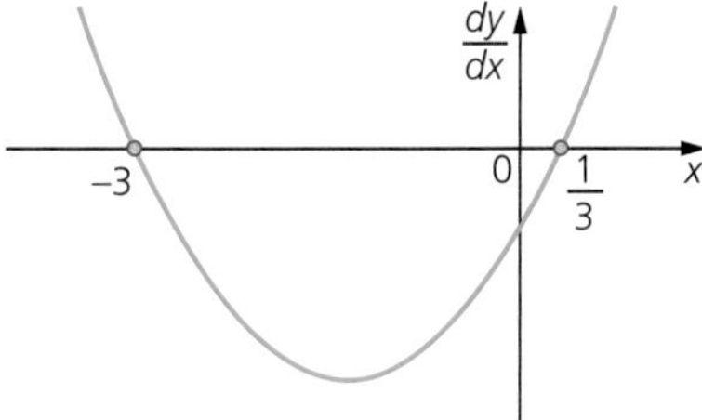

From the graph, the value of $3x^2 + 8x - 3$ is positive on the parts of the graph which are above the x-axis. Hence $\frac{dy}{dx} > 0$ when $x < -3$ and $x > \frac{1}{3}$ and so $y = x^3 + 4x^2 - 3x + 2$ is increasing when $x < -3$ and $x > \frac{1}{3}$.

The value of $3x^2 + 8x - 3$ is negative on the part of the graph which is below the x-axis. Hence $\frac{dy}{dx} < 0$ when $-3 < x < \frac{1}{3}$ so $y = x^3 + 4x^2 - 3x + 2$ is decreasing when $-3 < x < \frac{1}{3}$.

NOTE: You can find a reminder of how to solve quadratic inequalities on page 48.

Example 3

Show that the function $f(x) = x^3 - 6x^2 + 12x - 5$ is never decreasing.

SOLUTION

$$f'(x) = 3x^2 - 12x + 12$$
$$= 3(x^2 - 4x + 4)$$
$$= 3(x-2)^2$$

Now $(x-2)^2 \geq 0$ for all x.

Hence $3(x-2)^2 \geq 0$ for all x and so $f(x)$ is never decreasing.

Exercise 14.2

1 For each function state whether it is increasing or decreasing:

a) $y = x - x^2$ at $x = 3$
b) $f(x) = x^4 + 2x^3 + 4$ at $x = -1$
c) $y = \sqrt{x}(x-2)$ at $x = 4$
d) $f(x) = (x^2-1)(x+3)$ at $x = -2$

2 Find the intervals for which each function is increasing and decreasing:

a) $f(x) = x^2 - 7x$
b) $y = 9 + 8x - x^2$
c) $y = 2x^2 + 3x + 1$
d) $f(x) = \frac{1}{3}x^3 + 2x^2 - 5x + 4$
e) $y = 2x^3 - 5x^2 + 3$
f) $f(x) = 12x - x^3$
g) $y = x^3 + x^2 - x + 1$ HPQ
h) $f(x) = x^4 + 2x^3 - 3$
i) $f(x) = x^4 - 8x^2$

3 Show that $y = x^3 + x$ is increasing for all x.

4 Show that $y = 2 - x^5$ is never increasing. HPQ

5 Show that $y = \frac{3}{x}$, $x \neq 0$, is always decreasing.

6 Show that the function $f(x) = \frac{1}{3}x^3 + 2x^2 + 4x - 3$ is never decreasing.

7 Show that the function $f(x) = \frac{x^2 + 3x - 2}{x}$, $x \neq 0$, is always increasing. ACE

8 Show that the function $f(x) = 5 - 15x + 10x^3 - 3x^5$ is never increasing. ACE

9 Show that the function $f(x) = \frac{1}{(x+1)^3}$, $x \neq -1$, is always decreasing.

10 Show that the function $f(x) = \sin x + x$ is never decreasing.

Stationary points and values

The graph of the function $y = f(x)$ is shown below.

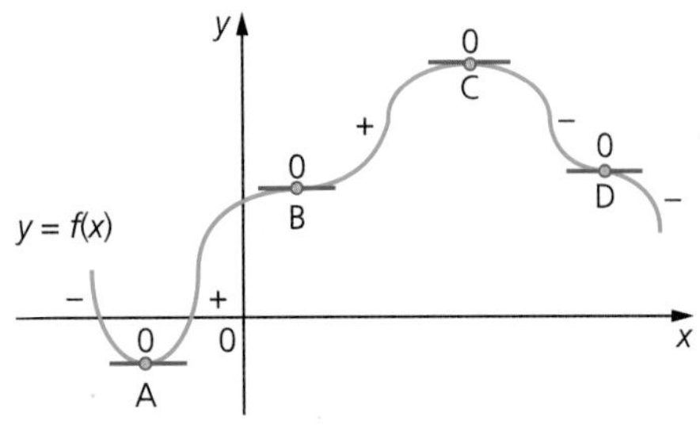

The tangents to the curve at the points A, B, C and D are horizontal, i.e. the curve has gradient zero at these points.

Points on the curve at which the gradient is zero are called **stationary points**.

If $f'(x) = 0$ when $x = a$ then

- $(a, f(a))$ are the coordinates of a stationary point
- $f(a)$ is a stationary value.

The stationary point may be a **maximum turning point,** a **minimum turning point** or a **point of inflexion**. The nature of the stationary point depends on the gradient on either side of it.

In the preceding graph

- A is a minimum turning point
- C is a maximum turning point
- B is a rising point of inflexion
- D is a falling point of inflexion.

Example 1

Find the stationary point on the curve $y = x^2 + 4x + 1$ and determine its nature.

SOLUTION

$\frac{dy}{dx} = 2x + 4$

Stationary points occur when $\frac{dy}{dx} = 0$.

$2x + 4 = 0$

$2x = -4$

$x = -2$

So $y = (-2)^2 + 4(-2) + 1 = -3$.

The stationary point is $(-2, -3)$.

Use a table to consider the gradient of the curve on either side of the stationary point.

x	$\leftarrow -2$	-2	$-2 \rightarrow$
$\frac{dy}{dx}$	$-$	0	$+$
slope	\	—	/

Hence this is a minimum turning point at $(-2, -3)$.

Example 2

Find the stationary points on the curve $f(x) = x^3 - \frac{1}{4}x^4$ and determine their nature.

SOLUTION

$f'(x) = 3x^2 - x^3$

Stationary points occur when $f'(x) = 0$.

$3x^2 - x^3 = 0$

$x^2(3 - x) = 0$

$x^2 = 0$ or $3 - x = 0$

$x = 0$ or $x = 3$

So $y = 0^3 - \frac{1}{4}(0)^4 = 0$, or $y = 3^3 - \frac{1}{4}(3)^4 = 6\frac{3}{4}$.

Calculus Skills

The stationary points are $(0,0)$ and $\left(3,6\frac{3}{4}\right)$.

x	$\leftarrow 0$	0	$0 \rightarrow$
x^2	+	0	+
$3-x$	+	+	+
$f'(x)$	+	0	+
slope	/	—	/

Rising point of inflexion at $(0,0)$

x	$\leftarrow 3$	3	$3 \rightarrow$
x^2	+	+	+
$3-x$	+	0	−
$f'(x)$	+	0	−
slope	/	—	\

Maximum turning point at $\left(3, 6\frac{3}{4}\right)$

Exercise 14.3

Find the stationary points on each of the following curves and determine their nature:

1 $f(x)=x^2-6x+5$ **2** $y=3x-x^2$ **3** $f(x)=12x-x^3$

4 $y=x^3+x^2$ **5** $f(x)=3x^4+4x^3$ **6** $y=x^4-2x^2+3$

Find the stationary values of each of the following functions and determine their nature:

7 $f(x)=(x+4)^2$ **8** $f(x)=x^3+7x^2-5x+1$ **9** $f(x)=\dfrac{x^2+1}{x}$ HPQ

10 The height, h metres, of a rocket t seconds after it has been fired into the air is given by $h=15+28t-2t^2$. What is the maximum height reached by the rocket? ACE

Find the stationary points on each of the following curves and determine their nature:

11 $y=x+\cos x,\ 0<x<2\pi$ **12** $f(x)=(x^2-2)^4$

Curve sketching

To sketch the graph of a function find:

- the points of intersection (if any) with the coordinate axes
- the stationary points and their nature
- the behaviour of the curve for large positive and negative values of x.

Example

Sketch the curve whose equation is $y=6x^4-4x^3$.

SOLUTION

i) *Points of intersection with coordinate axes*

y-intercept: $x=0 \Rightarrow y=6(0)^4-4(0)^3=0$ i.e. $(0,0)$

x-intercepts: $y=0 \Rightarrow 6x^4-4x^3=0$

$$2x^3(3x-2)=0$$

$$2x^3=0 \text{ or } 3x-2=0$$

$$x=0 \text{ or } x=\frac{2}{3} \quad \text{i.e. } (0,0) \text{ and } \left(\frac{2}{3},0\right)$$

ii) *Stationary points*

$\frac{dy}{dx} = 24x^3 - 12x^2$

Stationary points occur when $\frac{dy}{dx} = 0$.

$24x^3 - 12x^2 = 0$

$12x^2(2x - 1) = 0$

$12x^2 = 0$ or $2x - 1 = 0$

$x = 0$ or $x = \frac{1}{2}$

$y = 2(0)^3[3(0) - 2] = 0 \times (-2) = 0$ or $y = 2\left(\frac{1}{2}\right)^3\left[3\left(\frac{1}{2}\right) - 2\right] = \frac{1}{4} \times -\frac{1}{2} = -\frac{1}{8}$

Note The calculations are eased by substituting into the factorised form of the original equation.

The stationary points are $(0, 0)$ and $\left(\frac{1}{2}, -\frac{1}{8}\right)$.

x	$\leftarrow 0$	0	$0 \rightarrow$
$12x^2$	+	0	+
$2x-1$	−	−	−
$\frac{dy}{dx}$	−	0	−
slope	\	—	\

Falling point of inflexion at $(0, 0)$

x	$\leftarrow \frac{1}{2}$	$\frac{1}{2}$	$\frac{1}{2} \rightarrow$
$12x^2$	+	+	+
$2x-1$	−	−	+
$\frac{dy}{dx}$	−	0	+
slope	\	—	/

Minimum turning point at $\left(\frac{1}{2}, -\frac{1}{8}\right)$

iii) *Large positive and negative values of x*

$y = 6x^4 - 4x^3$ behaves like $y = 6x^4$ for large positive and negative values of x.

Therefore as $x \to -\infty$, $y \to +\infty$, and as $x \to +\infty$, $y \to +\infty$.

Hence the graph has the following appearance:

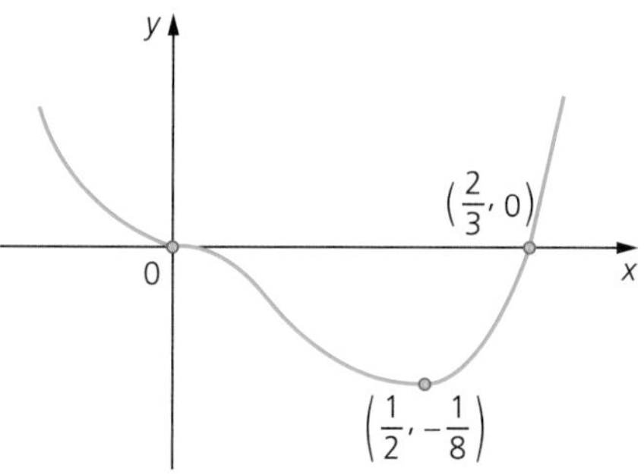

Calculus Skills

Exercise 14.4

Sketch the following curves and annotate them fully:

1 $y = x^2 + 2x - 8$

2 $y = 5 + 4x - x^2$

3 $y = x(x-1)^2$

4 $y = (x+1)(x-2)^2$

5 $y = x^3 + 6x^2$

6 $y = 2x^3 - x^4$

7 $y = (x^2-1)^2$

8 $y = (x^2+1)(x^2-9)$ HPQ

9 $y = x^3(x+4)$ HPQ

10 $y = (2x-1)^4$

11 $y = \cos^2 x + \cos x,\ 0 \leqslant x \leqslant 2\pi$

In Chapter 3 you learnt how to solve cubic equations. You will have to use this skill when sketching some curves.

Example

Sketch the curve whose equation is $y = 2x^3 - 7x^2 + 4x + 4$.

SOLUTION

Points of intersection with coordinate axes

y-intercept: $x = 0 \Rightarrow y = 2(0)^3 - 7(0)^2 + 4(0) + 4 = 4$ i.e. $(0, 4)$

x-intercepts: $y = 0 \Rightarrow 2x^3 - 7x^2 + 4x + 4 = 0$

Now factorise $2x^3 - 7x^2 + 4x + 4$.

2	2	−7	4	4
		4	−6	−4
	2	−3	−2	0

This gives $(x-2)(2x^2 - 3x - 2) = 0$

$$(x-2)(2x+1)(x-2) = 0$$

$$(x-2)^2(2x+1) = 0$$

$$x - 2 = 0 \text{ or } 2x + 1 = 0$$

$$x = 2 \text{ or } x = -\frac{1}{2}$$

i.e. $(2,0)$ and $\left(-\frac{1}{2}, 0\right)$

Stationary points

$$\frac{dy}{dx} = 6x^2 - 14x + 4$$

Stationary points occur when $\frac{dy}{dx} = 0$.

$$6x^2 - 14x + 4 = 0$$

$$2(3x^2 - 7x + 2) = 0$$

$$2(3x-1)(x-2) = 0$$

$$3x - 1 = 0 \text{ or } x - 2 = 0$$

$$x = \frac{1}{3} \text{ or } x = 2$$

So $y = \left(\frac{1}{3} - 2\right)^2\left(2\left(\frac{1}{3}\right) + 1\right) = \left(-\frac{5}{3}\right)^2\left(\frac{5}{3}\right) = \frac{125}{27} = 4\frac{17}{27}$ or $y = (2-2)^2(2(2)+1) = 0 \times 5 = 0$.

The stationary points are $\left(\frac{1}{3}, 4\frac{17}{27}\right)$ and $(2, 0)$.

x	$\leftarrow \frac{1}{3}$	$\frac{1}{3}$	$\frac{1}{3} \rightarrow$
$3x-1$	$-$	0	$+$
$x-2$	$-$	$-$	$-$
$\frac{dy}{dx}$	$+$	0	$-$
slope	/	—	\

Maximum turning point at $\left(\frac{1}{3}, 4\frac{17}{27}\right)$

x	$\leftarrow 2$	2	$2 \rightarrow$
$3x-1$	$+$	$+$	$+$
$x-2$	$-$	0	$+$
$\frac{dy}{dx}$	$-$	0	$+$
slope	\	—	/

Minimum turning point at $(2, 0)$

Large positive and negative values of x.

$y = 2x^3 - 7x^2 + 4x + 4$ behaves like $y = 2x^3$ for large positive and negative values of x.

Therefore as $x \rightarrow -\infty$, $y \rightarrow -\infty$ and as $x \rightarrow +\infty$, $y \rightarrow +\infty$.

Hence the graph has the following appearance:

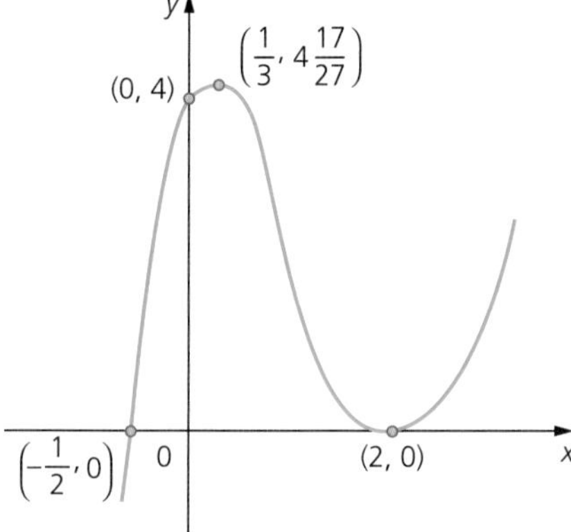

Exercise 14.5

Sketch the following curves and annotate them fully:

1 $y = x^3 - 5x^2 - 8x + 12$

2 $y = x^3 + x^2 - x - 1$

3 $y = x^3 - x^2 - 5x - 3$ HPQ

4 $y = x^3 - 6x^2 + 9x - 4$

5 $y = 2x^3 - 7x^2 + 9$

6 $y = x^3 + x^2 - 16x - 16$

Graph of the derived function

Note Although graphing the derived function is listed within the Algebraic and Trigonometric Skills section of the Higher Mathematics Course Specification, it fits appropriately with the other work on differentiation in this chapter.

You can sketch the graph of $y = f'(x)$ by looking at the features of the graph of $y = f(x)$.

The graph of $y = f(x)$ has stationary points at $(a,f(a)),(b,f(b)),(c,f(c))$ and $(d,f(d))$.

At each of the stationary points, $f'(x) = 0$ since the gradient of the curve is zero.

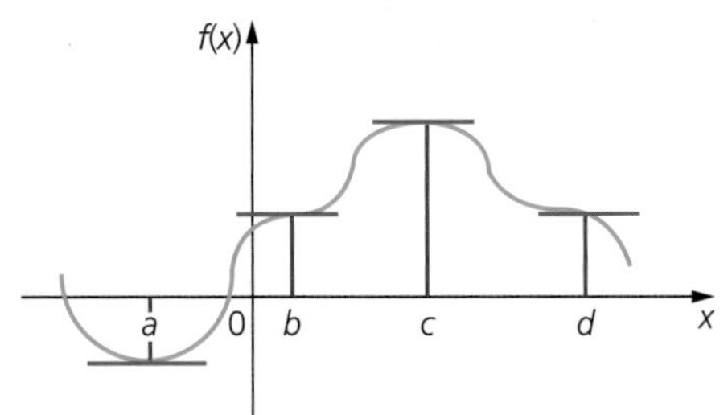

Hence the corresponding points on the graph of $y = f'(x)$ are $(a, 0), (b, 0), (c, 0)$ and $(d, 0)$.

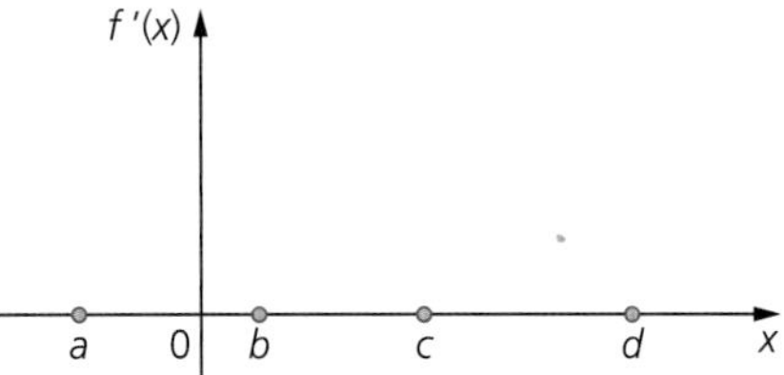

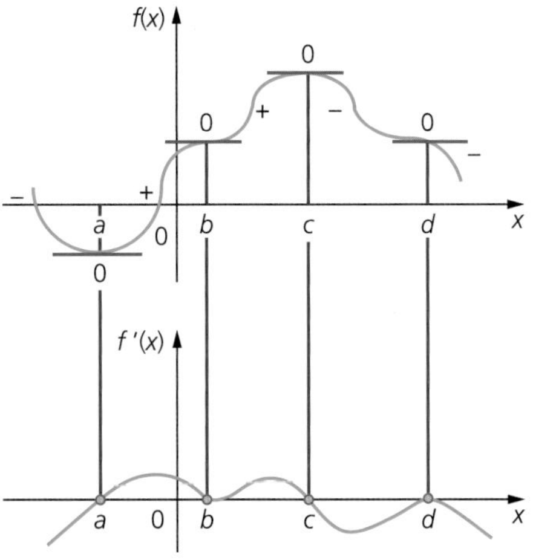

By considering the gradient of $y = f(x)$ on either side of each stationary point you can complete the sketch graph of $y = f'(x)$.

Example

Part of the graph of the function $y = f(x)$ is shown here, sketch the graph of the derived function.

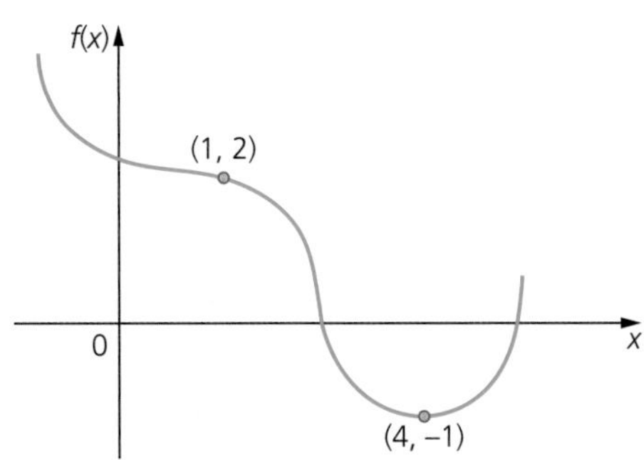

SOLUTION

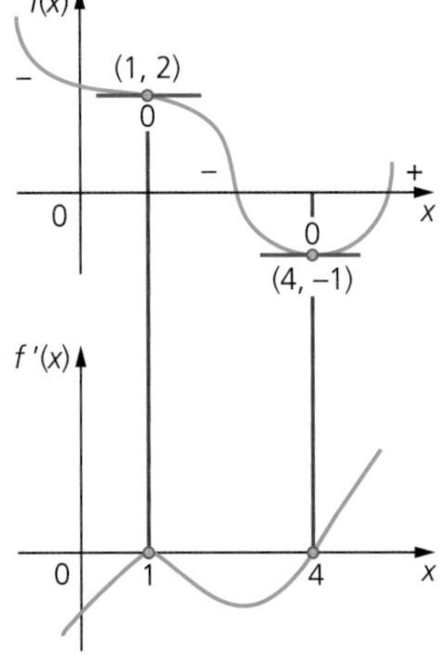

Exercise 14.6

For each function sketch the graph of its derived function.

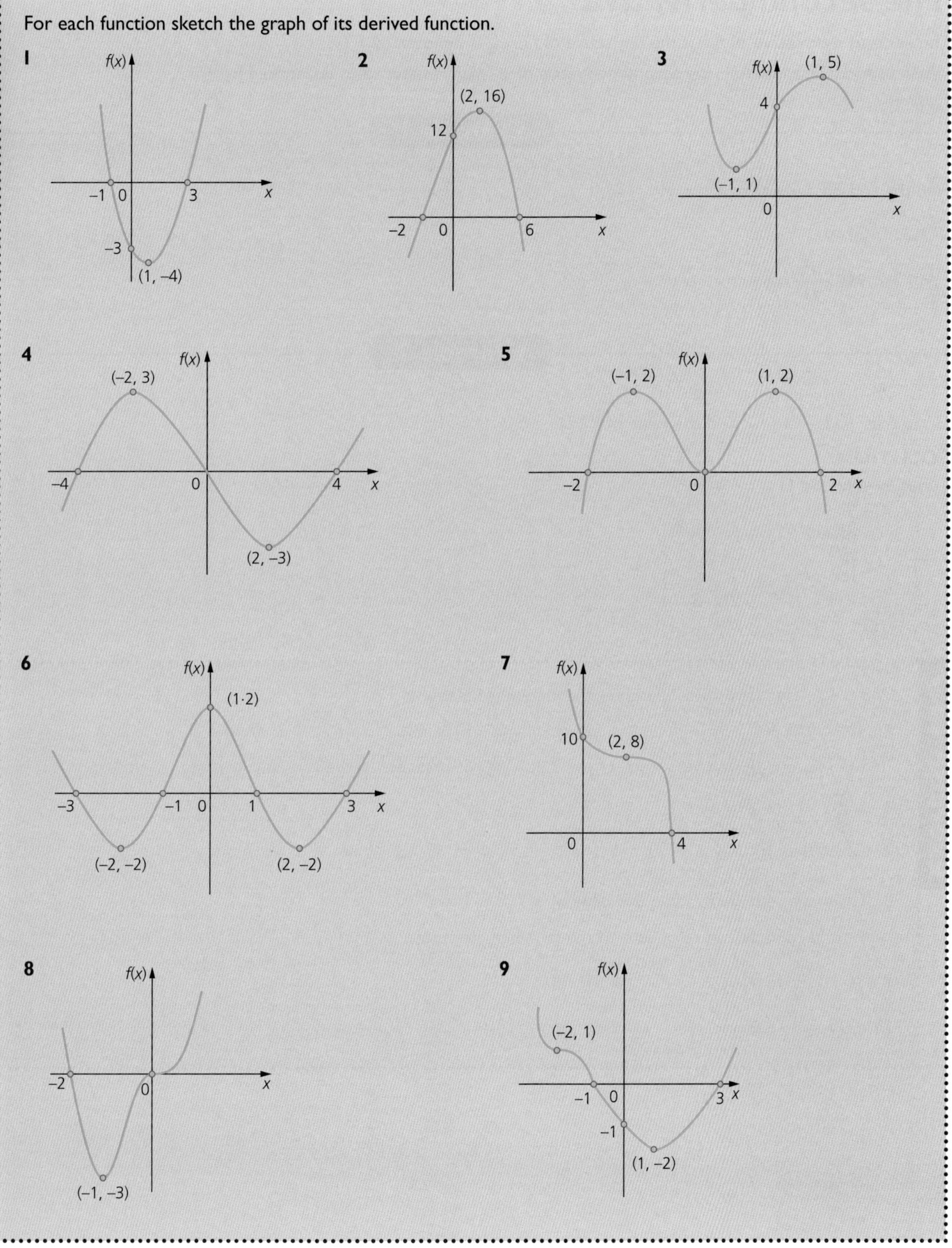

Calculus Skills

The second derivative

The **second derivative** of $f(x)$ is the derivative of $f'(x)$. It is denoted by $f''(x)$.

When using Leibniz notation, the second derivative of y with respect to x is denoted by $\frac{d^2y}{dx^2}$.

Example 1

Find the second derivative of $y = x^3$.

SOLUTION

$\frac{dy}{dx} = 3x^2$ and $\frac{d^2y}{dx^2} = 6x$

Example 2

Given that $f(x) = 4x + \frac{3}{x}$, find the value of $f''(2)$.

SOLUTION

$f(x) = 4x + 3x^{-1} \Rightarrow f'(x) = 4 - 3x^{-2}$

and $f''(x) = 6x^{-3} = \frac{6}{x^3}$

so $f''(2) = \frac{6}{2^3} = \frac{6}{8} = \frac{3}{4}$

Exercise 14.7

Find the second derivative of each of the following functions:

1 $f(x) = x^3 - 5x$ 2 $g(x) = (x+7)(x-2)$ 3 $h(t) = \frac{2}{t}$

Find the second derivative of each of the following with respect to the relevant variable:

4 $y = x^4 - x^3 + x^2 - x + 1$ 5 $A = (b^3+2)^2$ 6 $r = \frac{s^4 - 1}{s^2}$

7 Given that $f(x) = \frac{1}{3}x^4 + \frac{1}{2}x^3 - x^2$, find the value of $f''(-2)$. HPQ

8 Given that $g(t) = \sqrt{t^5}$, find the value of $g''(16)$. HPQ

Find the second derivative of each of the following functions:

9 $f(x) = \left(\frac{1}{2}x + 3\right)^4$ 10 $g(x) = \sqrt{(2x+1)^3}$

11 $h(t) = \frac{1}{1-t}$ 12 $f(\theta) = \sin(5\theta - \pi)$

Using the second derivative

The second derivative can be used to determine the nature of the stationary points on a curve.

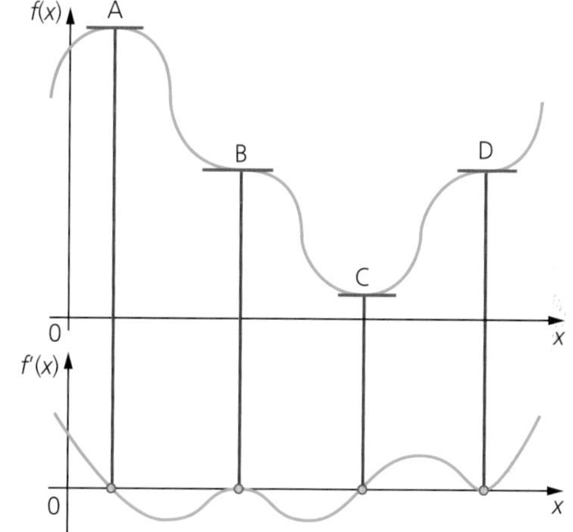

The diagram opposite shows the graph of a function $y = f(x)$ and the corresponding graph of $y = f'(x)$ plotted against x.

The gradient of the graph of $f'(x)$ is given by $\frac{d}{dx}(f'(x))$,

i.e. $f''(x)$ or $\frac{d^2y}{dx^2}$.

The maximum turning point A corresponds to a point at which $f'(x)$ has a negative gradient; hence $f''(x) < 0$ for a maximum turning point.

The minimum turning point C corresponds to a point at which $f'(x)$ has a positive gradient; hence $f''(x) > 0$ for a minimum turning point.

The points of inflexion, B and D, correspond to turning points on the graph of $y = f'(x)$, i.e. points at which the gradient of $f'(x)$ is zero; hence $f''(x) = 0$ for points of inflexion.

In fact $f''(x)$ may also be zero at maximum or minimum turning points for some functions. For example, consider $f(x) = x^4$. Then $f'(x) = 4x^3$ and $f''(x) = 12x^2$.

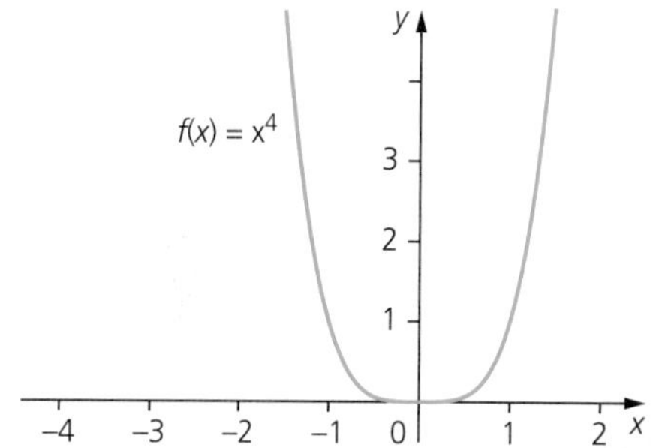

Stationary point occurs when $f'(x) = 0$. So

$4x^3 = 0$

$x = 0$

$f(0) = 0^4 = 0 \Rightarrow (0,0)$ is a stationary point.

$f''(0) = 12(0)^2 = 0$ but from the graph $(0,0)$ is a minimum turning point.

A stationary point on a curve occurs when $f'(x) = 0$. The nature of the stationary point can be determined using the second derivative as follows:

- if $f''(x) < 0$, then it is a maximum turning point
- if $f''(x) > 0$, then it is a minimum turning point
- if $f''(x) = 0$, then it could be a minimum, maximum or point of inflexion.

If $f''(x) = 0$, test the values of $f'(x)$ on either side of the stationary point as described earlier in this chapter.

Example

Find the stationary points on the curve $y = x^4 - 4x^3$ and determine their nature.

SOLUTION

$\frac{dy}{dx} = 4x^3 - 12x^2 = 4x^2(x - 3)$

Stationary points occur when $\frac{dy}{dx} = 0$.

$4x^2(x - 3) = 0$

$4x^2 = 0$ or $x - 3 = 0$

$x = 0$ or $x = 3$

$y = 0^4 - 4(0)^3 = 0$ or $y = 3^4 - 4(3)^3 = -27$

The stationary points are $(0,0)$ and $(3, -27)$.

$\frac{d^2y}{dx^2} = 12x^2 - 24x$

When $x = 0$, $\frac{d^2y}{dx^2} = 12(0)^2 - 24(0) = 0 \Rightarrow (0,0)$ may be a minimum, maximum or point of inflexion.

So test the values of $\frac{dy}{dx}$ on either side of the stationary point to determine its nature.

x	$\leftarrow 0$	0	$0 \rightarrow$
$4x^2$	+	0	+
$x-3$	–	–	–
$\frac{dy}{dx}$	–	0	–
slope	╲	—	╲

$(0,0)$ is a falling point of inflexion.

When $x = 3$, $\frac{d^2y}{dx^2} = 12(3)^2 - 24(3) = 36 \Rightarrow (3, -27)$ is a minimum turning point since $\frac{d^2y}{dx^2} > 0$.

Exercise 14.8

Find the stationary points on each of the following curves and determine their nature:

1 $f(x) = 2x^3 + 3x^2 - 12x + 20$

2 $f(x) = x^2 + 2x + 6$

3 $y = 7 + 9x + 3x^2 - x^3$

4 $y = 5 + 4x - x^2$

5 $f(x) = \frac{1}{2}x^4 + 2x^3$ HPQ

6 $y = x^5 - 15x^3$

Sketch the following curves and annotate them fully:

7 $y = x^3 - 8x^2 + 5x + 14$

8 $y = 2x^3 + x^4$ HPQ

9 $y = 5x^4 - x^5$

Checkout

1 Find the equation of the tangent to the curve $y = \frac{1}{3x}$ at the point where $x = 2$.

2 A tangent is drawn to the parabola with equation $y = 4x^2 + 5x - 1$.
The tangent is parallel to the line with equation $3x + y + 6 = 0$.
Find the coordinates of the point of contact of the tangent with the parabola.

3 For what values of x is the function $f(x) = \frac{1}{3}x^3 - 3x^2 - 7x + 2$ decreasing?

4 Show that the function $f(x) = x^3 - 3x^2 + 3x - 1$ is never decreasing.

5 A curve has equation $y = \frac{3x^4}{2} - x^3$.
Find the coordinates of its stationary points and determine their nature.

6 Find the stationary values of the function f defined by $f(x) = 5 + 15x^2 - 2x^3$, and determine the nature of each.

7 A curve has equation $y = (x-1)^2(x-4)$.
a) For this curve find the coordinates of:
(i) the points at which it meets the coordinate axes
(ii) the stationary points and determine their nature.
b) Make a sketch of the curve and annotate it fully.

8 The diagram shows a sketch of part of the parabola $y = f(x)$.

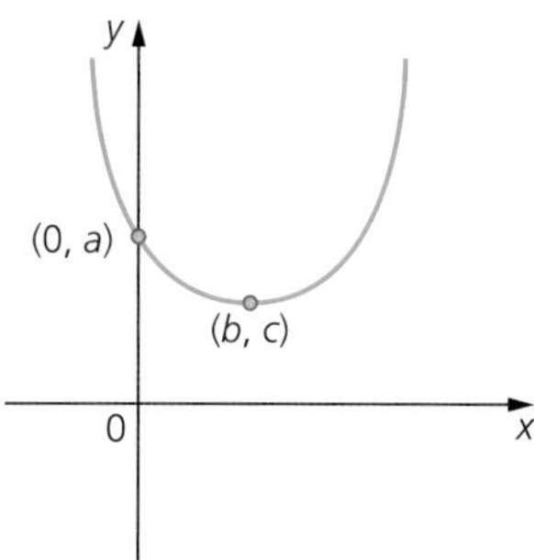

The parabola crosses the y-*axis* at $(0,a)$ and has a minimum turning point at (b,c).
Sketch the graph of $y = f'(x)$.

9 The diagram shows a sketch of part of the graph of $y = f(x)$.

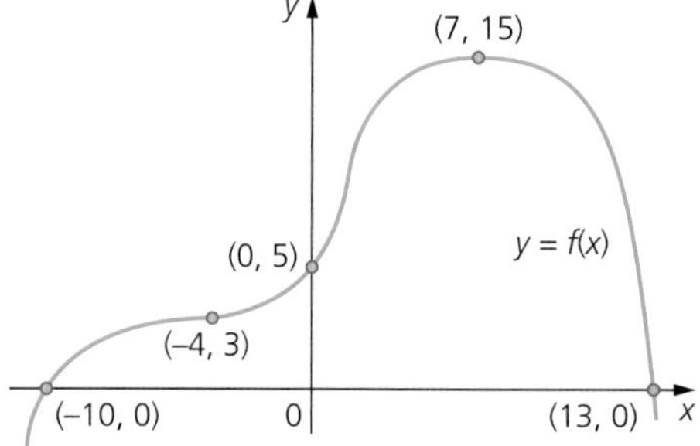

The graph crosses the coordinate axes at $(-10,0)$, $(0, 5)$ and $(13, 0)$, has a maximum turning point at $(7, 15)$ and a rising point of inflexion at $(-4, 3)$.
Sketch the graph of $y = f'(x)$.

Summary

Using Differentiation to Investigate the Nature and Properties of Functions

1 The equation of the tangent to the curve $y = f(x)$ at the point $P(a, b)$ on the curve, is given by $y - b = m(x - a)$ where the gradient is $m = f'(a)$.

2 When $f(x)$ has:
- a positive gradient it is *increasing*, i.e. if $f'(x) > 0$ then $f(x)$ is increasing
- a negative gradient it is *decreasing*, i.e. if $f'(x) < 0$ then $f(x)$ is decreasing.

3 A stationary point on a curve is a point at which the gradient is zero.
It occurs when $f'(x) = 0$.

4 The nature of a stationary point can be determined by considering the values of $f'(x)$ (i.e. the gradient of the curve) on either side of the stationary point.
Stationary points may be one of the four types illustrated below.
- A is a minimum turning point
- C is a maximum turning point
- B is a rising point of inflexion
- D is a falling point of inflexion

Calculus Skills

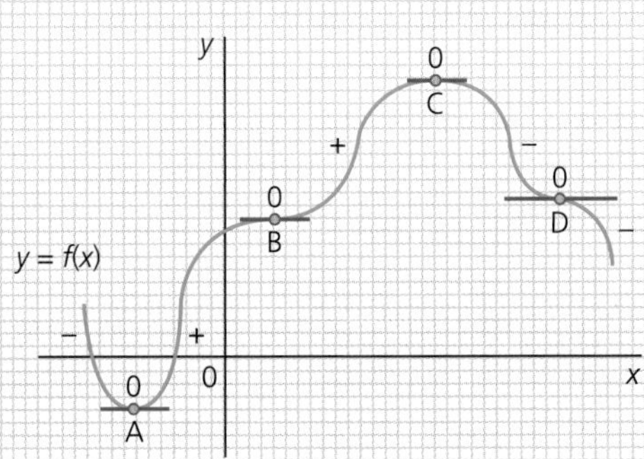

5 The nature of a stationary point can also be determined by using the second derivative as follows:

* if $f''(x) < 0$, then it is a maximum turning point
* if $f''(x) > 0$, then it is a minimum turning point
* if $f''(x) = 0$, then it could be a minimum, maximum or point of inflexion. In this case, test the values of $f'(x)$ on either side of the stationary point as explained above.

6 The second derivative of $f(x)$, $f''(x)$, is the derivative of $f'(x)$.
In Leibniz notation, the second derivative of y with respect to x is denoted by $\frac{d^2y}{dx^2}$.

7 To sketch the graph of a function find:

* the points of intersection with the coordinate axes
* the stationary points and their nature
* the behaviour of the curve for large positive and negative values of x.

CHAPTER

15 Integrating Functions

In this chapter you will learn that the inverse process to differentiation is called integration. You will look at how to integrate a range of algebraic and trigonometric functions and how to solve simple differential equations.

What I am learning

* To integrate algebraic functions which can be reduced to expressions involving powers of x
* To integrate functions of the form $f(x) = (x + q)^n,\ n \neq -1$
* To integrate functions of the form $f(x) = p\sin x$ and $f(x) = p\cos x$
* To integrate functions of the form $f(x) = (px + q)^n,\ n \neq -1$
* To integrate functions of the form $f(x) = p\sin(qx + r)$ and $f(x) = p\cos(qx + r)$
* To solve differential equations of the form $\frac{dy}{dx} = f(x)$
* To solve problems like this:
  The speed of a roller-coaster is given by $d'(t) = 20t - 5$, where t is the time in seconds after the start of the ride. Find $d(t)$ given that 3 seconds after the start of the ride the roller-coaster had travelled 75 metres.

What I should already know/be able to do

* Differentiate algebraic functions which can be reduced to expressions involving powers of x
* Differentiate $k\sin x$ and $k\cos x$
* Differentiate composite functions using the chain rule
* Work with radians

Quick check!

Find the derivative of each of the following:

1 $f(x) = (x+7)(x-2)$

2 $y = \frac{3}{x^2}$

3 $g(z) = 4\sqrt{z}$

4 $s = \frac{2t^4 - 1}{t}$

5 $P(n) = (5n+2)^3$

6 $y = 3\sin\theta - \cos 4\theta$

7 Convert to degrees:

a) $\frac{\pi}{3}$ radians

b) $\frac{\pi}{4}$ radians

c) $\frac{3\pi}{2}$ radians

d) $\frac{11\pi}{6}$ radians

Quick check! – *Solutions*

1 $f'(x) = 2x + 5$

2 $\frac{dy}{dx} = -\frac{6}{x^3}$

3 $g'(z) = \frac{2}{\sqrt{z}}$

4 $\frac{ds}{dt} = 6t^2 + \frac{1}{t^2}$

5 $P'(n) = 15(5n+2)^2$

6 $\frac{dy}{d\theta} = 3\cos\theta + 4\sin 4\theta$

7 a) 60° b) 45° c) 270° d) 330°

The inverse of differentiation

If you know the equation of a curve, say $y = f(x)$ then, by differentiation, you can find the gradient function $\frac{dy}{dx} = f'(x)$.

If you are given the gradient function $\frac{dy}{dx} = f'(x)$, you can work in reverse to obtain an equation for the curve.

Example

Find the equation of the curve which has gradient function $\frac{dy}{dx} = 2x$.

SOLUTION

The function $y = x^2$ differentiates to give $\frac{dy}{dx} = 2x$, but there are many other functions which also differentiate to give $\frac{dy}{dx} = 2x$, e.g. $y = x^2+1$, $y = x^2+4$, $y = x^2-2$, etc.

Hence there is a family of curves which have gradient function $\frac{dy}{dx} = 2x$.

Each curve in the family has an equation of the form $y = x^2 + C$, where C is a constant.

Exercise 15.1

Find the equation for the family of curves with gradient function:

1 $\frac{dy}{dx} = 3x^2$ 2 $\frac{dy}{dx} = 4x^3$ 3 $\frac{dy}{dx} = 5x^4$ 4 $\frac{dy}{dx} = 10x^9$ 5 $\frac{dy}{dx} = nx^{n-1}$

6 $\frac{dy}{dx} = x^2$ 7 $\frac{dy}{dx} = x^3$ 8 $\frac{dy}{dx} = x^4$ 9 $\frac{dy}{dx} = x^9$ 10 $\frac{dy}{dx} = x^n$

Integration

The inverse process to differentiation is called **integration**. For example, when you differentiate $x^2 + C$ you obtain the derivative $2x$.

When you integrate $2x$, you obtain the integral $x^2 + C$. Using the integral notation, you write $\int 2x\,dx = x^2 + C$.

$\int 2x\,dx$ is read as 'the indefinite integral of $2x$ with respect to x'; the 'dx' signifies that the integration is carried out with respect to the variable x; C is called the **constant of integration**. The function being integrated, $2x$ in this case, is called the **integrand**.

In general, $\int f'(x)\,dx = f(x) + C$.

It can be deduced from the answer to question 10 in Exercise15.1 that $\int x^n\,dx = \frac{x^{n+1}}{n+1} + C$.

This result can be verified by differentiation:

If $f(x) = \frac{x^{n+1}}{n+1} + C$ then $f'(x) = \frac{(n+1)x^{(n+1)-1}}{n+1}$

$= x^n$ as required.

In general, $\int x^n\,dx = \frac{x^{n+1}}{n+1} + C$ for $n \neq -1$.

Note This will not apply when $n = -1$, because in this case $\frac{x^0}{0}$ is undefined.

Calculus Skills

Examples

1 Find $\int x^8\,dx$.

2 Find $\int u^{-9}\,du$.

3 Find $\int t^{\frac{1}{3}}dt$.

SOLUTIONS

1 $\int x^8\,dx = \frac{x^{8+1}}{8+1} + C$

$= \frac{1}{9}x^9 + C$

2 $\int u^{-9}\,du = \frac{u^{-9+1}}{-9+1} + C$

$= -\frac{1}{8}u^{-8} + C$

$= -\frac{1}{8u^8} + C$

3 $\int t^{\frac{1}{3}}\,dt = \frac{t^{\frac{1}{3}+1}}{\frac{1}{3}+1} + C$

$= \frac{t^{\frac{4}{3}}}{\frac{4}{3}} + C$

$= \frac{3t^{\frac{4}{3}}}{4} + C$

Exercise 15.2

Find:

1 $\int x^5\,dx$ 2 $\int u^6\,du$ 3 $\int t^7\,dt$ 4 $\int v\,dv$ HPQ 5 $\int dx$ (i.e. $\int 1\,dx$)

6 $\int x^{-2}\,dx$ 7 $\int r^{-3}\,dr$ 8 $\int k^{-8}\,dk$ 9 $\int x^{\frac{1}{2}}\,dx$ HPQ 10 $\int p^{\frac{3}{2}}\,dp$

11 $\int t^{\frac{2}{3}}\,dt$ 12 $\int z^{-\frac{1}{4}}\,dz$ 13 $\int x^{-\frac{3}{5}}\,dx$ 14 $\int u^{-\frac{4}{3}}\,du$ HPQ

Reminders $\frac{1}{x^n} = x^{-n}$ $\sqrt[n]{x^m} = x^{\frac{m}{n}}$

Examples

1 Find $\int \frac{dx}{x^5}$.

2 Find $\int \sqrt[5]{p^2}\,dp$.

SOLUTIONS

1 $\int \frac{dx}{x^5} = \int \frac{1}{x^5}\,dx$

$= \int x^{-5}\,dx$

$= \frac{x^{-5+1}}{-5+1} + C$

$= -\frac{1}{4}x^{-4} + C$

$= -\frac{1}{4x^4} + C$

2 $\int \sqrt[5]{p^2}\,dp = \int p^{\frac{2}{5}}\,dp$

$= \frac{p^{\frac{2}{5}+1}}{\frac{2}{5}+1} + C$

$= \frac{p^{\frac{7}{5}}}{\frac{7}{5}} + C$

$= \frac{5p^{\frac{7}{5}}}{7} + C$

$= \frac{5\sqrt[5]{p^7}}{7} + C$

Exercise 15.3

Find:

1 $\int \frac{dx}{x^4}$ 2 $\int \frac{dr}{r^6}$ 3 $\int \frac{dv}{v^{10}}$ HPQ 4 $\int \sqrt[3]{x^4}\,dx$ 5 $\int \sqrt[3]{h}\,dh$

6 $\int \sqrt[4]{t}\,dt$ 7 $\int \sqrt{z^5}\,dz$ HPQ 8 $\int \frac{dn}{\sqrt[3]{n^2}}$ 9 $\int \frac{dx}{\sqrt{x^3}}$ 10 $\int \frac{ds}{\sqrt[3]{s}}$ HPQ

Rules for integration

From the rules for differentiation used in Chapter 13, it follows that:

- $\int ax^n\,dx = a\int x^n\,dx = \frac{ax^{n+1}}{n+1} + C$ for $n \neq -1$
- $\int (f(x) + g(x) + \ldots)\,dx = \int f(x)\,dx + \int g(x)\,dx + \int \ldots dx$

Examples

1 Find $\int 10x^4\,dx$.

2 Find $\int (2y^2 - 4y + 3)\,dy$.

SOLUTIONS

1
$$\int 10x^4\,dx = 10\int x^4\,dx = 10\left(\frac{x^5}{5}\right) + C = 2x^5 + C$$

2
$$\int (2y^2 - 4y + 3)dy = 2\int y^2\,dy - 4\int y^1\,dy + 3\int y^0\,dy = 2\left(\frac{y^3}{3}\right) - 4\left(\frac{y^2}{2}\right) + 3\left(\frac{y^1}{1}\right) + C = \frac{2y^3}{3} - 2y^2 + 3y + C$$

Exercise 15.4

Find:

1 $\int 9x^2\,dx$ 2 $\int 8t\,dt$ 3 $\int 7\,dx$ 4 $\int 2x^3\,dx$ HPQ 5 $\int 4u^5\,du$

6 $\int \frac{1}{2}v^2\,dv$ 7 $\int (x^2 + 3x - 2)\,dx$ 8 $\int (u^4 - 6u^2)\,du$ 9 $\int (8r^5 - 6r^3 + 1)\,dr$ 10 $\int (t - 3t^7)\,dt$

Examples

1 Find $\int \frac{dx}{2x^6}$.

2 Find $\int \frac{3\,ds}{\sqrt{s}}$.

SOLUTIONS

1 $\int \frac{dx}{2x^6} = \frac{1}{2}\int \frac{1}{x^6}dx$

$= \frac{1}{2}\int x^{-6}dx$

$= \frac{1}{2} \times \left(\frac{x^{-5}}{-5}\right) + C$

$= -\frac{1}{10x^5} + C$

2 $\int \frac{3ds}{\sqrt{s}} = 3\int \frac{1}{\sqrt{s}}ds = 3\int s^{-\frac{1}{2}}ds$

$= 3\frac{s^{\frac{1}{2}}}{\frac{1}{2}} + C$

$= 6s^{\frac{1}{2}} + C$

$= 6\sqrt{s} + C$

Exercise 15.5

Find:

1 $\int \frac{8\,dx}{x^3}$ 2 $\int \frac{-9\,dr}{r^4}$ 3 $\int \frac{5\,dp}{p^2}$ 4 $\int \frac{-6\,dk}{k^8}$ 5 $\int \frac{dx}{3x^5}$

6 $\int \frac{2\,du}{5u^7}$ HPQ 7 $\int 3\sqrt{x}\,dx$ 8 $\int 2\sqrt{v^7}\,dv$ 9 $\int 4\sqrt[5]{t^3}\,dt$ HPQ 10 $\int \frac{\sqrt[6]{z}\,dz}{2}$

11 $\int \frac{5\,dx}{\sqrt{x}}$ 12 $\int \frac{3\,dt}{\sqrt[4]{t^3}}$ 13 $\int \frac{du}{4\sqrt{u^3}}$ 14 $\int \frac{ds}{6\sqrt[3]{s^4}}$ 15 $\int \frac{-3\,dr}{2\sqrt[4]{r^7}}$ HPQ

Integrating products and quotients

Before integrating a function, it should be expressed as a sum of individual terms.

Examples

1 Find $\int (2x-3)^2\,dx$.

2 Find $\int \frac{u+1}{\sqrt{u}}du$.

SOLUTIONS

1 $\int (2x-3)^2\,dx = \int (4x^2 - 12x + 9)\,dx$

$= 4\left(\frac{x^3}{3}\right) - 12\left(\frac{x^2}{2}\right) + 9x + C$

$= \frac{4x^3}{3} - 6x^2 + 9x + C$

2 $\int \frac{u+1}{\sqrt{u}}du = \int \left(\frac{u}{\sqrt{u}} + \frac{1}{\sqrt{u}}\right)du$

$= \int \left(\frac{u}{u^{\frac{1}{2}}} + \frac{1}{u^{\frac{1}{2}}}\right)du$

$= \int \left(u^{\frac{1}{2}} + u^{-\frac{1}{2}}\right)du$

$= \frac{u^{\frac{3}{2}}}{\frac{3}{2}} + \frac{u^{\frac{1}{2}}}{\frac{1}{2}} + C$

$= \frac{2u^{\frac{3}{2}}}{3} + 2u^{\frac{1}{2}} + C$

$= \frac{2\sqrt{u^3}}{3} + 2\sqrt{u} + C$

Calculus Skills

Exercise 15.6

Find:

1 $\int (x-2)(x+1)\,dx$ **2** $\int (3u-1)^2\,du$ **3** $\int t(t+3)(t-1)\,dt$ **4** $\int 4p(p+2)^2\,dp$ HPQ

5 $\int \left(x+\frac{1}{x}\right)^2 dx$ **6** $\int 3\sqrt{s}\left(1-\sqrt{s}\right)ds$ **7** $\int \left(v+\frac{2}{v}\right)\left(v-\frac{2}{v}\right)dv$ **8** $\int \frac{x^3+5}{x^2}\,dx$

9 $\int \frac{r-2}{r^3}\,dr$ **10** $\int \frac{2x+\sqrt{x}}{3x}\,dx$ **11** $\int \frac{3-u^2}{\sqrt{u}}\,du$ HPQ **12** $\int \frac{6n^2+n-7}{n\sqrt{n}}\,dn$

Integrating $(ax+b)^n$

The chain rule for differentiation can be used to investigate integrals of the form $\int (ax+b)^n\,dx$.

1 $\frac{d}{dx}(x+1)^4 = 4(x+1)^3 \quad \Rightarrow \quad \int 4(x+1)^3 dx = (x+1)^4 + C$

hence $\int (x+1)^3 dx = \frac{(x+1)^4}{4} + C.$

2 $\frac{d}{dx}(5x+1)^4 = 20(x+1)^3 \quad \Rightarrow \quad \int 20(5x+1)^3 dx = (5x+1)^4 + C$

hence $\int (5x+1)^3 dx = \frac{(5x+1)^4}{20} + C.$

3 $\frac{d}{dx}(3x+2)^7 = 21(3x+2)^6 \quad \Rightarrow \quad \int 21(3x+2)^6 dx = (3x+2)^7 + C$

hence $\int (3x+2)^6 dx = \frac{(3x+2)^7}{21} + C.$

4 $\frac{d}{dx}(ax+b)^n = an(ax+b)^{n-1} \quad \Rightarrow \quad \int an(ax+b)^{n-1} dx = (ax+b)^n + C$

hence $\int (ax+b)^{n-1} dx = \frac{(ax+b)^n}{an} + C.$

These examples lead to the general rule: $\int (ax+b)^n dx = \frac{(ax+b)^{n+1}}{a(n+1)} + C, \; n \neq -1.$

Examples

1 Find $\int (7x+2)^4 dx.$

2 Find $\int \sqrt{1-2u}\,du.$

SOLUTIONS

1 $\int (7x+2)^4 dx = \frac{(7x+2)^5}{7\times 5} + C$

$= \frac{(7x+2)^5}{35} + C$

2 $\int \sqrt{1-2u}\,du = \int (1-2u)^{\frac{1}{2}} du$

$= \frac{(1-2u)^{\frac{3}{2}}}{-2\times\frac{3}{2}} + C$

$= \frac{\sqrt{(1-2u)^3}}{-3} + C$

$= -\frac{\sqrt{(1-2u)^3}}{3} + C$

Exercise 15.7

Find:

1 $\int (x+2)^3\,dx$
2 $\int (3u-1)^4\,du$
3 $\int (9-4t)^5\,dt$ HPQ
4 $\int (p+5)^{-2}\,dp$
5 $\int (2x+7)^{-3}\,dx$
6 $\int (4-v)^{\frac{1}{2}}\,dv$
7 $\int (5r+2)^{\frac{3}{2}}\,dr$
8 $\int (12s+7)^{\frac{3}{4}}\,ds$
9 $\int \frac{1}{(3u+2)^4}\,du$
10 $\int \frac{9}{(1+6x)^2}\,dx$
11 $\int \frac{3}{(1-2n)^5}\,dn$ HPQ
12 $\int \sqrt{4z-5}\,dz$
13 $\int \sqrt[3]{8x+5}\,dx$
14 $\int \frac{1}{\sqrt{3-7t}}\,dt$
15 $\int \frac{4}{\sqrt[3]{2u+9}}\,du$ HPQ
16 $\int \frac{2}{\sqrt{(5-r)^3}}\,dr$

Integrating trigonometric functions

The derivatives of the sine and cosine functions can be used to investigate their integrals.

$$\frac{d}{dx}(\sin x) = \cos x \quad \Rightarrow \quad \int \cos x\,dx = \sin x + C$$

$$\frac{d}{dx}(\cos x) = -\sin x \quad \Rightarrow \quad \int \sin x\,dx = -\cos x + C$$

Extensions to the above integrals can be found by using the chain rule for differentiation.

$$\frac{d}{dx}(\sin(ax+b)) = a\cos(ax+b) \quad \Rightarrow \quad \int a\cos(ax+b)\,dx = \sin(ax+b)+C$$

$$\text{hence} \int \cos(ax+b)\,dx = \frac{1}{a}\sin(ax+b)+C, \quad a \neq 0.$$

$$\frac{d}{dx}(\cos(ax+b)) = -a\sin(ax+b) \quad \Rightarrow \quad \int a\sin(ax+b)\,dx = -\cos(ax+b)+C$$

$$\text{hence} \int \sin(ax+b)\,dx = -\frac{1}{a}\cos(ax+b)+C, \quad a \neq 0.$$

Note These rules for the integrals of trigonometric functions are only true when the angle is in radians.

Examples

Integrate:

1 $6\sin x - \cos 6x$
2 $\sin(\pi - 5t)$

SOLUTIONS

1 $\int (6\sin x - \cos 6x)\,dx = -6\cos x - \frac{1}{6}\sin 6x + C$

2 $\int \sin(\pi - 5t)\,dt = -\frac{1}{5} \times -\cos(\pi - 5t) + C = \frac{1}{5}\cos(\pi - 5t) + C$

Exercise 15.8

Find:

1 $\int 4\cos x\,dx$

2 $\int \cos 4x\,dx$

3 $\int 4\cos 4x\,dx$

4 $\int 3\sin\theta\,d\theta$

5 $\int \sin 3\theta\,d\theta$

6 $\int 3\sin 3\theta\,d\theta$

7 $\int \frac{1}{2}\cos t\,dt$

8 $\int \cos\frac{1}{2}t\,dt$

9 $\int \frac{1}{2}\cos\frac{1}{2}t\,dt$

10 $\int (2\cos x - \sin 2x)\,dx$ HPQ

11 $\int (5\sin\theta - \cos 5\theta)\,d\theta$

12 $\int \left(\frac{1}{3}\cos t + \sin\frac{1}{3}t\right)dt$

13 $\int \sin(4x+\pi)\,dx$

14 $\int \cos\left(3u - \frac{\pi}{2}\right)du$ HPQ

15 $\int \sin(2\pi - \theta)\,d\theta$

16 $\int \cos(5+2t)\,dt$

17 $\int (2\cos(5v-1) + \frac{1}{2}\sin(7+6v))\,dv$

18 Using the fact that $\cos 2\theta = 2\cos^2\theta - 1 = 1 - 2\sin^2\theta$ ACE

a) express $\cos^2\theta$ in terms of $\cos 2\theta$ and hence find $\int \cos^2\theta\,d\theta$

b) express $\sin^2\theta$ in terms of $\cos 2\theta$ and hence find $\int \sin^2\theta\,d\theta$.

Solving differential equations

At the beginning of this chapter we investigated how to find the equation of a curve given its gradient function.

For example, we found that there is a family of curves which has gradient function $\frac{dy}{dx} = 2x$. Each curve in the family had an equation of the form $y = x^2 + C$, where C is a constant.

Equations like $\frac{dy}{dx} = 2x$ are called **differential equations.**

Differential equations are solved by integration, e.g. $\int 2x\,dx = x^2 + C$.

Therefore $y = x^2 + C$ is the general solution of the differential equation $\frac{dy}{dx} = 2x$.

If we are given some additional information, we can evaluate the constant of integration and obtain a particular solution to the equation.

For example, if we know that the curve above passes through the point $(2, 7)$, we can substitute $x = 2$ and $y = 7$ into $y = x^2 + C$:

$$\text{so } 7 = 2^2 + C$$
$$\text{and } C = 3.$$

Therefore $y = x^2 + 3$ is a particular solution of the differential equation $\frac{dy}{dx} = 2x$.

Example 1

Solve the differential equation $\frac{du}{dt} = 10t - 7$ if $u = 50$ when $t = 4$.

SOLUTION

$u = \int (10t - 7)\,dt = 5t^2 - 7t + C$

$u = 50$ when $t = 4 \Rightarrow 50 = 5(4)^2 - 7(4) + C$

so $50 = 52 + C$

and $C = -2$

Therefore $u = 5t^2 - 7t - 2$.

Example 2

The rate of change of a function is given by $f'(x) = 2\sqrt{x}$.
Find $f(x)$ given that $f(4) = 12$.

SOLUTION

$$f(x) = \int 2\sqrt{x}\,dx = \frac{2x^{\frac{3}{2}}}{\frac{3}{2}} + C = \frac{4x^{\frac{3}{2}}}{3} + C = \frac{4\sqrt{x^3}}{3} + C.$$

$$\text{Hence } f(4) = 12 \Rightarrow 12 = \frac{4\sqrt{4^3}}{3} + C$$

$$\Rightarrow 12 = \frac{32}{3} + C$$

$$\Rightarrow C = \frac{4}{3}$$

Therefore $f(x) = \dfrac{4\sqrt{x^3}}{3} + \dfrac{4}{3}$.

Exercise 15.9

1 Find the equations of the curves which satisfy the following conditions:

a) $\dfrac{dy}{dx} = 6x$ and the curve passes through the point (2, 5).

b) $\dfrac{dy}{dx} = x^2 - 2x + 1$ and the curve passes through the point (3, 8).

c) $\dfrac{dy}{dx} = \sqrt{4x+1}$ and the curve passes through the point (2, 6).

d) $\dfrac{dy}{dx} = \cos 2x$ and the curve passes through the point $\left(\dfrac{\pi}{12}, 1\right)$.

2 Find the solutions of these differential equations.

a) $\dfrac{ds}{dt} = 3t^2 + 4t + 5$ if $s = 1$ when $t = -1$.

b) $\dfrac{ds}{dt} = 2t - \dfrac{20}{t^2}$ if $s = 13$ when $t = -4$.

c) $\dfrac{dv}{dt} = \sqrt[3]{t}$ if $v = 5$ when $t = 8$.

d) $\dfrac{dv}{dt} = 3\sin(4t - \pi)$ if $v = 1$ when $t = \dfrac{\pi}{2}$.

3 The gradient of the tangent to a curve at the point (x, y) is given by $\dfrac{dy}{dx} = \dfrac{9 + 2x^3}{x^2}$. HPQ
If the curve passes through the point $(-3, 10)$, find its equation.

4 The rate of change of a function is given by $f'(x) = (2x - 3)^3$.
Find $f(x)$ given that $f(2{\cdot}5) = 4$.

5 The rate of change of a function is given by $g'(\theta) = 2\cos 3\theta$.
Find $g(\theta)$ given that $g\left(\dfrac{\pi}{6}\right) = 2$.

6 The speed of a roller-coaster is given by $d'(t) = 20t - 5$, where t is the time in seconds after the start of the ride.
Find $d(t)$ given that 3 seconds after the start of the ride the roller-coaster had travelled 75 metres. ACE

Checkout

Find:

1 $\int(2x^3+4x+1)\,dx$

2 $\int u(9u+2)\,du$

3 $\int \frac{8}{t^5}\,dt$

4 $\int\left(3\sqrt{p}+\frac{1}{p^3}\right)dp$

5 $\int\frac{4r^5-1}{2r^2}\,dr$

6 $\int\frac{(v+1)(v-2)}{\sqrt{v^3}}\,dv$

7 $\int\left(\frac{1}{2}x+1\right)^9 dx$

8 $\int\sqrt{6s-1}\,ds$

9 $\int\frac{12}{(5-3u)^2}\,du$

10 $\int\frac{1}{\sqrt[3]{(2n+3)}}\,dn$

11 $\int(\cos 10x+2)\,dx$

12 $\int(\cos(10x+2))\,dx$

13 $\int(\sin 7\theta-4)\,d\theta$

14 $\int(\sin(7\theta-4))\,d\theta$

15 $\int(3\cos 4t-2\sin t)\,dt$

16 $\int\left(\frac{1}{2}\sin 3t+3\cos\frac{1}{2}t\right)dt$

17 Find the solution of the differential equation $\frac{ds}{dt}=t^3+\frac{1}{t^2}-\frac{1}{4}$, given that $s=8$ when $t=1$.

18 A curve with equation $y=f(x)$ passes through the point (2, 1) and is such that $f'(x)=3x(x-2)$. Find the equation of the curve.

Summary

Integrating Functions

1 Integration is the inverse process to differentiation.

2 $\int f'(x)\,dx=f(x)+C$, where C is the constant of integration.

3 $\int x^n\,dx=\frac{x^{n+1}}{n+1}+C$ for $n\neq-1$

4 $\int ax^n\,dx=a\int x^n\,dx=\frac{ax^{n+1}}{n+1}+C$, for $n\neq-1$

$\int(f(x)+g(x)+....)\,dx=\int f(x)\,dx+\int g(x)\,dx+\int...dx$

5 $\int(ax+b)^n dx=\frac{(ax+b)^{n+1}}{a(n+1)}+C$, for $n\neq-1$

6 $\int\cos(ax+b)\,dx=\frac{1}{a}\sin(ax+b)+C$

$\int\sin(ax+b)\,dx=-\frac{1}{a}\cos(ax+b)+C$

These rules for the integrals of trigonometric functions are only true when the angle is in radians.

7 The general solution of the differential equation $\frac{dy}{dx}=f(x)$ is $y=\int f(x)\,dx$.

Given some additional information, a particular solution can be found.

Calculus Skills

CHAPTER

16 Using Integration to Calculate Definite Integrals

Problems involving area are studied in the branch of mathematics called **integral calculus**. This chapter provides an introduction to finding the area under a curve as well as looking at how to evaluate definite integrals.

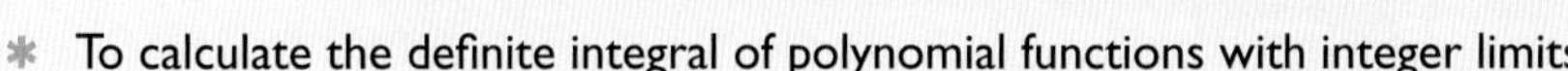

What I am learning

* To calculate the definite integral of polynomial functions with integer limits
* To calculate the definite integral of functions with limits which are integers, radians, surds, or fractions
* To solve problems like:
  Find the value of a given that $\int_2^a (x+1)\,dx = 20$.

What I should already know/be able to do

* To integrate algebraic functions which can be reduced to expressions involving powers of x
* To integrate functions of the form $f(x) = (x+q)^n, n \neq -1$
* To integrate functions of the form $f(x) = p \sin x$ and $f(x) = p \cos x$
* To integrate functions of the form $f(x) = (px+q)^n, n \neq -1$
* To integrate functions of the form $f(x) = p \sin(qx+r)$, and $f(x) = p \cos(qx+r)$

Quick check!

Find:

1. $\int (x^2+1)(x-2)\,dx$
2. $\int \left(6\sqrt{t} + \frac{1}{t^3}\right) dt$
3. $\int \frac{u^4-8}{4u^2}\,du$
4. $\int (x-7)^3\,dx$
5. $\int (2p+1)^4\,dp$
6. $\int \sqrt{4s-9}\,ds$
7. $\int \frac{2}{(5-u)^2}\,du$
8. $\int (3\cos x - 2\sin x)\,dx$
9. $\int \cos 6t\,dt$
10. $\int 8\sin 4\theta\,d\theta$
11. $\int \sin(2x+3)\,dx$
12. $\int \cos(5\theta-\pi)\,d\theta$

Quick check! – *Solutions*

1. $\frac{x^4}{4} - \frac{2x^3}{3} + \frac{x^2}{2} - 2x + C$
2. $4\sqrt{t^3} - \frac{1}{2t^2} + C$
3. $\frac{u^3}{12} + \frac{2}{u} + C$
4. $\frac{(x-7)^4}{4} + C$
5. $\frac{(2p+1)^5}{10} + C$
6. $\frac{\sqrt{(4s-9)^3}}{6} + C$
7. $\frac{2}{5-u} + C$
8. $3\sin x + 2\cos x + C$
9. $\frac{1}{6}\sin 6t + C$
10. $-2\cos 4\theta + C$
11. $-\frac{1}{2}\cos(2x+3) + C$
12. $\frac{1}{5}\sin(5\theta-\pi) + C$

Investigating the area under a curve

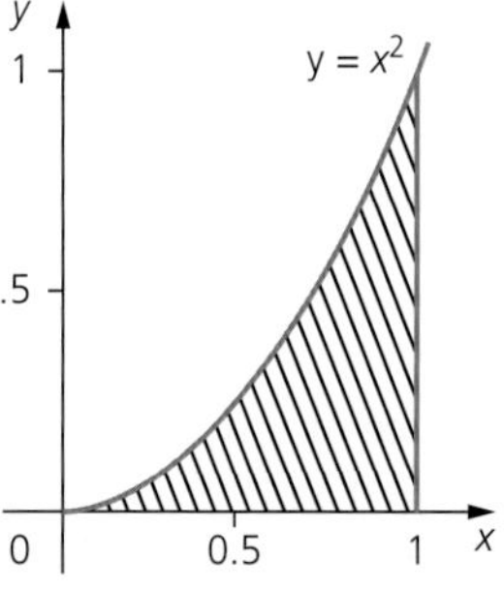

How can you find the area under the curve $y = x^2$, bounded by the x-axis and say the line $x = 1$?

One way to estimate the area is to divide it into 10 strips each 0·1 units wide.

You can then draw rectangles either below or above the curve $y = x^2$ as shown below.

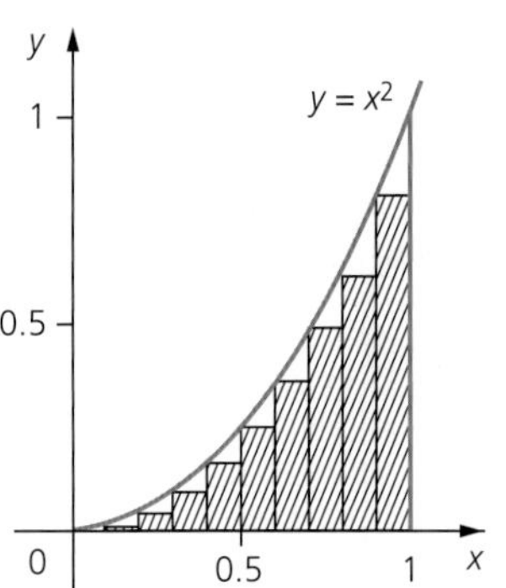

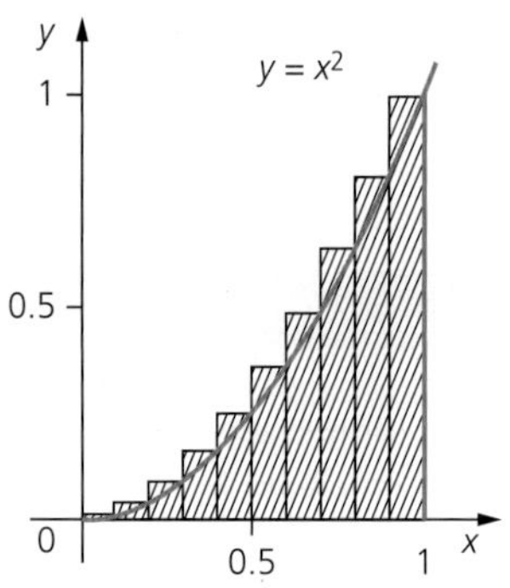

The sum of the areas of the rectangles:

- below the curve gives the lower bound of the area under the curve
- above the curve gives the upper bound of the area under the curve.

The lower bound $= 0{\cdot}1 \times (0^2 + 0{\cdot}1^2 + 0{\cdot}2^2 + 0{\cdot}3^2 + 0{\cdot}4^2 + 0{\cdot}5^2 + 0{\cdot}6^2 + 0{\cdot}7^2 + 0{\cdot}8^2 + 0{\cdot}9^2)$

$= 0{\cdot}1 \times 2{\cdot}85$

$= 0{\cdot}285$ square units

The upper bound $= 0{\cdot}1 \times (0{\cdot}1^2 + 0{\cdot}2^2 + 0{\cdot}3^2 + 0{\cdot}4^2 + 0{\cdot}5^2 + 0{\cdot}6^2 + 0{\cdot}7^2 + 0{\cdot}8^2 + 0{\cdot}9^2 + 1^2)$

$= 0{\cdot}1 \times 3{\cdot}85$

$= 0{\cdot}385$ square units

Therefore $0{\cdot}285$ square units $<$ area under curve $< 0{\cdot}385$ square units.

A better estimate is found when the area is divided into 100 strips each 0·01 units wide.

In this case,

the lower bound $= 0{\cdot}01 \times (0^2 + 0{\cdot}01^2 + 0{\cdot}02^2 + 0{\cdot}03^2 + \ldots + 0{\cdot}97^2 + 0{\cdot}98^2 + 0{\cdot}99^2)$

$= 0{\cdot}01 \times 32{\cdot}835$

$= 0{\cdot}32835$ square units

and the upper bound $= 0{\cdot}01 \times (0{\cdot}01^2 + 0{\cdot}02^2 + 0{\cdot}03^2 + 0{\cdot}04^2 + \ldots + 0{\cdot}98^2 + 0{\cdot}99^2 + 1^2)$

$= 0{\cdot}01 \times 33{\cdot}835$

$= 0{\cdot}33835$ square units

Therefore $0{\cdot}32835$ square units $<$ area under curve $< 0{\cdot}33835$ square units

As we increase the number of strips, the bounds converge to the same value, which is the area under the curve.

Finding the area under a curve using this method is extremely time-consuming and cumbersome.

Such areas can be found easily, however, with a graphing calculator or by using an appropriate software package.

Use a graphing calculator or an appropriate software package to confirm that the area under the curve $y = x^2$ bounded by the x-axis and the line $x = 1$ is $0{\cdot}\dot{3}$ square units or $\frac{1}{3}$ square units.

Calculus Skills

Exercise 16.1

1 The table below shows the areas under the curve $y = x^2$ bounded by the x-axis and the lines $x = 1$, $x = 2$, $x = 3$ and $x = 4$.

Line	$x = 1$	$x = 2$	$x = 3$	$x = 4$	$x = a$
Area (units^2)	$\frac{1}{3}$	$\frac{8}{3}$	$\frac{27}{3}$	$\frac{64}{3}$	

a) Use a graphing calculator or an appropriate software package to confirm that the areas shown in the table are correct.

b) Complete the final row of the table by stating an expression for the area under the curve $y = x^2$ bounded by the x-axis and the line $x = a$.

2 The table below shows the areas under the curve $y = x^3$, bounded by the x-axis and the lines $x = 1$, $x = 2$, $x = 3$ and $x = 4$.

Line	$x = 1$	$x = 2$	$x = 3$	$x = 4$	$x = a$
Area (units^2)	$\frac{1}{4}$	$\frac{16}{4}$	$\frac{81}{4}$	$\frac{256}{4}$	

a) Use a graphing calculator or an appropriate software package to confirm that the areas shown in the table are correct.

b) Complete the final row of the table by stating an expression for the area under the curve $y = x^3$ bounded by the x-axis and the line $x = a$.

3 The table below shows the areas under the curve $y = x^4$ bounded by the x-axis and the lines $x = 1$, $x = 2$, $x = 3$ and $x = 4$.

Line	$x = 1$	$x = 2$	$x = 3$	$x = 4$	$x = a$
Area (units^2)	$\frac{1}{5}$	$\frac{32}{5}$	$\frac{243}{5}$	$\frac{1024}{5}$	

a) Use a graphing calculator or an appropriate software package to confirm that the areas shown in the table are correct.

b) Complete the final row of the table by stating an expression for the area under the curve $y = x^4$ bounded by the x-axis and the line $x = a$.

4 Use your answers to questions 1, 2 and 3 to complete the table below for the area under each curve bounded by the x-axis and the line $x = a$.

Equation of curve	$y = x^2$	$y = x^3$	$y = x^4$	$y = x^n$
Area (square units)	$\frac{a^3}{3}$			

5 Make a conjecture about the connection between $\int x^n \, dx$ and the area under the curve $y = x^n$, bounded by the x-axis and the line $x = a$.

Calculus Skills

Using integration to find the area under a curve

If we use the notation $F(x)$ to denote $\int f(x)\,dx$, where $F'(x) = f(x)$, then the area under the curve $y = f(x)$ bounded by the x-axis and the line $x = a$ is equal to $F(a)$. Similarly, the area under the curve $y = f(x)$ bounded by the x-axis and the line $x = b$ is equal to $F(b)$.

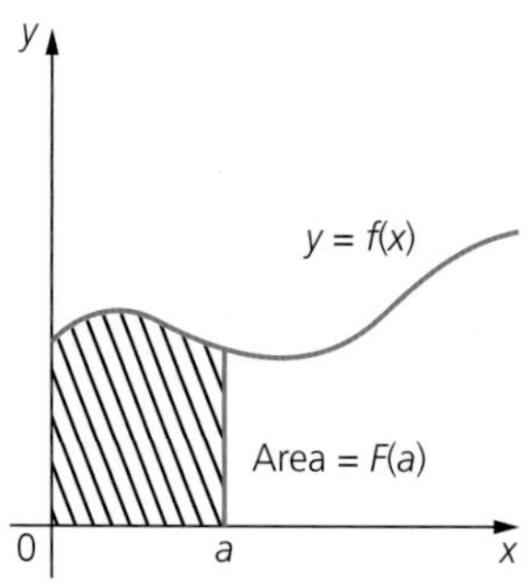

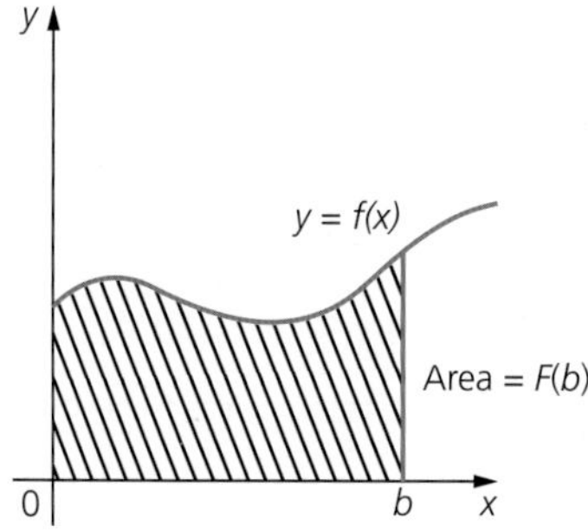

Therefore the area under the curve $y = f(x)$ bounded by the x-axis, the line $x = a$ and the line $x = b$ $(a < b)$ is equal to $F(b) - F(a)$.

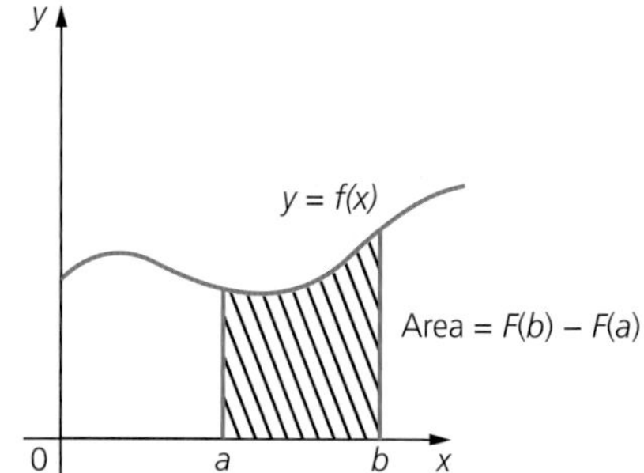

We use the notation $\int_a^b f(x)\,dx$ for $F(b) - F(a)$. This is called a **definite integral** with lower limit a and upper limit b.

The indefinite integral must include a constant of integration, i.e. $\int f(x)\,dx = F(x) + C$.

Note that $\int_a^b f(x)\,dx = (F(b) + C) - (F(a) + C) = F(b) - F(a)$. The constants cancel out, so a definite integral does not include a constant of integration.

The result $\int_a^b f(x)\,dx = F(b) - F(a)$ is known as the **Fundamental Theorem of Calculus**; it links differentiation and integration.

Example

Calculate the shaded area in the diagram.

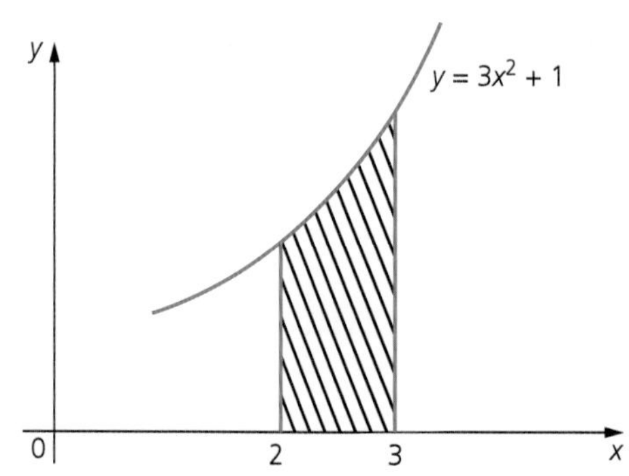

SOLUTION

$$\text{Shaded area} = \int_2^3 (3x^2 + 1)\,dx$$

$$= \left[3 \times \frac{x^3}{3} + x\right]_2^3$$

$$= \left[x^3 + x\right]_2^3$$

$$= (3^3 + 3) - (2^3 + 2)$$

$$= 30 - 10$$

$$= 20 \text{ square units.}$$

Exercise 16.2

Calculate the shaded area in each diagram.

1
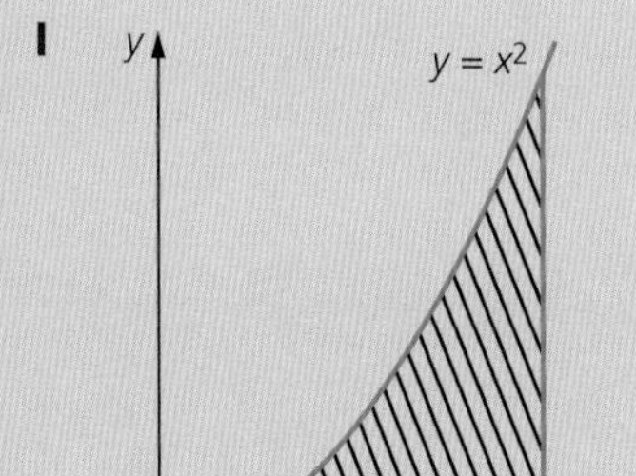

2
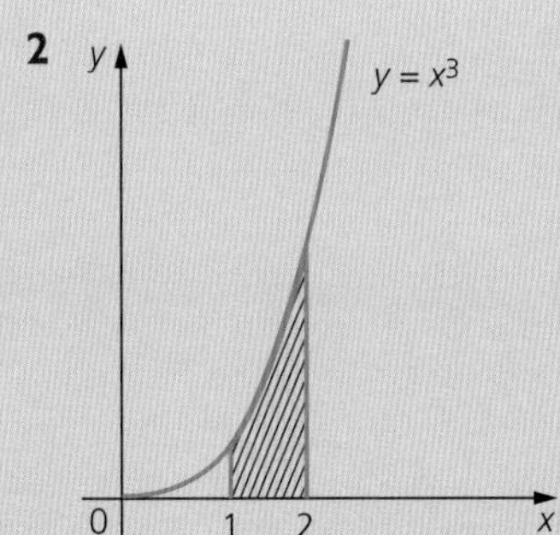

3
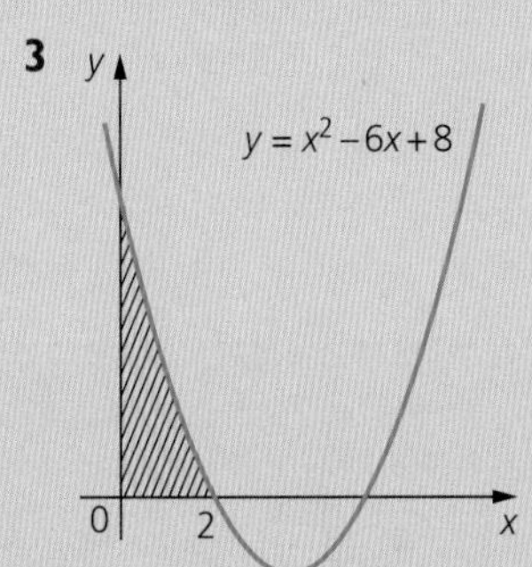

4
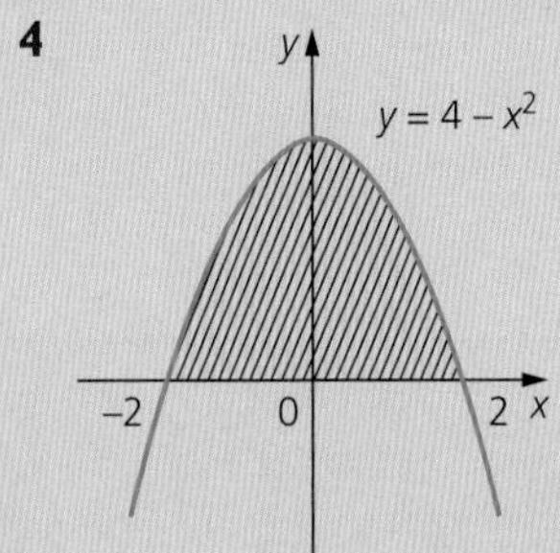

5
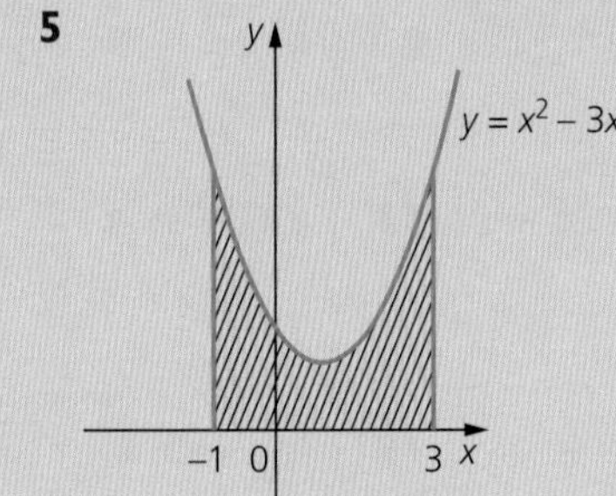

6
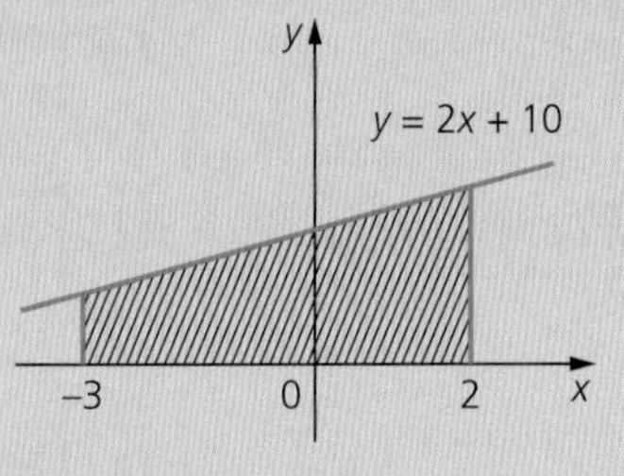

7
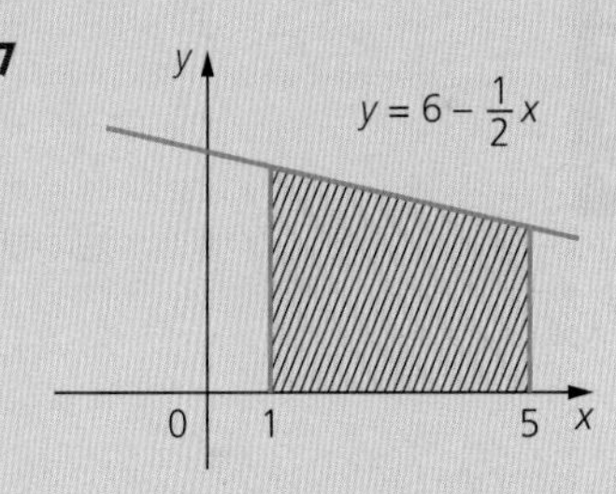

Evaluating definite integrals

Examples

Evaluate:

1 $\int_1^2 \frac{x^4 - 1}{x^3}\,dx$

2 $\int_4^9 \frac{dt}{\sqrt{t}}$

Calculus Skills

SOLUTIONS

1 $$\int_1^2 \frac{x^4-1}{x^3}dx = \int_1^2 \left(\frac{x^4}{x^3}-\frac{1}{x^3}\right)dx$$
$$= \int_1^2 (x - x^{-3})dx$$
$$= \left[\frac{x^2}{2} - \frac{x^{-2}}{-2}\right]_1^2$$
$$= \left[\frac{x^2}{2} + \frac{1}{2x^2}\right]_1^2$$
$$= \left(2+\frac{1}{8}\right) - \left(\frac{1}{2}+\frac{1}{2}\right)$$
$$= 1\frac{1}{8}$$

2 $$\int_4^9 \frac{dt}{\sqrt{t}} = \int_4^9 t^{-\frac{1}{2}}\,dt$$
$$= \left[\frac{t^{\frac{1}{2}}}{\frac{1}{2}}\right]_4^9$$
$$= \left[2\sqrt{t}\right]_4^9$$
$$= \left(2\sqrt{9}\right) - \left(2\sqrt{4}\right)$$
$$= 6 - 4$$
$$= 2$$

Exercise 16.3

Evaluate:

1 $\int_1^3 (x^2+2x)\,dx$ 2 $\int_{-1}^2 (4-t^3)\,dt$ 3 $\int_{-2}^4 (6u+1)\,du$ 4 $\int_{\frac{1}{3}}^{\frac{1}{2}} \frac{dx}{x^2}$

5 $\int_{-1}^2 \frac{6}{t^4}\,dt$ 6 $\int_{\sqrt{2}}^{\sqrt{3}} \frac{dr}{2r^3}$ 7 $\int_4^9 \sqrt{v}\,dv$ 8 $\int_1^8 \sqrt[3]{s}\,ds$

9 $\int_1^4 \frac{\sqrt{p^3}}{2}\,dp$ 10 $\int_{-3}^3 (x+1)(x+2)\,dx$ 11 $\int_{-1}^2 3z(2-z)\,dz$ HPQ 12 $\int_{\sqrt{5}}^{\sqrt{6}} t(2t^2-3)\,dt$

13 $\int_1^2 \frac{2n^5-1}{n^3}\,dn$ 14 $\int_1^9 \frac{1+2u}{\sqrt{u}}\,du$ HPQ 15 $\int_1^4 \frac{5+\sqrt{x}}{x^2}\,dx$ 16 $\int_{\frac{1}{4}}^{\frac{1}{3}} \frac{3-2r}{r^4}\,dr$

17 Find the value of a in each case given that:

a) $\int_2^a (x+1)\,dx = 20$ ACE **b)** $\int_1^a (10-2u)\,du = 16$ **c)** $\int_0^a \sqrt{t}\,dt = 18$

d) $\int_{-2}^a \frac{12}{n^4}\,dn = -1$ **e)** $\int_0^a p(p-2)\,dp = 0$ **f)** $\int_a^4 \frac{x^2-8}{x^2}\,dx = -3.$ ACE

Reminders

$$\int (ax+b)^n dx = \frac{(ax+b)^{n+1}}{a(n+1)} + C,\ n \neq -1$$
$$\int \cos(ax+b)\,dx = \frac{1}{a}\sin(ax+b) + C$$
$$\int \sin(ax+b)\,dx = -\frac{1}{a}\cos(ax+b) + C$$

Calculus Skills

Examples

Evaluate:

1 $\displaystyle\int_{-1}^{2} \frac{2}{(1-x)^3}\,dx$

2 $\displaystyle\int_{0}^{4} \sqrt{2u+1}\,du$

3 $\displaystyle\int_{\frac{\pi}{6}}^{\frac{\pi}{4}} \cos\left(2\theta-\frac{\pi}{3}\right)d\theta$

SOLUTIONS

1 $$\int_{-1}^{2} \frac{2}{(1-x)^3}\,dx = \int_{-1}^{2} 2(1-x)^{-3}dx$$

$$= \left[2\times\frac{(1-x)^{-2}}{-1\times-2}\right]_{-1}^{2}$$

$$= \left[\frac{1}{(1-x)^2}\right]_{-1}^{2}$$

$$= \frac{1}{(1-2)^2} - \frac{1}{(1-(-1))^2}$$

$$= 1-\frac{1}{4}$$

$$= \frac{3}{4}$$

2 $$\int_{0}^{4} \sqrt{2u+1}\,du = \int_{0}^{4} (2u+1)^{\frac{1}{2}}du$$

$$= \left[\frac{(2u+1)^{\frac{3}{2}}}{2\times\frac{3}{2}}\right]_{0}^{4}$$

$$= \left[\frac{\sqrt{(2u+1)^3}}{3}\right]_{0}^{4}$$

$$= \frac{\sqrt{(2(4)+1)^3}}{3} - \frac{\sqrt{(2(0)+1)^3}}{3}$$

$$= \frac{\sqrt{(9)^3}}{3} - \frac{\sqrt{(1)^3}}{3}$$

$$= \frac{3^3}{3} - \frac{1^3}{3}$$

$$= 9-\frac{1}{3}$$

$$= 8\frac{2}{3}$$

3 $$\int_{\frac{\pi}{6}}^{\frac{\pi}{4}} \cos\left(2\theta-\frac{\pi}{3}\right)d\theta = \left[\frac{1}{2}\sin\left(2\theta-\frac{\pi}{3}\right)\right]_{\frac{\pi}{6}}^{\frac{\pi}{4}}$$

$$= \left(\frac{1}{2}\sin(2\left(\frac{\pi}{4}\right)-\frac{\pi}{3})\right) - \left(\frac{1}{2}\sin(2\left(\frac{\pi}{6}\right)-\frac{\pi}{3})\right)$$

$$= \left(\frac{1}{2}\sin\frac{\pi}{6}\right) - \left(\frac{1}{2}\sin 0\right)$$

$$= \left(\frac{1}{2}\times\frac{1}{2}\right) - \left(\frac{1}{2}\times 0\right)$$

$$= \frac{1}{4}$$

Exercise 16.4

Evaluate:

1 $\displaystyle\int_{0}^{1} (3x-1)^3dx$

2 $\displaystyle\int_{-1}^{1} (u+2)^4du$

3 $\displaystyle\int_{\frac{1}{2}}^{\frac{3}{4}} (3-4t)^3dt$ HPQ

4 $\displaystyle\int_{1}^{6} \sqrt{10-n}\,dn$

5 $\displaystyle\int_{-2}^{3} \frac{1}{(4s+3)^2}\,ds$

6 $\displaystyle\int_{5}^{8} \frac{6}{\sqrt{3x+1}}\,dx$ HPQ

7 $\displaystyle\int_{0}^{\frac{\pi}{2}} (\cos x-\sin x)dx$

8 $\displaystyle\int_{0}^{\frac{\pi}{4}} \sqrt{2}\cos\theta\,d\theta$

→

9 $\int_{\frac{\pi}{3}}^{\frac{\pi}{2}} \cos 3t\, dt$ **10** $\int_{\frac{1}{2}}^{1} \sin \pi x\, dx$ **11** $\int_{0}^{\pi} \cos\left(\theta+\frac{\pi}{2}\right) d\theta$ HPQ **12** $\int_{\frac{\pi}{4}}^{\frac{\pi}{3}} \sin(4u-\pi)\, du$

Evaluate correct to three significant figures:

13 $\int_{2}^{5} (4\cos x-1)\, dx$ **14** $\int_{2}^{5} \cos(4x-1)\, dx$ **15** $\int_{1}^{3} (\sin 5\theta+2)\, d\theta$ **16** $\int_{1}^{3} \sin(5\theta+2)\, d\theta$ HPQ

17 Show that $\int_{\frac{\pi}{3}}^{\frac{\pi}{2}} (\sin 2t+2\cos t)\, dt = \frac{9-4\sqrt{3}}{4}$.

18 Show that $\int_{0}^{\pi} \left(\cos\frac{1}{4}x+\frac{1}{4}\sin x\right) dx = \frac{4\sqrt{2}+1}{2}$. ACE

19 Using the relationships $\cos 2\theta = 2\cos^2\theta - 1 = 1-2\sin^2\theta$: ACE

a) express $\cos^2\theta$ in terms of $\cos 2\theta$ and hence find the exact value of $\int_{\frac{\pi}{4}}^{\frac{\pi}{2}} \cos^2\theta\, d\theta$

b) express $\sin^2\theta$ in terms of $\cos 2\theta$ and hence find the exact value of $\int_{0}^{\frac{\pi}{6}} \sin^2\theta\, d\theta$.

Checkout

Evaluate:

1 $\int_{\sqrt{2}}^{\sqrt{5}} x^5 dx$ 2 $\int_{-1}^{2} (t+2)(3t-1)\, dt$ 3 $\int_{1}^{4} \frac{u-2}{\sqrt{u}} du$

4 $\int_{0}^{2} (p+3)^3 dp$ 5 $\int_{1}^{6} \frac{2}{\sqrt{8z+1}} dz$ 6 $\int_{-4}^{1} \frac{3}{(7-2v)^2} dv$

7 Show that $\int_{\frac{\pi}{6}}^{\frac{\pi}{3}} 3\cos 4x\, dx = -\frac{3\sqrt{3}}{4}$. 8 Show that $\int_{\frac{\pi}{4}}^{\frac{\pi}{2}} \sin\left(3\theta-\frac{\pi}{2}\right) d\theta = \frac{\sqrt{2}+1}{3\sqrt{2}}$.

9 Evaluate $\int_{0}^{1} (\cos t+\sin t)\, dt$ correct to three significant figures.

Summary

Using Integration to Calculate Definite Integrals

1 $\int_{a}^{b} f(x)dx$ is called a definite integral with lower limit a and upper limit b.

2 The Fundamental Theorem of Calculus:

If $\int f(x)\, dx = F(x)+C$ where $F'(x)=f(x)$ then $\int_{a}^{b} f(x)dx = F(b)-F(a)$ $(a<b)$.

CHAPTER 17 Applying Differential Calculus

In this chapter we will look at how to use differentiation to solve optimisation problems and problems involving rate of change.

What I am learning

* To determine the greatest/least value of a function on a closed interval
* To determine the optimal solution for a given problem
* To solve problems using rate of change
* To solve problems like:
  A sector of a circle with radius r cm has area $100\,cm^2$.
  a) Show that the perimeter P cm of the sector is given by $P = 2r + \frac{200}{r}$.
  b) Find the least possible perimeter of the sector.

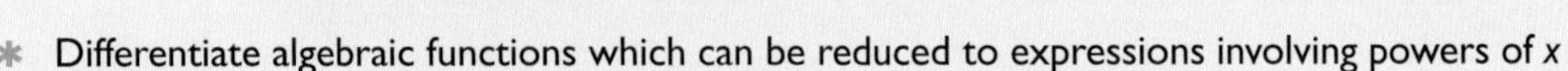

What I should already know/be able to do

* Differentiate algebraic functions which can be reduced to expressions involving powers of x
* Find the stationary values of a function and determine their nature
* Construct a formula to model information

Quick check!

1 Find the derivative of each of the following:

a) $f(x) = 3\sqrt{x}$ b) $h = t(t+1)^2$ c) $C(n) = \frac{3n^2 - 2}{n}$

2 Find the stationary values of $f(x) = \frac{1}{3}x^3 + x^2 - 3x + 2$ and determine their nature.

3 a) A rectangle of length x cm has perimeter 40 cm.

Construct a formula for the area, $A\,cm^2$, of the rectangle in terms of x.

b) A rectangle of length x cm has area $40\,cm^2$.

Construct a formula for the perimeter, P cm, of the rectangle in terms of x.

Quick check! – *Solutions*

1 a) $f'(x) = \frac{3}{2\sqrt{x}}$ b) $\frac{dh}{dt} = 3t^2 + 4t + 1$ c) $C'(n) = 3 + \frac{2}{n^2}$

2 Maximum = 11, minimum = $\frac{1}{3}$

3 a) $A = 20x - x^2$ b) $P = 2x + \frac{80}{x}$

Greatest and least values of a function within a closed interval

The graph of the function $y = f(x)$ within the closed interval $-2 \leqslant x \leqslant 5$ is as shown.

The greatest value of f within the interval is 4 and the least value is −3.

The least and greatest values of f within other closed intervals are shown in the table below.

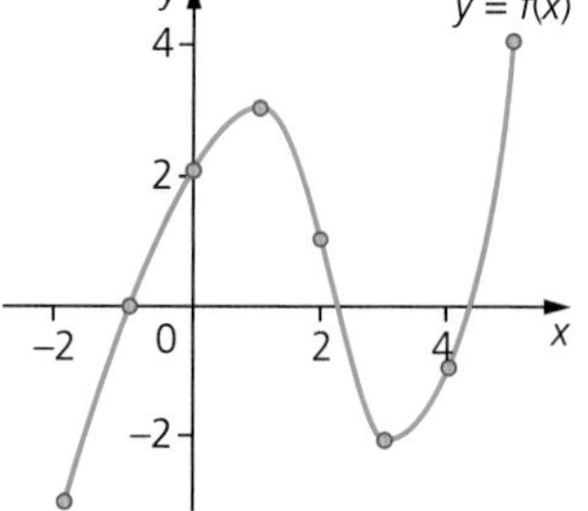

Closed interval	Greatest value of f	Least value of f
$-1 \leqslant x \leqslant 4$	3	−2
$0 \leqslant x \leqslant 2$	3	1
$2 \leqslant x \leqslant 4$	1	−2

Within a closed interval the greatest and least values of a function are either at a stationary point or at end points of the interval.

Example

Find the greatest and least values of $f(x) = x^3 - x^2 - x + 5$ in the closed interval $0 \leqslant x \leqslant 2$.

SOLUTION

$f'(x) = 3x^2 - 2x - 1$

Stationary points occur when $f'(x) = 0$

$3x^2 - 2x - 1 = 0$

$(3x + 1)(x - 1) = 0$

$3x + 1 = 0$ or $x - 1 = 0$

$x = -\frac{1}{3}$ or $x = 1$ (disregard $x = -\frac{1}{3}$ since it lies outside the interval $0 \leqslant x \leqslant 2$)

$f(1) = 1^3 - 1^2 - 1 + 5 = 4$

x	$\leftarrow 1$	1	$1 \rightarrow$
$3x+1$	+	+	+
$x-1$	−	0	+
$f'(x)$	−	0	+
slope	\	—	/

So the minimum turning value in the interval is 4.

(Alternatively, $f''(x) = 6x - 2$; so $f''(1) = 4$ and therefore 4 is a minimum turning value as $f''(1) > 0$.)

The values of f at the end points of the closed interval are $f(0) = 0^3 - 0^2 - 0 + 5 = 5$ and $f(2) = 2^3 - 2^2 - 2 + 5 = 7$.
Hence the greatest value of f in the closed interval is 7 and the least value is 4.

Exercise 17.1

Find the greatest and least values of the following functions in the given closed intervals.

1. $f(x) = 6 + 2x - x^2, \ -3 \leqslant x \leqslant 3$
2. $g(x) = x^2 - x + 2, \ -2 \leqslant x \leqslant 2$
3. $y = 3 + 3x^2 - x^3, \ 1 \leqslant x \leqslant 4$
4. $f(t) = 32t - t^4, \ -2 \leqslant t \leqslant 3$
5. $h(x) = (x-2)(x+1)^2, \ 0 \leqslant x \leqslant 3$
6. $C = 2n^3 - 3n^2 - 12n + 23, \ -2 \leqslant n \leqslant 4$
7. $s = p^3 - 2p^2 - 7p + 4, \ -3 \leqslant p \leqslant 2$ HPQ
8. $g(r) = r^4 - 4r^2 + 5, \ -1 \leqslant r \leqslant 3$ HPQ

Optimisation problems

There are many real-life problems where, based on a given set of constraints, you must maximise something, like an area to be fenced in, or minimise something, like the cost of producing a container. These are called **optimisation problems**, since you must find an optimum value. They involve finding the greatest or least value of a function over a given closed interval and can be solved therefore using differential calculus.

Example

A farmer uses 200 metres of fencing to form an enclosure against a wall.
What is the greatest rectangular area that can be enclosed?

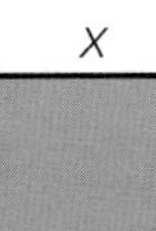

SOLUTION

Let the breadth of the enclosure be x metres; then the length is $(200 - 2x)$ metres.

Breadth $> 0 \Rightarrow x > 0$

Length $> 0 \Rightarrow 200 - 2x > 0$

$\Rightarrow 200 > 2x$

$\Rightarrow x < 100$

i.e. $0 < x < 100$

The area of the enclosure in square metres is given by $A(x) = x(200 - 2x) = 200x - 2x^2$.

The maximum turning value of $A(x)$ occurs at a stationary point, i.e. when $A'(x) = 0$.

$$A'(x) = 0 \Rightarrow 200 - 4x = 0$$
$$\Rightarrow 200 = 4x$$
$$\Rightarrow x = 50$$

x	$\leftarrow 50$	50	$50 \rightarrow$
$A'(x) = 200 - 4x$	+	0	−
slope	/	—	\

So the maximum turning value is $A(50) = 200(50) - 2(50)^2$
$= 10000 - 5000$
$= 5000.$

(Alternatively, $A''(x) = -4$, so $A''(50) = -4$ and therefore $A(50) = 5000$ is a maximum turning value as $A''(50) < 0$.)

Calculus Skills

At the end points of the interval $0 < x < 100$,

$A(0) = 200(0) - 2(0)^2 = 0$ and $A(100) = 200(100) - 2(100)^2 = 20000 - 20000 = 0$.

The greatest area that can be enclosed is therefore $5000\,\text{m}^2$.

Exercise 17.2

All the questions in Exercise 17.2 are ACE questions.

1 A farmer uses 60 metres of fencing to form a rectangular pen in a field.

a) Given that the pen has breadth x m, find an expression for its area.
b) Find the greatest area that can be enclosed by the pen.

2 Another farmer uses 60 metres of fencing to form two congruent rectangular pens side by side as shown below.

a) Given that the pens have breadth x m, show that the **total** area of the pens is given by

$$A(x) = 30x - \frac{3x^2}{2}.$$

b) Find the maximum **total** area that can be enclosed by the pens.

3 A yacht club is designing a new flag. The flag is to consist of a blue triangle on a white rectangular background.
In the white rectangle PQRS, PS is 4 feet and SR is 6 feet.
T and U lie on PQ and QR, x feet from P and Q as shown in the diagram.

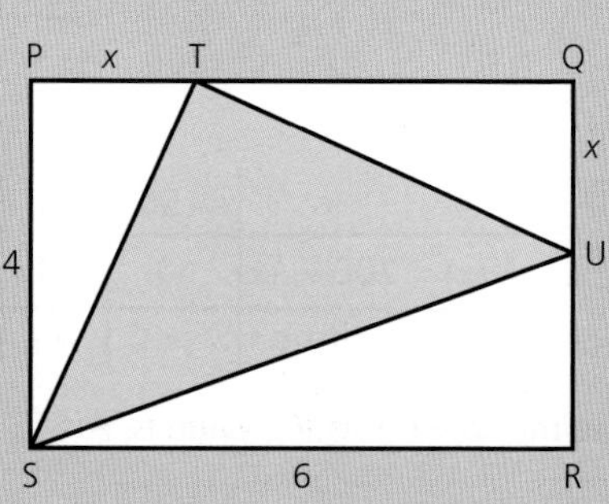

a) Show that the area, A square feet, of the blue triangle STU is given by $A(x) = \frac{x^2}{2} - 2x + 12$.
b) Hence find the greatest and least possible values of the area of triangle STU.

4 Squares of side x cm are cut from the corners of a cardboard square of side 20 cm. The flaps are then bent up and taped to form an open cuboid. HPQ

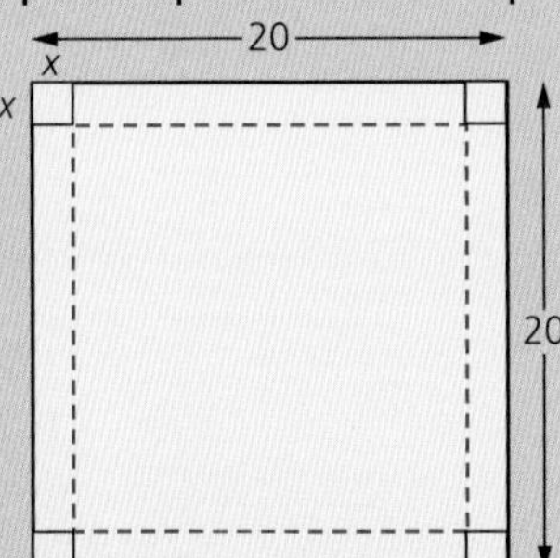

a) Show that the volume of the cuboid is given by $V(x) = 4x^3 - 80x^2 + 400x$.

b) Find the value of x for which this cuboid will have the greatest volume.

5 A rectangular sheet of metal 12 feet by 9 feet is to have a square of side x feet cut from each corner. The flaps are then bent up and taped to form an open cuboid, which will be used as a tray.

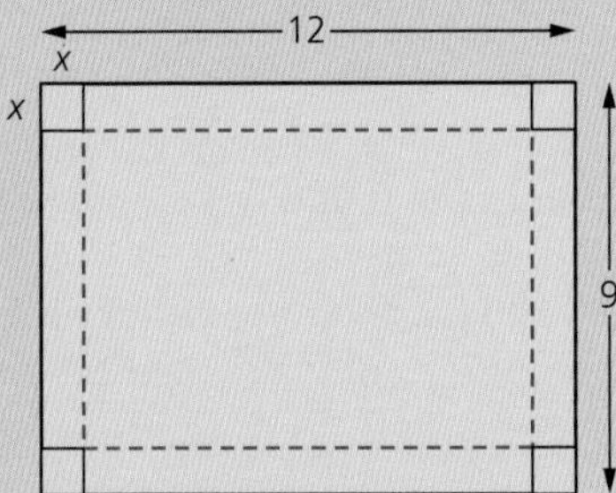

a) Show that the volume of the tray is given by $V(x) = 4x^3 - 42x^2 + 108x$.

b) Find the value of x, correct to one decimal place, for the tray to have maximum volume.

6 In the diagram B lies on the line joining points (0, 15) and (5, 0).

OABC is a rectangle, where A and C lie on the axes and OC = t.

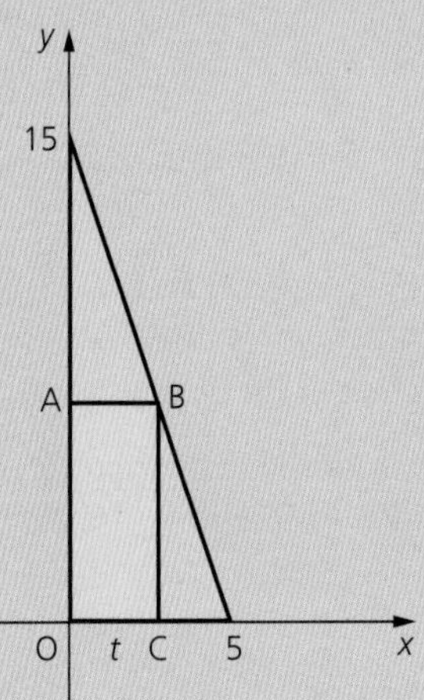

a) Show that $BC = 15 - 3t$.

b) Find the coordinates of B for which the rectangle has a maximum area.

Calculus Skills

7 The points P and Q lie on the curve $y = 12 - x^2$ as shown in the diagram.

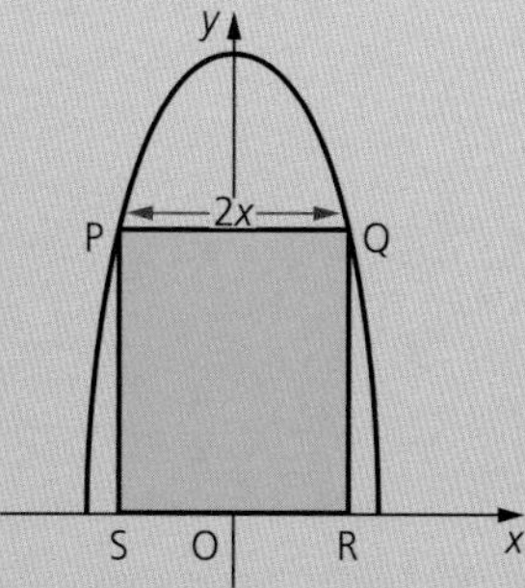

Find the coordinates of Q so that the shaded area of rectangle PQRS is maximised.

8 The cost, £C million, of laying one kilometre of an oil pipeline is given by the formula

$C = \frac{450}{a} + 8a$, where a is the cross-sectional area of the pipe in square metres.

a) Find the cross-sectional area of the most economical pipe to use.
b) Calculate the minimum cost of laying one kilometre of pipe.

9 When a ship is travelling at a speed of v kilometres per hour it consumes $(1 + 0{\cdot}0005v^3)$ tonnes of fuel per hour.
a) Show that the amount of fuel, F tonnes, used on a voyage of 5000 kilometres at a speed of v kilometres per hour is given by $F = \frac{5000}{v} + 2{\cdot}5v^2$.

b) Find the speed which gives the greatest fuel economy for this voyage and the amount of fuel used.

10 A conical container has vertical height h centimetres and slanted height of 3 metres.

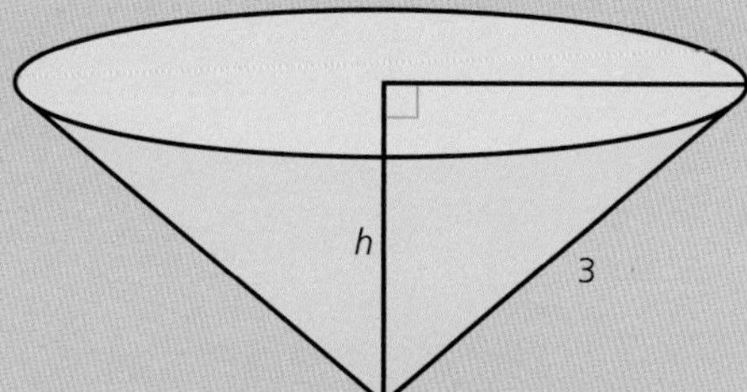

a) Show that the volume, V cubic centimetres, of the container is given by $V = \frac{1}{3}\pi h(9 - h^2)$.

b) The maximum volume of the cone is $k\pi$ cubic centimetr. Find the exact value of k.

11 An offshore gas production platform is to be connected by a pipeline to an onshore distribution centre. The cost, £C million, of laying the pipeline is given by the formula $C(x) = 2x + 50 - \sqrt{x^2 - 36}$, where x kilometres of the pipeline is undersea.
Find the exact value of x which minimises the cost of laying the pipeline.

Calculus Skills

Further optimisation problems

Often in optimisation problems, the function to be maximised or minimised contains two variables. In order to be able to differentiate the function, we use some additional information which allows us to express the function in terms of only one variable.

Example

An open box with a square base has a volume of 864 cubic centimetres.

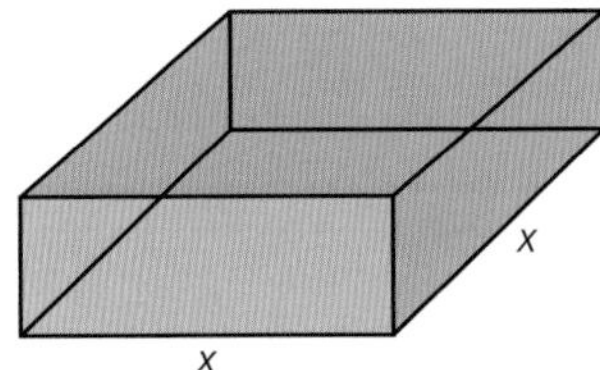

a) Given that the length of the base is x centimetres, show that the surface area of the box is given by $A = x^2 + \frac{3456}{x}$.

b) Find the dimensions of the box that will minimise the surface area and calculate this area.

SOLUTION

a) Let $A\,\text{cm}^2$ be the surface area and h cm be the height of the cuboid; then $A = x^2 + 4xh$.

In order to express A in terms of x alone, we need to substitute an expression for h in terms of x into the formula for the surface area.

Since the volume is $864\,\text{cm}^3$, then $x^2h = 864$

$$\Rightarrow h = \frac{864}{x^2}$$

Hence $A = x^2 + 4xh$

$$= x^2 + 4x\left(\frac{864}{x^2}\right)$$

$$= x^2 + \frac{3456}{x}$$

b) The minimum turning value of A occurs at a stationary point. That is, when $\frac{dA}{dx} = 0$.

$$\frac{dA}{dx} = 0 \Rightarrow 2x - \frac{3456}{x^2} = 0$$

$$\Rightarrow 2x = \frac{3456}{x^2}$$

$$\Rightarrow 2x^3 = 3456$$

$$\Rightarrow x^3 = 1728$$

$$\Rightarrow x = 12$$

x	←12	12	12→
$\frac{dA}{dx} = 2x - \frac{3456}{x^2}$	–	0	+
slope	╲	—	╱

So the minimum turning value is $12^2 + \frac{3456}{12} = 432$

(Alternatively, $\frac{d^2A}{dx^2} = 2 + \frac{6912}{x^3}$, so when $x = 12$, $\frac{d^2A}{dx^2} = 2 + \frac{6912}{12^3} = 6$, and therefore 432 is a minimum turning value as $\frac{d^2A}{dx^2} > 0$.)

When $x = 12$, the dimensions of the box that will minimise the surface area are length = 12 cm, breadth = 12 cm and height $= \frac{864}{12^2} = 6\,\text{cm}$. The minimum surface area is $432\,\text{cm}^3$.

Exercise 17.3

All the questions in Exercise 17.3 are ACE questions.

1 A water tank, cuboid in shape, has a square base and no top. Its volume is 4 cubic metres (m^3).

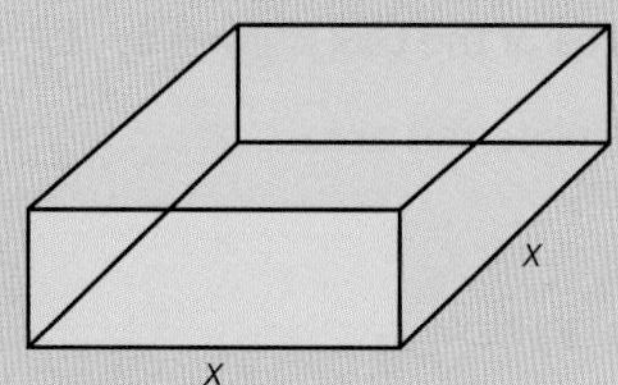

a) Given that the length of the base is x metres, show that the surface area of the tank is given by $A = x^2 + \frac{16}{x}$.

b) Find the dimensions of the tank that will minimise the surface area and calculate this area.

2 The height of a cuboid is twice the length of its base. Its volume is $9000\,\text{cm}^3$.

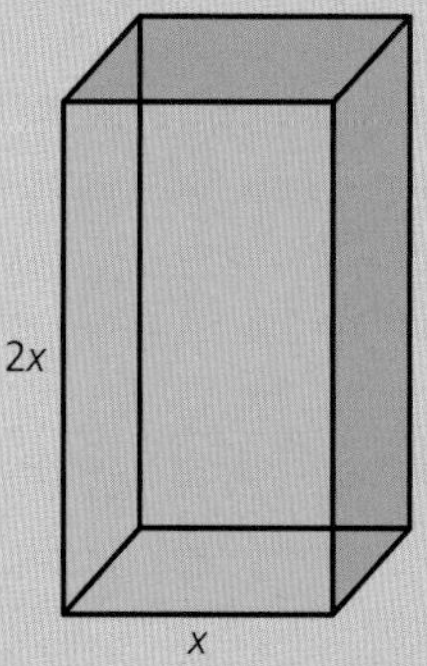

a) Given that the length of the base is x centimetres, show that the surface area of the tank is given by $A = 4x^2 + \frac{27\,000}{x}$.

b) Find the dimensions of the cuboid that will minimise the surface area and calculate this area.

3 The length of a cuboid is three times its width. Its surface area is $288\,\text{cm}^2$.

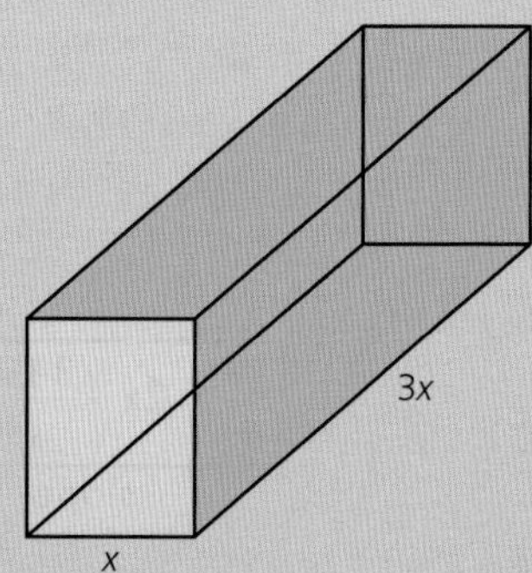

a) Given that the length of the base is x centimetres, show that the volume of the tank is given by $V = \frac{x}{4}(432 - 9x^2)$.

b) Find the dimensions of the cuboid that will maximise the volume and calculate this volume.

→

Calculus Skills

4 A cylindrical can of radius r cm has volume 500 cm^3.

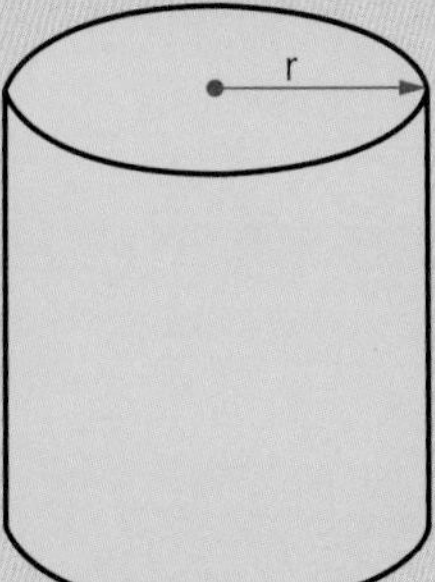

a) Show that the surface area of the cylinder is given by $A(r) = \frac{1000}{r} + 2\pi r^2$.

b) Find the dimensions of the cylinder that will minimise the surface area and calculate this area.

5 A sector of a circle with radius r cm has area 100 cm^2.

a) Show that the perimeter P cm of the sector is given by $P = 2r + \frac{200}{r}$.

b) Find the least possible perimeter of the sector.

6 A window is in the shape of a rectangle surmounted by a semicircle. The rectangle measures $2x$ metres by h metres. The perimeter of the window is 10 metres.

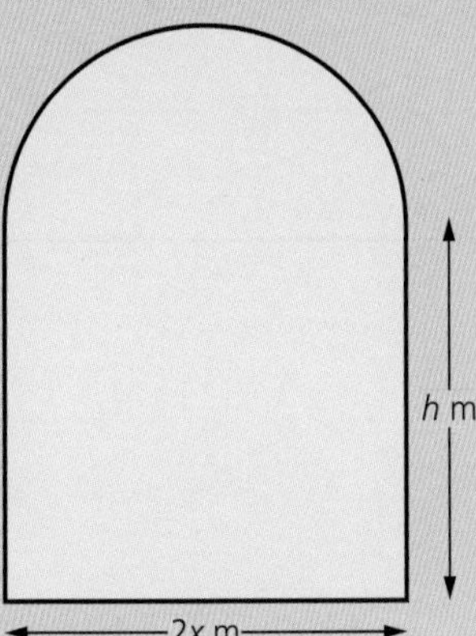

a) Show that the area of the window is given by $A = 10x - 2x^2 - \frac{1}{2}\pi x^2$.

b) Find the maximum possible area of the window.

Rate of change problems

Differentiation can be used to solve problems involving rates of change such as:

- Speed (S) = rate of change of distance (D) with respect to time (T): $S = \frac{dD}{dT}$
- Velocity (v) = rate of change of displacement (s) with respect to time (t): $v = \frac{ds}{dt}$
- Acceleration (a) = rate of change of velocity (v) with respect to time (t): $a = \frac{dv}{dt}$

Example 1

The displacement (position) of a particle, relative to the origin, is given by $s = t^3 - 2t^2 - 5t + 4$ where s is the displacement in centimetres and t is the time in seconds.

a) Find its initial displacement relative to the origin.
b) What is its velocity after 3 seconds?
c) When is its acceleration $0\,\text{cm/s}^2$?

SOLUTION

a) At $t = 0$, $s = 0^3 - 2(0)^2 - 5(0) + 4 = 4$

The particle is initially 4 cm from the origin.

b) $v = \dfrac{ds}{dt} = 3t^2 - 4t - 5$

At $t = 3$, $v = 3(3)^2 - 4(3) - 5 = 10$.

The velocity is 10 cm/s after 3 seconds

c) $a = \dfrac{dv}{dt} = 6t - 4$

$$a = 0 \Rightarrow 6t - 4 = 0 \Rightarrow 6t = 4 \Rightarrow t = \frac{2}{3}$$

The acceleration is $0\,\text{cm/s}^2$ after $\frac{2}{3}$ second.

Example 2

A water tank of height 1·2 metres has a square base.

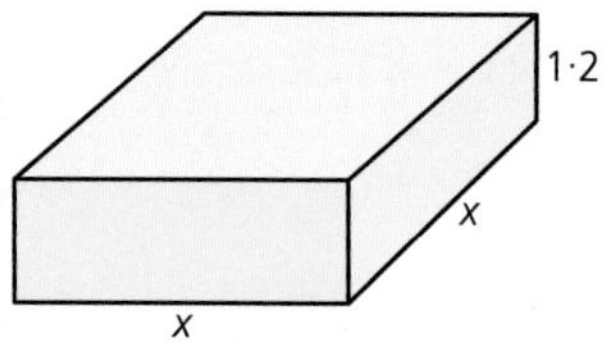

Find the rate at which the volume of the tank is changing with respect to the length of the base when the length is 2 metres.

SOLUTION

$V = 1{\cdot}2x^2 \Rightarrow \dfrac{dV}{dx} = 2{\cdot}4x$

When $x = 2$, $\dfrac{dV}{dx} = 2{\cdot}4 \times 2 = 4{\cdot}8$

The rate of change of the volume with respect to the length of the base is $4{\cdot}8\ \text{m}^3/\text{m}$.

Exercise 17.4

1 The height, h metres, of a missile fired upwards is given by $h = 5t(15-t)$, where t is the time in seconds since it was fired. Find the speed of the missile 4 seconds after it was fired.

2 A ball is thrown upwards. After t seconds its height is h metres, where $h = 1 \cdot 2 + 19 \cdot 6t - 4 \cdot 9t^2$.

a) When is the speed of the ball 0 m/s?

b) Find the speed of the ball when it returns to its starting point.

3 A particle moves along a straight line such that its displacement, s metres, after t seconds is given by $s = 15 + 4t^2 - t^3$ HPQ

Find its displacement, velocity and acceleration after 2 seconds.

4 The displacement s metres at time t seconds of an object moving in a straight line is given by the formula $s = t^3 - 5t^2 + 3t + 1$

a) What is its initial velocity?

b) When is its velocity 0 m/s?

5 The displacement s metres at time t seconds of a body moving in a straight line is given by the formula $s = 2t^3 - 3t^2$

a) What is its initial acceleration?

b) When is its acceleration 0 m/s^2?

6 The equation of motion of a body is $s = \sqrt{(4t+1)^3}$, where the displacement is s metres after t seconds. Find its displacement, velocity and acceleration after 2 seconds.

7 Find the rate at which the area of a circle is changing with respect to the radius when the radius is 4 cm. $[A = \pi r^2]$

8 Find the rate at which the volume of a spherical bubble is changing with respect to the radius when the radius is 3 cm. $[V = \frac{4}{3}\pi r^3]$ HPQ

9 The length, L centimetres, of a pendulum and the time, t seconds, of its swing are related by the formula $T = 0 \cdot 2\sqrt{L}$. Find the rate of change of time with respect to the length of the pendulum when the length is 25 cm.

10 The current, I amps, in a circuit is given by $I = \frac{500}{R}$, where R is the resistance in ohms. Find the rate of change of the current with respect to resistance for a resistance of 100 ohms.

11 The resistance, R ohms, to a current passing through a copper wire is given by $R = \frac{0{\cdot}018}{d^2}$, where d millimetres is the diameter of the wire.

Find the rate of change of the resistance with respect to diameter for a diameter of 2 mm.

12 A particle is moving so that its distance, s metres, from the origin at time t seconds is given by $s = 1 - \cos\left(2t + \frac{\pi}{2}\right)$.

a) Find the velocity of the particle at $t = 0$.

b) Find the times $(0 \leq t \leq \pi)$ at which the particle is stationary.

c) Find the time $(0 \leq t \leq \pi)$ at which the acceleration is a maximum.

13 The depth, d metres, of water in a harbour, t hours after midnight is given by $d = 4\sin\left(\frac{\pi}{6}t - \frac{\pi}{3}\right)$.

A buoy floats on the water, rising and falling with the tide.

a) Find the depth of the water at 3 a.m.

b) Find the velocity and acceleration of the buoy at 3 a.m.

Checkout

1 Find the greatest and least values of the function $f(x) = 4x^3 - 15x^2 + 12x + 4$ in the interval $0 \leqslant x \leqslant 3$.

2 A farmer wants to fence off six individual sheep pens.

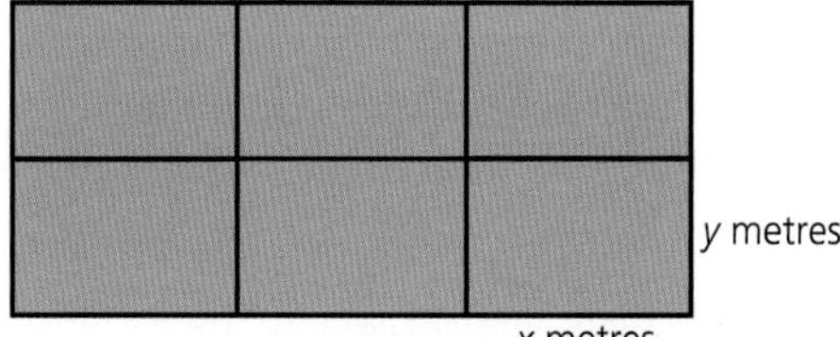

Each pen is a rectangle measuring x metres by y metres, as shown in the diagram.

a) (i) Express the total length of fencing in terms of x and y.

(ii) Given that the total length of fencing is 360 m, show that the total area, A m^2, of the six pens is given by $A(x) = 270x - \frac{27}{4}x^2$.

b) Find the maximum total area of the six pens.

3 A plastic trough, in the shape of a triangular prism, has a capacity of 32 litres. The triangular cross-section of the trough is right-angled and isosceles, with equal sides of length x centimetres. The length of the trough is l centimetres.

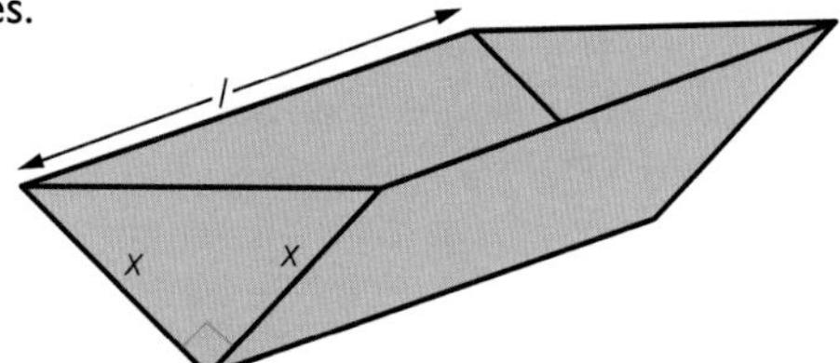

a) Show that the surface area, A cm^2, of the trough is given by $A(x) = x^2 + \frac{128\,000}{x}$.

b) Find the minimum surface area of the trough.

4 The surface area of a sphere is given by the formula $A = 4\pi r^2$. What is the rate of change of A, with respect to r, at $r = 1 \cdot 5$?

5 The effect of a crash on a car is tested by accelerating the car straight into a wall on a test site. The displacement, s metres, of the car from its starting point after t seconds is given by $s = 12\sqrt{t^3}$. The car hits the wall after 4 seconds.

a) How far from the wall was the car's starting point?

b) Find the velocity and acceleration at the time of impact.

Summary

Applying Differential Calculus

1 The greatest and least values of a function within a closed interval are either at a stationary point or at the end points of the interval.

2 Where real-life problems can be modelled by a function, the optimal solution will be the greatest or least values of the function within a closed interval.

3 The derivative of a function represents the rate of change of the function.

- Velocity (v) = rate of change of displacement (s) with respect to time (t): $v = \frac{ds}{dt}$
- Acceleration (a) = rate of change of velocity (v) with respect to time (t): $a = \frac{dv}{dt}$

CHAPTER

18 Applying Integral Calculus

In this chapter you will look at how to use integration to find the area between a curve and straight line or between two curves, and how to solve problems involving rate of change.

What I am learning

* To find the area between a curve and the x-axis
* To find the area between a straight line and a curve or between two curves
* To determine and use a function from a given rate of change and initial conditions
* To solve problems like:

  a) The shaded part of the diagram represents one of the blades of an aircraft's propeller.

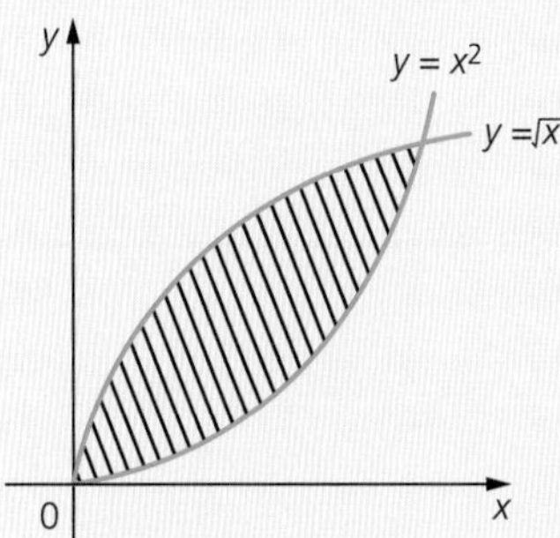

  The shaded region is enclosed by the curves with equations $y=\sqrt{x}$ and $y=x^2$. Calculate the area of the blade.

  b) The population of a town is growing at a rate of $50+3\sqrt{t}$ people per year. The present population is 10 000. Find a formula for P, the population after t years.

What I should already know/be able to do

* To calculate the definite integral of polynomial functions with integer limits
* To calculate the definite integral of functions with limits which are integers, radians, surds or fractions

Quick check!

Evaluate:

1 $\displaystyle\int_{-2}^{3}(3x-1)(x+2)\,dx$

2 $\displaystyle\int_{4}^{9}3\sqrt{t}\,dt$

3 $\displaystyle\int_{1}^{\sqrt{3}}\frac{u^6-3}{u^3}\,du$

4 $\displaystyle\int_{-\frac{3}{2}}^{\frac{3}{2}}(2x+1)^3\,dx$

5 $\displaystyle\int_{\frac{\pi}{6}}^{\frac{\pi}{3}}2\sin(\pi-3\theta)\,d\theta$

6 $\displaystyle\int_{1}^{4}5\cos 2t\,dt$

Quick check! – *Solutions*

1 $37\frac{1}{2}$	2 38	3 1	4 30	5 $\frac{2}{3}$	6 0·2

The area under a curve

You discovered in Chapter 16 that the area under the curve $y = f(x)$ bounded by the x-axis and the lines $x = a$ and $x = b$ $(a < b)$ is given by the definite integral $\int_a^b f(x)\,dx$.

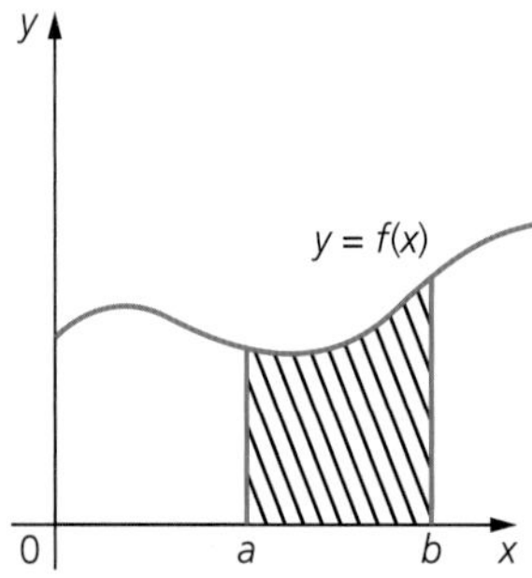

Example

Show by shading in a sketch the area associated with $\int_2^4 \frac{8}{x}\,dx$.

SOLUTION

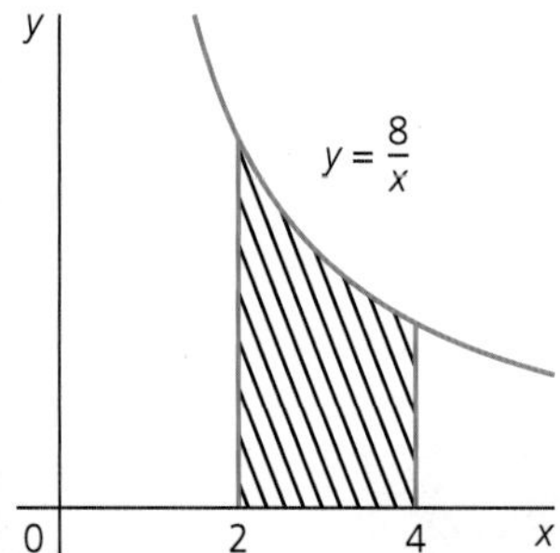

Exercise 18·1

Show by shading in sketches the areas associated with:

1 $\int_{-2}^{3} (x^2 + 1)\,dx$ 2 $\int_{-2}^{2} (4 - x^2)\,dx$ 3 $\int_{-1}^{2} (x + 1)\,dx$

4 $\int_{-1}^{3} (3 - x)\,dx$ 5 $\int_{0}^{\pi} \sin x\,dx$ 6 $\int_{0}^{\frac{\pi}{2}} \cos x\,dx$

Example 1

Calculate the shaded area in the diagram.

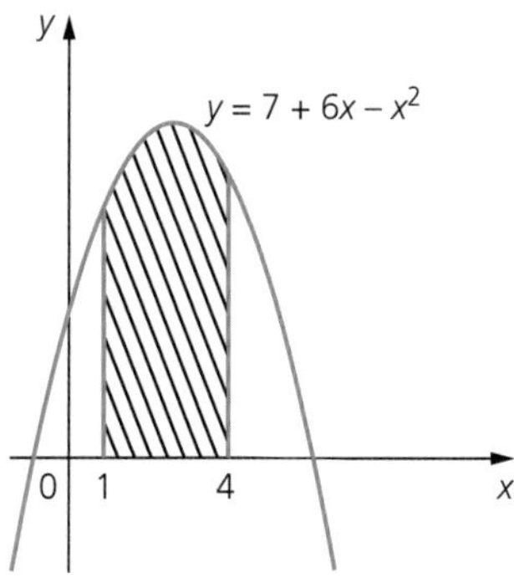

SOLUTION

$$\text{Shaded area} = \int_1^4 (7 + 6x - x^2)\,dx$$

$$= \left[7x + 3x^2 - \frac{x^3}{3}\right]_1^4$$

$$= \left(7(4) + 3(4)^2 - \frac{4^3}{3}\right) - \left(7(1) + 3(1)^2 - \frac{1^3}{3}\right)$$

$$= \left(28 + 48 - \frac{64}{3}\right) - \left(7 + 3 - \frac{1}{3}\right)$$

$$= 54\frac{2}{3} - 9\frac{2}{3}$$

$= 45$ square units

Example 2

Calculate the shaded area in the diagram.

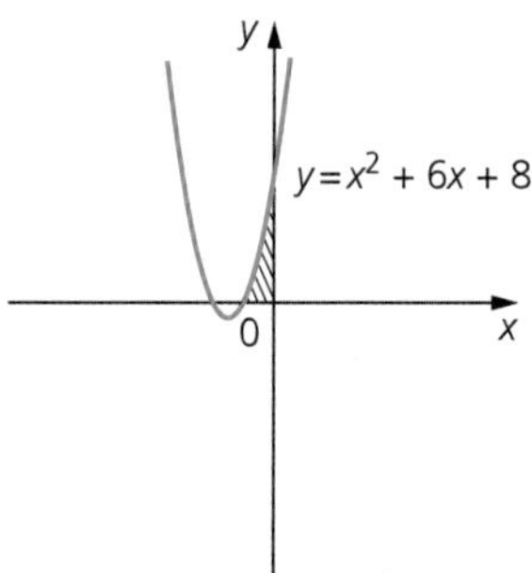

SOLUTION

The lower limit of the definite integral is one of the points where the curve cuts the x-axis.

The curve cuts the x-axis where $x^2 + 6x + 8 = 0$

$$\Rightarrow (x + 4)(x + 2) = 0$$

$$\Rightarrow x = -4 \text{ or } x = -2$$

Calculus Skills

So the curve cuts the x-axis at $(-4, 0)$ and $(-2, 0)$.

$$\text{Shaded area} = \int_{-2}^{0} (x^2 + 6x + 8)\,dx$$

$$= \left[\frac{x^3}{3} + 3x^2 + 8x\right]_{-2}^{0}$$

$$= \left(\frac{0^3}{3} + 3(0)^2 + 8(0)\right) - \left(\frac{(-2)^3}{3} + 3(-2)^2 + 8(-2)\right)$$

$$= (0) - \left(-\frac{8}{3} + 12 - 16\right)$$

$$= 0 - \left(-6\frac{2}{3}\right)$$

$$= 6\frac{2}{3} \text{ square units}$$

Exercise 18·2

Calculate the shaded area in each diagram.

1

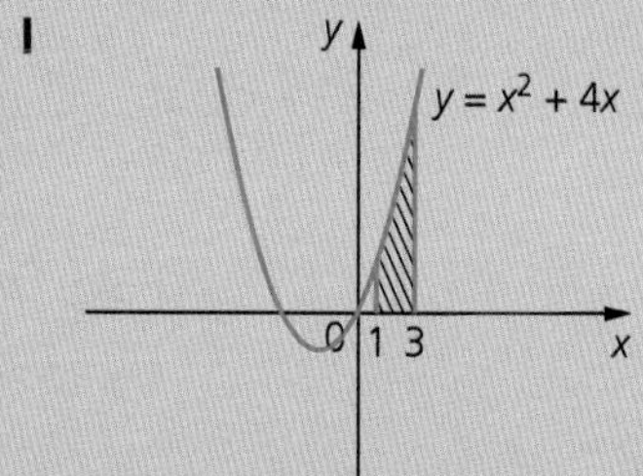

2

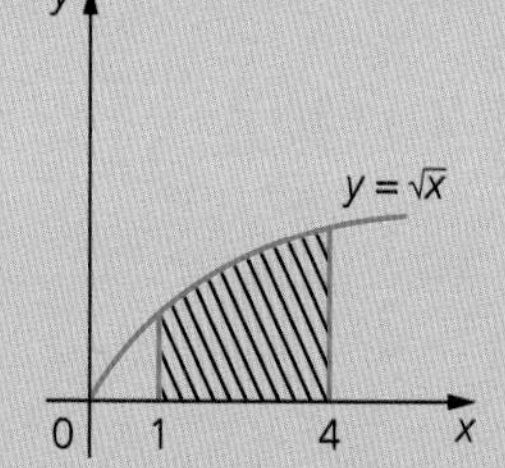

3

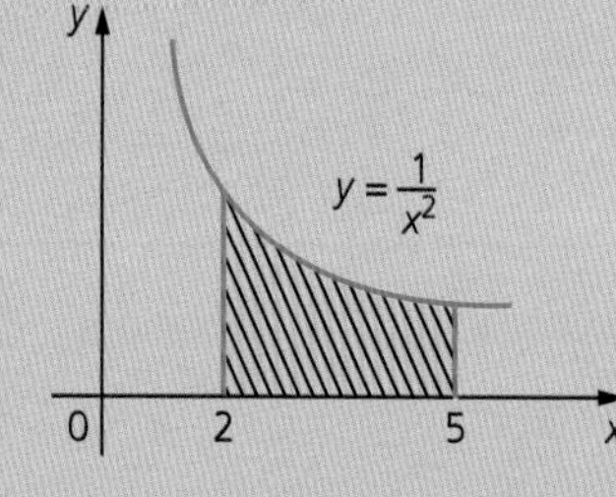

4

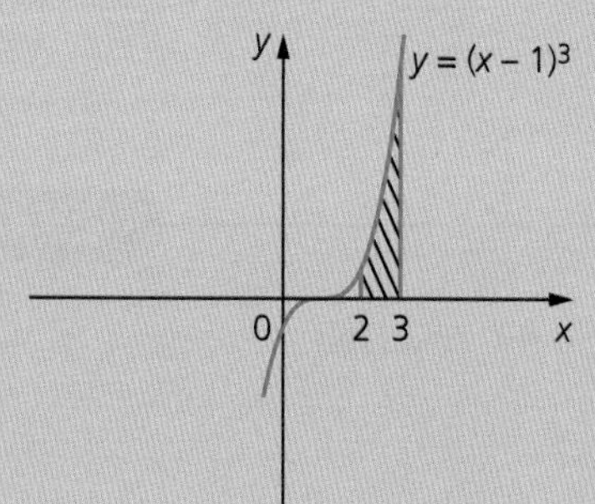

5

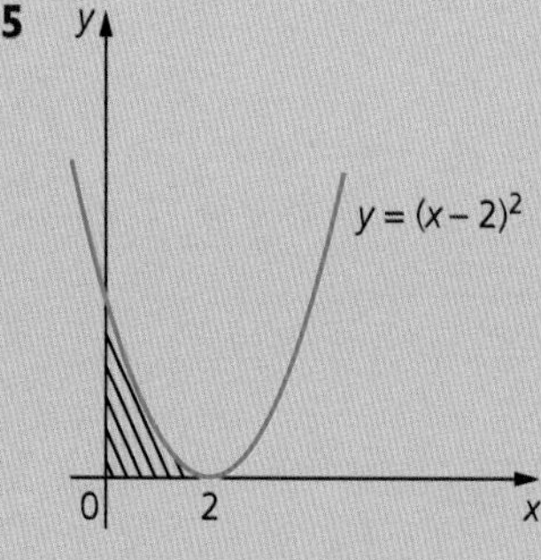

6

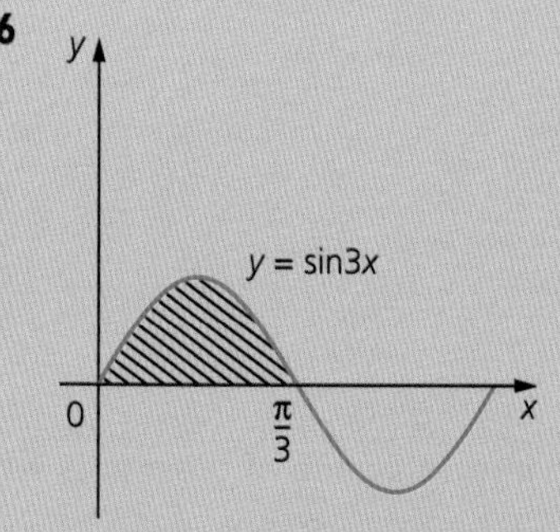

→

Calculus Skills

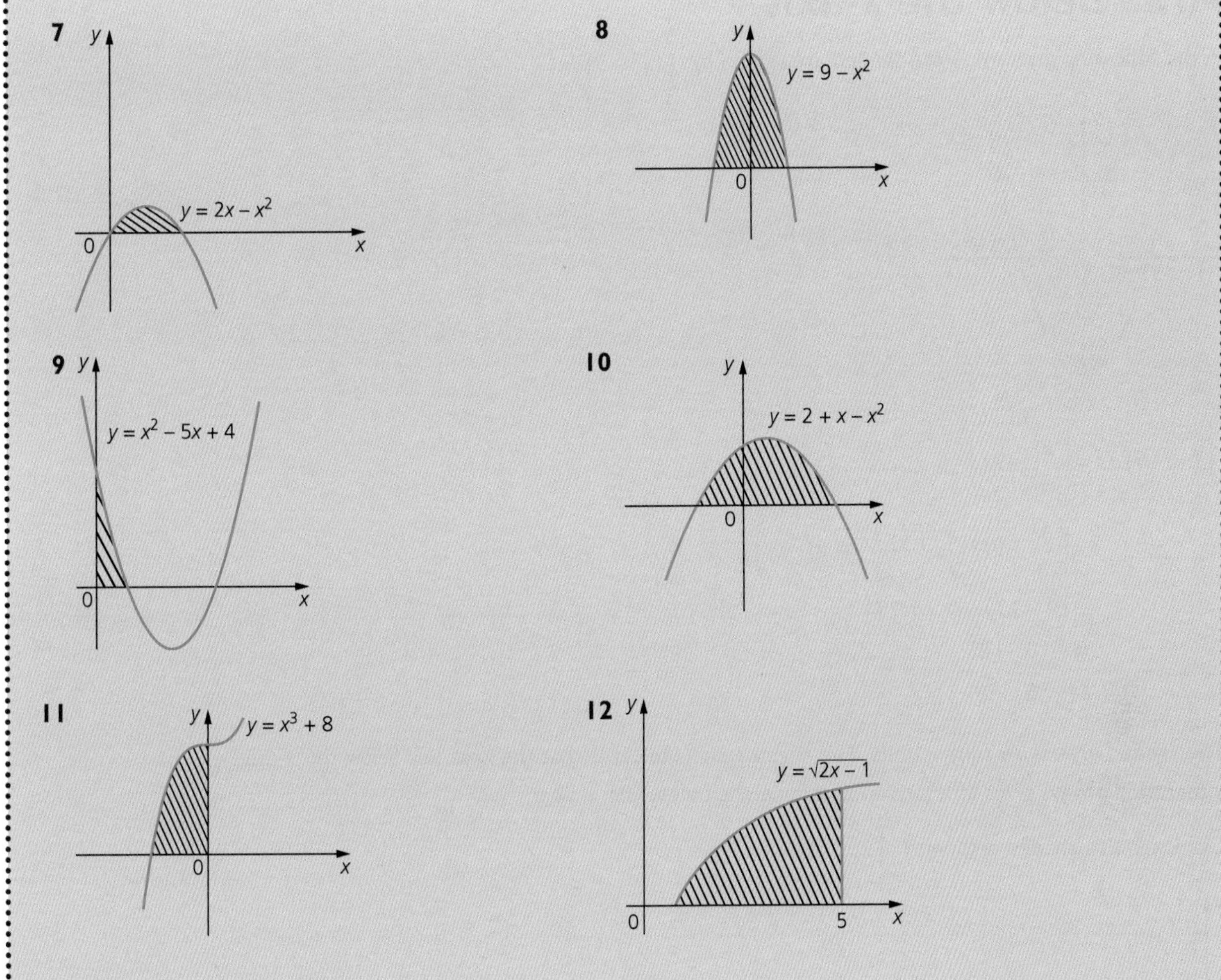

13

$y = 4\cos x$

0, $\frac{\pi}{6}$, 2π

14

$y = \frac{4}{(x+1)^2} - 1$

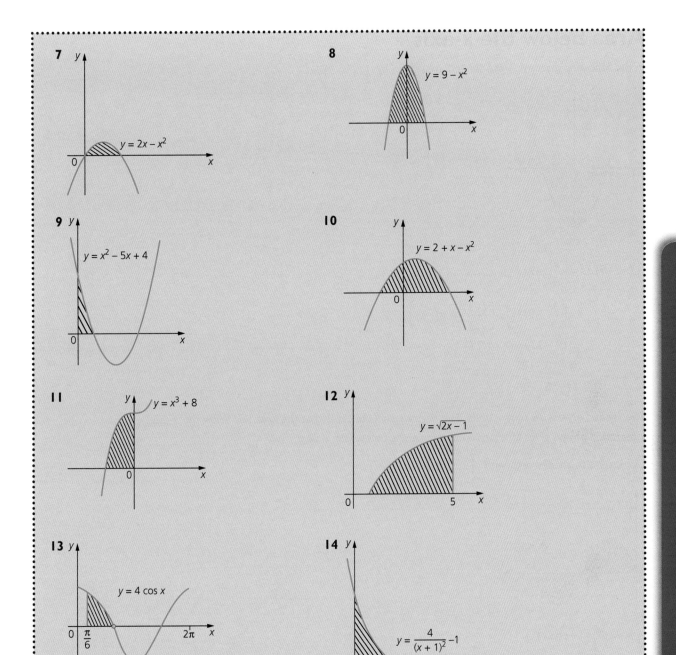

Area below the x-axis

In the following diagram, is the shaded area given by $\int_{-3}^{3}(x^2-9)dx$?

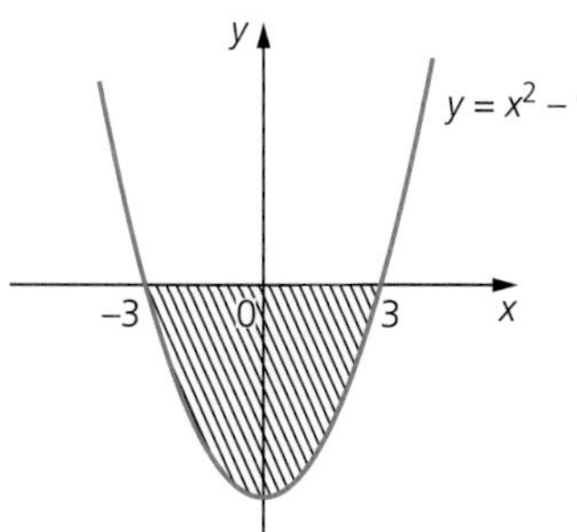

$$\int_{-3}^{3}(x^2-9)\,dx=\left[\frac{x^3}{3}-9x\right]_{-3}^{3}$$
$$=\left(\frac{3^3}{3}-9(3)\right)-\left(\frac{(-3)^3}{3}-9(-3)\right)$$
$$=(9-27)-(-9+27)$$
$$=-18-18$$
$$=-36$$

The shaded area is 36 square units. The *negative* sign indicates that the area lies *below* the x-axis.

Integration always gives a negative value for areas below the x-axis.

Compare this shaded area with $\int_{0}^{2\pi}\sin x\,dx$.

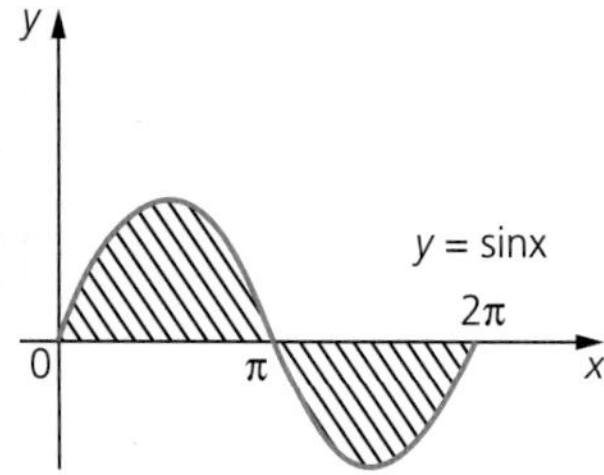

$$\int_{0}^{2\pi}\sin x\,dx=[-\cos x]_0^{2\pi}$$
$$=(-\cos 2\pi)-(-\cos 0)$$
$$=-1-(-1)$$
$$=0$$

The shaded area cannot be 0 square units!

In a case like this you must calculate the areas above and below the x-axis separately then add them.

Area above x-axis: $\int_{0}^{\pi}\sin x\,dx=[-\cos x]_0^{\pi}$
$$=(-\cos\pi)-(-\cos 0)$$
$$=(1)-(-1)$$
$$=2$$

Area above x-axis = 2 square units

Area below x-axis: $\int_{\pi}^{2\pi}\sin x\,dx=[-\cos x]_{\pi}^{2\pi}$
$$=(-\cos 2\pi)-(-\cos\pi)$$
$$=(-1)-(1)$$
$$=-2$$

Area below x-axis = 2 square units

Total shaded area = 2 + 2 = 4 square units

Always calculate the areas above and below the x-axis separately then add them.

Calculus Skills

Example

Calculate the shaded area in the diagram.

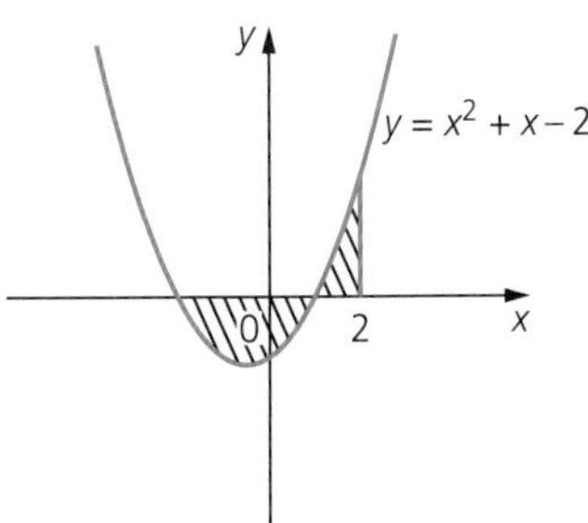

SOLUTION

The curve cuts the x-axis where $x^2 + x - 2 = 0$

$$\Rightarrow (x+2)(x-1) = 0$$

$$\Rightarrow x = -2 \text{ or } x = 1$$

So the curve cuts the x-axis at $(-2, 0)$ and $(1, 0)$.

Area below x-axis: $\int_{-2}^{1} (x^2 + x - 2)\,dx$

$$= \left[\frac{x^3}{3} + \frac{x^2}{2} - 2x\right]_{-2}^{1}$$

$$= \left(\frac{1}{3} + \frac{1}{2} - 2\right) - \left(\frac{-8}{3} + 2 + 4\right)$$

$$= \left(-1\frac{1}{6}\right) - \left(3\frac{1}{3}\right)$$

$$= -4\frac{1}{2}$$

Area above x-axis: $\int_{1}^{2} (x^2 + x - 2)\,dx$

$$= \left[\frac{x^3}{3} + \frac{x^2}{2} - 2x\right]_{1}^{2}$$

$$= \left(\frac{8}{3} + 2 - 4\right) - \left(\frac{1}{3} + \frac{1}{2} - 2\right)$$

$$= \left(\frac{2}{3}\right) - \left(-1\frac{1}{6}\right)$$

$$= 1\frac{5}{6}$$

Area below x-axis = $4\frac{1}{2}$ square units

Area above x-axis = $1\frac{5}{6}$ square units

Total shaded area = $4\frac{1}{2} + 1\frac{5}{6} = 6\frac{1}{3}$ square units

Exercise 18·3

Calculate the shaded area in each diagram.

1

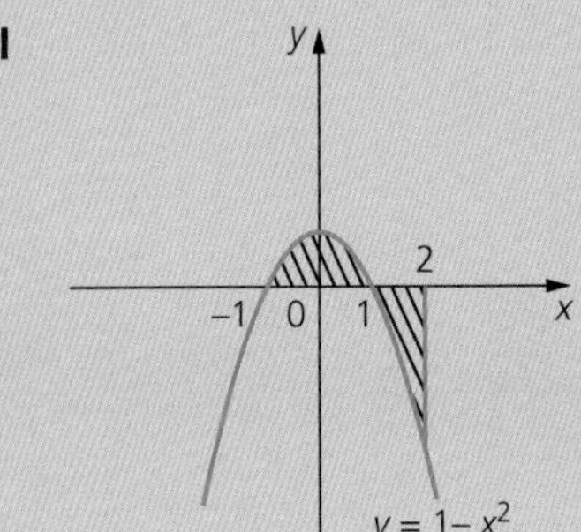

2

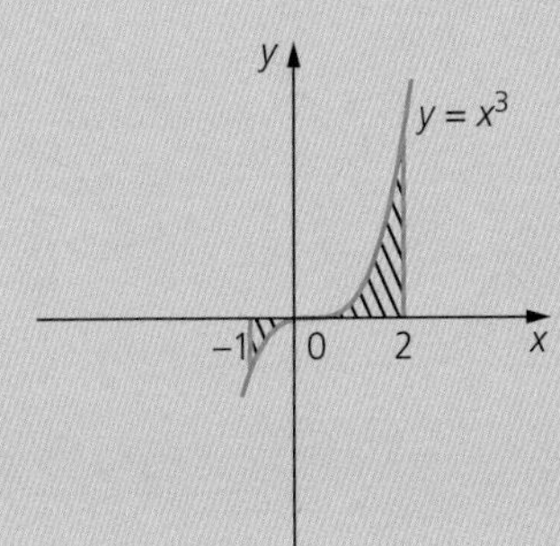

➜

Calculus Skills

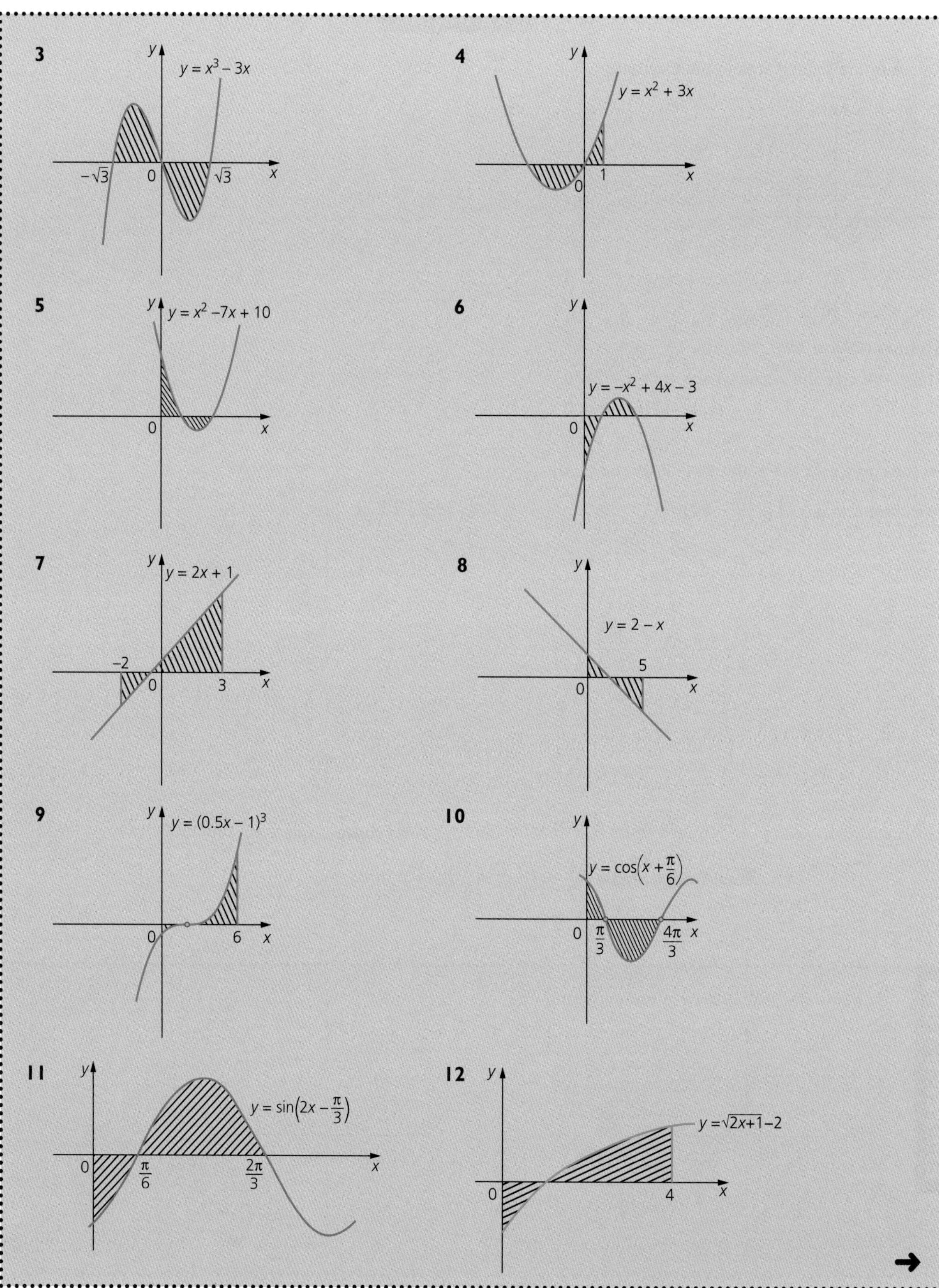

Calculus Skills

13 Find the points of intersection of each of the following curves with the x-axis.
Hence find the area enclosed by each curve and the x-axis.
a) $y = x^2 + 2x - 15$
b) $y = 3x(x+1)(x-2)$
c) $y = 2x - x^3$

14 Show that the area enclosed by the curve $y = \cos\left(x - \frac{\pi}{4}\right)$, $0 \le x \le \frac{5\pi}{4}$, and the x-axis is $\frac{4+\sqrt{2}}{2}$. ACE

Area between two curves

The area enclosed between the curves $y = f(x)$ and $y = g(x)$ from $x = a$ to $x = b$ is given by $\int_a^b (f(x) - g(x))\,dx$ when $f(x) \ge g(x)$ and $a < x < b$.

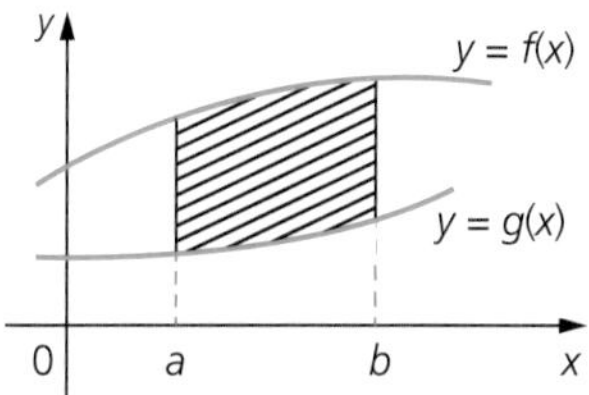

Note

$f(x)$ is the 'Top' function
$g(x)$ is the 'Bottom' function
so $\int f(x) - g(x)$ is $\int \text{Top} - \text{Bottom}$

Example

Calculate the area enclosed by the graphs of the functions $y = 9 - x^2$ and $y = x + 3$.

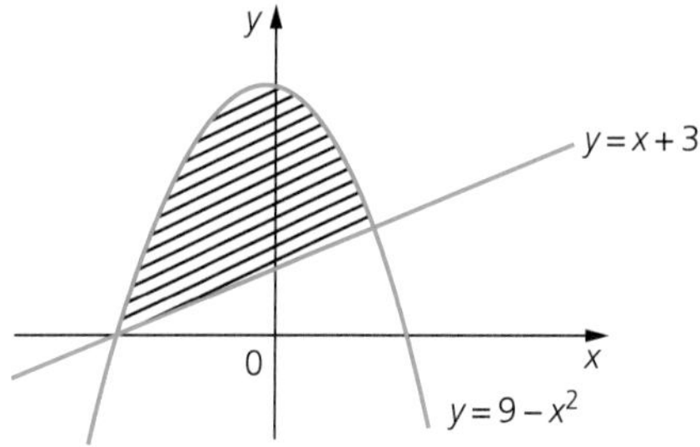

SOLUTION

The graphs intersect where $x + 3 = 9 - x^2$

$$\Rightarrow \quad x^2 + x - 6 = 0$$
$$\Rightarrow (x+3)(x-2) = 0$$
$$\Rightarrow \quad x = -3 \text{ or } x = 2$$

So the graphs intersect at $(-3, 0)$ and $(2, 5)$.

Calculus Skills

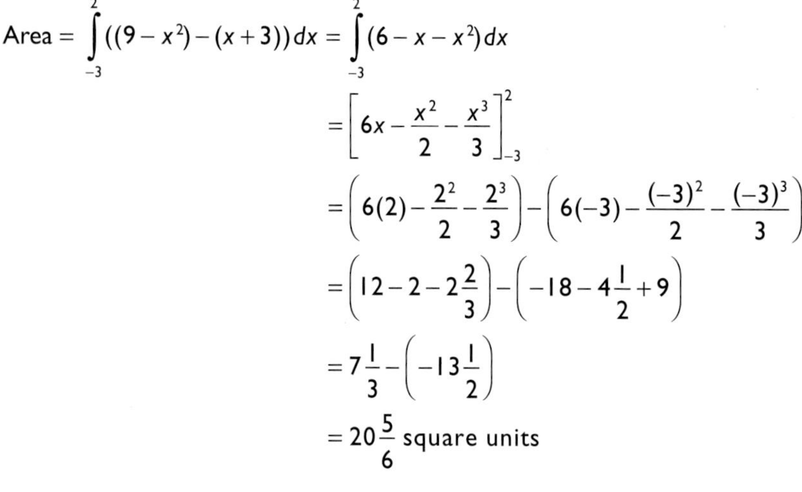

$$\text{Area} = \int_{-3}^{2}((9 - x^2) - (x + 3))\,dx = \int_{-3}^{2}(6 - x - x^2)\,dx$$

$$= \left[6x - \frac{x^2}{2} - \frac{x^3}{3}\right]_{-3}^{2}$$

$$= \left(6(2) - \frac{2^2}{2} - \frac{2^3}{3}\right) - \left(6(-3) - \frac{(-3)^2}{2} - \frac{(-3)^3}{3}\right)$$

$$= \left(12 - 2 - 2\frac{2}{3}\right) - \left(-18 - 4\frac{1}{2} + 9\right)$$

$$= 7\frac{1}{3} - \left(-13\frac{1}{2}\right)$$

$$= 20\frac{5}{6} \text{ square units}$$

Exercise 18·4

Calculate the area shaded in each diagram.

1 $y = x^2$, $y = 6 - x$ (shaded between $x = -3$ and $x = 2$)

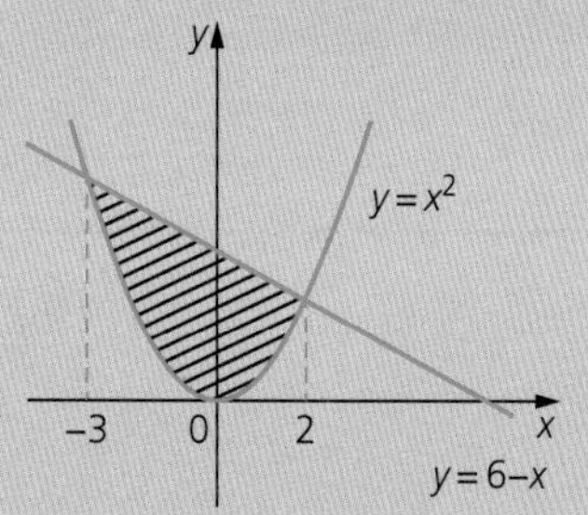

2 $y = x^2 - 4$, $y = 2x - x^2$ (axis marks -2, -1, 0, 2, -2, -4)

3 $y = x^3 - x^2 - 2x$, $y = x^2 + x$ (axis marks -1, 0, 3) HPQ

4 $y = \cos x$, $y = \sin x$ (axis marks 0, $\frac{\pi}{4}$, $\frac{5\pi}{4}$, 2π)

5 $y = \cos 2x$, $y = \cos x$ (axis marks 0, $\frac{2\pi}{3}$, π, 2π)

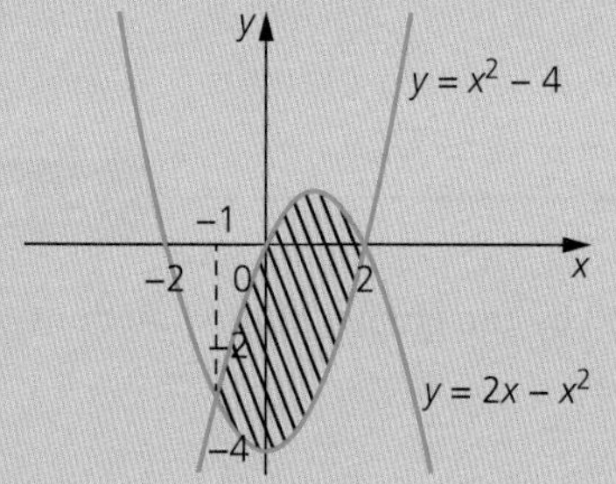

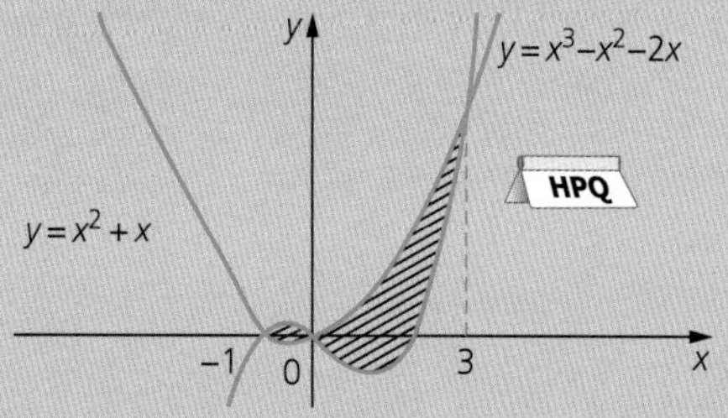

6 $y = \cos 2x$, $y = \sin x$ (axis marks 0, $\frac{\pi}{6}$, $\frac{5\pi}{6}$, π, 2π) HPQ

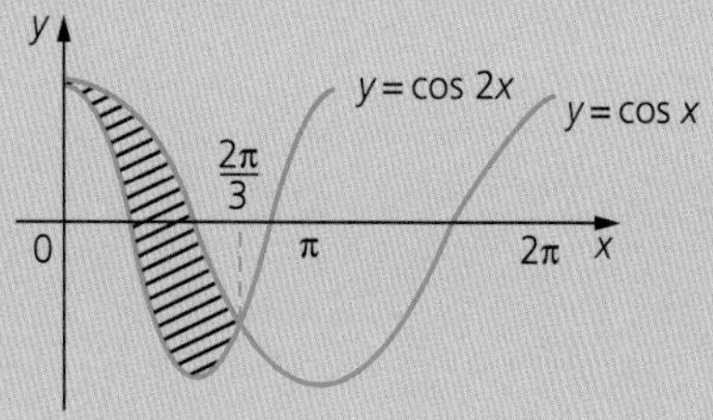

Calculus Skills

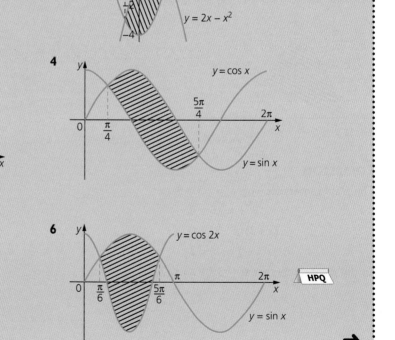

7

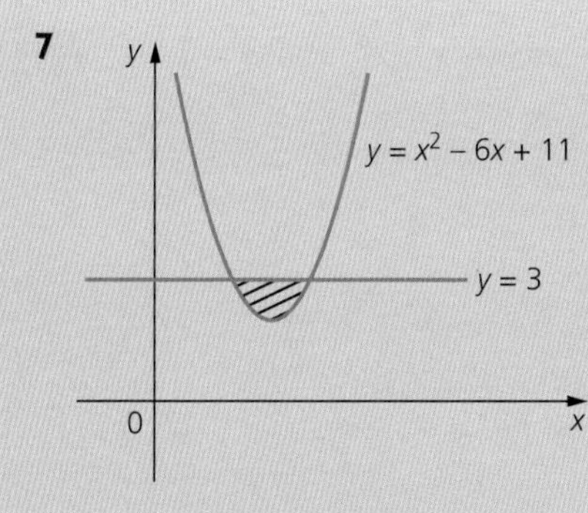

8

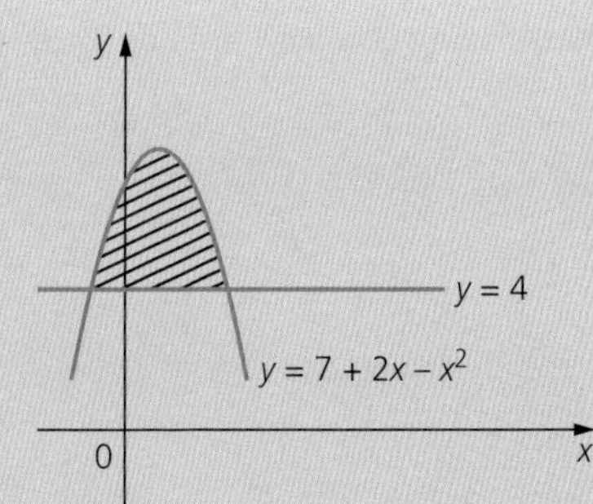

9

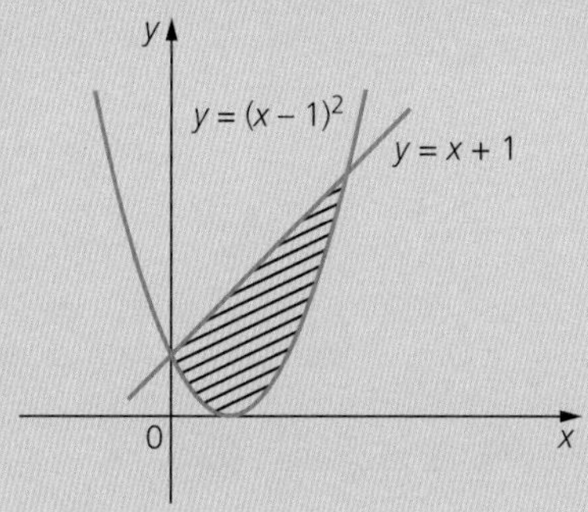

10

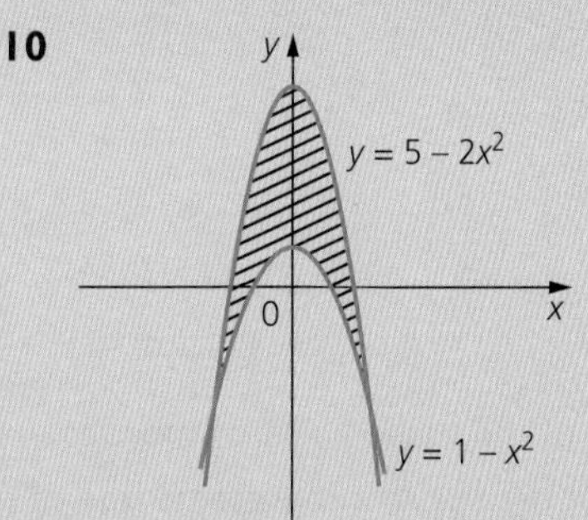

11

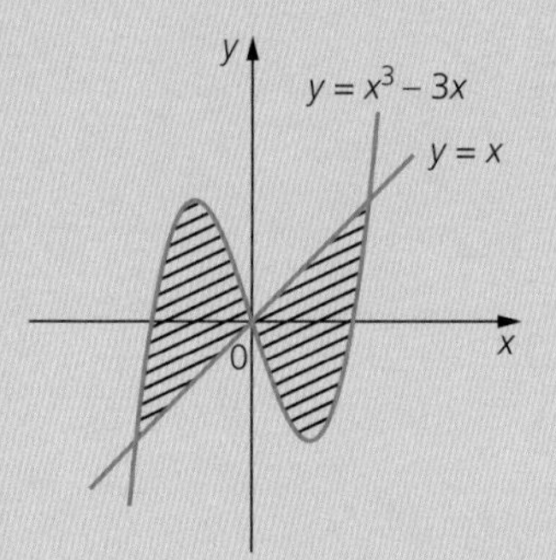

12

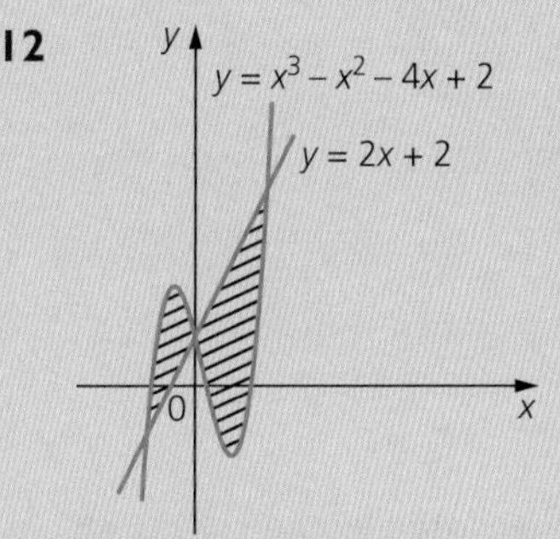

13

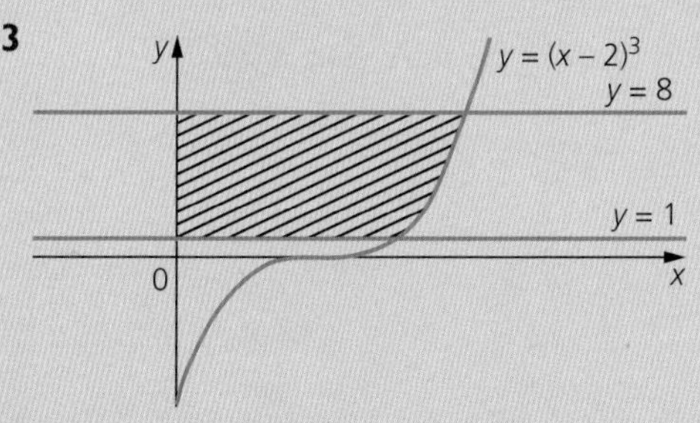

14

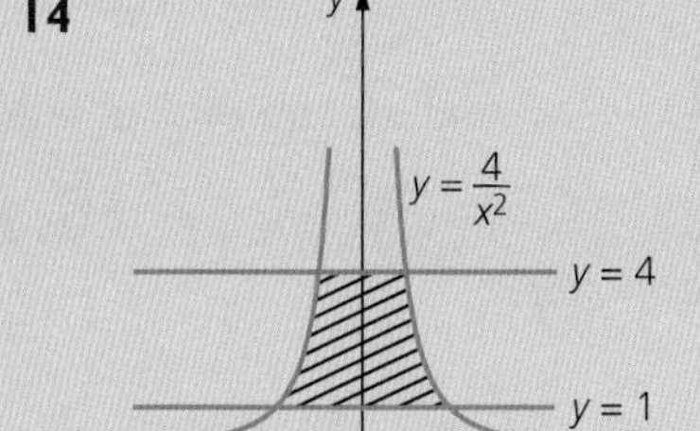

15

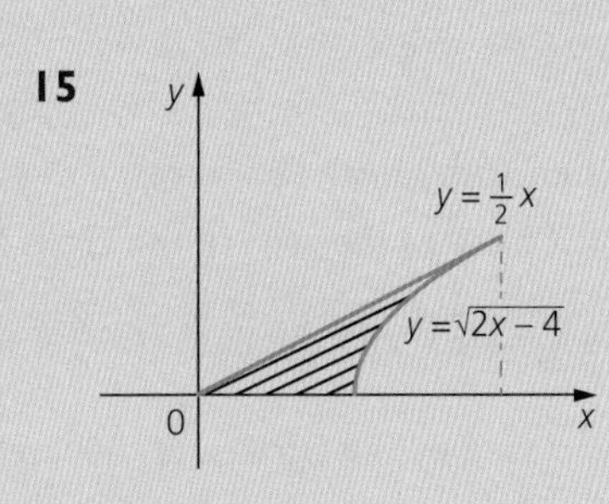

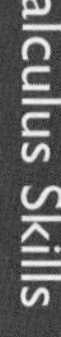

➜

16 The logo of a hat-making company was designed using parts of the curves $y = x^2$ and $y = 8 - x^2$. ACE

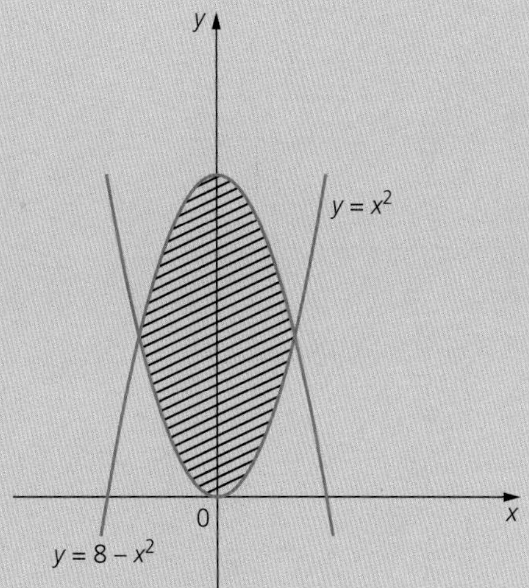

Calculate the area of the shaded part of the logo.

17 The shaded part of the diagram represents one of the blades of an aircraft's propeller. ACE

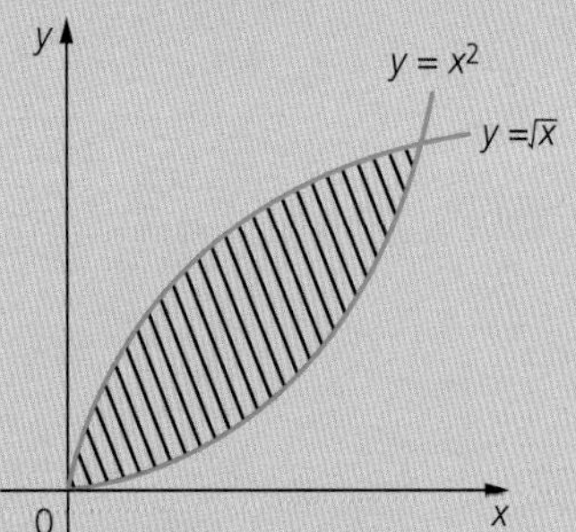

The shaded region is enclosed by the curves with equations $y = \sqrt{x}$ and $y = x^2$.

Calculate the area of the blade.

18 The shaded part of the diagram represents the cross-section of an aeroplane's wing. ACE

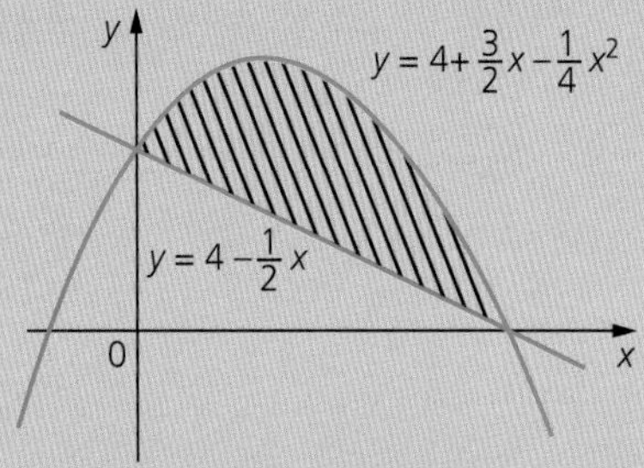

The shaded region is enclosed by the parabola with equation $y = 4 + \frac{3}{2}x - \frac{1}{4}x^2$ and the straight line with equation $y = 4 - \frac{1}{2}x$. Calculate the area of the cross-section.

19 Verify that the curve $y = \sin x$ and the line $y = \frac{2}{\pi}x$ intersect at 0 and $\frac{\pi}{2}$. ACE

Calculate the area enclosed by the curve and the line for $0 \leqslant x \leqslant \frac{\pi}{2}$

Calculus Skills

Rate of change problems

Integration can be used to solve problems where you know the rate of change of one variable with respect to another and you wish to find the relationship between the two variables.
$\frac{dy}{dx}$ is the rate of change of y with respect to x. If $\frac{dy}{dx} = f(x)$ then $y = \int f(x)\,dx$.

Example 1

The population of a town is growing at a rate of $50 + 3\sqrt{t}$ people per year.
The present population is 10 000. Find a formula for P, the population after t years.

SOLUTION

Rate of growth $= \frac{dP}{dt}$

$$\frac{dP}{dt} = 50 + 3\sqrt{t} \Rightarrow P = \int (50 + 3\sqrt{t})\,dt$$
$$= 50t + \frac{3t^{\frac{3}{2}}}{\frac{3}{2}} + C$$
$$= 50t + 2\sqrt{t^3} + C$$

$P = 10000$ when $t = 0$.
Substitute into $P = 50t + 2\sqrt{t^3} + C$.

$$10\,000 = 50(0) + 2\sqrt{(0)^3} + C$$

So $\quad C = 10000$

Hence $\quad P = 50t + 2\sqrt{t^3} + 10000$

We have already seen in Chapter 17 that, where displacement is given as a function of time, $s = f(t)$, then the velocity is given by $v = \frac{ds}{dt}$ and the acceleration is given by $a = \frac{dv}{dt}$.

Using integration we can now reverse these rules, so that velocity is given by $v = \int a\,dt$ and displacement is given by $s = \int v\,dt$.

Example 2

The velocity, v m/s, of a car after t seconds is given by the formula $v = 10 + 8t$.
Calculate how far, s metres, the car travelled in the first 5 seconds, given that $s = 0$ when it was first observed.

SOLUTION

$$v = \frac{ds}{dt} \Rightarrow s = \int v\,dt$$
$$= \int (10 + 8t)\,dt$$
$$= 10t + 4t^2 + C$$

Substitute $s = 0$ and $t = 0$ into $s = 10t + 4t^2 + C$.

$0 = 10(0) + 4(0^2) + C$

So $C = 0$

Hence $s = 10t + 4t^2$

So, when $t = 5$, $s = 10(5) + 4(5^2) = 150$ m.

Exercise 18·5

1 The velocity, v m/s (metres per second), of an object after t seconds is given by the formula $v = 3t^2 - 6t$. Find a formula for the displacement, s metres, given that $s = 2$ when $t = 0$.

2 A particle moves along a straight line such that its velocity, v m/s, after t seconds is given by $v = t^2 - 4t + 2$. Find its displacement, s metres, after 2 seconds, given that its displacement after 3 seconds is 4 metres.

3 The acceleration, a m/s^2, at time t seconds of a body moving in a straight line is given by the formula $a = 2 - t$. Find formulae for its velocity, v m/s, and displacement, s metres, given that $v = 3$ and $s = 1\frac{2}{3}$ when $t = 2$. HPQ

4 The acceleration, a m/s^2, at time t seconds of a particle moving in a straight line is given by the formula $a = 6t - 10$. Find the displacement of the particle after 4 seconds given that its initial velocity is 7 m/s and its initial displacement is 2 metres.

5 An object is moving in a straight line so that, at time t seconds, its distance from a fixed point is s metres. Its acceleration, a m/s^2, is given by $a = \dfrac{6}{\sqrt{(2t+1)}}$.

Find a formula for its distance from the fixed point after t seconds given that it starts from rest.

6 A piston moves vertically up and down in a cylinder so that, after t seconds, its height above the bottom of the cylinder is h centimetres.

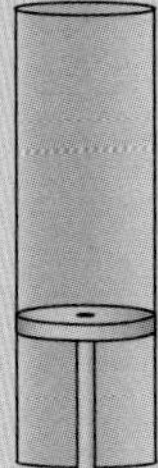

The piston's velocity, v cm/s, is given by $v = 3\sin\frac{1}{2}t$.

Express h in terms of t given that its initial height is 2 centimetres.

7 A ball is thrown vertically upwards so that, after t seconds, its speed, v m/s, is given by $v = 10 - 10t$. Find a formula for h, its height in metres, in terms of t given that its height is 3 metres after 1 second. HPQ

8 The number of bacteria in a culture grows at a rate of $6t^2 + 500$ per hour. Find a formula for N, the number of bacteria in the culture after t hours, given that there were initially 800 bacteria in the culture. ACE

9 A cylindrical tank has sprung a leak part of the way down one side and is losing water at the rate of $8 - t$ litres per minute. After 8 minutes it has lost 50 litres of water. Find a formula for V, the volume (in litres) of water lost from the tank after t minutes. ACE

10 A hospital patient is given an antibiotic, the amount of which in her bloodstream changes at a rate of $\dfrac{5}{\sqrt{t}} - 1$ milligrams per minute. After 1 minute, there are 15 milligrams of the antibiotic in her bloodstream. Find a formula for A, the amount (in milligrams) of antibiotic in her bloodstream after t minutes. ACE

Checkout

Show by shading in sketches the areas associated with:

1 $\int_{-1}^{4}\left(\frac{1}{2}x+3\right)dx$ 2 $\int_{0}^{2}(x-2)^2\,dx$ 3 $\int_{0}^{\frac{3\pi}{2}}\cos x\,dx$

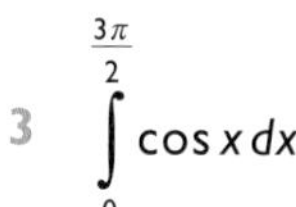

Calculate the shaded area in each of the following diagrams.

4

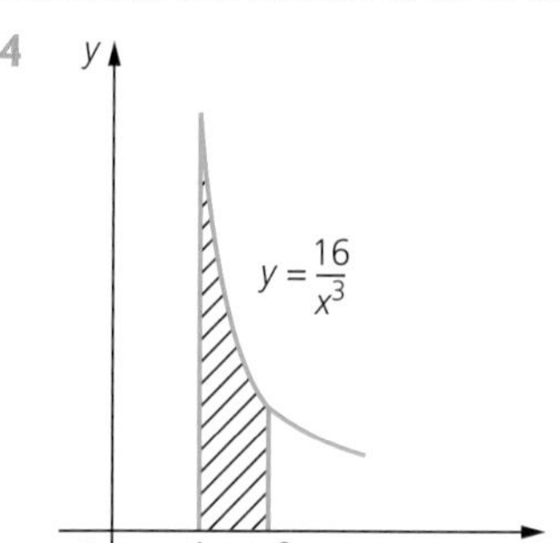

5

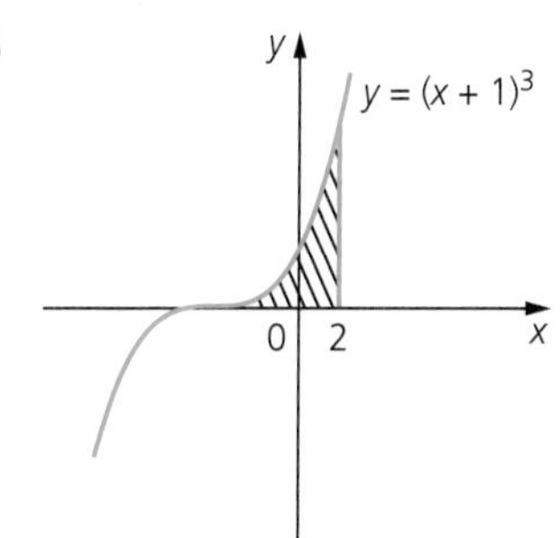

6

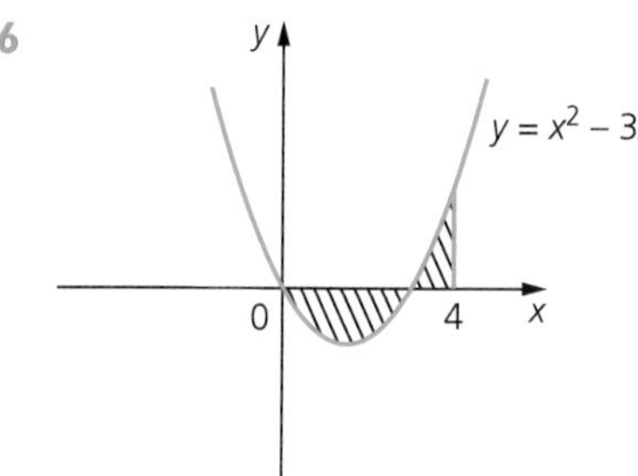

7

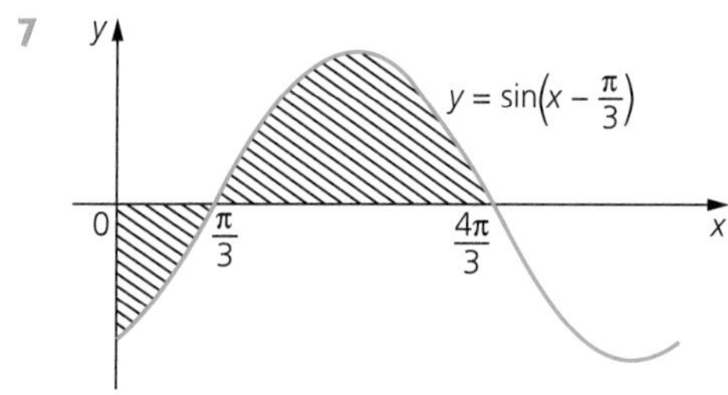

8

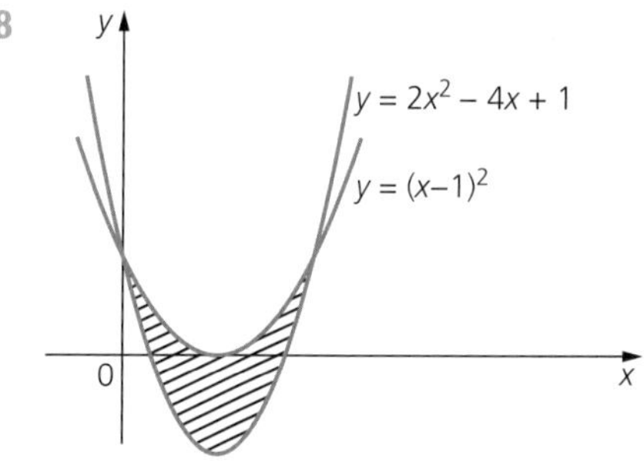

9

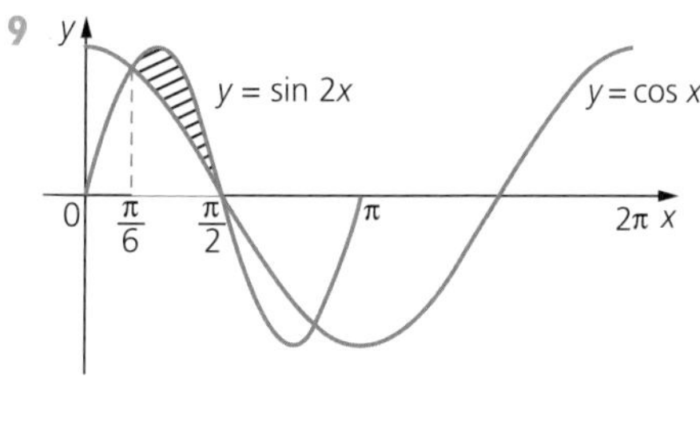

10

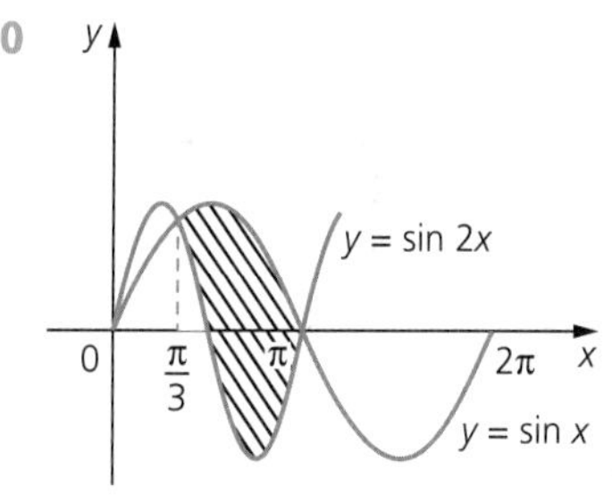

11 Find the points of intersection of the curve $y=(x^2-1)(x-3)$ with the x-axis. Hence find the area enclosed by the curve and the x-axis.

12 Find the points of intersection of the line $y=x+5$ and the curve $y=x^3+6x^2+4x-5$. Hence find the area enclosed by the line and the curve.

13 A wall at the end of a tunnel is in the shape of a rectangle measuring 10 metres by 9 metres with a parabolic space for the tunnel.

The equation of the parabola is $y=8-\frac{1}{2}x^2$.

Calculate the area of the wall.

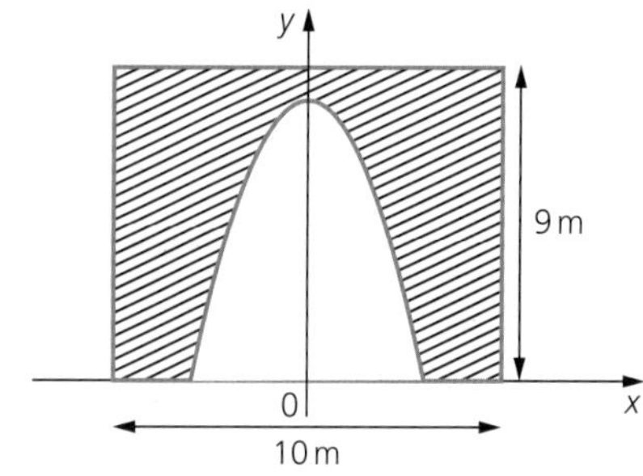

14 The hold of a fishing boat is 40 feet long.
The shaded part of the diagram represents the uniform cross-section of this hold.

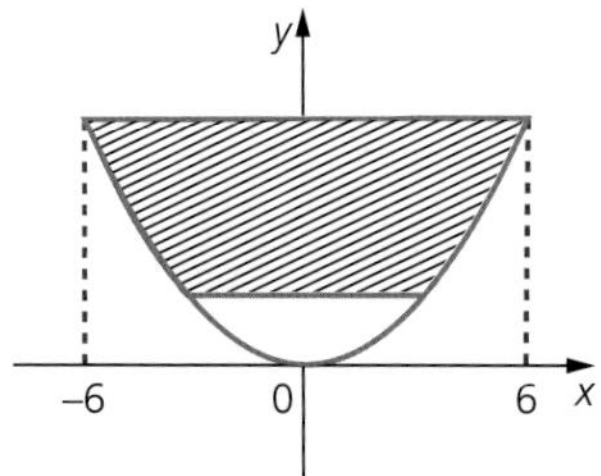

The shaded region is enclosed by the parabola with equation $y = \frac{1}{3}x^2,\ -6 \le x \le 6,$ and the lines $y = 3$ and $y = 12$.
Find the area of the cross-section and the volume of the hold.

15 The acceleration, a m/s^2, at time t seconds of a particle moving in a straight line is given by the formula $a = 3\sqrt{t} - 2$.
Find formulae for its velocity, v m/s, and displacement, s metres, given that it starts from rest.

16 The Garden Hut Company's annual profit, $P(h)$, depends on the number of huts, h, that it sells. The rate at which its profit changes with respect to sales is given by $90 - 0{\cdot}2h$.
Find the profit function $P(h)$ given that $P(0) = -3000$.

Summary

Applying Integral Calculus

1 The area under the curve $y = f(x)$ bounded by the x-axis and the lines $x = a$ and $x = b$ $(a < b)$ is given by the definite integral $\int_a^b f(x)\,dx$.

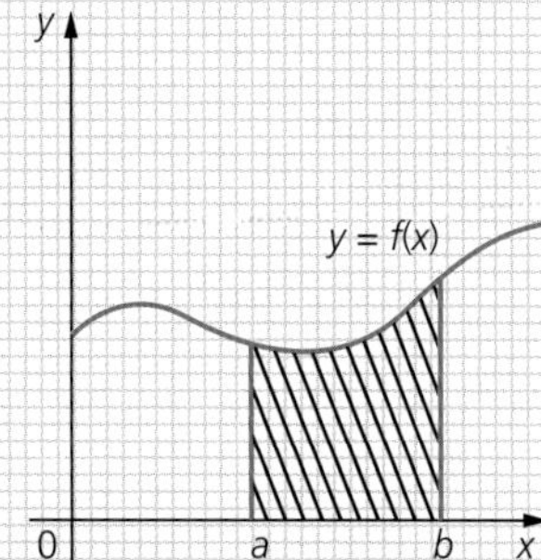

2 For areas below the x-axis, $\int_a^b f(x)\,dx$ is negative.

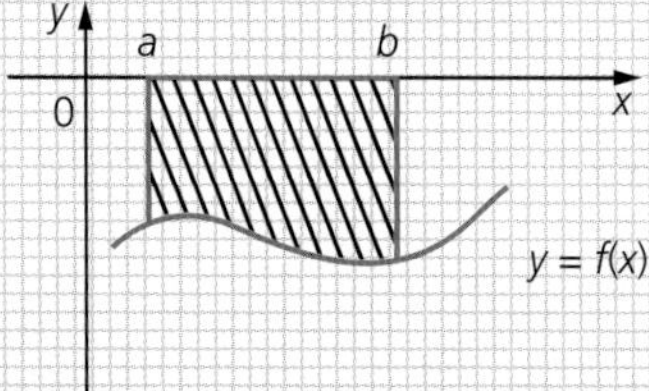

Ignore the negative sign as it merely indicates that the area lies below the x-axis.

Calculus Skills

3 Calculate areas above and below the x-axis separately (ignoring negative signs for areas below the x-axis) and then add.

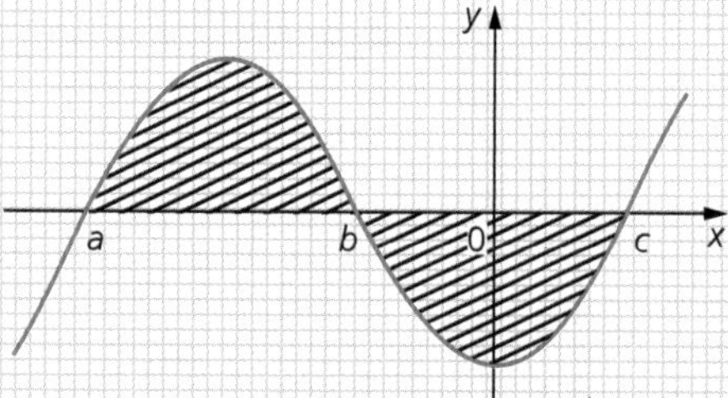

4 The area enclosed between the curves $y = f(x)$ and $y = g(x)$ from $x = a$ to $x = b$ is given by $\int_a^b (f(x) - g(x))\,dx$ when $f(x) \geq g(x)$ and $a < x < b$.

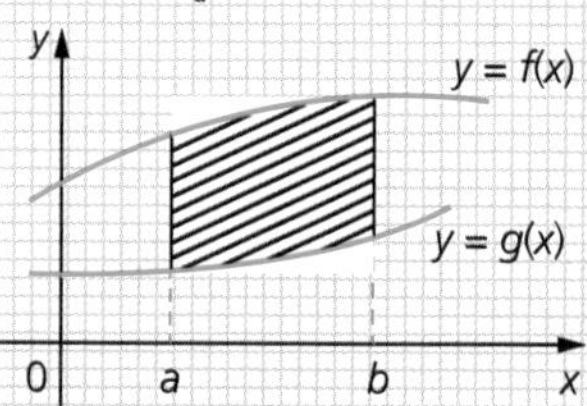

5 $\frac{dy}{dx}$ is the rate of change of y with respect to x. If $\frac{dy}{dx} = f(x)$ then $y = \int f(x)\,dx$.

6 $s = \int v\,dt$ and $v = \int a\,dt$, where s = displacement, v = velocity and a = acceleration after time t.

ANSWERS

Chapter 1

Exercise 1.1

1 a) $\sqrt{10}$
b) 5
c) $\sqrt{13}$
d) $\sqrt{58}$
e) 13
f) 5
g) $2\sqrt{2}$
h) $\sqrt{34}$
i) $\sqrt{41}$

2 Proof

3 Proof

4 Proof

5 Proof

6 $k=-7$ or $k=1$

Exercise 1.2

1 a) (6,4)
b) (1,−1)
c) (3,−4)
d) (1,−1)
e) (−2, 1)
f) $\left(-\frac{1}{2},\frac{1}{2}\right)$
g) (3,−4)
h) (−8,−2)
i) (7,−4)

2 (14,−1)

3 (9,−5)

4 a) (5, 6)
b) (5, 6)
c) They bisect each other.

5 a) (−3, 6)
b) $3x-5y+39=0$

Exercise 1.3

1 a) 76·0°
b) 30·0°
c) 135·0°
d) 26·6°
e) 120·0°
f) 89·0°

2 a) 0·36
b) −1·73
c) 1·43
d) Undefined
e) 5·00
f) −0·29

3 a) $\frac{1}{3}$
b) 18·4°

4 a) $-\frac{5}{7}$
b) 144·5°

5 80·5°

6 45·0°

7 45·0°

8 a) 1·00
b) −2·75
c) −0·36

9 −1·6 and 0·4

10 a) $a=76\cdot0°$, $b=166\cdot0°$
b) 90°

11 a) $a=71\cdot6°$, $b=161\cdot6°$
b) The lines are perpendicular.

Exercise 1.4

1 Proof

2 Proof

3 Proof

4 $k=11$

5 $t=3$

6 $q=-8$

7 Proof

8 (5, 11)

Exercise 1.5

1 a) GH and IJ
b) AB and EF, CD and KL

2 a) $-\frac{1}{4}$
b) $\frac{1}{3}$
c) −4
d) 2·5
e) $\frac{4}{3}$
f) $-\frac{2}{7}$

3 Because $4\times-\frac{1}{4}=-1$

Answers

4 **a)** $y = -\frac{1}{5}x$

b) $y = \frac{1}{2}x$

c) $y = -2x$

d) $y = 6x$

5 **a)** $\frac{1}{9}$

b) -9

6 **a)** $-\frac{5}{6}$

b) $6x - 5y + 8 = 0$

7 $x + 2y - 7 = 0$

8 $x + 5y - 32 = 0$

9 $5x - 11y + 32 = 0$

10 $3x + 2y - 10 = 0$

11 $2x + 3y + 8 = 0$

12 Proof

13 Proof

14 $3x - 4y - 12 = 0$

15 $2x - y - 5 = 0$

16 $7x - 2y + 28 = 0$

Exercise 1.6

1 **a)** $x + y = 10$

b) $3x - 2y + 5 = 0$

c) $5x + 3y - 2 = 0$

d) $3x - 4y + 1 = 0$

e) $y = -2$

f) $5x + 4y - 12 = 0$

2 $2x + y - 3 = 0$

3 $y = 3 \cdot 5$

Exercise 1.7

1 $x + y = 2$

2 $2x + y + 3 = 0$

3 **a)** $3x - 4y - 17 = 0$

b) $x - 3y - 14 = 0$

4 $x = 7,\ 2x + y = 14,\ x + 6y = 7$

5 $x + 3y = 0$

Exercise 1.8

1 $y = 3x - 7$

2 **a)** $x - 3y - 6 = 0$

b) $4x + 3y + 1 = 0$

3 $6x + y = 18,\ 9x + 8y = 40,\ 3x + 7y = 22$

4 **a)** $2x + 5y = 7$

b) $x - 3y = 11$

c) $x = 1$

5 **a)** $x - 4y + 13 = 0$

b) $x - 4y + 13 = 0$

c) Isosceles, since median and altitude are the same line

Exercise 1.9

1 **a)** $x - 3y - 6 = 0$

b) $4x + 3y + 1 = 0$

c) $\left(1, -\frac{5}{3}\right)$

2 **a)** $x = y$

b) $2x + 3y + 6 = 0$

c) $\left(-\frac{6}{5}, -\frac{6}{5}\right)$

3 **a)** $y = 4x + 4$

b) $2y = x + 8$

c) $(0, 4)$

4 **a)** $2x - y = 1$

b) $3x + y = 9$

c) $(2, 3)$

5 **a)** $y = 2$

b) $2x + y = 2$

c) $(0, 2)$

Exercise 1.10

1 (a) and (c)

2 $k = -6$

Exercise 1.11

1 **a)** $y = -3,\ 2x + 3y = 10,\ 6x + y = 54$

b) $(9 \cdot 5, -3)$

2 **a)** $2x + y + 3 = 0,\ y = 1,\ 2x - y + 5 = 0$

b) $(-2, 1)$

3 **a)** $3y = x - 4,\ 2y = x - 6,\ y = x - 8$

b) $(10, 2)$

4 $\left(0, -\frac{9}{7}\right)$

Checkout

1 $\sqrt{41}$
2 $y = 2x - 5$
3 $2x + y + 3 = 0$
4 $5x + 6y = 16$
5 Yes, they all pass through $(-1, 8)$.
6 $\sqrt{3}$
7 a) $x + y = 4$
 b) $135°$
8 Proof
9 Proof
10 a) $y = 2x - 1$
 b) $3x + y = 9$
 c) $(2, 3)$

Chapter 2

Exercise 2.1

1 a) 1, 3, 5, 7; 39
 b) $2\frac{1}{2}, 3, 3\frac{1}{2}, 4;\ 12$
 c) −6, −2, 2, 6; 70
 d) 5, 20, 45, 80; 2000
 e) 1, 8, 27, 64; 8000
 f) 3, 9, 27, 81; 3486784401
 g) $6, 6\frac{1}{2}, 6\frac{2}{3}, 6\frac{3}{4};\ 6\frac{19}{20}$
 h) −5, 5, −5, 5; 5
2 a) $u_n = 4n + 2$
 b) $u_n = 8n - 1$
 c) $u_n = 2n - 7$
 d) $u_n = 25 - 4n$
 e) $u_n = n^2$
 f) $u_n = 2^n$

Exercise 2.2

1 a) 607
 b) 4·25
 c) −409
 d) −1
2 a) 44·5, 90·5
 b) 5
3 a) −4·48, −5·344
 b) 6

Exercise 2.3

1 a) $u_{n+1} = 1\cdot025u_n + 50,\ u_0 = 100$
 b) £435·36
2 a) $u_{n+1} = 1\cdot05u_n - 15000,\ u_0 = 150000$
 b) No, after 14 years Dave would only have £3010·26 left, so after 15 years he would be £11 839·23 in the red.
3 a) $u_{n+1} = 1\cdot015u_n - 250,\ u_0 = 2000$
 b) November 1st; £146·95
4 a) $u_{n+1} = 1\cdot15u_n - 100,\ u_0 = 1500$
 b) 2343 ml (to the nearest ml)
 c) 7
5 a) $u_{n+1} = 0\cdot88u_n + 10,\ u_0 = 100$
 b) 91 ml (to the nearest ml)
6 $a = 0\cdot3,\ b = 7\cdot9$
7 $m = 0\cdot4,\ c = -10$
8 4%; £200
9 a) $u_1 = 2a - 4,\ u_2 = 2a^2 - 4a - 4$
 b) −3, 5
10 a) $u_1 = 3m + 1,\ u_2 = 3m^2 + m + 1$
 b) $-\frac{4}{3}, 1$

Exercise 2.4

1 i) b, d, g
 ii) a, c, e
 iii) f
2 b) 4
 d) 1·25
 g) −15
3 a) 12
 b) 12
 c) 12
4 a) $-8\frac{1}{3}$
 b) $-8\frac{1}{3}$
 c) $-8\frac{1}{3}$
5 Sequence converges to a limit if $-1 < a < 1$.

Exercise 2.5

1 a) Converges since $-1 < 0\cdot6 < 1$; limit = 30
 b) Converges since $-1 < 0\cdot25 < 1$; limit = −12
 c) Diverges since $2 > 1$
 d) Converges since $-1 < -0\cdot5 < 1$; limit = 2
 e) Diverges since $1 = 1$
 f) Converges since $-1 < -\frac{2}{3} < 1$; limit = −2·4

2 a) $-1 < 0{\cdot}3 < 1$
   b) $\frac{20}{7}$
3 a) $-1 < \frac{4}{7} < 1$
   b) $\frac{28}{3}$
4 a) u does not have a limit since $4 > 1$; w does have a limit since $-1 < 0\cdot4 < 1$
   b) 5
5 4
6 0·2
7 $p = 2q$
8 a) $a = 1\cdot5$, $b = 3$
   b) Limit does not exist since $1\cdot5 > 1$

Exercise 2.6

1 a) $t_{n+1} = 0\cdot65t_n + 800$
   b) 2286
   c) In the long run the number of tadpoles in the pond converges to 2286.
2 a) $u_{n+1} = 0\cdot73u_n + 20$, $u_0 = 200$
   b) $-1 < 0\cdot73 < 1$
   c) 74
   d) In the long run the number of chickens converges to 74.
3 a) $u_{n+1} = 0\cdot45u_n + 275$
   b) In the long run the mass of algae in the pond converges to 500 g.
4 It is unsafe, since in the long run the level of drug in the patient's system converges to 53·8 mg. This is more than 50 mg at which level the consequences are very serious.
5 Yes, in the long run the amount of pollutant chemicals in the loch would converge to 2·86 tonnes. This is below the safe level of 3 tonnes.
6 a) 3·53 kg
   b) In the long run the amount of sticky gum on the pavements will converge to 2·35 kg.
7 a) In the long term the number of members will converge to 1200.
   b) 35
8 a) 3·75 m
   b) 30%

Investigation

We'R'Electric 36 000; Edison Electrics 54 000

Checkout

1 a) 13, 17·5
   b) 7
2 a) $-1 < 0\cdot4 < 1$
   b) $\frac{25}{3}$
3 $-0\cdot25$
4 $p = \frac{4}{3}q$
5 $a = -0\cdot2$; Limit $= \frac{25}{3}$
6 a) $m = \frac{1}{3}$, $c = 11$
   b) 16·5
7 £81 657·53
8 Bugs Away will be more effective in the long run since using this pesticide will result in the number of pests converging to 308, compared to 313 if OutBug is used.

Chapter 3

Exercise 3.1

1 a) 3
   b) −8
   c) 0
2 a) 1
   b) 5
   c) 3
3 a) 3
   b) 0
   c) −4
   d) −6
   e) 15
4 a) 1
   b) 4
   c) 6
   d) 2
   e) 3
   f) 4
5 a) and b)
6 a) $25x^2 + 10x + 1$
   b) $x^3 - 8x^2 + 16x$
7 a) $3 - 4x + x^2 - 5x^3$
   b) $8 + 12x + 6x^2 + x^3$

Answers

8 a) −16
b) 3
c) 4
9 9
10 a) 24
b) 21
c) −1
d) 46

Exercise 3.2

1 a) 46
b) 0
c) 553
d) −69
e) 41
f) 205
g) 14
h) −19
2 a) 18
b) 8
c) 0·2
d) 1·5
3 7

Exercise 3.3

1 a) x^2+4x; 2
b) x^2-4x+9; -25
c) x^3+2x^2+4x+5; 4
d) $x^2-8x+18$; -52
e) $x^2+4x+16$; 59
f) $2x^2-14x+57$; -232
g) x^2+3x+6; 0
h) $6x^2-7x-20$; 0
i) $-x^3-x^2-x-1$; -1
j) $3x^4-13x^3+53x^2-209x+836$; -3344
2 $a=8$
3 $h=-14$
4 $p=3$
5 $q=4$

Exercise 3.4

1 a) x^2+2x-2; -9
b) $2x^2-4x+1$; 11
c) x^2+3x+3; -2
d) x^2+2x+5; -7
e) $2x^3+3x+4$; 5

Exercise 3.5

1 $(x-2)(x+1)(x-3)$
2 $(x-2)(x-1)^2$
3 $(x+2)(x+4)(x-3)$
4 $(x-2)(x+2)(x-4)$
5 $(x+1)(2x^2-1)$
6 a) Proof
b) $(x-1)(x-2)(x+3)$
7 a) Proof
b) $(x+3)(x-1)^2$
8 a) $(x+2)(x-1)(x-3)$
b) $x(x-2)(x+1)$
c) $(x+2)(2x-1)(x+3)$
d) $(x+2)(2x+1)(x+3)$
e) $(t+4)(2t-1)(t-5)$
9 $(2x-1)(x-1)(x+2)$
10 $(3x+1)(x+2)(x-1)$
11 $(2x+1)(x^2-5x+3)$
12 a) Proof
b) $(x+2)(x+1)^3$
13 a) Proof
b) $(x^2+2x+3)(x+1)^2$
14 a) $c=-4$
b) $(x-2)(x+2)(x+1)$
15 $b=3$
16 $a=-1$, $b=-2$
17 $p=-18$, $q=9$

Exercise 3.6

1 a) Proof
b) 1, −4, 2
2 a) Proof
b) $-1, -\frac{2}{3}, \frac{1}{2}$
3 a) Proof
b) −1, 1, 2
4 a) 2, 3, −2
b) 1, −3, −4
c) 2, 4, 6
d) $1, \frac{1}{2}, -\frac{2}{5}$
5 Proof; $\frac{2}{3}, -\frac{1}{2}, 1$
6 a) 0, 1, 3, −2
b) 1, 2
c) $-1, 1, 2, \frac{1}{2}$

Answers

7 **a)** $k=-7$
b) Proof
8 **a)** $(-2, 0), (1, 0), (6, 0)$
b) $(-1, 0), (3, 0)$

Exercise 3.7

1 $f(x)=(x+2)(x-5)$
2 $f(x)=-2(x+4)(x-1)$
3 $f(x)=-(x+3)(x+1)(x-4)$
4 $f(x)=2(x+5)(x-1)(x-2)$
5 $f(x)=-\frac{1}{2}(x+2)^2(x-3)$
6 $f(x)=3(x+3)(x-1)^2$
7 $f(x)=\frac{1}{2}(x+3)(x+1)(x-2)(x-4)$
8 $f(x)=-\frac{1}{3}(x+4)(x+1)(x-3)(x-5)$
9 $f(x)=-(x+2)(x-1)^2(x-4)$
10 $f(x)=\frac{1}{4}(x+3)^2(x-2)^2$

Exercise 3.8

1 **a)** Proof
b) $\left(-\frac{5}{2}, -\frac{3}{2}\right)$, $(-1, 3)$
2 $(-3, -4), (0, 8), (3, 20)$
3 A $(-1, 4)$, B $(2, 4)$
4 $(1, 5), (-1, 1), (-2, -1)$
5 $(1, 2), (2, 5), \left(-\frac{1}{2}, -\frac{5}{2}\right)$
6 $(1, -1), (-2, 5)$
7 $(0, 1), (2, -7)$
8 $(1, 7), \left(-\frac{1}{2}, -\frac{13}{8}\right), \left(\frac{1}{3}, \frac{73}{27}\right)$

Exercise 3.9

1 **a)** Distinct real (irrational) roots
b) No real roots
c) Equal (rational) roots
d) Distinct real (rational) roots
2 Distinct real (irrational) roots
3 Proof
4 Proof
5 Proof
6 **a)** $\frac{1}{2}$
b) $\frac{1}{6}$
c) $\frac{1}{3}$
7 **a)** $p=9$
b) $p<9$
c) $p>9$
8 $k=7$ or -9
9 $q=-3$ or 13
10 $k<-\frac{1}{6}$
11 **a)** Proof
b) $k\le\frac{1}{4}$
12 Proof
13 Proof
14 Proof
15 $p=1$ or 5
16 $k=-7$
17 $y=8x-3$; $(1, 5)$

Exercise 3.10

1 $x<-3$ and $x>-2$
2 $-4<x<2$
3 $x\le-2$ and $x\ge3$
4 $-5\le x\le3$
5 $x<-\frac{5}{2}$ and $x>-\frac{3}{5}$
6 $-\frac{1}{2}<x<\frac{5}{2}$
7 $x\le-2$ and $x\ge8$
8 $-5\le x\le5$
9 $x<0$ and $x>\frac{4}{3}$
10 $-5<k<7$
11 $t\le0$ and $t\ge4$
12 $p<-4$ and $p>4$
13 $-2<k<3$

Investigation

1.53

Checkout

1 x^2+1; 4
2 a) Proof
b) $(x-1)^2(2x+5)$
c) $1, -\frac{5}{2}$
3 $(-1, -2)$
4 a) Proof
b) $3, \frac{1}{2}, -\frac{1}{2}$
5 a) Proof
b) $(x-1)(x+4)(x+5)$
6 a) $a=6$
b) $(0, 6)$
c) $(2, 0), \left(\frac{1}{2}, 0\right)(-3, 0)$
7 $a=1, b=0, c=-7, d=6$
8 $p=\frac{9}{8}$
9 $t<0$ or $t>4$
10 $-4 \le x \le 8$

Chapter 4

Exercise 4.1

1 a) $x^2+y^2=4$
b) $x^2+y^2=36$
c) $x^2+y^2=64$
d) $x^2+y^2=225$
2 a) $(0, 0)$; 7
b) $(0, 0)$; 10
c) $(0, 0)$; 5
d) $(0, 0)$; 9
3 a) $x^2+y^2=169$
b) $x^2+y^2=25$
c) $x^2+y^2=16$
d) $x^2+y^2=100$
4 a) $x^2+y^2=144$
b) $x^2+y^2=40$
5 a) 8
b) 8π
c) 16π
6 a) Proof
b) $x^2+y^2=25$
c) $x^2+y^2<25$
7 Inside
8 Outside
9 ± 8
10 a)

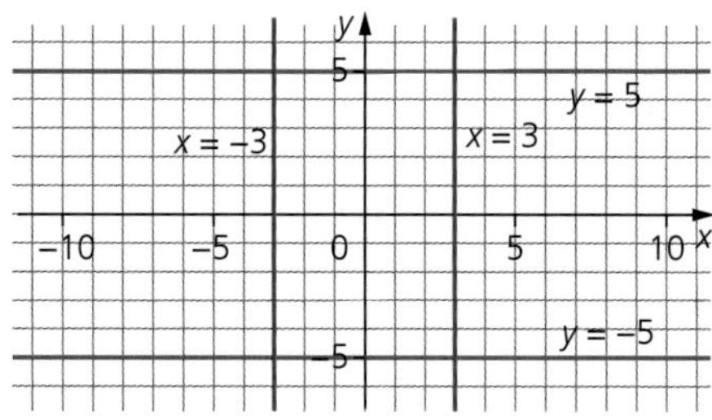

b) $x^2+y^2=34$
11 $(-6, 4)$

Exercise 4.2

1 $(x-3)^2+(y-5)^2=16$
2 $(x-3)^2+(y+1)^2=49$
3 $(x+5)^2+(y+7)^2=25$
4 $(x+4)^2+y^2=12{\cdot}25$
5 a) $(5, 7)$, 4
b) $(3, -6)$, 2
c) $(0, 3)$, 2·5
d) $(-2, -2)$, $\sqrt{47}$
6 a) $(x-3)^2+(y-2)^2=25$
b) $(x+2)^2+(y-2)^2=100$
c) $(x+4)^2+(y+3)^2=169$
d) $x^2+(y+3)^2=18$
e) $(x-x_1)^2+(y-y_1)^2=(x_2-x_1)^2+(y_2-y_1)^2$
7 $(x-7)^2+(y-24)^2=625$
8 $(x-3)^2+(y+4)^2=16$
9 $(x-1)^2+(y+3)^2=49$
10 Outside
11 Inside
12 $(x-3)^2+(y-6)^2=106$
13 $(x+5)^2+(y-7)^2=10$
14 $(-1, -5)$
15 a) <POQ is the angle in a semi-circle
b) $(x-4)^2+(y-3)^2=25$

16 The circles touch since the distance between their centres, 10, equals the sum of their radii, $(6+4)$.

Exercise 4.3

1 $(1, 2), \sqrt{8}$
2 $(-2, -3), \sqrt{13}$
3 $(-3, 2), 5$
4 $(4, -5), 6$

Exercise 4.4

1 **a)** $(2, 4), 2$
b) $(3, 5), 6$
e) $(4, 1), 2$
f) $(-2, -3), 3$
c) and **d)** do not represent circles.
2 **a)** $(5, 3), 6$
b) $(-3, -2), 3$
c) $(-4, 0), 2$
d) $(4, -2), \sqrt{3}$
e) $(-5, 7), 3$
3 $(x+1)^2+(y-2)^2=108$
4 A is on the circle; B and C are outside.
5 $(-3, 2), 6$
6 **a)** $(-2, 3), 5$
b) $(-3, -4), 5$
7 $(1, 5)$
8 $m=3$ or -9
9 **a)** $4g+10f=-36, \ -4g+2f=-12$
b) $g=1, f=-4$
c) $x^2+y^2+2x-8y+7=0$
d) $(-1, 4), \sqrt{10}$
10 $x^2+y^2-8x+6y=0$

Exercise 4.5

1 **a)** $x-3y+5=0$
b) $x-2y+5=0$
2 $y=2x-9$
3 $x-2y+4=0$
4 $y=2x+11$
5 **a)** Proof
b) $y=2x-11$
6 **a)** $2x+y+3=0$
b) $(x+0{\cdot}5)^2+(y+2)^2=1{\cdot}25$
7 **a)** $(x+2)^2+(y-3)^2=18$
b) $x+y=7$

Exercise 4.6

1 **a)** Yes, $(4, 1), (-4, 1)$
b) Yes, $(5, 3), (-5, 3)$
c) No
d) Yes, $(1, 2), (-2, -1)$
e) Yes, $(1, -7), (3, -1)$
2 **a)** $(4, 0)$
b) $(-1, 3)$
c) $(3, 2)$
3 $(4, -2)$
4 $(1, 5)$
5 $(1, 0), (3, 0)$
6 $(1, 8), (-4, -7)$
7 $(-2, -6), (4, 0)$
8 $(-6, -4)$ and $(-2, 4)$
9 $(0, 1), (5, 6)$
10 **a)** $(4, 2), \sqrt{20}$
b) A $(2, 6)$, B $(8, 0)$
c) $(5, 3)$
d) $(x-4)^2+(y-2)^2=2$
11 **a)** $(3, 5)$
b) $x+y=10$
c) $(5, 7)$
12 $(-1, -1)$
13 $k=6$ or -6

Exercise 4.7

1 Touch internally
2 Yes
3 **a)** Do not touch (and the circles are separate)
b) Do not touch (and one circle is enclosed by the other)
4 Proof
5 **a)** Proof
b) $(0, 4)$
6 **a)** Proof
b) 4
7 $(x-10)^2+(y-11)^2=34$
8 $(x-17)^2+(y-15)^2=25$
9 $(x+6)^2+(y-6)^2=100, \ (x-10)^2+(y+6)^2=100$

Checkout

1 $(x-5)^2+(y+1)^2=9$

2 $x^2+y^2=20$

3 a) (5, 2), 6
b) Inside
c) No

4 Proof

5 $(x-3)^2+(y-12)^2=4$

6 $3x+2y=14$

7 Proof

8 Proof

9 a) (−2, 1), 4
b) $(0,\ 1+2\sqrt{3})$ and $(0,\ 1-2\sqrt{3})$

10 Proof

11 $(x+7)^2+(y+1)^2=100$ and $(x-3)^2+(y+1)^2=100$

12 7·0

Chapter 5

Exercise 5.1

1 a)

x	−3	−2	−1	0	1	2	3
$f(x)$	$\frac{1}{27}$	$\frac{1}{9}$	$\frac{1}{3}$	1	3	9	27

b)

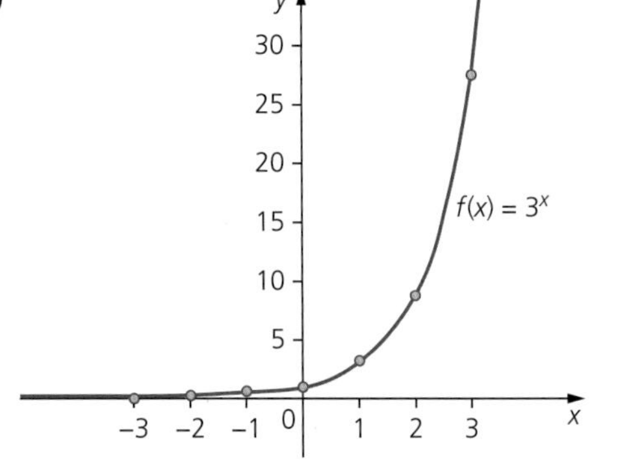

2 a)

x	−3	−2	−1	0	1	2	3
$f(x)$	8	4	2	1	$\frac{1}{2}$	$\frac{1}{4}$	$\frac{1}{8}$

b)

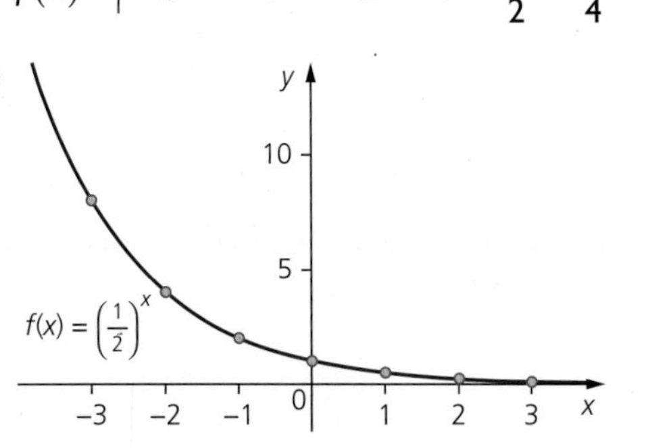

3 a)

x	−3	−2	−1	0	1	2	3
$f(x)$	27	9	3	1	$\frac{1}{3}$	$\frac{1}{9}$	$\frac{1}{27}$

b)

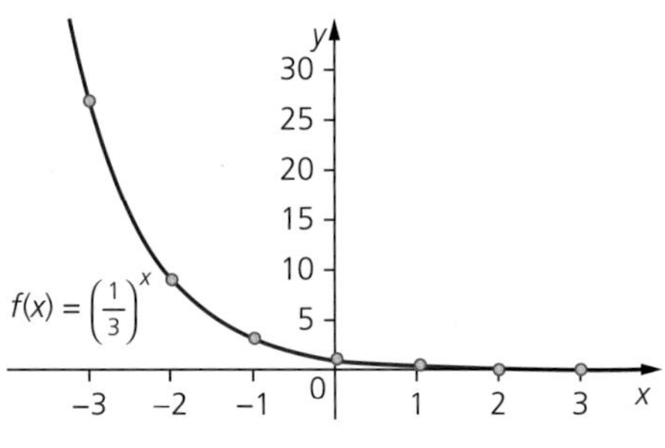

4

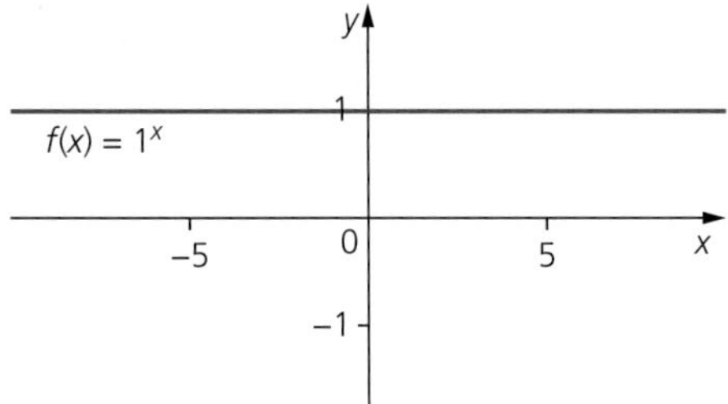

5 a) $\frac{1}{100}$ b) $\frac{1}{10}$
c) 1 d) 10
e) 100 f) 1000

6 a) 100 b) 10
c) 1 d) $\frac{1}{10}$
e) $\frac{1}{100}$ f) $\frac{1}{1000}$

7 $a=5$

8 $k=2$

Exercise 5.2

1 a)

x	−3	−2	−1	0	1	2	3
$f(x)$	0·0	0·1	0·4	1·0	2·7	7·4	20·1

b)

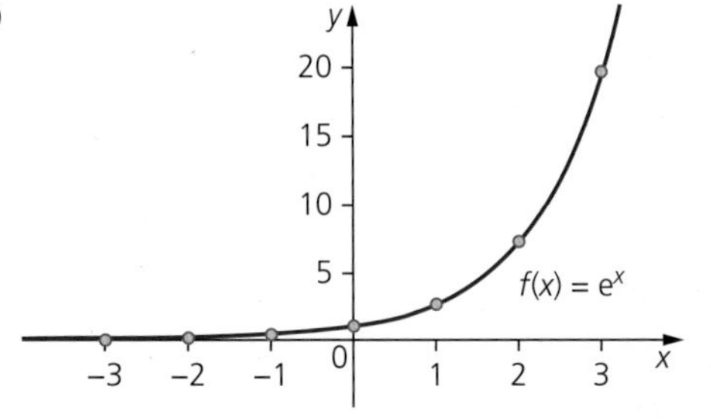

2 **a)** 2·01
b) 5·47
c) 0·0821
d) 2980
e) 0·301
f) 0·124

Exercise 5.3

1 **a)** $P_n = 1{\cdot}15^n \times 12000$
b) 27 757
2 **a)** $V_n = 0{\cdot}88^n \times 25000$
b) £6962·52
3 **a)** $P_n = 1{\cdot}0125^n \times 6{\cdot}08$ billion
b) 7·417 billion
4 **a)** $W_h = 0{\cdot}85^h \times 500$
b) 261 ml
5 £1014·59
6 10 years
7 4 hours
8 **a)** 500
b) 24 701
9 **a)** 200 mg
b) 134 mg

Exercise 5.4

1 **a)** $\log_2 16 = 4$
b) $\log_{10} 1000 = 3$
c) $\log_3 9 = 2$
d) $\log_8 8 = 1$
e) $\log_7 1 = 0$
f) $\log_3 \frac{1}{27} = -3$
g) $\log_6 \frac{1}{6} = -1$
h) $\log_{10} \frac{1}{100} = -2$
i) $\log_a q = p$
j) $\log_m k = 5$
2 **a)** $3^4 = 81$
b) $7^2 = 49$
c) $6^3 = 216$
d) $3^1 = 3$
e) $8^0 = 1$
f) $5^{-2} = \frac{1}{25}$
g) $7^{\frac{1}{2}} = \sqrt{7}$
h) $4^{-3} = 1/64$
i) $c^e = d$
j) $d^e = f$
3 **a)** $x = 25$
b) $x = 64$
c) $x = 3$
d) $x = \frac{1}{1000}$
4 **a)** $x = 9$
b) $x = 4$
c) $x = \sqrt{3}$
d) $x = 9$
5 **a)** 7
b) 2
c) −2
d) −4
e) 4
f) $\frac{3}{2}$
g) 6
h) $-\frac{4}{3}$

Exercise 5.5

1 **a)** 0·301
b) 0·477
c) 0·699
d) 2·954
e) 0·500
f) −0·097
2 **a)** 0·693
b) 1·099
c) 1·609
d) 6·802
e) 1·151
f) −0·223
3 **a)**

	$\log_{10} ab$	$\log_{10} a \times \log_{10} b$	$\log_{10} a + \log_{10} b$
$a = 2, b = 3$	0·778	0·144	0·778
$a = 4, b = 7$	1·447	0·509	1·447
$a = 8, b = 6$	1·681	0·703	1·681

b) $\log_{10} ab = \log_{10} a + \log_{10} b$

4 a)

	$\ln ab$	$\ln a \times \ln b$	$\ln a + \ln b$
$a=2, b=3$	1·792	0·762	1·792
$a=4, b=7$	3·332	2·698	3·332
$a=8, b=6$	3·871	3·726	3·871

b) $\ln ab = \ln a + \ln b$

5 a)

	$\log_{10}\frac{a}{b}$	$\frac{\log_{10} a}{\log_{10} b}$	$\log_{10}a - \log_{10}b$
$a=12, b=4$	0·477	1·792	0·477
$a=26, b=2$	1·114	4·700	1·114
$a=15, b=3$	0·699	2·465	0·699

b) $\log_{10}\frac{a}{b} = \log_{10}a - \log_{10}b$

6 a)

	$\ln\frac{a}{b}$	$\frac{\ln a}{\ln b}$	$\ln a - \ln b$
$a=12, b=4$	1·099	1·792	1·099
$a=26, b=2$	2·565	4·700	2·565
$a=15, b=3$	1·609	2·465	1·609

b) $\ln\frac{a}{b} = \ln a - \ln b$

7 a)

	$\log_{10}a^b$	$(\log_{10}a)^b$	$b \log_{10}a$
$a=5, b=2$	1·398	0·489	1·398
$a=4, b=3$	1·806	0·218	1·806
$a=2, b=6$	1·806	0·001	1·806

b) $\log_{10}a^b = b \log_{10}a$

8 a)

	$\ln a^b$	$(\ln a)^b$	$b\ln a$
$a=5, b=2$	3·219	2·590	3·219
$a=4, b=3$	4·159	2·664	4·159
$a=2, b=6$	4·159	0·111	4·159

b) $\ln a^b = b\ln a$

Exercise 5.6

1 a) $\log_4 6$
b) $\log_5 3$
c) $\log_3 100$
d) $\log_5 48$
e) $\log_7 18$
f) $\log_3 2$
g) $\log_{10} 6$
h) $\log_e 16$
i) $\ln 24$

2 a) $x = 28$
b) $x = 6$
c) $x = 20$
d) $x = 72$

3 a) 2
b) 2
c) 3
d) 4
e) -1
f) 0
g) 0·5
h) 1
i) 4
j) 3
k) 2

4 Proof

5 Proof

6 a) $f + g$
b) $f - g$
c) $5f$

7 a) $2\log_{10}2 + \log_{10}3$
b) $2\log_{10}2 + 2\log_{10}3$

8 $b = \frac{c^2d^3}{\sqrt{f}}$

9 $1 + 2x - y$

10 $\log_2\left(\frac{16}{2}\right)$ should be $\log_2 16^{\frac{1}{2}}$ $(= \log_2 4)$; the next-to-last line should be $\log_2\left(25 \times \frac{5}{4} \times 4\right)$ leading to $\log_2 125$.

Exercise 5.7

1 a) $x = 5$
b) $x = 6$
c) $x = 1$
d) $x = 7$

2 a) $x = 6$
b) $x = \frac{7}{8}$

Answers

c) $x = \frac{27}{5}$
d) $x = 40$
e) $x = 3$
f) $x = 3$
g) $x = 2$
h) $x = \frac{5}{2}$

3 a) $x = 4$
b) $x = 10$
c) $x = 2$
d) $x = 3$

4 a) $x = 2{\cdot}06$
b) $y = 5{\cdot}13$
c) $a = 1{\cdot}46$
d) $b = 0{\cdot}70$
e) $x = 1{\cdot}29$
f) $m = -0{\cdot}61$

5 a) 2·77
b) 2·12

6 a) (16, 0)
b) (7, 0)
c) $\left(-\frac{1}{2}, 0\right)$

Exercise 5.8

1 a) $k = 0{\cdot}358$
b) 10·9 hours

2 167 105

3 16·7 years

4 a) 3·47 million
b) Around 2032 – 2033

5 38·6 years

6 The population in January 2000; the growth rate (1·9%)

7 a) $k = 0{\cdot}462$
b) 5080 km²

8 a) 100 mg
b) $k = -0.00193$

9 $k = -0{\cdot}073$

10 a) $k = -0{\cdot}000128$
b) (i) 853 hPa
(ii) 327 hPa

11 a) $k = -0{\cdot}000121$
b) 78·5%

Exercise 5.9

1 a) $\ln y = 0{\cdot}75 \ln x + 1{\cdot}5$
b) $a = 4{\cdot}48$ and $b = 0{\cdot}75$

2 (0, 0·7)

3 a) $a = 5$, $b = 6$
b) $a = 31{\cdot}6$, $b = -1{\cdot}5$

4 a) $a = 5{\cdot}25$, $b = 2{\cdot}51$
b) $a = 3981$, $b = 0{\cdot}631$

5 a)

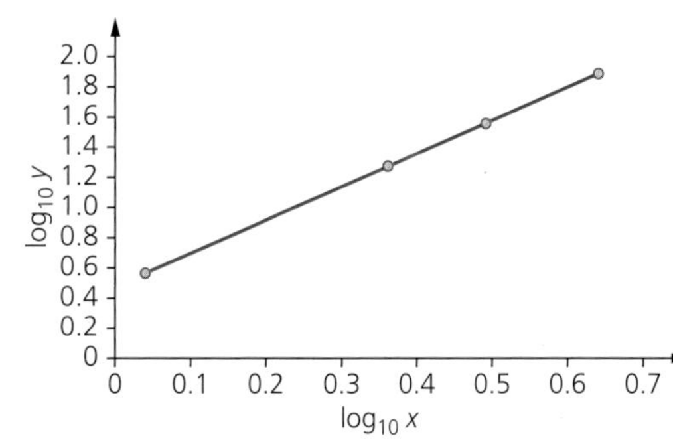

b) $a = 3$, $b = 2{\cdot}2$

6 a)

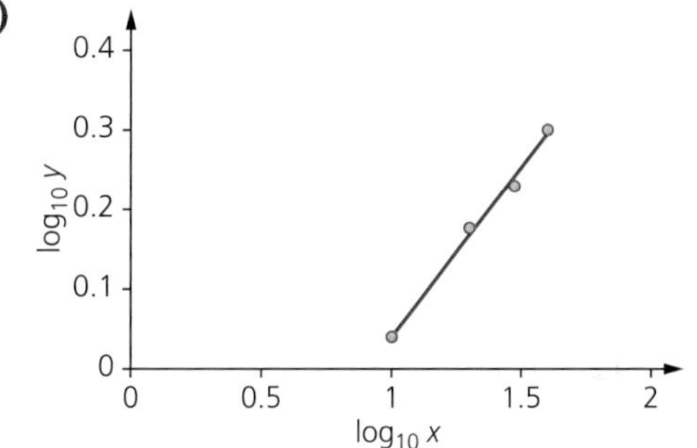

b) $a = 0{\cdot}41$, $b = 0{\cdot}43$

7 a)

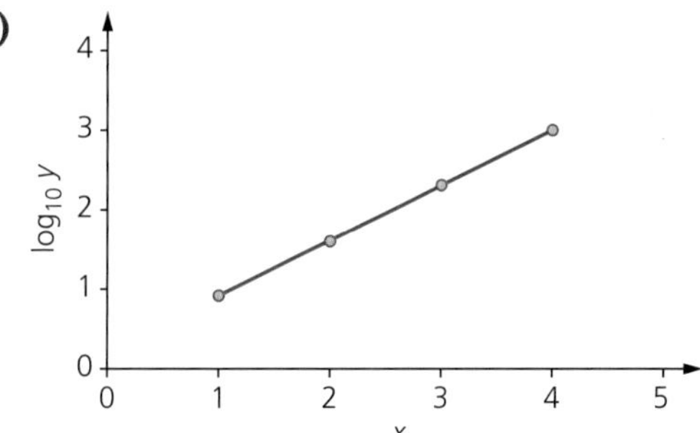

b) $a = 1{\cdot}7$, $b = 5$

8 a) $a = \frac{1}{2}$
b) $b = \frac{3}{2}$
c) $\log_{10} 4$

9 a) Proof
b) $k = 3{\cdot}17$, $n = 1{\cdot}7$

Answers

Checkout

1 $\log_3 243 = 5$
2 $6^p = 7$
3 $\log_{10} 4$
4 2
5 $x = 5$
6 $x = \frac{4}{3}$
7 $x = 2{\cdot}80$
8 21·4 mg
9 51·7 minutes
10 Proof
11 $a = 5$, $b = -4$

Chapter 6

Exercise 6.1

1 a) $\sin 57°$
b) $-\sin 35°$
c) $-\sin 63°$
d) $\sin 82°$
e) $-\sin 32°$

2 a) $\cos 62°$
b) $\cos 10°$
c) $-\cos 55°$
d) $\cos 17°$
e) $-\cos 70°$

3 a) $\tan a°$
b) $-\sin y°$
c) $\cos m°$
d) $\sin b°$

Exercise 6.2

1 a) $\frac{1}{2}$
b) 1
c) $-\frac{1}{2}$
d) $-\frac{\sqrt{3}}{2}$
e) $\frac{\sqrt{3}}{2}$
f) $-\frac{1}{\sqrt{3}}$
g) $-\frac{1}{\sqrt{2}}$
h) $-\frac{\sqrt{3}}{2}$
i) -1
j) $-\frac{\sqrt{3}}{2}$

2 a) 210, 330
b) 30, 330
c) 135, 315
d) 0, 180, 360
e) 180
f) 90, 270

3 a) 30, 210
b) 150, 210

4 a) $\frac{7}{12}$
b) $\sqrt{3}$

Exercise 6.3

1 a) 0, 19·5, 160·5, 180, 360
b) 120, 240
c) 48·2, 131·8, 228·2, 311·8
d) 30, 150
e) 60, 300
f) 30, 150, 194·5, 345·5

Exercise 6.4

1 a) 45, 225
b) 20, 40, 140, 160, 260, 280
c) 30, 90, 150, 210, 270, 330
d) 105, 165, 285, 345

2 a) 7·2, 82·8, 187·2, 262·8
b) 16·1, 103·9, 136·1, 223·9, 256·1, 343·9

Exercise 6.5

1

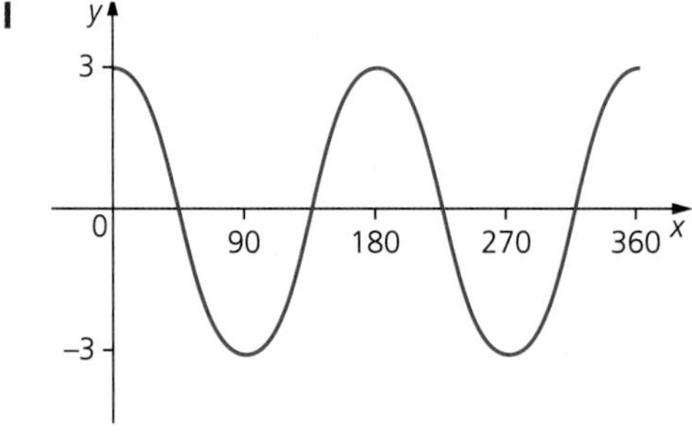

2

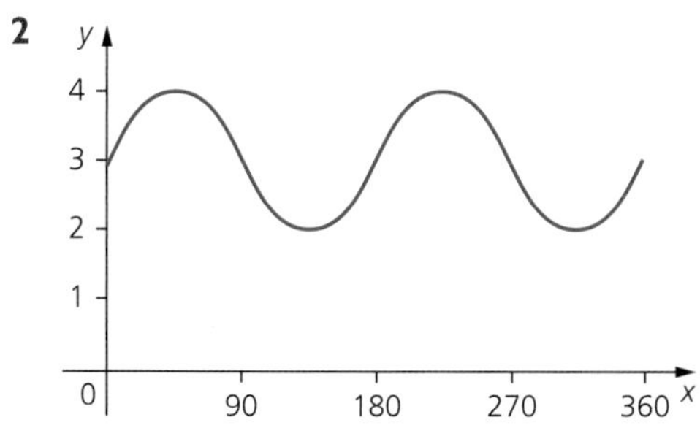

3

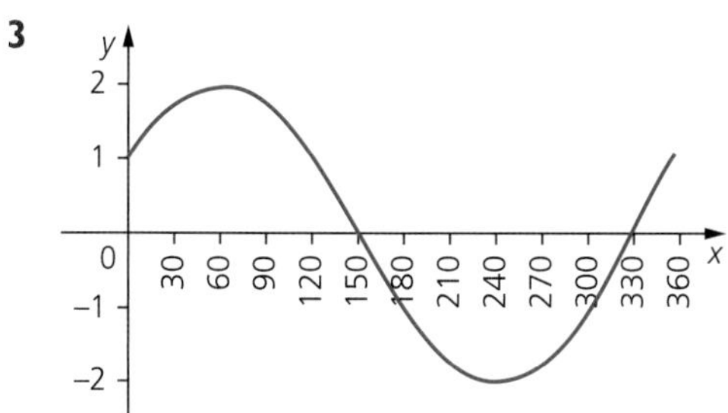

4

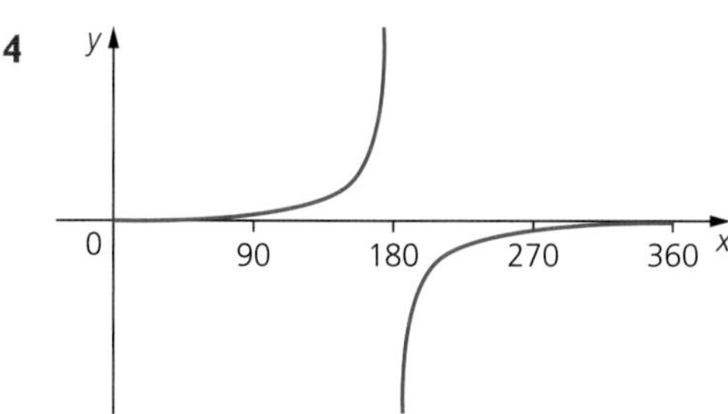

5 $y = 2\sin(x - 30)^\circ$

6 $y = 4\cos 2x^\circ + 3$

Exercise 6.6

All answers in Exercise 6.6 are proof.

Exercise 6.7

1 a) 90°
b) 270°
c) 45°
d) 30°
e) 120°
f) 315°
g) 210°
h) 36°

2 a) $\frac{5\pi}{6}$
b) $\frac{\pi}{3}$
c) $\frac{3\pi}{4}$
d) $\frac{5\pi}{3}$
e) $\frac{11\pi}{6}$
f) $\frac{3\pi}{10}$

3

	$\frac{\pi}{6}$	$\frac{\pi}{4}$	$\frac{\pi}{3}$
sin	$\frac{1}{2}$	$\frac{1}{\sqrt{2}}$	$\frac{\sqrt{3}}{2}$
cos	$\frac{\sqrt{3}}{2}$	$\frac{1}{\sqrt{2}}$	$\frac{1}{2}$
tan	$\frac{1}{\sqrt{3}}$	1	$\sqrt{3}$

4 a) $\frac{\sqrt{3}}{2}$
b) $-\frac{1}{\sqrt{3}}$
c) $-\frac{1}{\sqrt{2}}$
d) $-\frac{1}{\sqrt{2}}$
e) $\frac{1}{2}$

5 a) $\frac{\pi}{6}, \frac{5\pi}{6}$
b) $\frac{\pi}{4}, \frac{5\pi}{4}$
c) $\frac{5\pi}{6}, \frac{7\pi}{6}$
d) $\frac{\pi}{3}, \frac{5\pi}{3}$

6 $y = 4\sin 2x$

7 a) $\frac{4\pi}{3}, \frac{5\pi}{3}$
b) $\frac{\pi}{3}, \frac{5\pi}{3}$
c) $\frac{\pi}{12}, \frac{5\pi}{12}, \frac{13\pi}{12}, \frac{17\pi}{12}$
d) $\frac{\pi}{3}, \pi, \frac{5\pi}{3}$

8 a) 0·795, 5·488
b) 1·159, 5·124
c) 0·163, 1·408, 3·304, 4·550

Answers

Investigation

1 a) 14·7 cm
b) 37·7°
c) 42·0°

Checkout

1 20 cm²

2 $\frac{\sqrt{3}}{2}$

3 135, 225

4 90°

5 199·5, 340·5

6 225, 315

7 4

8 $\frac{7\pi}{4}$

Chapter 7

Exercise 7.1

1 a) $\sin p\cos q - \cos p\sin q$

b) $\cos x^\circ\cos y^\circ - \sin x^\circ\sin y^\circ$

c) $\sin 3m\cos n + \cos 3m\sin n$

d) $\cos c\cos d + \sin c\sin d$

e) $\cos 4a\cos 3b + \sin 4a\sin 3b$

f) $\sin z^\circ\cos 2y^\circ - \cos z^\circ\sin 2y^\circ$

g) $\sin x\cos a - \cos x\sin a$

h) $\cos\theta\cos\omega + \sin\theta\sin\omega$

2 a) $\sin(P+Q)$

b) $\cos(2x-y)$

c) 1

d) $\cos 5x$

e) $\frac{1}{2}$

3 Proofs

4 $\frac{63}{65}$

5 $\frac{84}{85}$

6 $-\frac{16}{65}$

7 Proof

8 Proof

9 Proof

10 a) $\cos x^\circ\cos 30^\circ - \sin x^\circ\sin 30^\circ$

b) Proof

11 $-\frac{16}{65}$

12 $-\frac{56}{65}$

13 $\frac{33}{65}$

14 Proof

15 $\frac{1}{2}$

16 $-\frac{1}{2}$

Exercise 7.2

1 a) $2\sin C\cos C$

b) $2\sin 2A\cos 2A$

c) $2\sin 3X\cos 3X$

d) $2\sin 5p\cos 5p$

e) $2\sin\frac{1}{2}A\cos\frac{1}{2}A$

2 a) $\cos^2 3B - \sin^2 3B$, $2\cos^2 3B - 1$, $1 - 2\sin^2 3B$

b) $\cos^2 y^\circ - \sin^2 y^\circ$, $2\cos^2 y^\circ - 1$, $1 - 2\sin^2 y^\circ$

c) $\cos^2\frac{1}{2}Q - \sin^2\frac{1}{2}Q$, $2\cos^2\frac{1}{2}Q - 1$, $1 - 2\sin^2\frac{1}{2}Q$

d) $\cos^2 2E - \sin^2 2E$, $2\cos^2 2E - 1$, $1 - 2\sin^2 2E$

e) $\cos^2 6A - \sin^2 6A$, $2\cos^2 6A - 1$, $1 - 2\sin^2 6A$

3 a) $\sin 2Y$

b) $\cos 2F$

c) $\cos 4A$

d) $\sin 4z$

e) $\cos 6p$

f) $\frac{1}{2}$

g) 1

h) $\frac{1}{2}$

i) $\frac{\sqrt{3}}{2}$

4 $\frac{24}{25}$

5 a) $\frac{120}{169}$
b) $\frac{119}{169}$
c) $\frac{120}{119}$

6 $-\frac{1}{10}$

7 $\frac{240}{289}$

8 $\frac{4\sqrt{5}}{9}$

9 a) $\cos^2 A = \frac{1}{2}(1 + \cos 2A)$
b) $\sin^2 A = \frac{1}{2}(1 - \cos 2A)$

10 a) $\frac{4}{5}$
b) $\frac{3}{5}$

11 a) $\frac{24}{25}$
b) $\frac{336}{625}$

12 $\frac{3}{5}$

13 $\frac{3}{5}$

14 a) $\frac{1}{\sqrt{10}}$
b) $\frac{3}{5}$
c) $\frac{4}{5}$

15 $6\cos^2 x - \cos x - 5$

Exercise 7.3

1 a) Proof
b) Proof
c) Proof
2 a) Proof
b) Proof
3 Proof
4 Proof
5 Proof

Checkout

1 0
2 a) $\cos x^\circ \cos 45^\circ + \sin x^\circ \sin 45^\circ$
b) Proof
3 $\frac{56}{65}$
4 a) $\frac{2\sqrt{2}}{3}$
b) $\frac{1}{3}$
c) $2\sqrt{2}$
5 Proof

Chapter 8

Exercise 8.1

1 a) 30, 90, 150, 270
b) 0, 120, 180, 240, 360
c) 90, 199·5, 270, 340·5
2 0, 60, 300, 360
3 a) 120, 240
b) 90
c) 30, 150, 228·6, 311·4
d) 60, 300
e) 120, 180, 240
f) 48·2, 75·5, 284·5, 311·8
g) 0, 180, 360
h) 90, 221·8, 270, 318·2
i) 90, 228·6, 311·4
4 a) 51·3, 128·7
b) 32·1, 327·9
5 a) $\frac{\pi}{2}, \frac{3\pi}{2}$
b) $\frac{\pi}{3}, \pi, \frac{5\pi}{3}$
c) $\frac{\pi}{2}, \frac{7\pi}{6}, \frac{11\pi}{6}$
6 a) 2·26, 4·02
b) 0·57, 2·21, 4·08, 5·72
7 15, 75, 195, 255
8 $\frac{\pi}{4}, \frac{5\pi}{4}$
9 $\frac{\pi}{6}, \frac{5\pi}{6}$

Checkout

1 0, 84·3, 180, 275·7, 360
2 48·2, 104·5, 255·5, 311·8

Chapter 9

Exercise 9.1

1 a) $k = \sqrt{2}$, $\alpha = 45$
b) $k = 5$, $\alpha = 36\cdot9$
c) $k = \sqrt{5}$, $\alpha = 116\cdot6$
d) $k = 13$, $\alpha = 337\cdot4$
e) $k = \sqrt{3}$, $\alpha = 54\cdot7$
f) $k = \sqrt{10}$, $\alpha = 198\cdot4$

2 a) $k = 2$, $\alpha = \frac{\pi}{6}$
b) $k = \sqrt{8}$, $\alpha = \frac{7\pi}{4}$

Exercise 9.2

1 a) $\sqrt{2}\cos(x - 135)^\circ$
b) $5\cos(x - 126\cdot9)^\circ$
c) $\sqrt{52}\cos(x - 326\cdot3)^\circ$
d) $\sqrt{8}\cos(x - 135)^\circ$

2 a) $\sqrt{6}\cos(x + 335\cdot9)^\circ$
b) $\sqrt{52}\cos(x + 76\cdot1)^\circ$
c) $\sqrt{17}\cos(x + 104\cdot0)^\circ$
d) $25\cos(x + 73\cdot7)^\circ$

3 a) $\sqrt{5}\sin(x + 116\cdot6)^\circ$
b) $17\sin(x + 61\cdot9)^\circ$
c) $3\sin(x + 109\cdot5)^\circ$
d) $\sqrt{13}\sin(x + 123\cdot7)^\circ$

4 a) $4\sin(x - 75\cdot5)^\circ$
b) $\sqrt{20}\sin(x - 26\cdot6)^\circ$
c) $\sqrt{10}\sin(x - 18\cdot4)^\circ$
d) $\sqrt{41}\sin(x - 308\cdot7)^\circ$

5 a) $2\cos\left(x - \frac{5\pi}{3}\right)$
b) $\sqrt{32}\cos\left(x - \frac{7\pi}{4}\right)$

6 $15\sin(x - 0\cdot927)$

Exercise 9.3

1 Max = 4 when $x = 25$; min = −4 when $x = 205$; zeros at $x = 115$ and $x = 295$

2 Max = $\sqrt{10}$ when $x = 17$; min = $-\sqrt{10}$ when $x = 197$; zeros at $x = 107$ and $x = 287$

3 a) $\sqrt{28}\sin(x - 70\cdot9)^\circ$
b) Max = $\sqrt{28}$ when $x = 160\cdot9$; min = $-\sqrt{28}$ when $x = 340\cdot9$; zeros at $x = 70\cdot9$ and $x = 250\cdot9$

4 a) Max = $\sqrt{11}$ when $x = 25\cdot2$; min = $-\sqrt{11}$ when $x = 205\cdot2$; zeros at $x = 115\cdot2$ and $x = 295\cdot2$
b) Max = $\sqrt{20}$ when $x = 206\cdot6$; min = $-\sqrt{20}$ when $x = 26\cdot6$; zeros at $x = 116\cdot6$ and $x = 296\cdot6$
c) Max = $\sqrt{136}$ when $x = 149\cdot0$; min = $-\sqrt{136}$ when $x = 329\cdot0$; zeros at $x = 59\cdot0$ and $x = 239\cdot0$

5 Max = $\sqrt{2}$ when $x = \frac{3\pi}{4}$; min = $-\sqrt{2}$ when $x = \frac{7\pi}{4}$; zeros at $x = \frac{\pi}{4}$ and $x = \frac{5\pi}{4}$

Exercise 9.4

1 a)

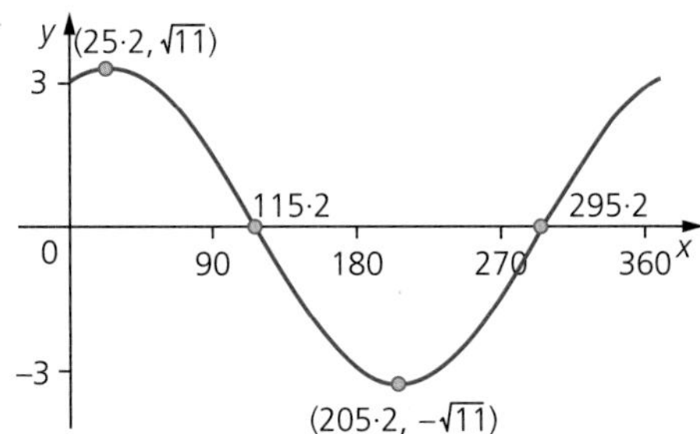

b)

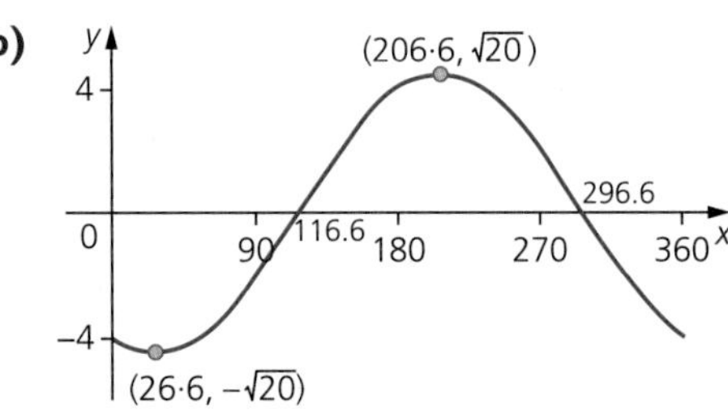

c)

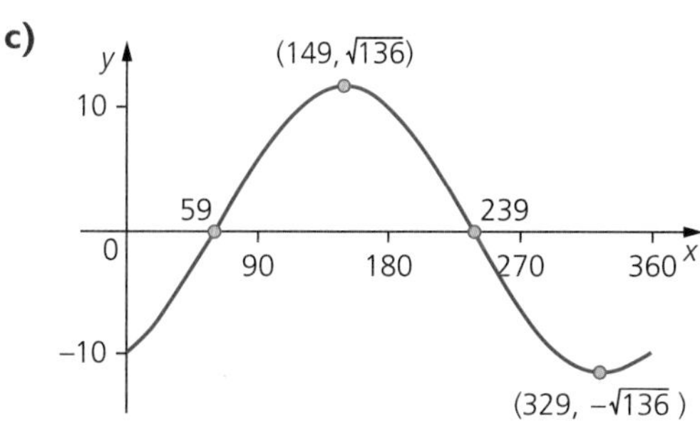

2 a) $\sqrt{17}\cos(x-14)^\circ$

b) Max = $\sqrt{17}$ when $x = 14$; min = $-\sqrt{17}$ when $x = 194$

c)

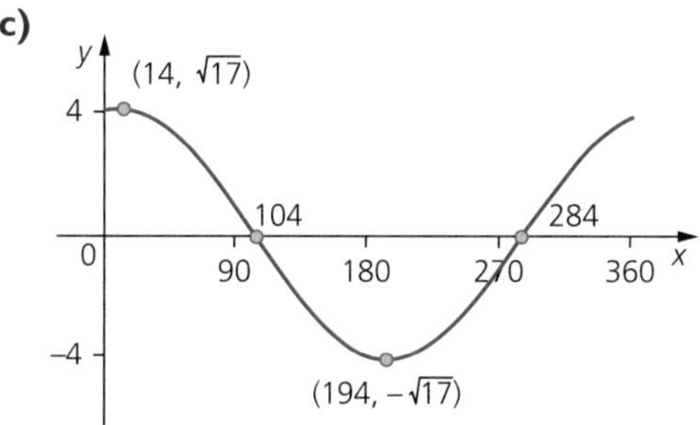

3

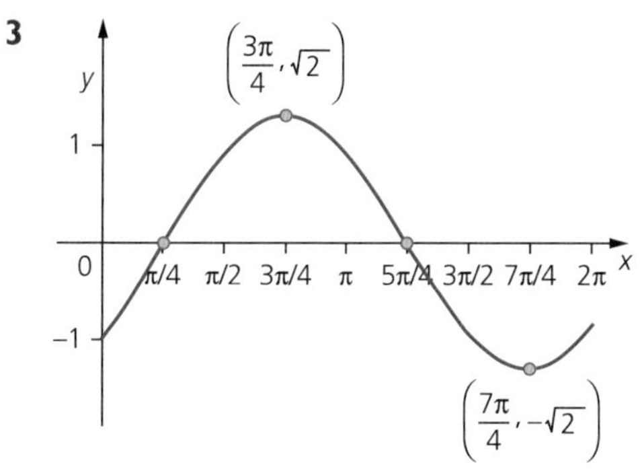

Checkout

1 $\sqrt{13}\cos(x+56{\cdot}3)^\circ$

2 $2\sin\left(x+\frac{2\pi}{3}\right)$

3 a) $\sqrt{50}\sin(x-8{\cdot}1)^\circ$

b) Max = $\sqrt{50}$ when $x = 98{\cdot}1$; min = $-\sqrt{50}$ when $x = 278{\cdot}1$; zeros at $x = 8.1$ and $x = 188.1$

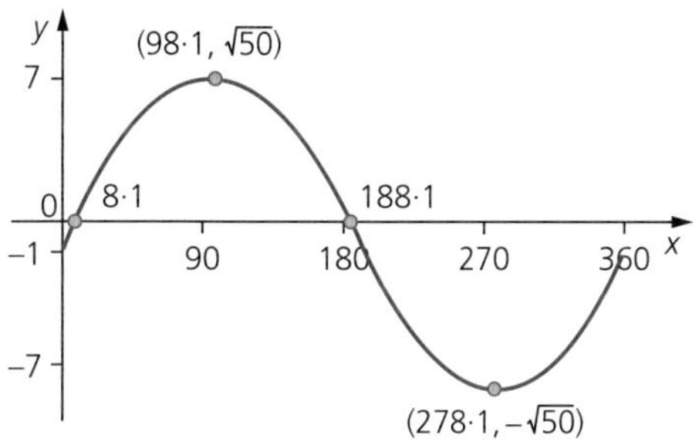

Chapter 10

Exercise 10.1

1 69·4, 346·6

2 64·4, 335·6

3 a) $\sqrt{20}\sin(x+63{\cdot}4)^\circ$

b) 90, 323·1

4 a) $\sqrt{10}\cos(x-71{\cdot}6)^\circ$

b) 0, 143.1, 360

5 a) $\sqrt{11}\sin(x-64{\cdot}8)^\circ$

b) 82·3, 227·2

6 a) $\sqrt{5}\cos(x+153{\cdot}4)^\circ$

b) 180, 233·1

7 a) $10\sin(x-53{\cdot}1)^\circ$

b) 117·3, 169·0

8 41·5, 117·7

9 a) $0, \frac{\pi}{2}, 2\pi$

b) $\frac{\pi}{2}, \frac{11\pi}{6}$

10 0·311, 2·263

Exercise 10.2

1 a) 18 hours

b) 91·25 days

2 a) $5\cos(3x-36{\cdot}9)^\circ$

b) 50·1, 94·5, 170·1, 214·5, 290·1, 334·5

3 a) $\sqrt{29}\cos(2x+21\cdot8)^\circ$

b) 10·1, 148·1, 190·1, 328·1

4 Yes, the minimum frequency is 510 cps which is less than 550 cps

5 a) $h=80\sqrt{5}\cos(30t-26\cdot6)^\circ$

b) High: 0053 and 1253; low: 0653 and 1853

c) 0314, 1032, 1514, 2232

Investigation

1 39·0, 159·9

Checkout

1 a) $20\sin(x-53\cdot1)^\circ$

b) 83·1, 203·1

2 a) $\sqrt{15}\cos(2x+50\cdot8)^\circ$

b) 12·1, 117·1, 192·1, 297·1

Chapter 11

Exercise 11.1

1 $y=-x-5,\ y=3-x^3$

2 a) $\{x:x\in R,\ x\geq0\}$

b) $\{x:x\in R,\ x\neq0\}$

c) $\{x:x\in R,\ x\geq2\}$

d) $\{x:x\in R,\ x\geq1\}$

e) $\{x:x\in R,\ x\neq4\}$

f) $\{x:x\in R,\ x\neq-3\}$

g) $\left\{x:x\in R,\ x\leq\frac{1}{2}\right\}$

h) $\{x:x\in R,\ x\neq-5\}$

3 a) $\{y:y\in R,\ -3\leq y\leq3\}$

b) $\{y:y\in R,\ y\geq0\}$

c) $\{y:y\in R,\ y\geq-2\}$

d) $\{y:y\in R,\ -1\leq y\leq1\}$

4 a) $\{x:x\in R,\ x\neq-3,\ \ x\neq16\}$

b) $\{x:x\in R,\ x\leq-3,\ \ x\geq5\}$

Exercise 11.2

1 a) $2(x+1)^2-1$

b) $2(x-4)^2-27$

c) $2(x-2)^2$

d) $4(x+3)^2-45$

e) $3(x+2)^2-14$

f) $2(x-5)^2+30$

g) $2(x-1\cdot5)^2-3\cdot5$

2 a) $11-(x+1)^2$

b) $24-(x+3)^2$

c) $43-(x-5)^2$

d) $16-(x+3)^2$

e) $61-(x-6)^2$

3

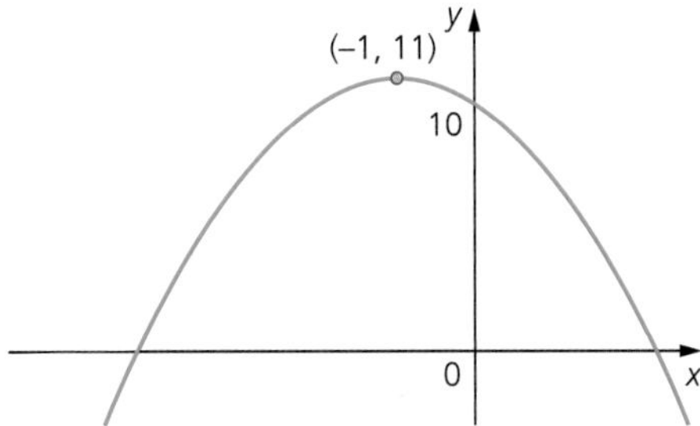

4 a) $32-2(x+3)^2$

b) $19-2(x+2)^2$

c) $9-3(x-1)^2$

d) $12-5(x-1)^2$

e) $41-2(x+3)^2$

f) $63-3(x-4)^2$

5 a) $x=4\pm\sqrt{31}$

b) $x=-1\pm\sqrt{\frac{1}{2}}$

6 $x=\dfrac{-b\pm\sqrt{b^2-4ac}}{2a}$

Exercise 11.3

1

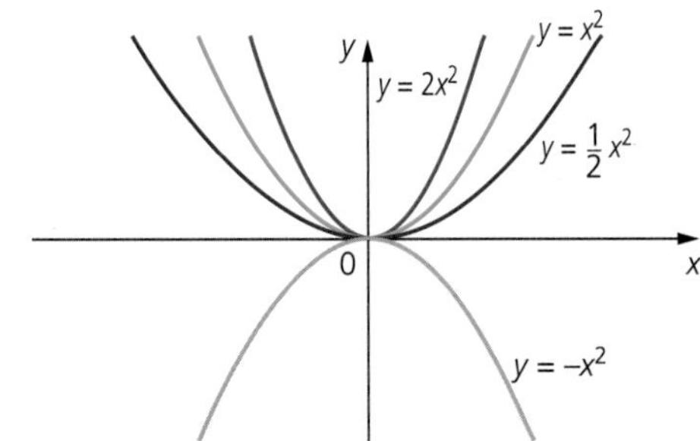

2

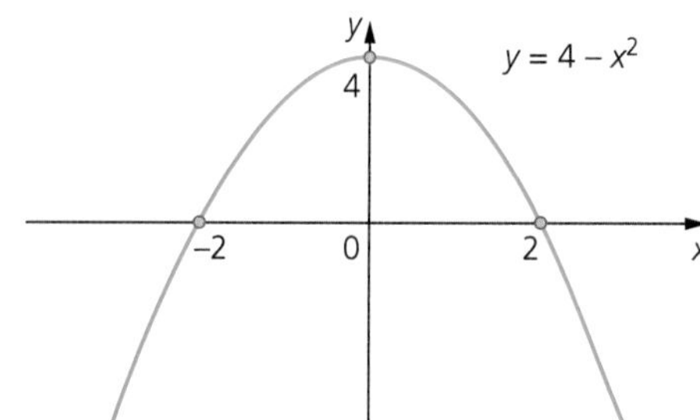

3 a)

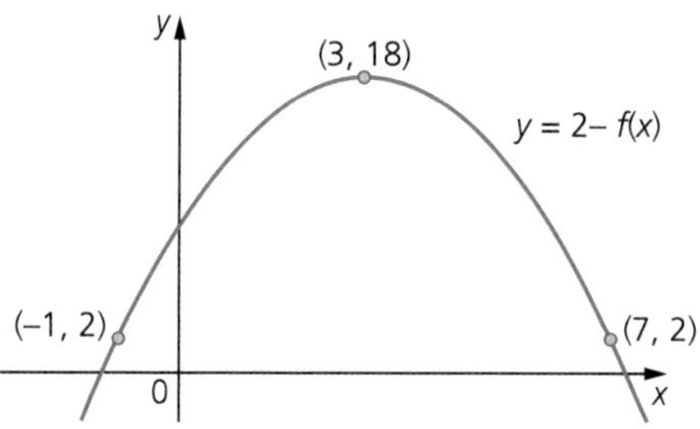

b)

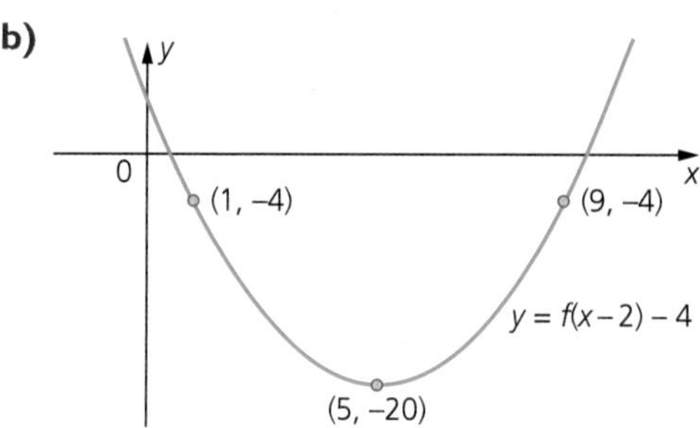

4

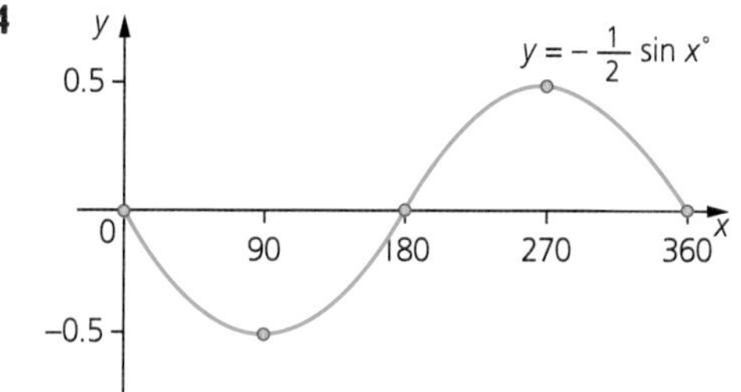

5 a)

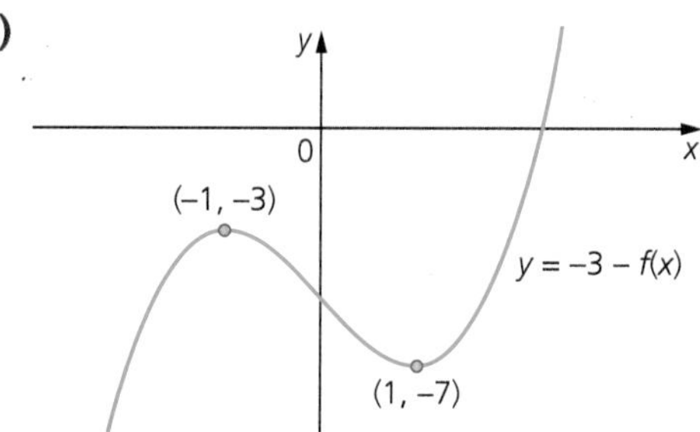

b)

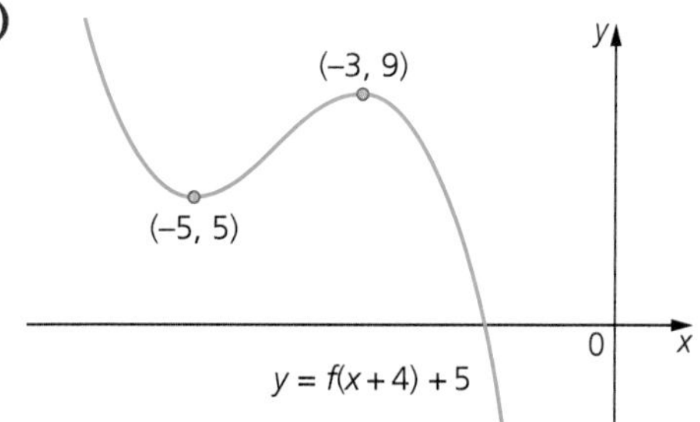

Exercise 11.4

1 a)

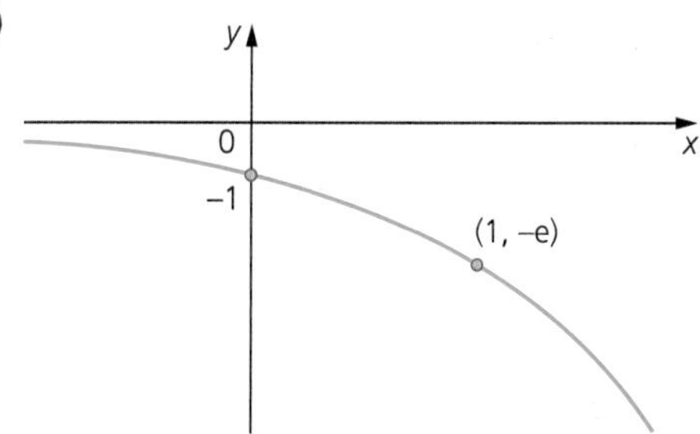

b)

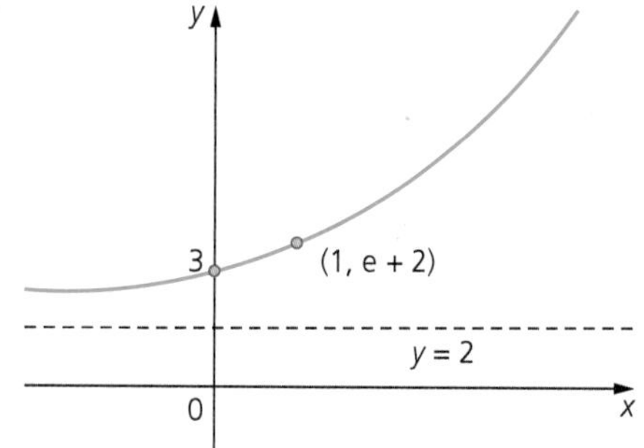

c)

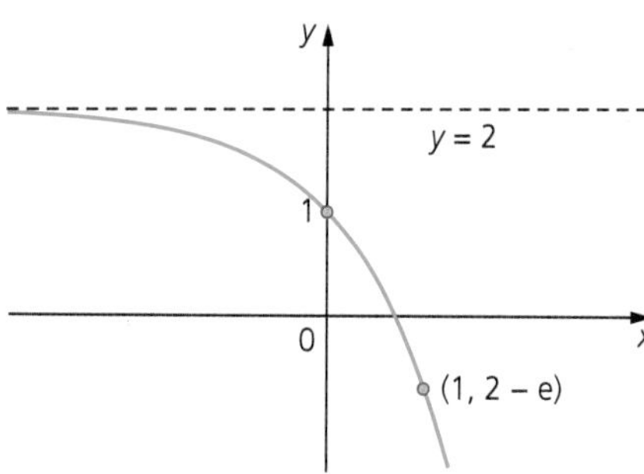

2 a)

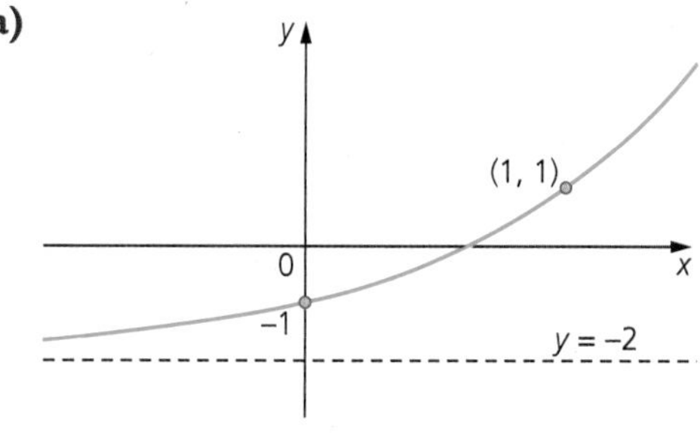

Answers

b)

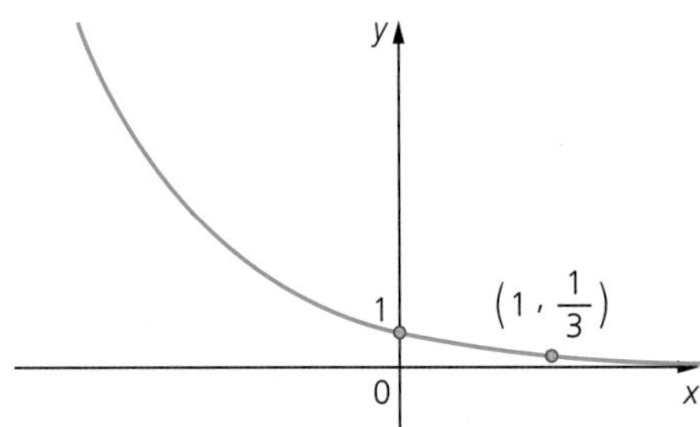

3

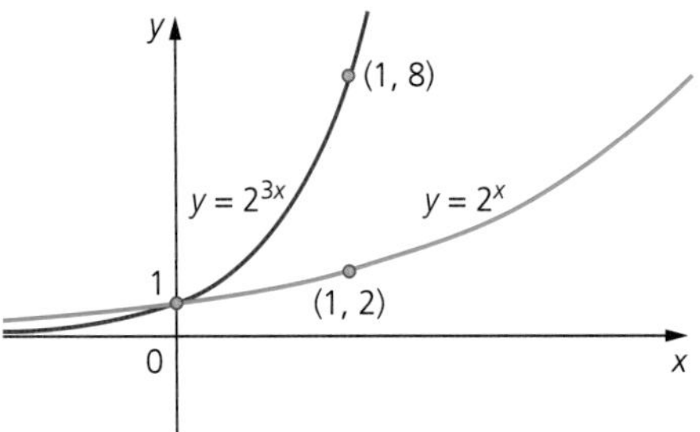

4 a) $p = 1$, $q = 4$

b)

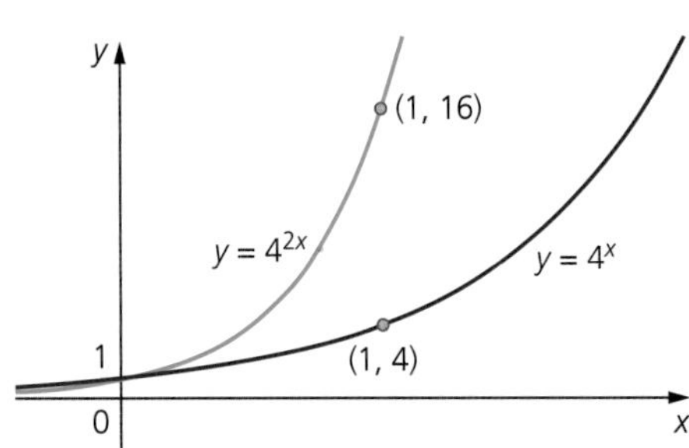

c) $(1, 16)$

5 a) $a = 2$

b) $(3, 8{\cdot}96)$

Exercise 11.5

1 a)

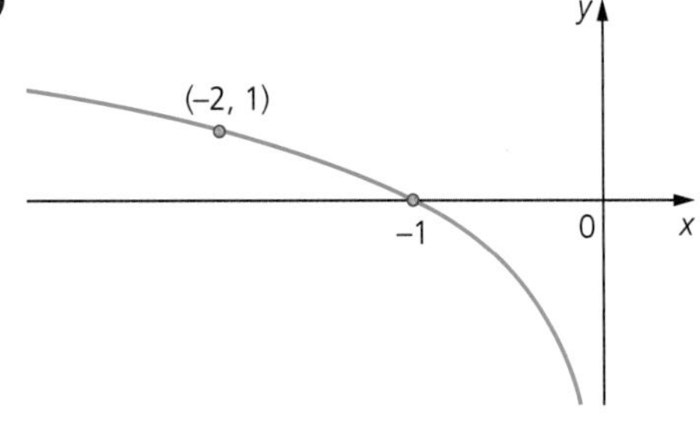

b)

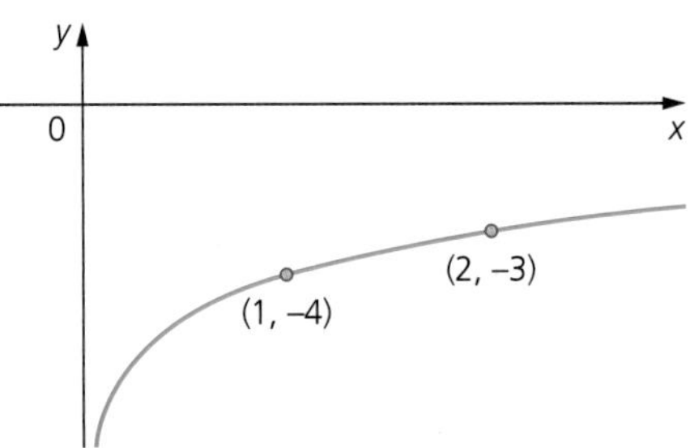

c)

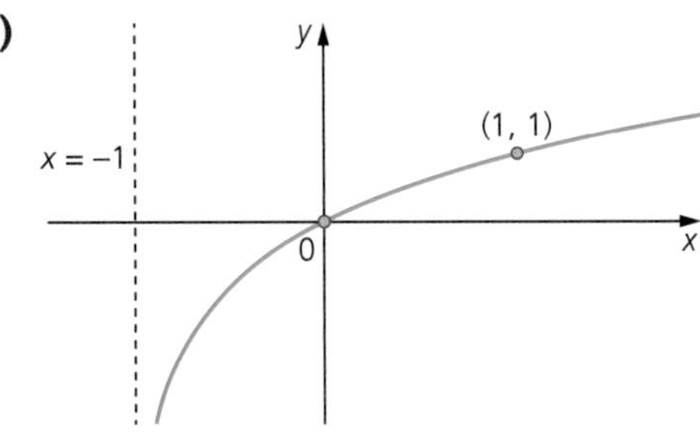

2 a)

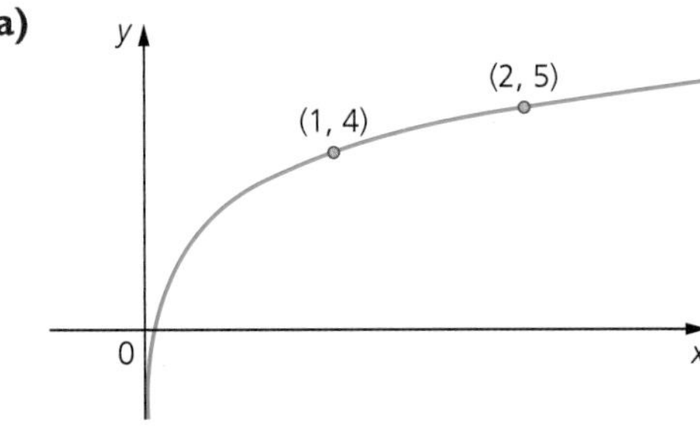

b) $\left(\frac{1}{16}, 0\right)$

3 a)

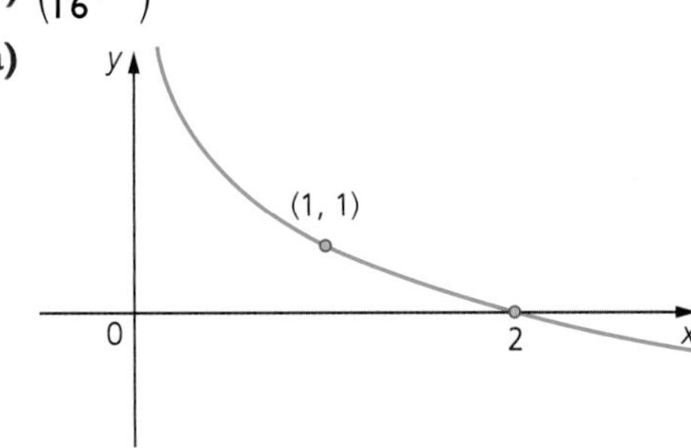

b)

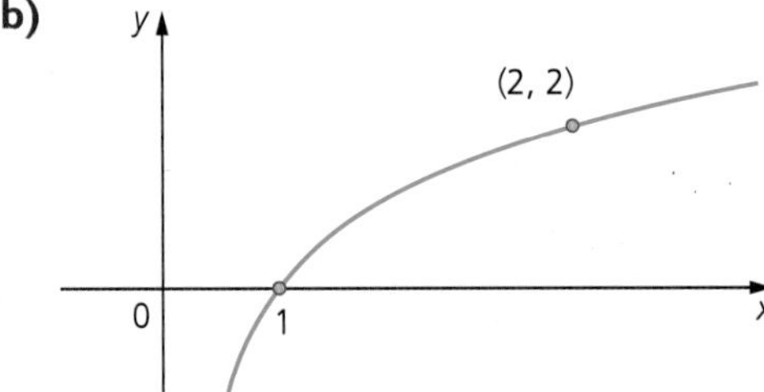

Answers

c)

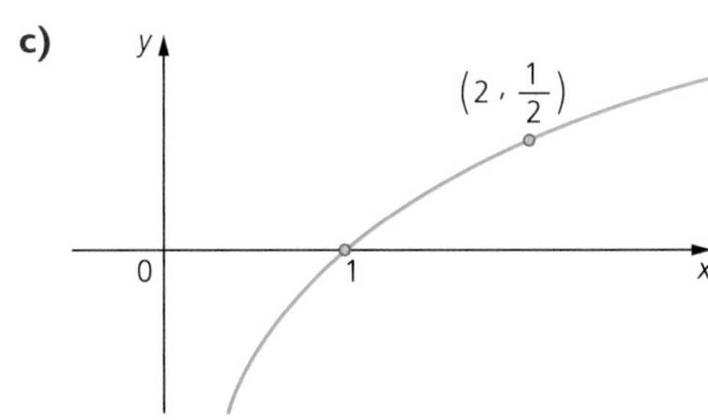

4 $a = 3, b = 1$

5 $a = 3, b = 4$

6 a)

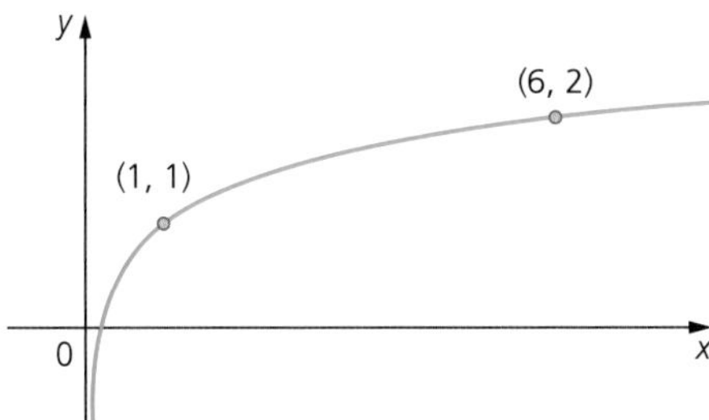

b) $\left(\frac{1}{6}, 0\right)$

c)

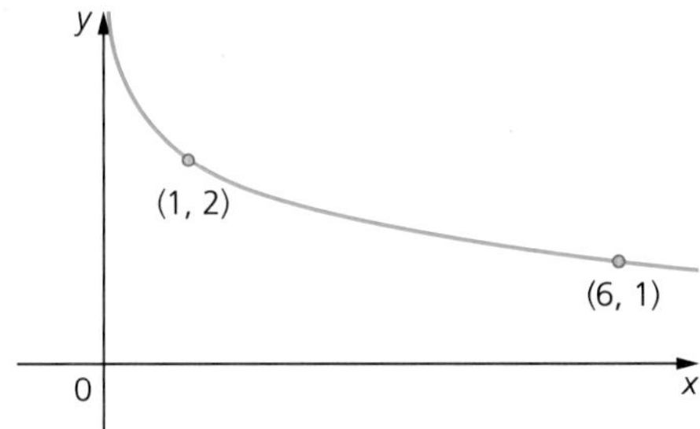

7 $b = 4$

8 a) $a = 1, b = 3$

b)

y
$x = 4$
(31, 5)
(5, 2)
0
x

9 a) $m = 2, n = 1$

b) $\{x : x \in R,\ x > 1\}$

Exercise 11.6

1 a) 18

b) 30

c) −12

d) 8

e) −16

2 a) $f(g(x)) = 2x^2 - 2$

b) $g(f(x)) = 4x^2 - 16x + 17$

c) $f(f(x) = 4x - 12$

d) $g(g(x) = x^4 + 2x^2 + 2$

3 a) $h(x) = 4 - \frac{2}{x}$

b) $h(k(x)) = x + 3$

4 a) $f(h(x)) = 6x - 11$

b) $h(f(x)) = 6x - 3$

c) $f(g(x)) = \frac{x}{x - 2}$

d) $g(g(x)) = \frac{x - 2}{5 - 2x}$

e) $h(g(x)) = \frac{15 - 6x}{x - 2}$

5 $f(g(x)) = x$

6 a) (i) $f(g(x)) = \sin 2x°$

(ii) $g(f(x)) = 2\sin x°$

b) 0, 120, 180, 240, 360

7 a) $b = 11, c = 123$

b) $h(x) = 9x^2 - 6x + 3$

8 a) $h(x) = (x + 2)^2 + 5$

b) (i) $(-2, 5)$

(ii) $\{y : y \in R,\ y \geq 5\}$

9 a) Proof

b) $x(x + 4)(x - 1)$

c) −4, 0, 1

10 a) (i) $f(h(x)) = \sin\left(x - \frac{\pi}{3}\right)$

(ii) $g(k(x)) = \cos\left(x - \frac{\pi}{6}\right)$

b) (i) Proof

(ii) $x = \frac{2\pi}{3}, \frac{4\pi}{3}$

Exercise 11.7

1 $f(g(x)) = x$

2 a) $f^{-1}(x) = \frac{x}{5}$

b) $f^{-1}(x) = \frac{x + 3}{4}$

c) $f^{-1}(x) = \frac{8 - x}{3}$

d) $f^{-1}(x) = \frac{1}{x}$

Answers

e) $f^{-1}(x)=\sqrt[3]{\left(\frac{x}{2}\right)}$

f) $f^{-1}(x)=\frac{2-x}{5}$

g) $f^{-1}(x)=\frac{x-2}{6}$

3 a) $f^{-1}(x)=\sqrt[3]{\left(\frac{x+4}{3}\right)}$

b) 2

4 $f(x)$ and $g(x)$ are inverses of each other.

5 a) $f^{-1}(x)=\sqrt{x-3}$

b) $\{x : x \in R,\ x \geq 3\}$

6 a)

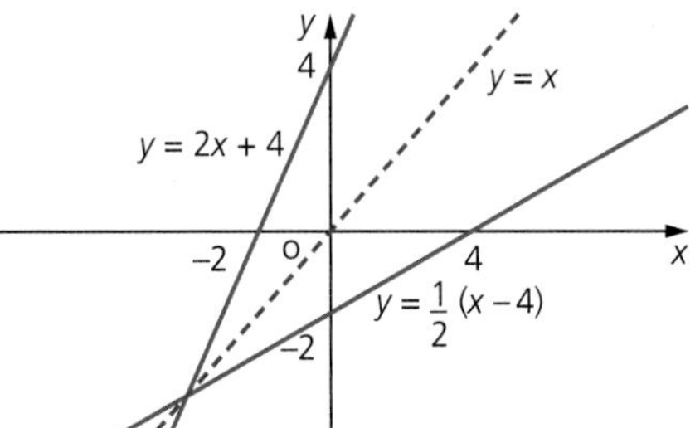

b) $f^{-1}(x)=\frac{x-4}{2}$

c) Reflection in the line $y=x$

7 a) $f^{-1}(x)=\log_2 x$

b) −5

8 a) $g(x)=8x^3+5$

b) 96

Exercise 11.8

1

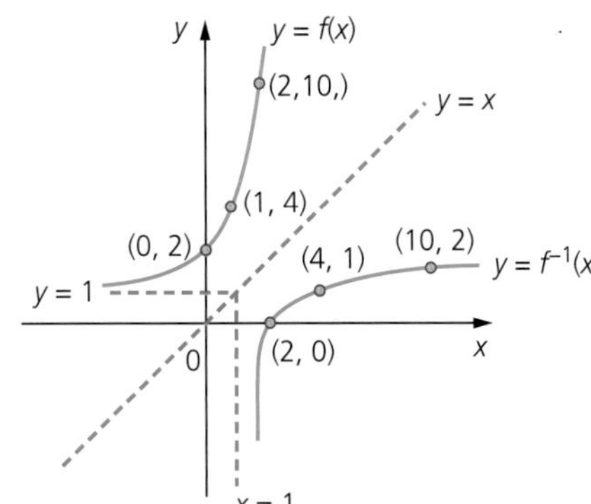

2

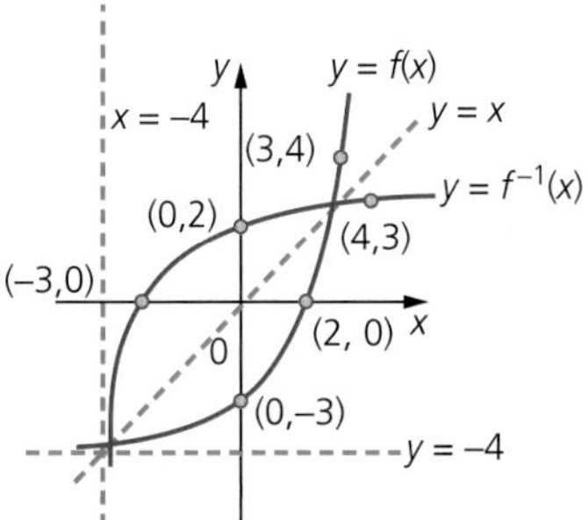

3

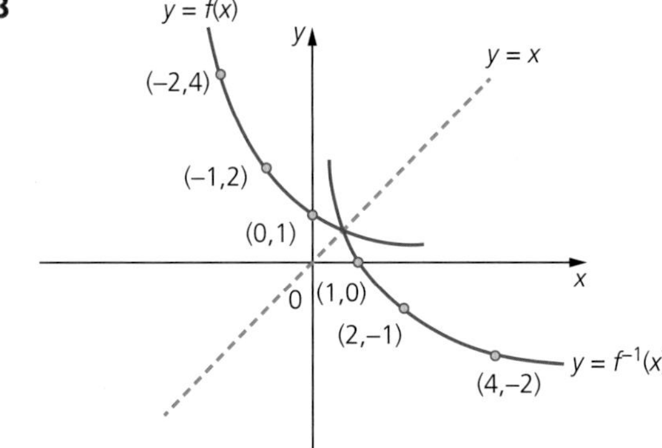

4

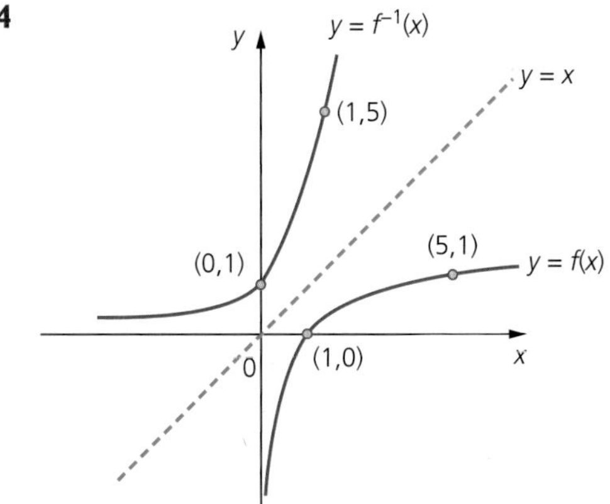

5

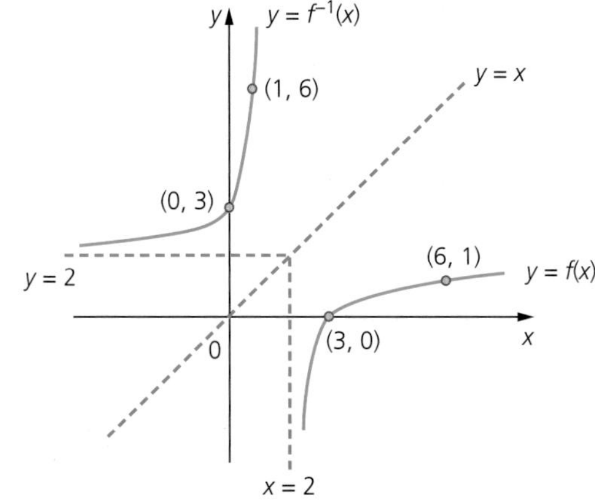

6

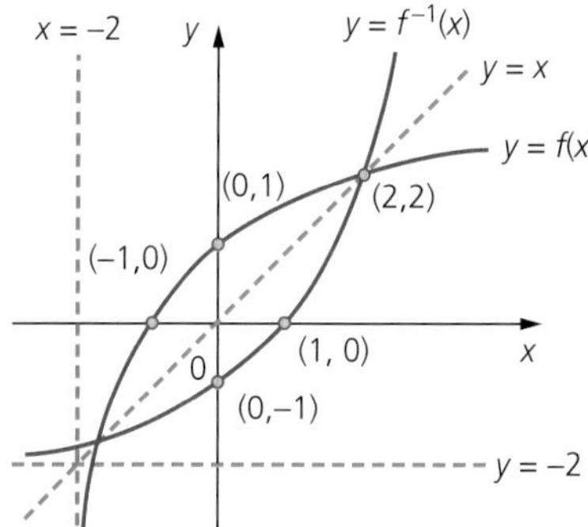

7

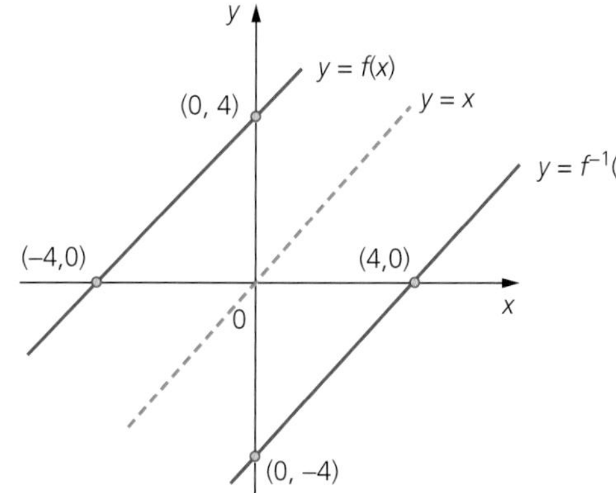

8

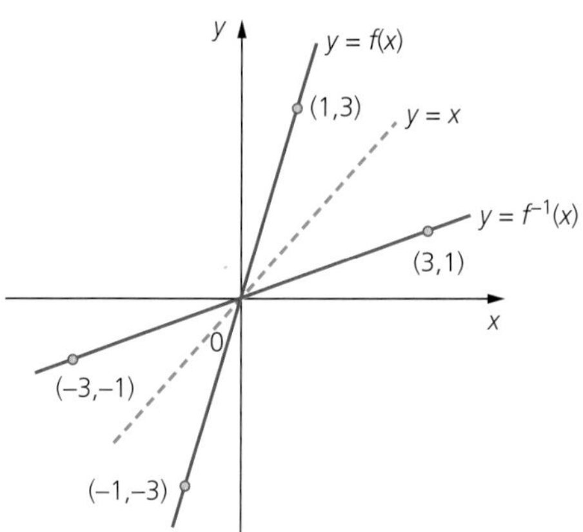

9

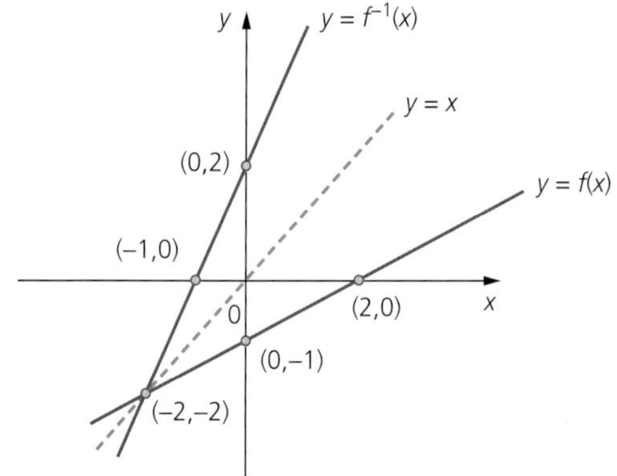

10

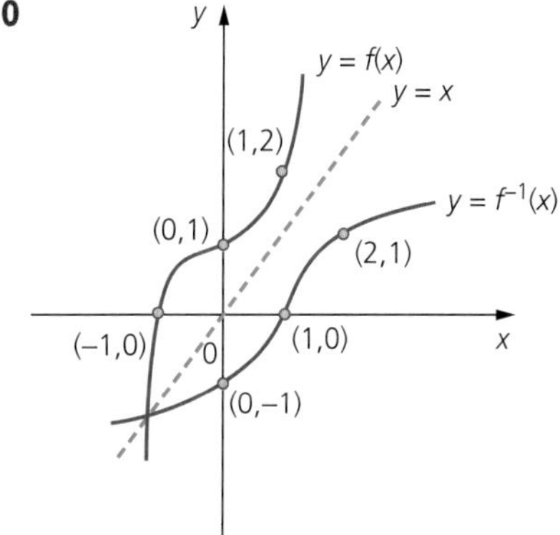

Exercise 11.9

1 $y = 3(x + 3)(x - 5)$

2 $y = -(x + 1)(x - 1)(x - 3)$

3 $y = -2x(x - 4)^2$

4 $y = 3(x - 6)(x + 2)^2$

Checkout

1 $\left\{x : x \in R,\ x \neq \frac{1}{3}\right\}$

2 $2(x-4)^2 - 34$

3

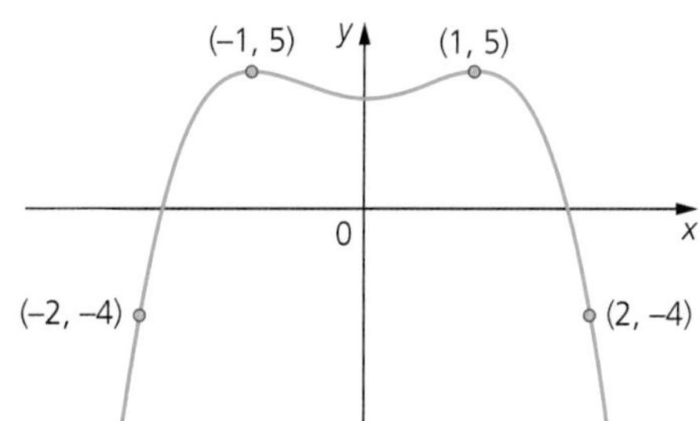

4

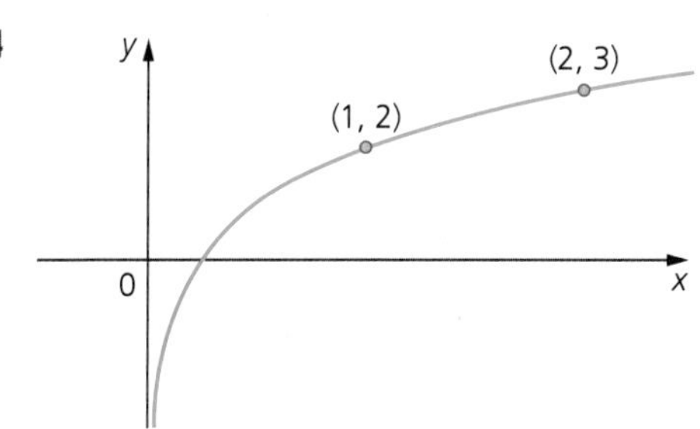

5 $a = 6,\ b = 5$

6 **a)** $f(g(x)) = 8 - 15x$

b) $g(f(x)) = 8 - 15x$

7 **a)** **(i)** $u(x) = 2x^2 + 1$

(ii) $v(x) = 4x^2 - 12x + 11$

b) $a = 2$

8 $k^{-1}(x) = \frac{7-x}{4}$

9 **a)** **(i)** $f(g(x)) = 4x^2 + 4x + 1 + p$
(ii) $g(f(x)) = 2x^2 + 2p + 1$
b) Proof
c) $p = -2$

10 $y = 4(x-1)(x-2)(x-3)$

11

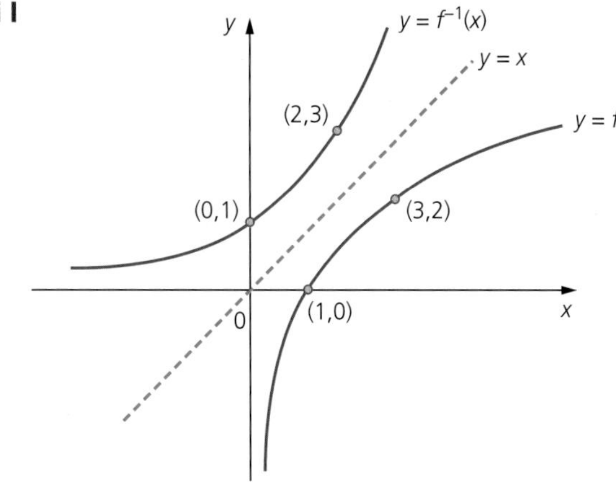

Chapter 12

Exercise 12.1

1 **a)** $\begin{pmatrix} 2 \\ -1 \\ 3 \end{pmatrix}$ **b)** $\sqrt{14}$

2 **a)** $\begin{pmatrix} 9 \\ 2 \\ -1 \end{pmatrix}$ **b)** $\begin{pmatrix} 3 \\ 6 \\ 6 \end{pmatrix}$

c) $\begin{pmatrix} -9 \\ -2 \\ 1 \end{pmatrix}$ **d)** $\begin{pmatrix} -6 \\ 4 \\ 7 \end{pmatrix}$

e) $\begin{pmatrix} -3 \\ -6 \\ -6 \end{pmatrix}$ **f)** $\begin{pmatrix} 6 \\ -4 \\ -7 \end{pmatrix}$

3 **a)** $\begin{pmatrix} 5 \\ -3 \\ 4 \end{pmatrix}$ **b)** $5\sqrt{2}$

4 13

5 **a)** 9 **b)** $\sqrt{62}$

c) $\sqrt{21}$ **d)** $\sqrt{145}$

e) $\sqrt{74}$ **f)** $\sqrt{45}$

g) $\sqrt{62}$

6 Proof

7 Proof

8 Proof

Exercise 12.2

1 **a)** $\begin{pmatrix} 3 \\ -2 \\ 1 \end{pmatrix}$

b) $\begin{pmatrix} 4 \\ 3 \\ -5 \end{pmatrix}$

c) $\begin{pmatrix} -4 \\ -2 \\ 3 \end{pmatrix}$

d) $\begin{pmatrix} 3 \\ 0 \\ -1 \end{pmatrix}$

2 $\sqrt{14}$, $\sqrt{50}$, $\sqrt{29}$, $\sqrt{10}$

3 **a)** **(i)** $\begin{pmatrix} 13 \\ -2 \\ -4 \end{pmatrix}$

(ii) $\begin{pmatrix} -16 \\ -14 \\ 22 \end{pmatrix}$

b) $\sqrt{589}, \sqrt{1661}$

4 **a)** $\overrightarrow{OF} = 8\mathbf{i} + 6\mathbf{j} + 4\mathbf{k}$
b) $\overrightarrow{GN} = 4\mathbf{i} - 6\mathbf{j} - 4\mathbf{k}$

5 $\sqrt{774}$

6 $\frac{1}{\sqrt{6}}\begin{pmatrix} -1 \\ 1 \\ 2 \end{pmatrix}$

7 **a)** $\frac{1}{5}\begin{pmatrix} 3 \\ 0 \\ 4 \end{pmatrix}$

b) $\frac{1}{\sqrt{14}}\begin{pmatrix} 2 \\ -3 \\ 1 \end{pmatrix}$

c) $\frac{1}{7}\begin{pmatrix} 6 \\ -3 \\ 2 \end{pmatrix}$

d) $\frac{1}{13}\begin{pmatrix} -4 \\ 12 \\ -3 \end{pmatrix}$

8 $m = \pm\sqrt{\frac{1}{2}}$

9 $m = \pm\sqrt{\frac{119}{144}}$

10 Proof

Exercise 12.3

1 1 : 2
2 1 : 2
3 2 : 1
4 1 : 2
5 2 : 7
6 1 : 4
7 3 : 2
8 1 : 3

Exercise 12.4

1 **a)** 2 : 3
b) 4 : 1
c) 1 : 3
d) 1 : 1
e) 1 : 4
2 (1, −5, 3)
3 **a)** (6, 10, 8)
b) (4, 4, −3)
c) (12, −3, 1)
d) (−5, 7, −2)
e) (4, 4, 1)
f) (1, 7, −10)
4 **a)** $\frac{1}{5}(4\mathbf{p}+\mathbf{q})$
b) $\frac{1}{9}(4\mathbf{p}+5\mathbf{q})$
c) $\frac{1}{10}(7\mathbf{p}+3\mathbf{q})$
5 **a)** Each of P, Q and R is (10, −2).
b) The medians are concurrent. The point of intersection divides each median in the ratio 2:1.
c) The centroid
6 **a)** 2 : 1
b) $x = 7$, $y = -9$
7 $p = -19$, $q = -6$
8 1 : 2

Exercise 12.5

1 **a)** $\overrightarrow{OS} = 2\mathbf{u} + \mathbf{v} + \mathbf{w}$
b) Proof
2 $\mathbf{x} - \mathbf{y} + \mathbf{z}$
3 **a)** $\overrightarrow{DE} = \mathbf{v} - \mathbf{u}$
b) $\overrightarrow{MG} = \frac{1}{2}\mathbf{w} - \mathbf{v} + \mathbf{u}$
4 **a)** $\overrightarrow{KN} = -4\mathbf{i} - 3\mathbf{j} - 2\mathbf{k}$
b) $\overrightarrow{MK} = 2\mathbf{i} - \mathbf{j} + 3\mathbf{k}$
5 **a)** $\begin{pmatrix} 10 \\ 4 \\ 0 \end{pmatrix}$
b) $\begin{pmatrix} 11 \\ 7 \\ 2 \end{pmatrix}$
c) $\begin{pmatrix} 5 \\ 4 \\ 2 \end{pmatrix}$
d) $\begin{pmatrix} -2 \\ -2 \\ 0 \end{pmatrix}$
e) $\begin{pmatrix} -3 \\ 2 \\ 2 \end{pmatrix}$
f) $\begin{pmatrix} 3 \\ 5 \\ 2 \end{pmatrix}$
g) $\begin{pmatrix} 9 \\ 1 \\ -2 \end{pmatrix}$
h) $\begin{pmatrix} 5 \\ 2 \\ 0 \end{pmatrix}$
6 **a)** $\begin{pmatrix} -7 \\ -11 \\ 34 \end{pmatrix}$
b) $\begin{pmatrix} 3 \\ 4 \\ 3 \end{pmatrix}$
c) $\begin{pmatrix} 10 \\ 15 \\ -31 \end{pmatrix}$
7 **a)** $\begin{pmatrix} 11 \\ 13 \\ 11 \end{pmatrix}$
b) $\begin{pmatrix} 17 \\ -11 \\ -1 \end{pmatrix}$
c) $\begin{pmatrix} 10 \\ 0 \\ -16 \end{pmatrix}$
8 **a)** $\overrightarrow{DO}$
b) $\overrightarrow{CG}$

Exercise 12.6

1 **a)** 48
b) −175
c) −35
d) 30
e) 45
f) 0

Answers

2 a) 144
b) –25
c) 0
3 a) 32
b) 32
c) –32
4 35
5 40
6 a) 0
b) **u** and **v** + **w**
7 112
8 32
9 a) 15
b) 2·5
10 Proof
11 a) $\frac{1}{2}$
b) $\frac{3}{4}$

Exercise 12.7

1 a) 4
b) 23
c) –38
d) 30
e) –2
f) –15
2 a) 10
b) 5
c) –8
d) –14
e) –26
3 $m = 2$
4 $k = 12$
5 a) $\begin{pmatrix} 1 \\ 5 \\ -9 \end{pmatrix}$
b) $\begin{pmatrix} -4 \\ 8 \\ -4 \end{pmatrix}$
c) 72
6 Proof
7 a) $\overrightarrow{ST} = \begin{pmatrix} 2 \\ 3 \\ 6 \end{pmatrix}$ and $\overrightarrow{UV} = \begin{pmatrix} 1 \\ 2 \\ 5 \end{pmatrix}$
b) $a = 3, b = -4$
c) $\frac{1}{7}\begin{pmatrix} 2 \\ 3 \\ 6 \end{pmatrix}$
8 a) $\begin{pmatrix} -9 \\ 12 \\ 3 \end{pmatrix}$
b) (2, 5, 9)
c) Proof
9 a) (3, –7, –1)
b) $p = -1$
10 a) $\left(\frac{4k+7}{k+1}, \frac{-k-5}{k+1}, \frac{5k+1}{k+1}\right)$
b) 9·25

Exercise 12.8

1 a) 141·3°
b) 63·4°
c) 78·9°
d) 112·3°
2 50·5°
3 73·9°
4 127·4°
5 49·7°
6 a) 2 : 1
b) $a = 5$
c) 70·5°
7 a) M (4, 6, 5), Q (8, 0, 5)
b) 56·3°
8 a) A (6, 0, 0), B (4, 4, 6)
b) $\overrightarrow{UA} = \begin{pmatrix} -2 \\ -4 \\ -6 \end{pmatrix}, \overrightarrow{UB} = \begin{pmatrix} -4 \\ 0 \\ 0 \end{pmatrix}$
c) 74·5°
9 a) (3, 4, 6)
b) 47·9°
10 a) (8, 8, 0)
b) $\overrightarrow{DA} = \begin{pmatrix} 4 \\ -4 \\ -9 \end{pmatrix}, \overrightarrow{DB} = \begin{pmatrix} 4 \\ 4 \\ -9 \end{pmatrix}$
c) 44·2°
11 a) (7, 10, –4)
b) 52·0°
12 a) Proof
b) Proof

Checkout

1 $\sqrt{105}$
2 $\sqrt{26}$
3 $\sqrt{162}$
4 $\begin{pmatrix} 10 \\ 2 \\ -11 \end{pmatrix}$
5 2 : 3
6 (10, 5, −11)
7 2
8 32
(−8, ·
9

10 a) 5 : 3
b) Proof
11 74·2°
12 a) (1, 1, −5)
b) 40·6°

Chapter 13

Exercise 13.1

1 a) (i) 2
(ii) 4
(iii) 8
(iv) 10
b) $2x$
2 a) (i) 3
(ii) 12
(iii) 27
(iv) 48
(v) 75
b) $3x^2$
3 a) (i) 4
(ii) 32
(iii) 108
(iv) 256
(v) 500
b) $4x^3$
4

$f(x)$	x x^2 x^3 x^4 x^5 x^n
Gradient of $f(x)$ at the point (x, y)	1 $2x$ $3x^2$ $4x^3$ $5x^4$ nx^{n-1}

Exercise 13.2

All answers in Exercise 13.2 are proof.

Exercise 13.3

1 $f'(x) = 6x^5$
2 $g'(x) = 20x^{19}$
3 $V'(x) = 1$
4 $r'(s) = 0$
5 $h'(x) = 14x^6$
6 $r'(x) = -6x$
7 $C'(n) = 4$
8 $s'(u) = 0$
9 $f'(p) = 2p^3$
10 $g'(t) = 8t^9$
11 $A'(x) = \frac{3}{2}x^5$
12 $P'(a) = \frac{10}{3}a^7$

Exercise 13.4

1 a) 32
b) 108
c) −4
d) $\frac{1}{2}$
2 80
3 $\frac{3}{4}$
4 −4
5 $a = 5$ or -5
6 (2,8)
7 $f'(x) = 15x^4$ so $f'(x) \geq 0$ as $x^4 \geq 0$ for all x, so the gradient of the curve $f(x) = 3x^5$ is never negative.

Exercise 13.5

1 $f'(x) = 4x^3 - 6x^2 + 8x - 5$
2 $g'(x) = 5 - 2x^2$
3 $h'(x) = 6x + 10$

4 $f'(t) = 2t - 6$

5 $g'(n) = 2n + 12$

6 $A'(r) = 8r - 12$

7 $V'(t) = 14 - 14t$

8 $m'(x) = 6x^2 + 2x + 8$

9 $f'(p) = 3p^2 + 18p + 23$

10 $S'(d) = 3d^2 + 12d + 12$

11 21

12 −9

13 16

14 24 m/s

15 3

16 $g'(3) = -2$, so the curve slopes down at the point (3,12) as $g'(3) < 0$.

17 $a = 4$ or -4

18 (1,2)

19 (6,1)

Exercise 13.6

1 $f'(x) = -2x^{-3}$

2 $f'(x) = -21x^{-8}$

3 $g'(x) = -3x^{-31}$

4 $g'(x) = \frac{5x^{\frac{3}{2}}}{2}$

5 $h'(x) = \frac{7x^{\frac{3}{4}}}{2}$

6 $f'(a) = \frac{2a^{\frac{1}{5}}}{5}$

7 $A'(h) = \frac{4h^{-\frac{3}{7}}}{7}$

8 $C'(n) = \frac{5n^{-\frac{1}{6}}}{2}$

9 $f'(t) = -\frac{t^{-\frac{6}{5}}}{5}$

10 $s'(u) = -5u^{-\frac{9}{4}}$

Exercise 13.7

1 $f'(x) = -\frac{3}{x^4}$

2 $g'(x) = -\frac{5}{x^6}$

3 $h'(x) = \frac{9\sqrt[4]{x^5}}{4}$

4 $f'(t) = \frac{5\sqrt{t^3}}{2}$

5 $m'(n) = \frac{2}{3\sqrt[3]{n}}$

6 $g'(t) = \frac{1}{2\sqrt{t}}$

7 $g'(u) = -\frac{7}{3\sqrt[3]{u^{10}}}$

8 $m'(a) = -\frac{2}{5\sqrt[5]{a^7}}$

9 $-\frac{1}{4}$

10 3

11 $-\frac{1}{9}$

12 $-\frac{1}{16}$

Exercise 13.8

1 $h'(t) = -\frac{2}{t^9}$

2 $f'(p) = -\frac{32}{p^9}$

3 $g'(t) = -\frac{15}{t^7}$

4 $h'(x) = 5\sqrt{x^3}$

5 $r'(s) = \frac{4}{\sqrt[3]{s}}$

6 $v'(x) = \frac{7}{2\sqrt{x}}$

7 $q'(r) = -\frac{5}{\sqrt{r^3}}$

8 $m'(a) = -\frac{6}{5\sqrt{a^5}}$

9 $h'(t) = 6t - \frac{1}{t^2}$

10 $r'(u) = 5\sqrt{u^3} + \frac{3}{u^5}$

11 $k'(x) = 8\sqrt[3]{x} - \frac{3}{\sqrt{x^3}}$

12 $u'(t) = 3\sqrt{t} + \frac{5\sqrt{t^3}}{2}$

13 $v'(u) = 1 - \frac{3}{\sqrt{u}}$

14 $f'(x) = 2x - \frac{12}{x^3}$

15 $h'(c) = 8c - \frac{4}{c^2} - \frac{4}{c^5}$

16 $g'(p) = -1 - \frac{3}{p^2}$

Exercise 13.9

1 $f'(x) = 3x^2 - \frac{2}{x^2}$

2 $g'(x) = \frac{9}{x^4} - \frac{1}{x^2}$

3 $h'(x) = \frac{4}{x^2} - \frac{2}{x^3}$

4 $k'(x) = -1 - \frac{6}{x^2}$

5 $B'(n) = \frac{2}{3} + \frac{1}{n^2}$

6 $g'(t) = \frac{4}{t^2} - \frac{16}{t^3}$

7 $f'(t) = \frac{3\sqrt{t}}{2} + \frac{3}{\sqrt{t}}$

8 $r'(s) = \frac{1}{\sqrt{s^3}} - \frac{3}{2\sqrt{s^5}}$

9 $h'(t) = \frac{5\sqrt[3]{t^2}}{3} + \frac{4}{3\sqrt[3]{t}} - \frac{1}{\sqrt[3]{t^4}}$

Exercise 13.10

1 **a)** $10x^4 + 9$

b) $1 + \frac{3}{t^4}$

c) $\frac{1}{\sqrt{u}} + \frac{3}{\sqrt[3]{u^2}}$

d) $6p + 10$

e) $32n + 40$

f) $\frac{3\sqrt{a}}{2} - \frac{2}{\sqrt{a}}$

g) $5 + \frac{4}{r^3}$

h) $\frac{1}{2\sqrt{x}} - \frac{9}{2\sqrt{x^3}}$

2 $8\frac{1}{4}$

3 -7

4 30 m/s

5 16

6 $\frac{3}{4}$

7 $(-1, 11)$ and $(3, -5)$

8 $(-2, -10)$ and $(2, 10)$

9 $(3, -8)$

10 $y = \frac{8}{x}$ is not defined for $x = 0$; $\frac{dy}{dx} = -\frac{8}{x^2}$, so $\frac{dy}{dx} < 0$ as $x^2 > 0$ for all x, $x \neq 0$; so the gradient of the curve $y = \frac{8}{x}$ is always negative.

11 $\frac{dy}{dx} = 3(x-1)^2$, so $\frac{dy}{dx} \geq 0$ as $(x-1)^2 \geq 0$ for all x; so the gradient of the curve $y = x^3 - 3x^2 + 3x - 1$ is never negative.

Exercise 13.11

1 $f'(x) = 4\cos x$

2 $g'(x) = -2\sin x$

3 $h'(t) = -\frac{1}{3}\cos t$

4 $f'(\theta) = 6\sin\theta$

5 $\frac{dy}{dx} = \cos x + 3\sin x$

6 $\frac{ds}{dr} = -\frac{1}{2}\sin r + \frac{3}{4}\cos r$

7 $\frac{dA}{db} = \frac{1}{2\sqrt{b}} - \cos b$

8 $\frac{dM}{dq} = 6q^2 - \frac{2}{3}\sin q$

9 $\frac{dv}{dt} = 8\cos t + 4\sin t + \frac{2}{3\sqrt[3]{t}}$

Answers

10 $\dfrac{dP}{d\theta} = -\sin\theta + 10\cos\theta + \dfrac{2}{\theta^3}$

11 1

12 5

13 a) 1

b) 0

c) -1

d) -1

Exercise 13.12

All answers in Exercise 13.12 are proof.

Exercise 13.13

1 $f'(x) = 6(x+2)^5$

2 $g'(x) = 12(3x-1)^3$

3 $h'(x) = -6(5-2x)^2$

4 $P'(x) = -7(4-x)^6$

5 $\dfrac{dy}{dx} = 6x(x^2+5)^2$

6 $\dfrac{ds}{dr} = -8r(3-r^2)^3$

7 $\dfrac{dA}{db} = 15b^2(b^3-2)^4$

8 $\dfrac{dM}{dq} = 12q^3(1+q^4)^2$

9 $f'(x) = 4(2x+3)(x^2+3x-2)^3$

10 $g'(n) = 8(3n^2+1)(n^3+n)^7$

11 $h'(t) = 10(2t-5)(t^2-5t+6)^9$

12 $C'(p) = 9(1-6p)(2+p-3p^2)^8$

13 $\dfrac{dy}{dx} = \dfrac{4}{\sqrt{8x-1}}$

14 $\dfrac{dm}{dk} = \dfrac{2}{\sqrt[3]{(6k+5)^2}}$

15 $\dfrac{dV}{dc} = -\dfrac{6}{(2c+9)^4}$

16 $\dfrac{dE}{dw} = \dfrac{5}{(7-w)^6}$

17 $f'(x) = \dfrac{5}{\sqrt{10x+3}}$

18 $s'(t) = -\dfrac{1}{\sqrt{5-2t}}$

19 $n'(c) = \dfrac{c}{\sqrt{c^2+9}}$

20 $g'(z) = \dfrac{2-z^2}{\sqrt[3]{(6z-z^3)^2}}$

21 $\dfrac{dy}{dx} = -\dfrac{14}{(7x+2)^3}$

22 $\dfrac{dA}{dr} = -\dfrac{12r}{(r^2-4)^4}$

23 $\dfrac{dp}{dy} = \dfrac{1}{(8-y)^2}$

24 $\dfrac{dF}{dg} = -\dfrac{12(g^3+3)}{(g^3+9g)^2}$

25 $g'(x) = -\dfrac{1}{\sqrt{(2x+1)^3}}$

26 $h'(t) = \dfrac{6}{\sqrt{(3-4t)^3}}$

27 $\dfrac{3}{16}$

28 $\dfrac{27}{2}$

29 $-\dfrac{3}{4}$

30 $-\dfrac{6}{5}$

Exercise 13.14

1 $f'(x) = 2\cos 2x$

2 $\dfrac{dy}{dx} = 12\cos 4x$

3 $g'(x) = 3\cos(3x-2)$

4 $\dfrac{ds}{dt} = 5\cos\left(\dfrac{1}{2}t+3\right)$

5 $f'(x) = -3\sin 3x$

6 $\dfrac{dy}{dx} = -10\sin 5x$

7 $h'(t) = 2\sin(1-2t)$

8 $\dfrac{dp}{dn} = 2\cos\left(\dfrac{1}{3}n+2\right)$

9 $g'(x) = 3\sin^2 x\cos x$

10 $\dfrac{dA}{d\theta} = 4\sin^3\theta\cos\theta$

11 $h'(u) = -2\cos u\sin u$

12 $\dfrac{dn}{d\theta} = -5\cos^4\theta\sin\theta$

13 $f'(x) = 3x^2\cos x^3$

14 $f'(x) = -\dfrac{3\cos x}{\sin^4 x}$

15 $\dfrac{dy}{dx} = \dfrac{\cos x}{2\sqrt{\sin x}}$

16 $\dfrac{dy}{dx} = \dfrac{\cos\sqrt{x}}{2\sqrt{x}}$

17 $f'(x) = -2x\sin x^2$

18 $f'(x) = \dfrac{\sin x}{\cos^2 x}$

19 $\dfrac{dy}{dx} = \dfrac{\sin x}{2\sqrt{\cos^3 x}}$

20 $\dfrac{dy}{dx} = 2\sin x(1 - \cos x)$

21 3

22 $-\dfrac{3\sqrt{3}}{4}$

23 $\dfrac{1}{2}$

24 a) $f'(x) = \dfrac{\pi}{180}\cos x^\circ$

b) $g'(x) = -\dfrac{\pi}{180}\sin x^\circ$

Checkout

1 a) $\dfrac{dy}{dx} = 6x^2 - 4x + 3$

b) $f'(x) = 50x + 20$

c) $g'(x) = -\dfrac{10}{x^3} + 6\sqrt{x}$

d) $\dfrac{ds}{dt} = 6t + \dfrac{14}{t^3}$

e) $f'(n) = -\dfrac{1}{3n^2}$

f) $\dfrac{du}{dv} = \dfrac{3\sqrt{v}}{2} + \dfrac{1}{2\sqrt{v^3}}$

2 a) $f'(x) = 6x(x^2 + 4)^2$

b) $\dfrac{dy}{dx} = 12\cos x(3\sin x + 1)^3$

c) $k'(x) = -\dfrac{\sin x}{2\sqrt{1 + \cos x}}$

d) $\dfrac{dh}{dt} = \dfrac{10}{(1 - 5t)^2}$

e) $g'(x) = \dfrac{2x}{\sqrt{(3 - 2x^2)^3}}$

f) $f'(\theta) = 6\cos(6\theta + 1)$

g) $\dfrac{dy}{dx} = 2\cos 2x + 12\sin 4x$

h) $g'(\theta) = -12\cos^2\theta\sin\theta$

i) $\dfrac{ds}{dt} = 2\sin 2t$ or $4\sin t\cos t$

3 $\dfrac{5}{128}$

4 12

5 $a = -1$, $a = 3$

6 27

7 10

8 23 m/s

9 1

10 5

11 $\dfrac{1}{3}$

12 $(-2, -4)$

13 $f'(\theta) = 4\sin^3\theta\cos\theta + 4\cos 4\theta + 4\cos\theta$

$$\Rightarrow f'\left(\frac{\pi}{4}\right) = 4\left(\frac{1}{\sqrt{2}}\right)^3\left(\frac{1}{\sqrt{2}}\right) + 4\times(-1) + 4\left(\frac{1}{\sqrt{2}}\right) = 2\sqrt{2} - 3$$

14 $\dfrac{dy}{dx} = 3(x + 2)^2$, so $\dfrac{dy}{dx} \geq 0$ as $(x + 2)^2 \geq 0$ for all x; so the gradient of the curve $y = x^3 + 6x^2 + 12x + 3$ is never negative.

Answers

Chapter 14

Exercise 14.1

1 $5x-y-17=0$

2 $2x-y+2=0$

3 $x+y+1=0$

4 $2x-3y+18=0$

5 $4x-y+5=0$

6 $2x+y-9=0$

7 Tangents are parallel since both have gradient 6.

$y=6x-8$ cuts y-axis at $(0,-8)$ and x-axis at $\left(\frac{4}{3}, 0\right)$.

$y=6x+8$ cuts y-axis at $(0,8)$ and x-axis at $\left(-\frac{4}{3}, 0\right)$.

8 $(-1,3)$

9 $(4,72)$ and $(-4,-72)$

10 $7x-y-9=0$

11 $4x-y-16=0$

12 $(-3,1)$

13 x-axis: $2x-y-2=0$, y-axis: $x-y-1=0$

14 $\left(1, \frac{1}{3}\right)$ and $(3,-1)$

15 $b=-5, c=8$

16 $4x-y-28=0$

17 $3x-5y+16=0$

18 $x-y+2-\pi=0$

19 $x-y=0$

20 $6x+2y-\pi=0$

21 $4x+4y-2-\pi=0$

Exercise 14.2

1 **a)** Decreasing
b) Increasing
c) Increasing
d) Decreasing

2 **a)** Increasing $x>\frac{7}{2}$, decreasing $x<\frac{7}{2}$

b) Increasing $x<4$, decreasing $x>4$

c) Increasing $x>-\frac{3}{4}$, decreasing $x<-\frac{3}{4}$

d) Increasing $x<-5$ and $x>1$, decreasing $-5<x<1$

e) Increasing $x<0$ and $x>\frac{5}{3}$, decreasing $0<x<\frac{5}{3}$

f) Increasing $-2<x<2$, decreasing $x<-2$ and $x>2$

g) Increasing $x<-1$ and $x>\frac{1}{3}$, decreasing $-1<x<\frac{1}{3}$

h) Increasing $x>-\frac{3}{2}, x\neq 0$, decreasing $x<-\frac{3}{2}$

i) Increasing $-2<x<0$ and $x>2$, decreasing $x<-2$ and $0<x<2$

3 $\frac{dy}{dx}=3x^2+1$, so $\frac{dy}{dx}\geq 1$ as $x^2\geq 0$ for all x; so y is increasing for all x.

4 $\frac{dy}{dx}=-5x^4$, so $\frac{dy}{dx}\leq 0$ as $x^4\geq 0$ for all x; so y is never increasing.

5 $\frac{dy}{dx}=-\frac{3}{x^2}$, so $\frac{dy}{dx}<0$ as $x^2>0$ for all x, $x\neq 0$;

so $y=\frac{3}{x}, x\neq 0$ is always decreasing.

6 $f'(x)=(x+2)^2$, so $f'(x)\geq 0$ as $(x+2)^2\geq 0$ for all x;

so $f(x)$ is never decreasing.

7 $f'(x)=1+\frac{2}{x^2}$, so $f'(x)>0$ as $x^2>0$ for all x, $x\neq 0$;

so $f(x)=\frac{x^2+3x-2}{x}, x\neq 0$ is always increasing.

8 $f'(x)=-15(x^2-1)^2$, so $f'(x)\leq 0$ as $(x^2-1)^2\geq 0$ for all x; so $f(x)$ is never increasing.

9 $f'(x)=\frac{-3}{(x+1)^4}$, so $f'(x)<0$ as $(x+1)^4>0$ for all x, $x\neq -1$; so $f(x)$ is always decreasing.

10 $f'(x)=\cos x+1$, so $0\leq f'(x)\leq 2$ as $-1\leq \cos x\leq 1$ for all x; so $f(x)$ is never decreasing.

Exercise 14.3

1 $(3, -4)$ min. t.p.

2 $\left(\frac{3}{2}, \frac{9}{4}\right)$ max. t.p.

3 $(-2, -16)$ min. t.p., $(2, 16)$ max. t.p.

4 $\left(-\frac{2}{3}, \frac{4}{27}\right)$ max. t.p., (0, 0) min. t.p.

5 (−1, −1) min. t.p., (0, 0) rising point of inflexion

6 (−1, 2) min. t.p., (0, 3) max. t.p., (1, 2) min. t.p.

7 min. stationary value = 0

8 min. stationary value = $\frac{4}{27}$, max. stationary value = 76

9 min. stationary value = 2, max. stationary value = −2

10 113 metres

11 $\left(\frac{\pi}{2}, \frac{\pi}{2}\right)$ rising point of inflexion

12 $(-\sqrt{2}, 0)$ min. t.p., (0,16) max. t.p., $(\sqrt{2}, 0)$ min. t.p.

Exercise 14.4

1

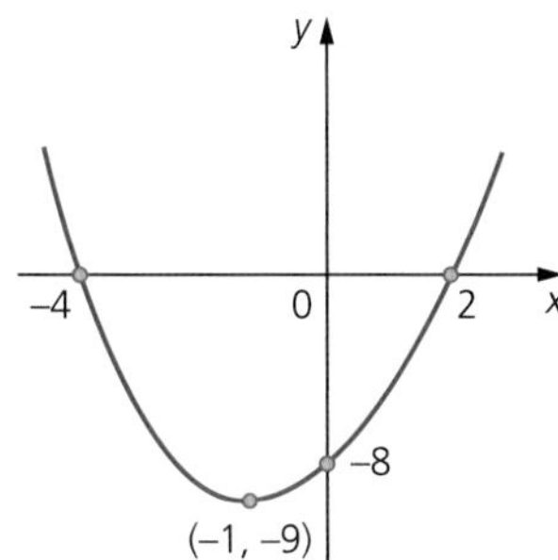

2

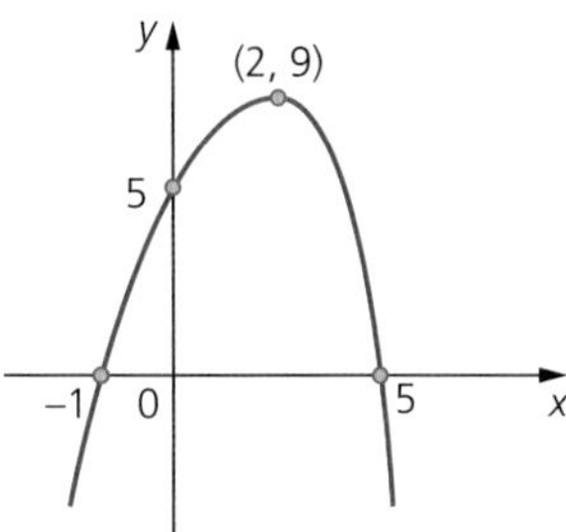

3

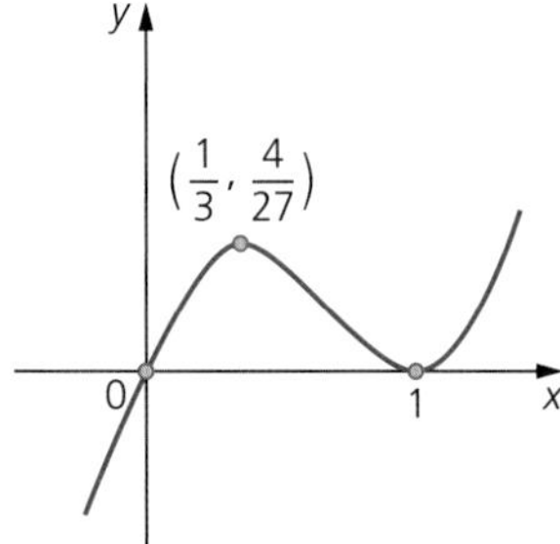

4

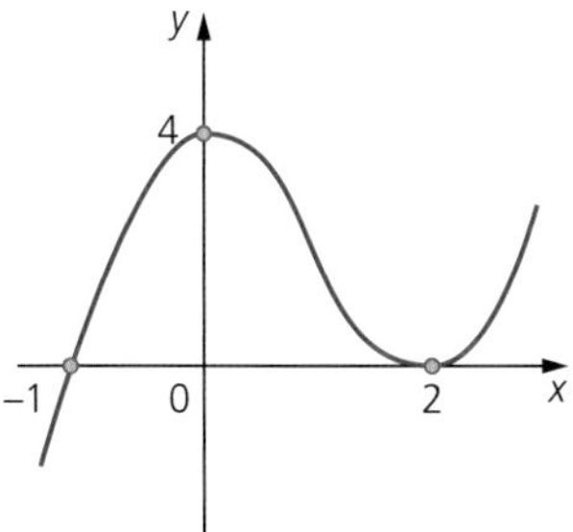

5

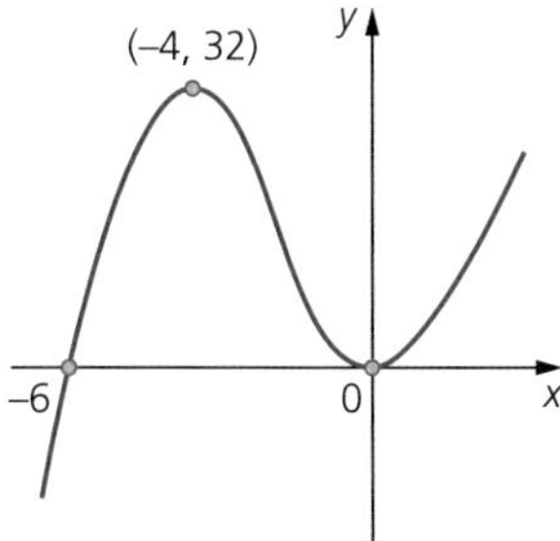

6

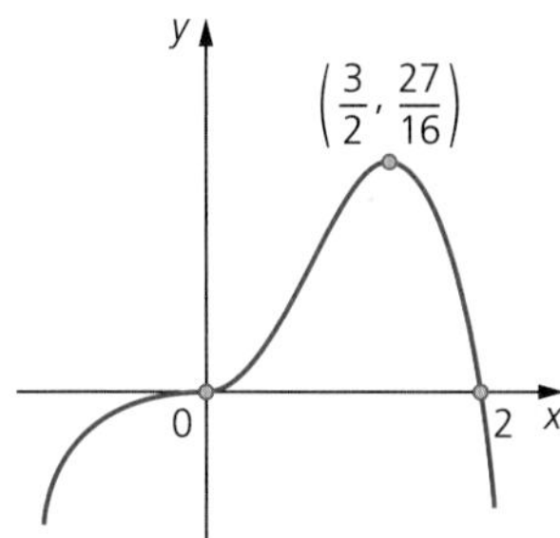

7

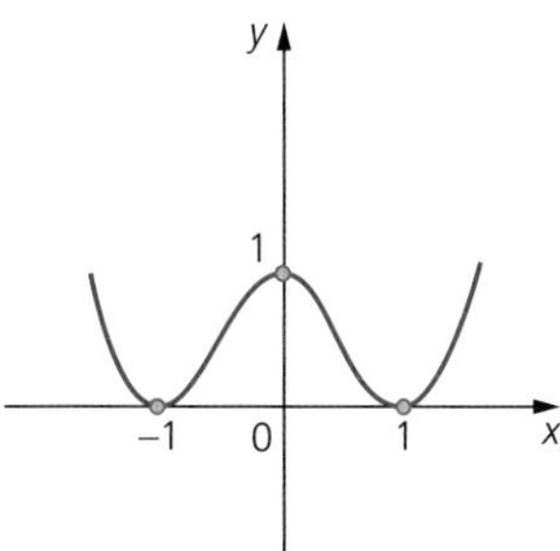

8

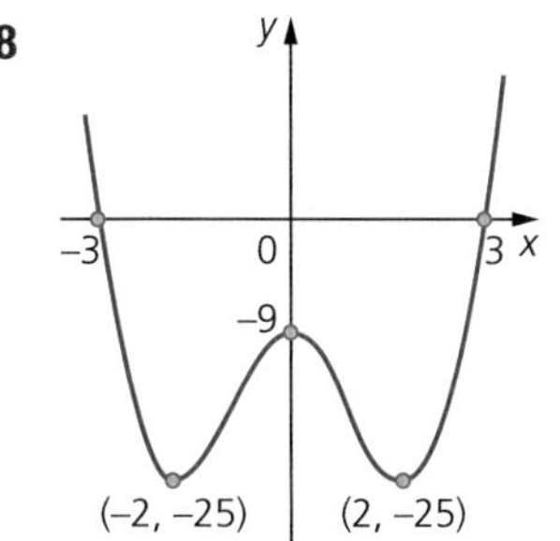

Answers

9

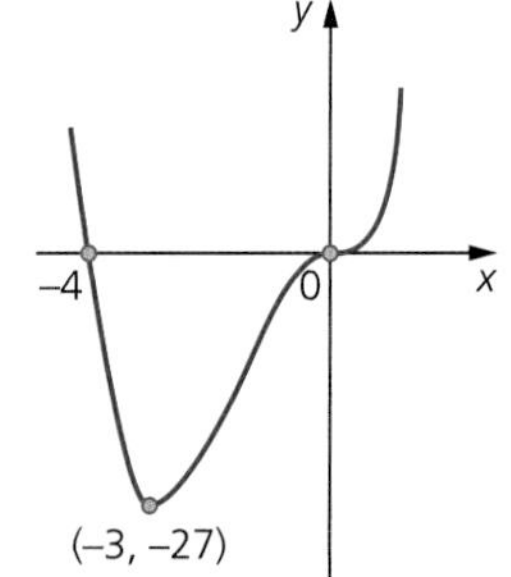

10

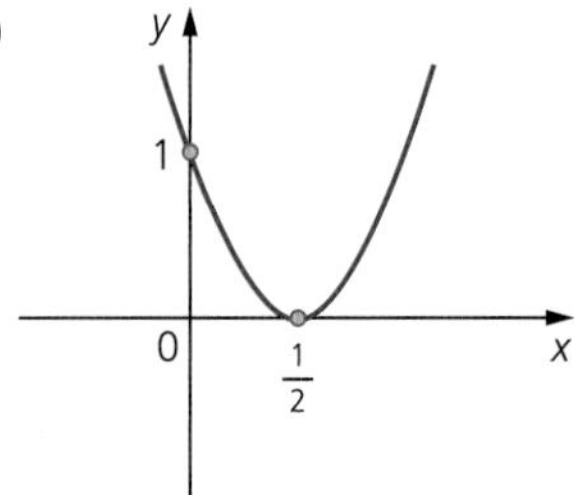

11

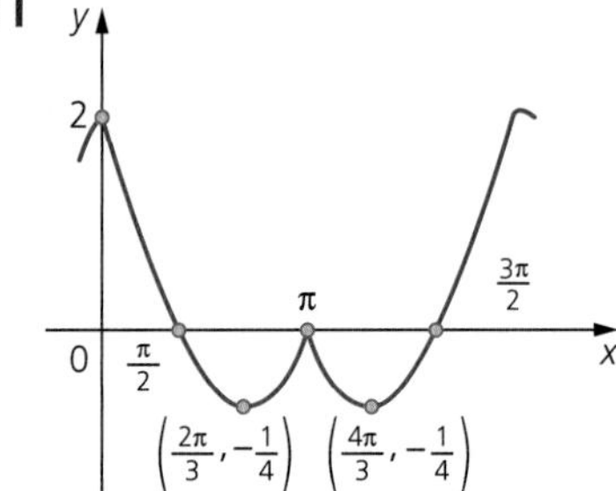

Exercise 14.5

1

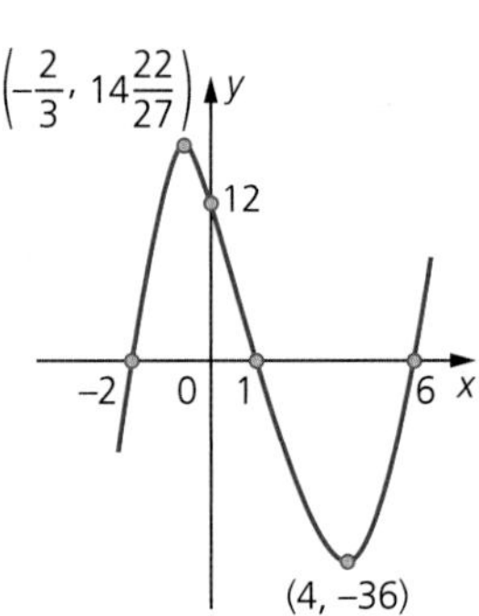

2

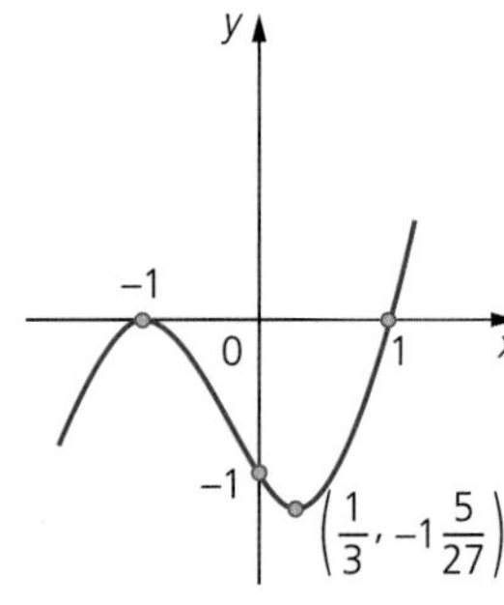

3

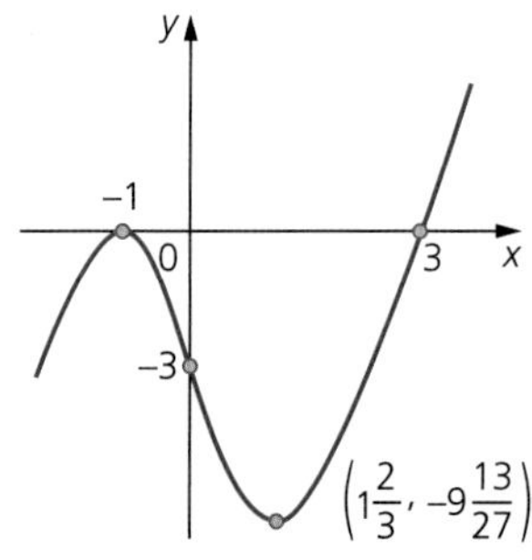

4

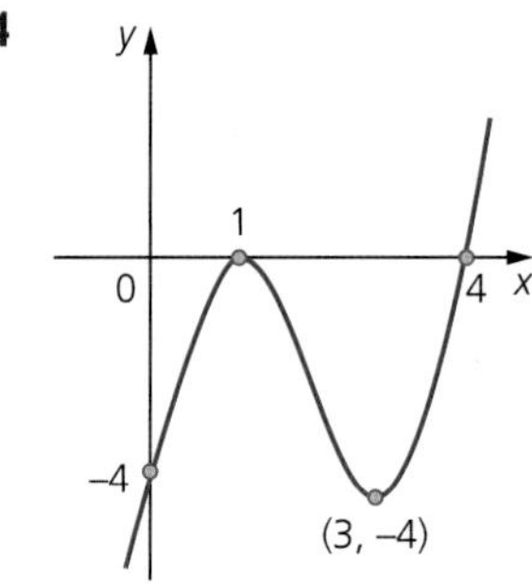

5

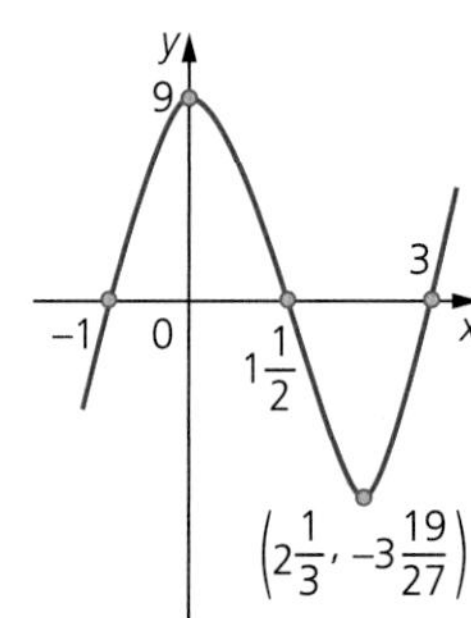

6

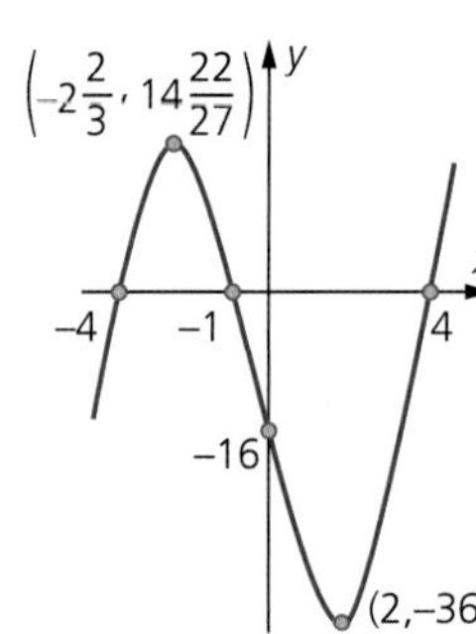

Exercise 14.6

1

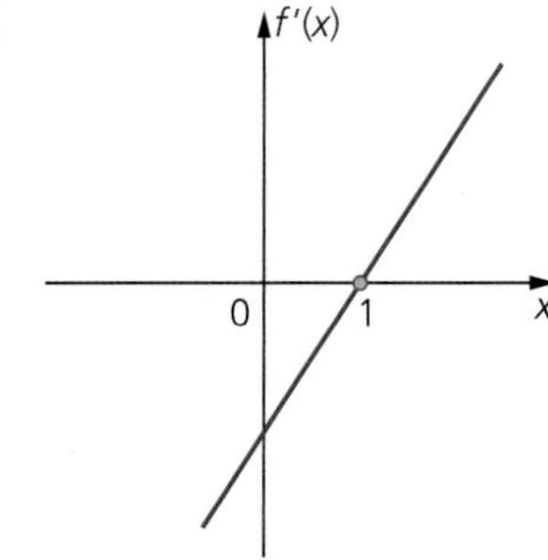

2

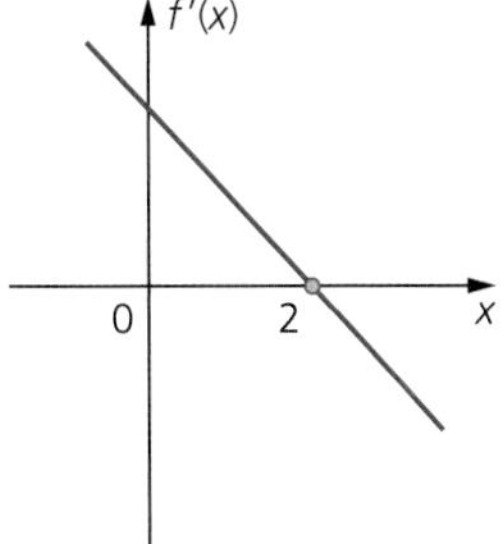

3

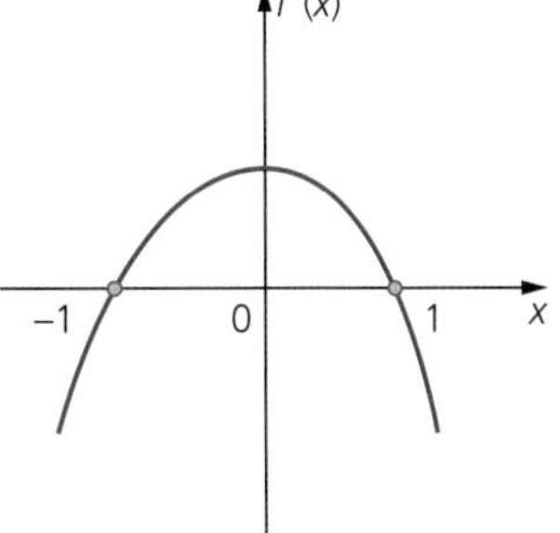

4

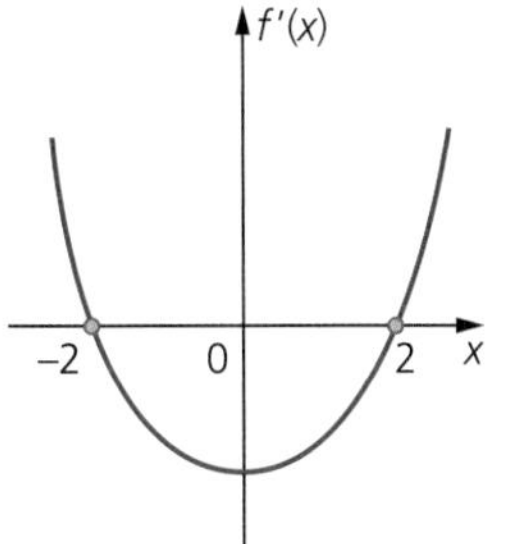

5

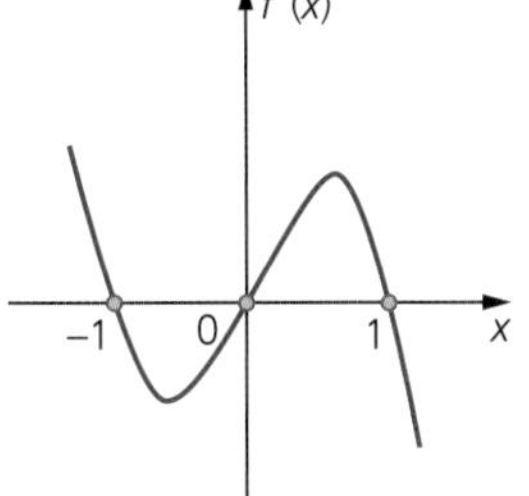

6

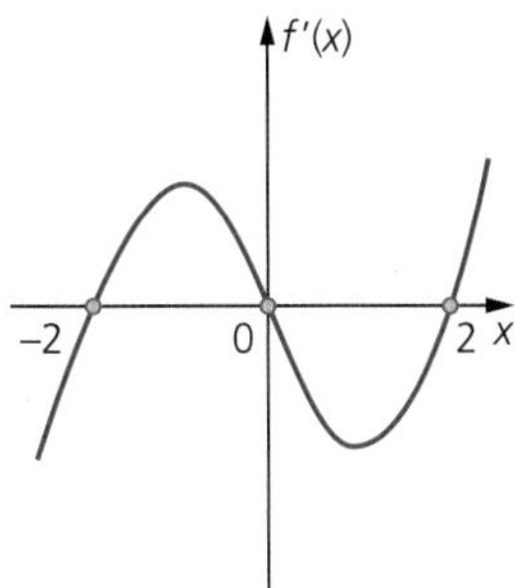

7

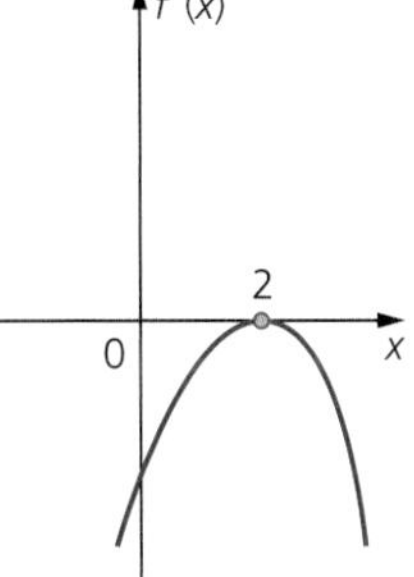

8

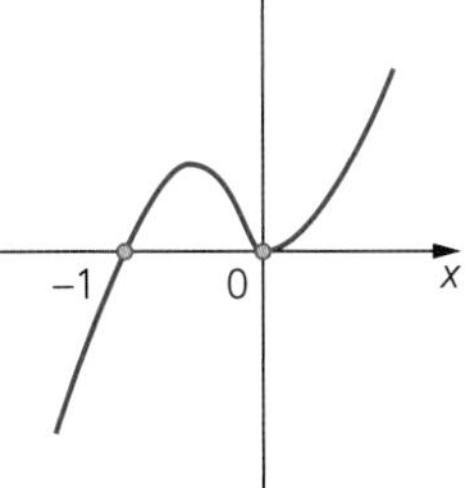

9

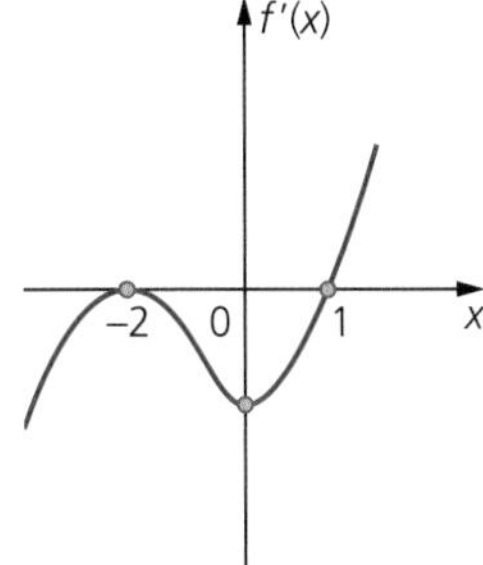

Exercise 14.7

1 $f''(x) = 6x$

2 $g''(x) = 2$

3 $h''(t) = \dfrac{4}{t^3}$

4 $\dfrac{d^2y}{dx^2} = 12x^2 - 6x + 2$

5 $\dfrac{d^2A}{db^2} = 30b^4 + 24b$

6 $\dfrac{d^2r}{ds^2} = 2 - \dfrac{6}{S^4}$

7 $f''(-2) = 8$

8 $g''(16) = 15$

9 $f''(x) = 3\left(\dfrac{1}{2}x + 3\right)^2$

Answers

10 $g''(x) = \dfrac{3}{\sqrt{2x+1}}$

11 $h''(t) = \dfrac{2}{(1-t)^3}$

12 $f''(\theta) = -25\sin(5\theta - \pi)$

Exercise 14.8

1 $(-2, 40)$ max. t.p., $(1, 13)$ min. t.p.

2 $(-1, 5)$ min. t.p.

3 $(-1, 2)$ min. t.p., $(3, 34)$ max. t.p.

4 $(2, 9)$ max. t.p.

5 $(-3, -13\frac{1}{2})$ min. t.p., $(0, 0)$ rising point of inflexion

6 $(-3, 162)$ max. t.p., $(0, 0)$ falling point of inflexion, $(3, -162)$ min. t.p.

7

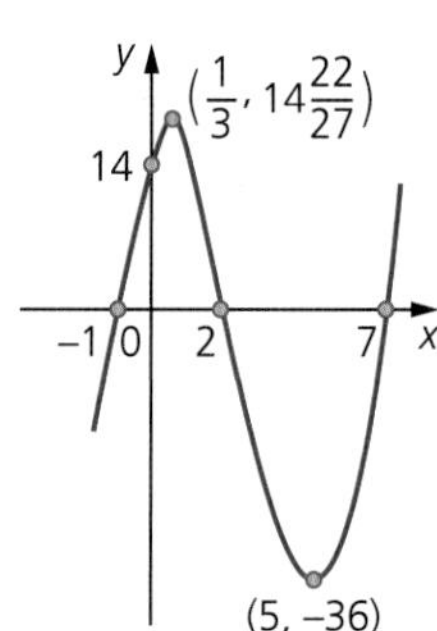

8

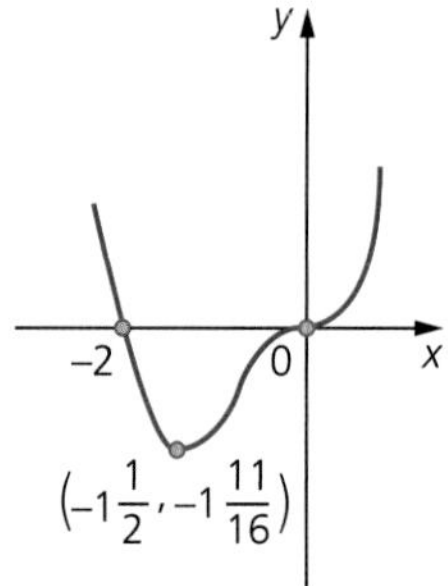

9

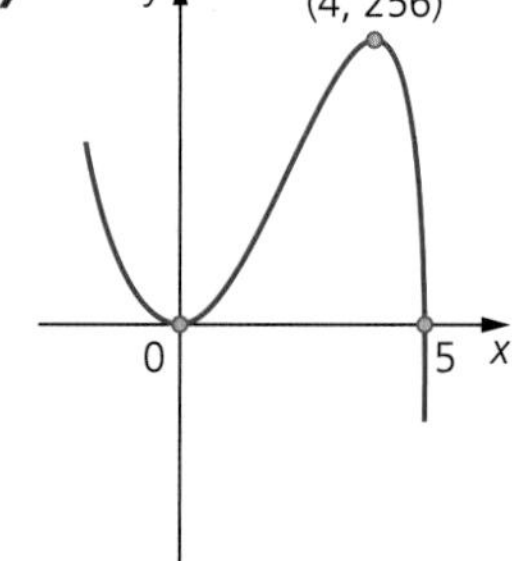

Checkout

1 $x + 12y - 4 = 0$

2 $(-1, -2)$

3 $-1 < x < 7$

4 $f'(x) = 3(x-1)^2$, so $f'(x) \geq 0$ as $(x-1)^2 \geq 0$ for all x; so $f(x)$ is never decreasing.

5 $(0, 0)$ falling point of inflexion, $\left(\frac{1}{2}, -\frac{1}{32}\right)$ min. t.p.

6 $(0, 5)$ min. t.p., $(5, 130)$ max. t.p.

7 a) (i) $(0, -4)$, $(1, 0)$ and $(4, 0)$

(ii) $(1, 0)$ max. t.p., $(3, -4)$ min. t.p.

b)

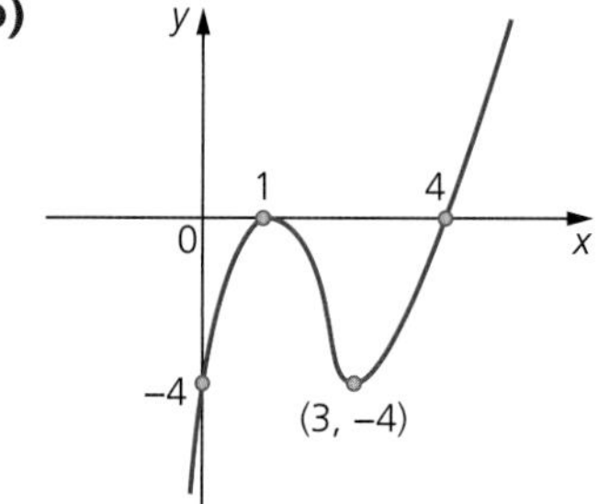

8

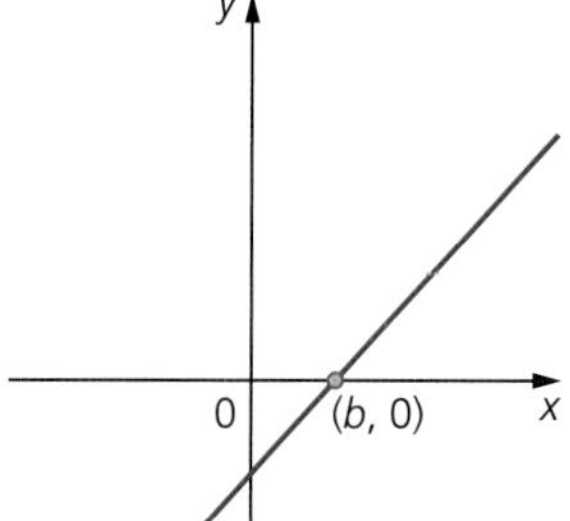

9

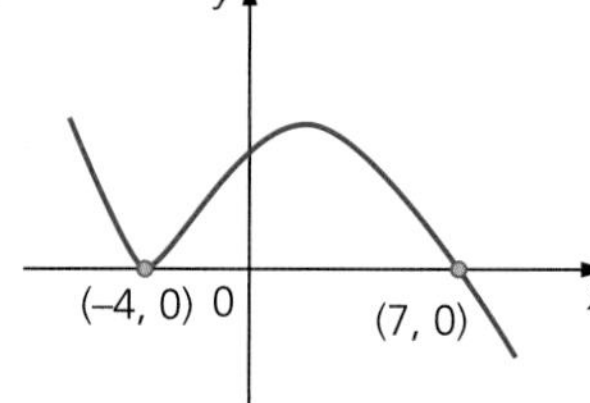

Chapter 15

Exercise 15.1

1 $y = x^3 + C$
2 $y = x^4 + C$
3 $y = x^5 + C$
4 $y = x^{10} + C$
5 $y = x^n + C$
6 $y = \frac{1}{3}x^3 + C$
7 $y = \frac{1}{4}x^4 + C$
8 $y = \frac{1}{5}x^5 + C$
9 $y = \frac{1}{10}x^{10} + C$
10 $y = \frac{1}{n+1}x^{n+1} + C$

Exercise 15.2

1 $\frac{1}{6}x^6 + C$
2 $\frac{1}{7}u^7 + C$
3 $\frac{1}{8}t^8 + C$
4 $\frac{1}{2}v^2 + C$
5 $x + C$
6 $-\frac{1}{x} + C$
7 $-\frac{1}{2r^2} + C$
8 $-\frac{1}{7k^7} + C$
9 $\frac{2x^{\frac{3}{2}}}{3} + C$
10 $\frac{2p^{\frac{5}{2}}}{5} + C$
11 $\frac{3t^{\frac{5}{3}}}{5} + C$
12 $\frac{4z^{\frac{3}{4}}}{3} + C$
13 $\frac{5x^{\frac{2}{5}}}{2} + C$
14 $-\frac{3}{u^{\frac{1}{3}}} + C$

Exercise 15.3

1 $-\frac{1}{3x^3} + C$
2 $-\frac{1}{5r^5} + C$
3 $-\frac{1}{9v^9} + C$
4 $\frac{3\sqrt[3]{x^7}}{7} + C$
5 $\frac{3\sqrt[3]{h^4}}{4} + C$
6 $\frac{4\sqrt[4]{t^5}}{5} + C$
7 $\frac{2\sqrt{z^7}}{7} + C$
8 $3\sqrt[3]{n} + C$
9 $-\frac{2}{\sqrt{x}} + C$
10 $\frac{3\sqrt[3]{s^2}}{2} + C$

Exercise 15.4

1 $3x^3 + C$
2 $4t^2 + C$
3 $7x + C$
4 $\frac{1}{2}x^4 + C$
5 $\frac{2}{3}u^6 + C$
6 $\frac{1}{6}v^3 + C$
7 $\frac{1}{3}x^3 + \frac{3}{2}x^2 - 2x + C$
8 $\frac{1}{5}u^5 - 2u^3 + C$
9 $\frac{4}{3}r^6 - \frac{3}{2}r^4 + r + C$
10 $\frac{1}{2}t^2 - \frac{3}{8}t^8 + C$

Exercise 15.5

1 $-\frac{4}{x^2} + C$
2 $\frac{3}{r^3} + C$
3 $-\frac{5}{p} + C$
4 $\frac{6}{7k^7} + C$

Answers

5 $-\frac{1}{12x^4}+C$

6 $-\frac{1}{15u^6}+C$

7 $2\sqrt{x^3}+C$

8 $\frac{4}{9}\sqrt{v^9}+C$

9 $\frac{5}{2}\sqrt[5]{t^8}+C$

10 $\frac{3}{7}\sqrt[6]{z^7}+C$

11 $10\sqrt{x}+C$

12 $12\sqrt[4]{t}+C$

13 $-\frac{1}{2\sqrt{u}}+C$

14 $-\frac{1}{2\sqrt[3]{s}}+C$

15 $\frac{2}{\sqrt[4]{r^3}}+C$

Exercise 15.6

1 $\frac{1}{3}x^3-\frac{1}{2}x^2-2x+C$

2 $3u^3-3u^2+u+C$

3 $\frac{1}{4}t^4+\frac{2}{3}t^3-\frac{3}{2}t^2+C$

4 $p^4+\frac{16}{3}p^3+8p^2+C$

5 $\frac{1}{3}x^3+2x-\frac{1}{x}+C$

6 $2\sqrt{s^3}-\frac{3}{2}s^2+C$

7 $\frac{1}{3}v^3+\frac{4}{v}+C$

8 $\frac{1}{2}x^2-\frac{5}{x}+C$

9 $-\frac{1}{r}+\frac{1}{r^2}+C$

10 $\frac{2}{3}x+\frac{2}{3}\sqrt{x}+C$

11 $6\sqrt{u}-\frac{2}{5}\sqrt{u^5}+C$

12 $4\sqrt{n^3}+2\sqrt{n}+\frac{14}{\sqrt{n}}+C$

Exercise 15.7

1 $\frac{(x+2)^4}{4}+C$

2 $\frac{(3u-1)^5}{15}+C$

3 $-\frac{(9-4t)^6}{24}+C$

4 $-\frac{1}{(p+5)}+C$

5 $-\frac{1}{4(2x+7)^2}+C$

6 $-\frac{2\sqrt{(4-v)^3}}{3}+C$

7 $\frac{2\sqrt{(5r+2)^5}}{25}+C$

8 $\frac{\sqrt[4]{(12s+7)^7}}{21}+C$

9 $-\frac{1}{9(3u+2)^3}+C$

10 $-\frac{3}{2(1+6x)}+C$

11 $\frac{3}{8(1-2n)^4}+C$

12 $\frac{\sqrt{(4z-5)^3}}{6}+C$

13 $\frac{3\sqrt[3]{(8x+5)^4}}{32}+C$

14 $-\frac{2\sqrt{3-7t}}{7}+C$

15 $3\sqrt[3]{(2u+9)^2}+C$

16 $\frac{4}{\sqrt{5-r}}+C$

Exercise 15.8

1 $4\sin x+C$

2 $\frac{1}{4}\sin 4x+C$

3 $\sin 4x+C$

4 $-3\cos\theta+C$

5 $-\frac{1}{3}\cos 3\theta+C$

6 $-\cos 3\theta+C$

7 $\frac{1}{2}\sin t+C$

8 $2\sin\frac{1}{2}t+C$

9 $\sin\frac{1}{2}t+C$

10 $2\sin x+\frac{1}{2}\cos 2x+C$

11 $-5\cos\theta-\frac{1}{5}\sin 5\theta+C$

12 $\frac{1}{3}\sin t-3\cos\frac{1}{3}t+C$

13 $-\frac{1}{4}\cos(4x+\pi)+C$

14 $\frac{1}{3}\sin(3u-\frac{\pi}{2})+C$

15 $\cos(2\pi-\theta)+C$

16 $\frac{1}{2}\sin(5+2t)+C$

17 $\frac{2}{5}\sin(5v-1)-\frac{1}{12}\cos(7+6v)+C$

18 a) $\cos^2\theta=\frac{1}{2}(\cos 2\theta+1)$

$\Rightarrow\int\cos^2\theta d\theta=\frac{1}{4}\sin 2\theta+\frac{1}{2}\theta+C$

b) $\sin^2\theta=\frac{1}{2}(1-\cos 2\theta)$

$\Rightarrow\int\sin^2\theta d\theta=\frac{1}{2}\theta-\frac{1}{4}\sin 2\theta+C$

Exercise 15.9

1 a) $y=3x^2-7$

b) $y=\frac{1}{3}x^3-x^2+x+5$

c) $y=\frac{1}{6}\sqrt{(4x+1)^3}+\frac{3}{2}$

d) $y=\frac{1}{2}\sin 2x+\frac{3}{4}$

2 a) $s=t^3+2t^2+5t+5$

b) $s=t^2+\frac{20}{t}+2$

c) $v=\frac{3}{4}\sqrt[3]{t^4}-7$

d) $v=\frac{1}{4}(1-3\cos(4t-\pi))$

3 $y=x^2-\frac{9}{x}-2$

4 $f(x)=\frac{(2x-3)^4}{8}+2$

5 $g(\theta)=\frac{2}{3}(\sin 3\theta+2)$

6 $d(t)=10t^2-5t$

Checkout

1 $\frac{1}{2}x^4+2x^2+x+C$

2 $3u^3+u^2+C$

3 $-\frac{2}{t^4}+C$

4 $2\sqrt{p^3}-\frac{1}{2p^2}+C$

5 $\frac{1}{2}r^4+\frac{1}{2r}+C$

6 $\frac{2}{3}\sqrt{v^3}-2\sqrt{v}+\frac{4}{\sqrt{v}}+C$

7 $\frac{\left(\frac{1}{2}x+1\right)^{10}}{5}+C$

8 $\frac{\sqrt{(6s-1)^3}}{9}+C$

9 $\frac{4}{5-3u}+C$

10 $\frac{3\sqrt[3]{(2n+3)^2}}{4}+C$

11 $\frac{1}{10}\sin 10x+2x+C$

12 $\frac{1}{10}\sin(10x+2)+C$

13 $-\frac{1}{7}\cos 7\theta-4\theta+C$

14 $-\frac{1}{7}\cos(7\theta-4)+C$

15 $\frac{3}{4}\sin 4t+2\cos t+C$

16 $-\frac{1}{6}\cos 3t+6\sin\frac{1}{2}t+C$

17 $s=\frac{1}{4}t^4-\frac{1}{t}-\frac{1}{4}t+9$

18 $f(x)=x^3-3x^2+5$

Chapter 16

Exercise 16.1

1 $\frac{a^3}{3}$

2 $\frac{a^4}{4}$

Answers

3 $\frac{a^5}{5}$

4

Equation of curve	$y=x^2$	$y=x^3$	$y=x^4$	$y=x^n$
Area (square units)	$\frac{a^3}{3}$	$\frac{a^4}{4}$	$\frac{a^5}{5}$	$\frac{a^{n+1}}{n+1}$

5 The area under the curve $y=x^n$ bounded by the x-axis and the line $x=a$ is equal to the value of $\int x^n dx$ when $x=a$.

Exercise 16.2

1 21 square units
2 $3\frac{3}{4}$ square units
3 $6\frac{2}{3}$ square units
4 $10\frac{2}{3}$ square units
5 $13\frac{1}{3}$ square units
6 45 square units
7 18 square units

Exercise 16.3

1 $16\frac{2}{3}$
2 $8\frac{1}{4}$
3 42
4 1
5 $-2\frac{1}{4}$
6 $\frac{1}{24}$
7 $12\frac{2}{3}$
8 $11\frac{1}{4}$
9 $6\frac{1}{5}$
10 30
11 0
12 4
13 $4\frac{7}{24}$
14 $38\frac{2}{3}$
15 $4\frac{3}{4}$
16 30
17 **a)** 6
b) 5
c) 9
d) 2
e) 3
f) 1

Exercise 16.4

1 $1\frac{1}{4}$
2 $48\frac{2}{5}$
3 $\frac{1}{16}$
4 $12\frac{2}{3}$
5 $-\frac{1}{15}$
6 4
7 0
8 1
9 $-\frac{1}{3}$
10 $\frac{1}{\pi}$
11 -2
12 $\frac{1}{8}$
13 $-10\cdot5$
14 $-0\cdot127$
15 $4\cdot21$
16 $0\cdot206$
17 Proof
18 Proof
19 **a)** $\cos^2\theta=\frac{1}{2}(\cos 2\theta+1) \Rightarrow \int_{\frac{\pi}{4}}^{\frac{\pi}{2}} \cos^2\theta d\theta=\frac{\pi}{8}-\frac{1}{4}$

b) $\sin^2\theta=\frac{1}{2}(1-\cos 2\theta) \Rightarrow \int_{0}^{\frac{\pi}{6}} \sin^2\theta d\theta=\frac{\pi}{12}-\frac{\sqrt{3}}{8}$

Checkout

1 $19\frac{1}{2}$
2 $10\frac{1}{2}$
3 $\frac{2}{3}$
4 136
5 2
6 $\frac{1}{5}$
7 Proof
8 Proof
9 1·30

Chapter 17

Exercise 17.1

1 7, −9
2 8, $1\frac{3}{4}$
3 7, −13
4 48, −80
5 −4, 16
6 55, 3
7 8, −20
8 50, 1

Exercise 17.2

1 **a)** $30x - x^2$
b) 225 m^2
2 **a)** Proof
b) 150 m^2
3 **a)** Proof
b) Greatest = 12 ft^2, least = 10 ft^2
4 **a)** Proof
b) $\frac{10}{3}$
5 1·7
6 **a)** Proof
b) B (2·5, 7·5)
7 P (2, 8)
8 **a)** 7·5 m^2
b) £120 million
9 **a)** Proof
b) Speed = 10 km/h, amount of fuel = 750 tonnes
10 **a)** Proof
b) $2\sqrt{3}$
11 $4\sqrt{3}$

Exercise 17.3

1 **a)** Proof
b) Length = 2 m, breadth = 2 m, height = 1 m surface area = 12 m^2
2 **a)** Proof
b) Length = 15 cm, breadth = 20 cm, height = 30 cm, surface area = 2700 cm^2
3 **a)** Proof
b) Length = 4 cm, breadth = 12 cm, height = 6 cm, volume = 288 cm^3
4 **a)** Proof
b) Radius = 4·3 cm, height = 8·6 cm, surface area = 349 cm^2
5 **a)** Proof
b) Perimeter = 40 cm
6 **a)** Proof
b) 7 m^2

Exercise 17.4

1 35 m/s
2 **a)** After 2 seconds
b) 19·6 m/s
3 Displacement = 23 m, velocity = 4 m/s, acceleration = −4 m/s^2
4 **a)** 3 m/s
b) $\frac{1}{3}$ second and 3 seconds
5 **a)** −6 m/s^2
b) $\frac{1}{2}$ second
6 Displacement = 27 m, velocity = 18 m/s, acceleration = 4 m/s^2
7 8π cm^2/cm
8 36π cm^3/cm
9 0.02 s/cm
10 −0.05 ohms/amp
11 −0.0045 ohms/mm
12 **a)** 2m/s
b) $\frac{\pi}{4}, \frac{3\pi}{4}$ seconds
c) $\frac{3\pi}{4}$ seconds
13 **a)** 2 m
b) Velocity = $\frac{\sqrt{3}\pi}{3}$ m/h, acceleration = $-\frac{\pi^2}{18}$ m/h^2

Checkout

1 Greatest value = 13, least value = 0
2 a) (i) $9x + 8y$
(ii) Proof
b) 2700 m^2
3 a) Proof
b) 4800 cm^2
4 12π
5 a) 96 m
b) Velocity = 36 m/s, acceleration = 4·5 m/s^2

Chapter 18

Exercise 18.1

1

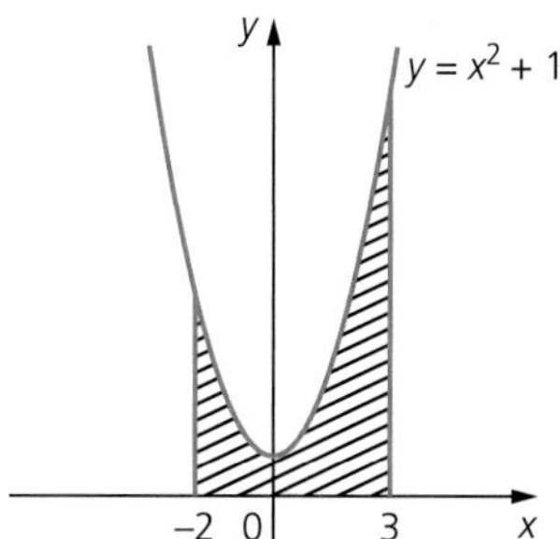

2

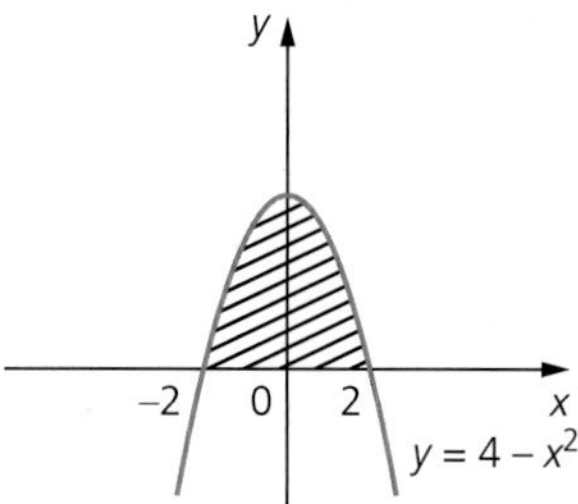

3

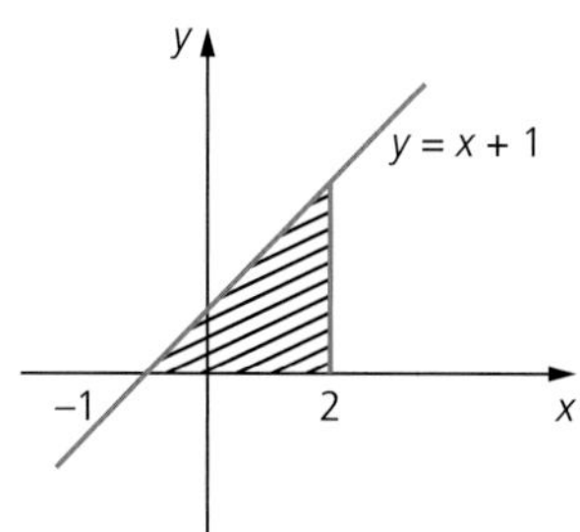

4

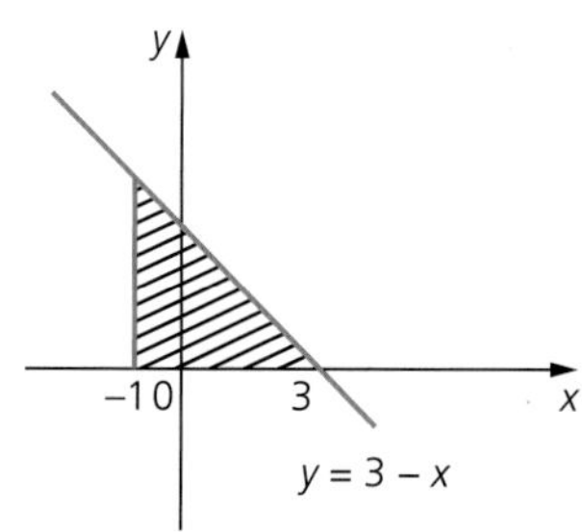

5

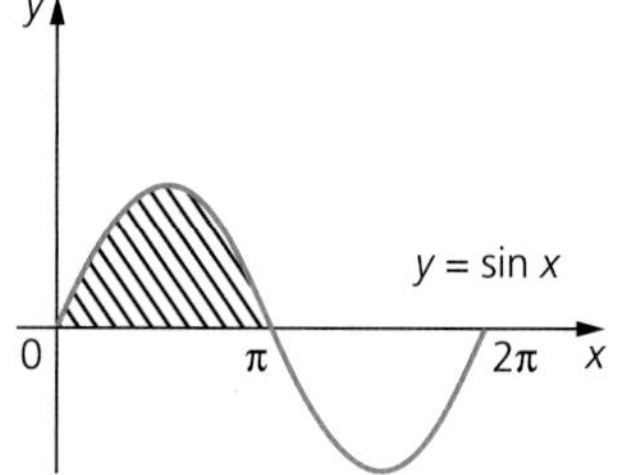

6

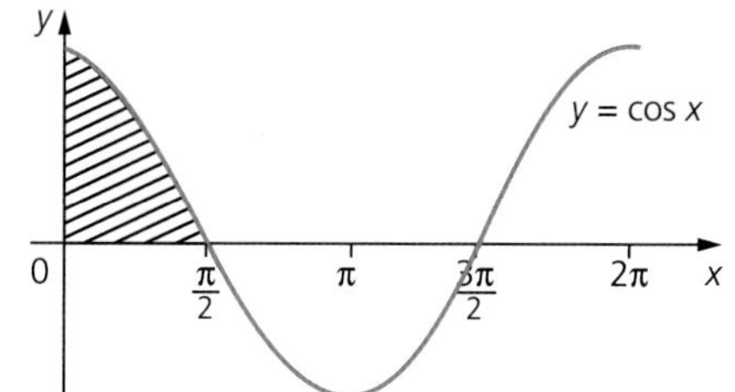

Exercise 18.2

1 $24\frac{2}{3}$ square units

2 $4\frac{2}{3}$ square units

3 $\frac{3}{10}$ square units

4 $3\frac{3}{4}$ square units

5 $2\frac{2}{3}$ square units

6 $\frac{2}{3}$ square units

7 $1\frac{1}{3}$ square units

8 36 square units

9 $1\frac{5}{6}$ square units

10 $4\frac{1}{2}$ square units

11 12 square units
12 9 square units
13 2 square units
14 1 square units

Exercise 18.3

1 $2\frac{2}{3}$ square units

2 $4\frac{1}{4}$ square units

3 $4\frac{1}{2}$ square units

4 $6\frac{1}{3}$ square units

5 $13\frac{1}{6}$ square units

6 $2\frac{2}{3}$ square units

7 $14\frac{1}{2}$ square units

8 $6\frac{1}{2}$ square units

9 $8\frac{1}{2}$ square units

10 $2\frac{1}{2}$ square units

11 $1\frac{1}{4}$ square units

12 2 square units

13 a) $(-5, 0), (3, 0)$; $85\frac{1}{3}$ square units

b) $(-1, 0), (0, 0), (2, 0)$; $9\frac{1}{4}$ square units

c) $(-\sqrt{2}, 0), (0, 0), (\sqrt{2}, 0)$; 2 square units

14 Proof

Exercise 18.4

1 $20\frac{5}{6}$ square units

2 9 square units

3 $11\frac{5}{6}$ square units

4 $2\sqrt{2}$ square units

5 $\frac{3\sqrt{3}}{4}$ square units

6 $\frac{3\sqrt{3}}{2}$ square units

7 $1\frac{1}{3}$ square units

8 $10\frac{2}{3}$ square units

9 $4\frac{1}{2}$ square units

10 $10\frac{2}{3}$ square units

11 8 square units

12 $21\frac{1}{12}$ square units

13 $25\frac{1}{4}$ square units

14 8 square units

15 $1\frac{1}{3}$ square units

16 $21\frac{1}{3}$ square units

17 $\frac{1}{3}$ square units

18 $21\frac{1}{3}$ square units

19 $\left(1-\frac{\pi}{4}\right)$ square units

Exercise 18.5

1 $s = t^3 - 3t^2 + 2$

2 $5\frac{2}{3}$ m

3 $v = 2t - \frac{1}{2}t^2 + 1, \quad s = t^2 - \frac{1}{6}t^3 + t - 3$

4 14 m

5 $2\sqrt{(2t+1)^3} - 6t - 2$

6 $h = 8 - 6\cos\frac{1}{2}t$

7 $h = 10t - 5t^2 - 2$

8 $N = 2t^3 + 500t + 800$

9 $V = 8t - \frac{1}{2}t^2 + 18$

10 $A = 10\sqrt{t} - t + 6$

Checkout

1

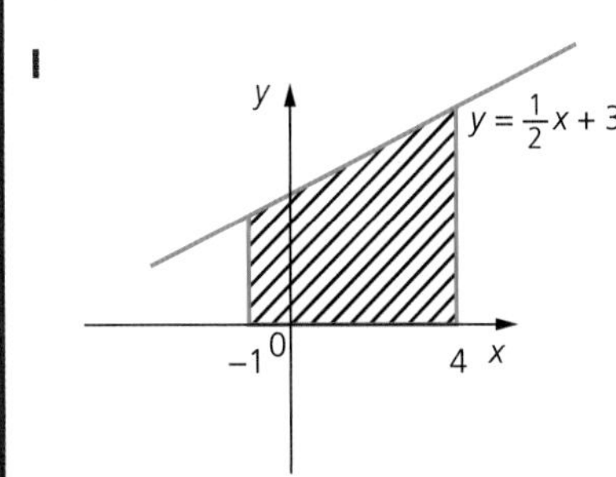

2

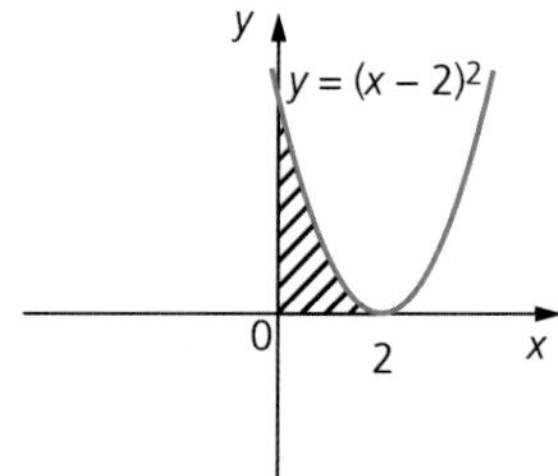

3

y
y = cos x
0
$\frac{\pi}{2}$
$\frac{3\pi}{2}$
x

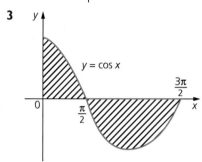

4 6 square units

5 $20\frac{1}{4}$ square units

6 $6\frac{1}{3}$ square units

7 $2\frac{1}{2}$ square units

8 $1\frac{1}{3}$ square units

9 $\frac{1}{4}$ square units

10 $2\frac{1}{4}$ square units

11 (–1, 0) (1, 0), (3, 0); 8 square units

12 (–5, 0), (–2, 3), (1, 6); $40\frac{1}{2}$ square units

13 $47\frac{1}{3}$ m^2

14 $A = 84\,\text{ft}^2, V = 3360\,\text{ft}^3$

15 $v = 2\sqrt{t^3} - 2t$, $s = \frac{4}{5}\sqrt{t^5} - t^2$

16 $P(h) = 90h - 0{\cdot}1h^2 - 3000$

Appendix 1

The list of formulae

When you sit your assessments, you will be provided with a list of formulae. This is invaluable. Check the list below to make sure you know what formulae are on it as you will need to memorise any other required formulae. During assessments you should refer to the list regularly. Even if you think you know all the formulae, check the list to ensure you are accurate. Also, take great care when copying formulae from the list as it is easy to make a transcription error.

Circle:

The equation $x^2 + y^2 + 2gx + 2fy + c = 0$ represents a circle centre $(-g, -f)$ and radius $\sqrt{g^2+f^2-c}$.
The equation $(x - a)^2 + (y - b)^2 = r^2$ represents a circle centre (a, b) and radius r.

Scalar product:

$$\mathbf{a}.\mathbf{b} = |\mathbf{a}||\mathbf{b}|\cos\theta, \text{ where } \theta \text{ is the angle between } \mathbf{a} \text{ and } \mathbf{b}.$$

or

$$\mathbf{a}.\mathbf{b} = a_1b_1 + a_2b_2 + a_3b_3 \text{ where } \mathbf{a} = \begin{pmatrix} a_1 \\ a_2 \\ a_3 \end{pmatrix} \text{ and } \mathbf{b} = \begin{pmatrix} b_1 \\ b_2 \\ b_3 \end{pmatrix}.$$

Trigonometric formulae:

$$\begin{aligned} \sin(A \pm B) &= \sin A \cos B \pm \cos A \sin B \\ \cos(A \pm B) &= \cos A \cos B \mp \sin A \sin B \\ \sin 2A &= 2 \sin A \cos A \\ \cos 2A &= \cos^2 A - \sin^2 A \\ &= 2\cos^2 A - 1 \\ &= 1 - 2\sin^2 A \end{aligned}$$

Table of standard derivatives:

$f(x)$	$f'(x)$
$\sin ax$	$a \cos ax$
$\cos ax$	$-a \sin ax$

Table of standard integrals:

$f(x)$	$\int f(x)dx$
$\sin ax$	$-\frac{1}{a}\cos ax + c$
$\cos ax$	$\frac{1}{a}\sin ax + c$

Appendix 2

In the Higher Mathematics Course Specification, the SQA include the following additional information. Added, where appropriate, are descriptions or definitions of the terms.

Additional information		
The following symbols, terms and sets may appear in the question papers. Candidates are expected to understand their use but they are not required to use them in their answers.		
Symbol or term	**Meaning**	**Example**
Set Member or element	A set is a collection of objects. The objects in a set are called the members or elements of the set and are listed inside curly brackets.	$\{1, 2, 3, 4, 5\}$
$\in$	$\in$ means 'is a member of'	$3 \in \{1, 2, 3, 4, 5\}$
$\notin$	$\notin$ means 'is not a member of'	$6 \notin \{1, 2, 3, 4, 5\}$
Subset	A set contained within a set	$\{3, 4\}$ is a subset of $\{3, 4, 5, 6\}$
Empty set	A set with no members	$\{\ \}$
Conventions for naming sets		
Symbol	**Name**	**Description**
$\mathbb{N}$	The set of natural numbers	$\{1, 2, 3, 4 \ldots\}$
$\mathbb{W}$	The set of whole numbers	$\{0, 1, 2, 3, 4 \ldots\}$
$\mathbb{Z}$	The set of integers	$\{\ldots -3, -2, -1, 0, 1, 2, 3 \ldots\}$
$\mathbb{Q}$	The set of rational numbers	Numbers that can be written as a ratio of two integers i.e. as a fraction. This set includes numbers like $-\frac{2}{3}$, $1{\cdot}25$, -7.
$\mathbb{R}$	The set of real numbers	All rational and irrational numbers. Numbers that can't be written as a ratio of two integers are irrational e.g. π and surds such as $\sqrt{2}$.

Appendix 3

If you are studying for the Free-standing units at Higher level, the table below indicates the groupings of chapters for each unit.

Free-standing unit	Relevant chapters
Expressions and functions	5, 6, 7, 9, 11, 12
Relationships and calculus	3, 8, 10, 13, 14, 15, 16
Applications	1, 2, 4, 17, 18

INDEX

L

M

N

O

P

Q

R

S

T

U

V

W

X

Z